Visualizing Categorical Data

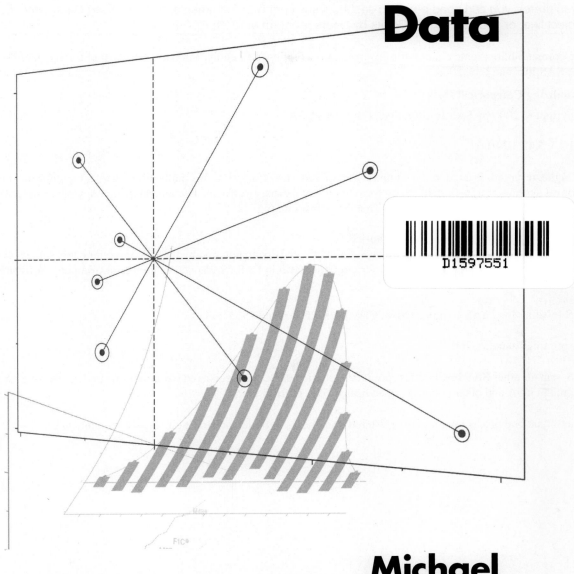

Michael Friendly

§sas.® | SAS Publishing

Comments or Questions?

The author assumes complete responsibility for the technical accuracy of the content of this book. If you have any questions about the material in this book, please write to the author at this address:

SAS Institute Inc.
Books by Users
Attn: Michael Friendly
SAS Campus Drive
Cary, NC 27513

If you prefer, you can send e-mail to sasbbu@sas.com with "comments on *Visualizing Categorical Data*" as the subject line, or you can fax the Books by Users program at (919) 677-4444.

The correct bibliographic citation for this manual is as follows: Friendly, Michael, *Visualizing Categorical Data,* Cary, NC: SAS Institute Inc., 2000.

Visualizing Categorical Data

ISBN 1-58025-660-0

SAS Institute Inc., SAS Campus Drive, Cary, North Carolina 27513.

1st printing, January 2001

Contents

Preface

> The *practical* power of a statistical test is the product of its statistical power times the probability that one will use it.
>
> J. W. Tukey, 1959

> Theory into Practice
>
> Chairman Mao Zedong, *The Little Red Book*

This book aims to provide a practically oriented, in-depth treatment of modern graphical methods and visualization techniques for categorical data—discrete response data and frequency data. It describes the underlying statistical theory and methods, and presents nearly 40 general-purpose SAS macros and programs to perform these specialized analyses and produce insightful visual displays.

The application of these techniques to a large number of substantive problems and datasets is another focus: how to analyze the data, produce the graphs, and understand what they have to say about the problem at hand. A number of these examples are reviewed from several different perspectives.

In a real sense, this book continues where *SAS System for Statistical Graphics, First Edition* leaves off. That book ends with a chapter titled "Displaying Categorical Data." It surveys some of the few graphical methods that were available for discrete data at the time of its publication, saying "while graphical display techniques are common adjuncts to analysis of variance and regression, methods for plotting contingency table data are not as widely used" (p. 499).

Not many graphical methods were available; many of those in the literature were designed for specialized situations (2-way tables, or simply 2×2 tables) and, except for correspondence analysis, very few were available in standard statistical software. Of the methods I had encountered, association plots and mosaic displays seemed sufficiently promising to include in that chapter with simple SAS programs and examples.

The disparity between availability and use of graphical methods for quantitative data, on the one hand, and analogous methods for categorical data, on the other, seemed particularly curious—almost paradoxical. The statistical methods for the later (log-linear models, logistic regression) are such close analogs of the standard method for the former (ANOVA, regression) that I found the contrast in visualization methods puzzling.

Since that time, I and others have worked actively on the development of new graphical methods for categorical data, with the goals of (a) providing visualization techniques for data exploration and model fitting comparable in scope to those used for quantitative data, (b) implementing these methods in readily available software, and (c) illustrating how these methods may be used in understanding real data—theory into practice.

Beginning somewhat earlier, the development of the generalized linear model (e.g., McCullagh and Nelder, 1989) created the statistical machinery to integrate many aspects of classical linear models for quantitative data with similar linear models for discrete responses and frequency data within a common framework. As a result, many of the commonly used diagnostic displays (normal probability plots of residuals, added-variable plots, influence plots, etc.) described in *SAS System for Statistical Graphics, First Edition* could be adapted and extended to categorical data.

Altogether, what seemed to deserve only a skeleton chapter in 1991 has progressed to meat on the bones, perhaps worthy of an extended treatment, to which you are now invited.

How to Use This Book

This book was written to make graphical methods for categorical data *available* and *accessible*.

Available methods should be conveniently collected, described, and illustrated. *Available* means that I try to show how graphs, some old and some quite novel, can be used to expose or summarize important features of categorical data. I try to collect and describe methods I consider useful all together here. In part, this is done by example. Quite a few examples are treated several times throughout the text from different perspectives or to illustrate different views of the same data. If you are looking for a graphical method to help you understand some particular type of data, the examples in this book may help you find some useful candidates. Use the Example Index to track the various analyses applied to a given dataset.

Accessible methods should be easy to use. *Accessible* reflects the opening quotations of this Preface. A technique may be well-described somewhere but is inaccessible because it is hard for you to use with your own data. I try to provide general tools, conceptual and computational, for *thinking about* and *doing* categorical data analysis guided by visualization. The statistical theory for the methods described is, of necessity, somewhat abbreviated but oriented toward understanding how to apply these methods. You may wish to refer to cited references for more detail. The programs developed for this book (described in Appendix A) reflect my aim to make it easy for you to use these methods with your own data. If you are not familiar with the use of SAS macros, it will take you a bit of effort to begin to use these programs, but I strongly believe that small effort will empower you greatly and help *you* convert theory into practice.

Beyond the *information* provided, I also tried to make the *structure* of this information available and accessible within the confines of a printed (and therefore linear) work. The following subsection provides a synopsis of the contents of each chapter of this book. Each chapter begins with thumbnail images of some of the graphical methods that are described within it, and a capsule summary. Each chapter ends with a summary of the main points and methods.

Overview

Chapter 1: "Introduction" introduces some aspects of categorical data, distinctions among different types of data, and different strategies for analysis of frequency data and discrete response data. I discuss the implications of these features of categorical data for visualization techniques and outline a strategy of data analysis focused on visualization.

Chapter 2: "Fitting and Graphing Discrete Distributions" describes the well-known discrete frequency distributions: the binomial, Poisson, negative binomial, geometric, and logarithmic series distributions, along with methods for fitting these to empirical data. Graphic displays are used to visualize goodness of fit, to diagnose an appropriate model, and determine the impact of individual observations on estimated parameters.

Chapter 3: "2-way Contingency Tables" presents methods of analysis designed mainly for 2-way tables of frequencies (contingency tables), along with graphical techniques for understanding the patterns of associations between variables. Different specialized displays are focused on visualizing an odds ratio (a fourfold display of 2×2 tables), or the general pattern of association (sieve diagrams), the agreement between row and column categories (agreement charts), and relations in $n \times 3$ tables (trilinear plots).

Chapter 4: "Mosaic Displays for *n*-Way Tables" introduces the mosaic display, a general method for visualizing the pattern of associations among variables in 2-way and larger tables. Extensions of this technique can reveal partial associations, marginal associations, and shed light on the structure of log-linear models themselves.

Chapter 5: "Correspondence Analysis" discusses correspondence analysis, a technique designed to provide visualization of associations in a 2-way contingency table in a small number of dimensions. Multiple correspondence analysis extends this technique to *n*-way tables. Other graphical methods, including mosaic matrices and biplots, provide complementary views of log-linear models for 2-way and *n*-way contingency tables.

Chapter 6: "Logistic Regression" introduces the model-building approach of logistic regression, designed to describe the relation between a discrete response, often binary, and a set of explanatory variables. Smoothing techniques are often crucial in visualizations for such discrete data. The fitted model provides both inference and prediction, accompanied by measures of uncertainty. Diagnostic plots help us to detect influential observations that may distort our results.

Chapter 7: "Log-linear and Logit Models" extends the model building approach to log-linear and logit models. These are most easily interpreted through visualizations, including mosaic displays and plots of associated logit models. As with logistic regression, diagnostic plots and influence plots help to assure that the fitted model is an adequate summary of associations among variables.

Appendix A: "SAS Programs and Macros" documents all the SAS macros and programs illustrated in the book.

Appendix B: "Datasets" lists the DATA steps used to create the principal datasets used in the book.

Appendix C: "Tables" lists two tables of the values of the χ^2 distribution, along with a SAS program that may be customized to provide similar information in any desired format.

Acknowledgments

Many colleagues, friends, students, and internet acquaintances have contributed directly and indirectly to the preparation of this book.

The seed for this book was planted during a staff seminar series on categorical data analysis held by the Statistical Consulting Service at York University in 1991–92; over several subsequent years I taught a short course on Graphical Methods for Categorical Data and received valuable feedback from many colleagues and students. I am grateful to my colleagues, friends, and students in the Statistical Consulting Service: John Fox, Georges Monette, Mirka Ondrack, Peggy Ng, Roman Konarski, Tom Buis, Ernest Kwan, and Tom Martin.

A number of people reviewed the book at various stages, offering helpful suggestions and comments: John Fox, Ernest Kwan, Rob Agnelli, Jim Ashton, Sanford Gayle, Duane Hayes, Lelia McConnell, Kevin Scott, Kathy Shelley, and Rick Wicklin. Russ Tyndall carefully reviewed the macro programs. I also benefited from discussions of some of the topics discussed with Forrest Young, Michael Greenacre, Antoine de Falguerolles, and Howard Wainer, and with the participants of the Workshop "Data Visualization in Statistics," organized by Andreas Buja.

At SAS Institute, David Baggett encouraged and supported this work. Julie Platt and later Patsy Poole served as editors, helping me to refine the text and produce a printed version with the look and feel I desired. Ed Huddleston, Sue Kocher, Josephine Pope, Tate Renner, Mary Rios, Gretchen Rorie, Helen Weeks, and Patricia Spain were involved in copyediting, production, and marketing. The lovely cover was designed by Laurin Smith Allen. It was a pleasure to work with them all.

Along the way, I faced many SAS programming challenges. As always, the contributors to "SAS-L" (news:comp.soft-sys.sas) were generous in their assistance. Among the many who helped, Jack Hamilton, Melvin Klassen, Ian Whitlock, and Matthew Zack deserve particular mention.

I wrote this book using LaTeX, and the learning curve was steeper than I imagined. Donald Arseneau, David Carlisle, David Kastrup, Bernd Schandl, Paul Thompson, and other contributors to comp.text.tex were generous with their time and expertise, helping me often to translate my ideas into boxes that looked right on the printed page. Demian Conway and others on the comp.lang.perl.* newsgroups helped me to construct some Perl tools that considerably eased the work.

At York University, Ryan McRonald provided heroic support and wizardry to keep my aging "Hotspur" workstation going and rescued me from several crises and catastrophes over the course of this work. Mike Street, Tim Hampton, and other members of the Academic Technical Support Group ably assisted me in setting up and tuning many software components needed during this project. Marshal Linfoot and other members of the UNIX Team answered numerous questions and provided invaluable support.

Finally, I am grateful to the National Sciences and Engineering Research Council of Canada for research support on my project, "Graphical Methods for Categorical Data" (Grant 8150), and to York University for a sabbatical leave and a research grant in 1998–99, during which most of this book was drafted.

Whatever defects remain, after all this help, are entirely my responsibility.

MICHAEL FRIENDLY

Chapter

1 Introduction

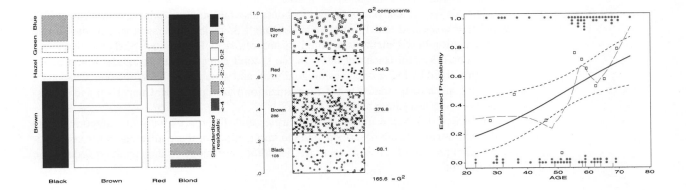

Categorical data consists of variables whose values comprise a set of discrete categories. Such data requires different statistical and graphical methods from those commonly used for quantitative data. The focus of this book is on visualization techniques and graphical methods designed to reveal patterns of relationships among categorical variables.

1.1 Data Visualization and Categorical Data

> Beauty is truth, truth beauty. — that is all
> Ye know on earth, and all ye need to know.
>
> John Keats, "Ode on a Grecian Urn"

"Data visualization" is an approach to data analysis that focuses on *insightful graphical display*. We can display the raw data, some summary statistics, or some indicators of the quality or adequacy of a fitted model. The word "insightful" suggests that the goal is (we hope) to reveal some aspects of the data that might not be perceived, appreciated, or absorbed by other means. The overall aims include both beauty and truth, though each of these is only as perceived by the beholder.

Methods for visualizing quantitative data have a long history. These methods are now widely used in both data analysis and data presentation, and in both popular and scientific media. However, graphical methods for categorical data have only recently developed and, consequently, are not as widely used. The goal of this book is to show, concretely, how data visualization can be usefully applied to categorical data.

"Categorical data" means different things in different contexts. The topic is introduced in Section 1.2, which contains some examples illustrating (a) types of categorical variables: binary, nominal, and ordinal; (b) data in case form vs. frequency form; (c) frequency data vs. count data; (d) univariate, bivariate, and multivariate data; and (e) the distinction between explanatory and response variables.

Methods for the analysis of categorical data also fall into two quite different categories, which are described and illustrated in Section 1.3. In the first category are the simple randomization-based methods typified by the classical Pearson χ^2, Fisher's exact test, and Cochran-Mantel-Haenszel tests. In the second category are the model-based methods represented by logistic regression, loglinear, and generalized linear models. Chapters 2 through 5 are mostly related to the randomization-based methods. Chapters 6 and 7 illustrate the model-based methods.

In Section 1.4, some important similarities and differences between categorical data and quantitative data are described, and the implications of these differences for visualization techniques are discussed. Section 1.5 outlines a strategy of data analysis focused on visualization.

1.2   What Is Categorical Data?

A *categorical variable* is a variable for which the possible measured or assigned values consist of a discrete set of categories. Here are some typical examples:

- Gender — Male, Female
- Marital Status — Never Married, Married, Separated, Divorced, Widowed
- Fielding Position (in baseball) — Pitcher, Catcher, 1st base, 2nd base,..., Left field
- Side Effects (in a pharmacological study) — None, Skin Rash, Sleep Disorder, Anxiety,...
- Political Preference — Left, Center, Right
- Treatment Outcome — No Improvement, Some Improvement, Marked Improvement
- Age — 0-9, 10-19, 20-29, 30-39,...
- Number of Children — 0, 1, 2, ...

As these examples suggest, categorical variables differ in the number of categories: **binary variables**, such as Gender, are distinguished from those that have more than two categories (called **polytomous**). For example, Table 1.1 gives data about 4526 applicants to graduate departments at the University of California at Berkeley in 1973, classified by two binary variables, gender and admission status.

Table 1.1   Admissions to Berkeley graduate programs

	Admitted	Rejected	Total
Males	1198	1493	2691
Females	557	1278	1835
Total	1755	2771	4526

Some categorical variables, such as Political Preference and Treatment Outcome, may have ordered categories and are called ***ordinal***; other variables, such as Marital Status, have unordered categories and are called ***nominal***.[1] For example, Table 1.2 shows a $2 \times 2 \times 3$ table of ordered outcomes (None, Some, or Marked Improvement) to an active treatment for rheumatoid arthritis in men and women compared to treatment with a placebo.

Table 1.2 Arthritis treatment data

		Improvement			
Treatment	Sex	None	Some	Marked	Total
Active	Female	6	5	16	27
	Male	7	2	5	14
Placebo	Female	19	7	6	32
	Male	10	0	1	11
Total		42	14	28	84

Finally, such variables differ in the fineness or level to which some underlying observation has been categorized for a particular purpose. From one point of view, *all* data may be considered categorical because the precision of measurement is necessarily finite, or an inherently continuous variable may be recorded only to limited precision. But this view is not helpful for the applied researcher because it neglects the phrase "for a particular purpose." Age, for example, might be treated as a quantitative variable in a study of native language vocabulary, or as an ordered categorical variable in terms of the efficacy or side-effects of treatment for depression, or even as a binary variable (Child vs. Adult) in an analysis of survival following an epidemic or a natural disaster.

1.2.1 Case Form vs. Frequency Form

In many circumstances, data is recorded about each individual or experimental unit. Data in this form is called case data or data in ***case form***. For example, the data in Table 1.2 was derived from the individual data listed in Appendix B.1. Whether or not the data variables and the questions we ask call for categorical or quantitative data analysis, we can always trace any observation back to its individual identifier or data record when the data is in case form.

Data in ***frequency form***, such as that shown in Table 1.2, has already been tabulated, by counting over the categories of the table variables. Data in frequency form may be analyzed by methods for quantitative data if there is a quantitative response variable (weighting each group by the cell frequency by using a `WEIGHT` or a `FREQ` statement). Otherwise, such data is generally best analyzed by methods for categorical data. In either case, however, an observation in a dataset in frequency form refers to all cases in the cell collectively, and it cannot be identified individually. Data in case form can always be reduced to frequency form, but the reverse is rarely possible.

---

[1] An ordinal variable may be defined as one whose categories are *unambiguously* ordered along a *single* underlying dimension. Both marital status and fielding position may be weakly ordered, but not on a single dimension, and not unambiguously.

1.2.2   Frequency Data vs. Count Data

In many cases, the observations that represent the classifications of events or variables are recorded from *operationally independent* experimental units or individuals, typically, a sample from some population. The tabulated data may be called *frequency data*. The data in Tables 1.1 and 1.2 are examples of frequency data because each observation that is tabulated comes from a different person.

However, if several events or variables are observed for the same units or individuals, those events are not operationally independent, and it is useful to use the term *count data* in this situation. These terms (following Lindsey, 1995) are by no means standard, but the distinction is often important, especially in statistical models for categorical data. In a tabulation of the number of male children within families (Table 1.3), for example, the number of male children in a specific family would be a count variable, taking values 0, 1, 2, ... The number of independent families with a specific number of male children is a frequency variable. Count data also arises when a sequence of events is tabulated over time or, under different circumstances, in a number of individuals.

1.2.3   Univariate, Bivariate, and Multivariate Data

Table 1.1 is an example of a bivariate (two-way) contingency table, and Table 1.2 classifies the observations by three variables. Yet, the Berkeley admisssions data also recorded the department to which potential students applied (giving a three-way table), and in the arthritis data, the age of subjects was also recorded.

Therefore, any contingency table records the marginal totals, summed over all variables not represented in the table. For data in case form, this means simply ignoring (or not recording) one or more variables; the observations remain the same. However, data in frequency form results in smaller tables when any variable is ignored; the observations are the cells of the contingency table.

In the limiting case, only one table variable may be recorded or available, giving the categorical equivalent of univariate data. For example, Table 1.3 gives data about the distribution of the number of male children in families that have 12 children, as discussed in Example 2.10. This data was part of a large tabulation of the sex distribution of families in Saxony in the nineteenth century, but the data in Table 1.3 has only one discrete classification variable, that is, the number of males. Without further information, the only statistical questions concern the form of the distribution. The methods for fitting and graphing such discrete distributions are discussed in Chapter 2. The remaining chapters relate to bivariate and multivariate data.

Table 1.3   Number of Males in 6115 Saxony Families That Have 12 Children

Males	0	1	2	3	4	5	6	7	8	9	10	11	12
Families	3	24	104	286	670	1033	1343	1112	829	478	181	45	7

1.2.4   Explanatory vs. Response Variables

Many statistical models make a distinction between *response* (or *dependent*, or *criterion*) variables and *explanatory* (or *independent*, or *predictor*) variables. In the standard (classical) linear models for regression and analysis of variance (ANOVA), for instance, we treat one (or more) variables as responses, to be explained by the other, explanatory variables. The explanatory variables may be quantitative or categorical (e.g., CLASS variables), but this affects only the details of how the model is specified for PROC GLM or PROC REG. For example, the response variable, treatment outcome, must be considered quantitative, and the model attempts to describe how the *mean* of the distribution of responses changes with the values or levels of the explanatory variables, such as age or gender.

However, when the response variable is categorical, the standard linear models do not apply because they assume a normal (Gaussian) distribution for the model residuals. For example, in Table 1.2 the response is Improvement, and even if numerical scores were assigned to the categories None, Some, and Marked, it may be unlikely that the assumptions of the classical linear models could be met.

Hence, a categorical *response variable* generally requires analysis using methods for categorical data, but categorical explanatory variables may be readily handled by either method.

1.3   Strategies for Categorical Data Analysis

Methods of analysis for categorical data can be classified into two broad categories: those concerned with hypothesis testing *per se*, and those concerned with model building.

1.3.1   Hypothesis-Testing Approaches

In many studies, the questions of substantive interest translate readily into questions concerning hypotheses about association between variables. If a non-zero association exists, we may want to characterize the strength of the association numerically and understand the pattern or nature of the association. For example, in Table 1.1, the question "Is there evidence of gender-bias in admission to graduate school?" may be expressed in terms of an association between gender and admission status in a 2×2 contingency table of applicants who are classified by these two variables. If so, we can assess the strength of the association by a variety of measures, including the difference in proportions admitted for men and women or the ratio of the odds of admission for men compared to women, as described in Section 3.2.2.

Similarly, in Table 1.2, questions about the efficacy of the treatment for rheumatoid arthritis can be answered in terms of hypotheses about the associations among the table variables: Treatment, Sex, and the Improvement categories. Although the main concern might be focused on the overall association between Treatment and Improvement, one would also want to know if this association is the same for men and women. A stratified analysis (Section 3.3) controls for the effects of background variables, such as Sex, and tests for *homogeneity of association* help determine if these associations are equal.

Questions involving tests of such hypotheses are answered most easily using the randomization-based methods provided by `PROC FREQ`. These include the familiar Pearson chi-square, the Cochran-Mantel-Haenszel test statistics, Fisher's exact test, and a wide variety of measures of strength of association. These tests make minimal assumptions, principally requiring that subjects or experimental units have been randomly assigned to the categories of experimental factors. The hypothesis testing approach is illustrated in Chapters 3 through 5, though the emphasis is on graphical methods that help to understand the nature of association between variables.

EXAMPLE 1.1   Hair color and eye color

Two graphical methods related to the hypothesis-testing approach are shown in Figure 1.1. The data concerns the relationship between hair color and eye color in a sample of nearly 600 students (see Table 3.2 and Appendix B.3). The standard analysis with `PROC FREQ` gives a Pearson χ^2 of 138.3 with 9 degrees of freedom (df), indicating substantial departure from independence. How do we understand the *nature* of this association between hair and eye color?

Figure 1.1 Graphical displays for hair color and eye color data.
Left: mosaic display; right: correspondence analysis 2-D solution.

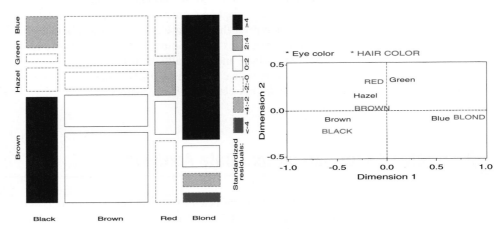

The left panel of Figure 1.1 is a mosaic display (Chapter 4) constructed so that the size of each rectangle is proportional to the observed cell frequency. The shading reflects the cell contribution to the χ^2 statistic: shades of blue, when the observed frequency is substantially greater than the expected frequency under independence; shades of red, when the observed freqency is substantially less, as shown in the legend.

The right panel of this figure shows the results of a correspondence analysis (Chapter 5), where the deviations of the hair-color and eye-color points from the origin account for as much of the χ^2 as possible in two dimensions.

We observe that both the hair colors and the eye colors are ordered from dark-to-light in the mosaic display and along Dimension 1 in the correspondence analysis plot. The deviations between observed and expected frequencies have an opposite-corner pattern in the mosaic display, except for the combination of red hair and green eyes, which also stand out as the largest values on Dimension 2 in the correspondence analysis plot. Displays such as these provide a means to understand *how* the variables are related. □

1.3.2   Model-Building Approaches

In other situations, model-based methods provide tests of equivalent hypotheses about associations, but (at the cost of additional assumptions) offer additional advantages not provided by the simpler hypotheses-testing approaches. As in the analysis of quantitative data, linear statistical models relate the expected value of a response to a linear function of the table variables, and also assume that residuals or deviations from the model follow a known parametric form.

For a dichotomous response variable, for example, it is convenient to construct a model relating a function of the probability, π, of one event to a linear combination of the explanatory variables. Logistic regression uses the logit function,

$$\text{logit}(\pi) = \log_e \frac{\pi}{1 - \pi}$$

which may be interpreted as the log odds of the given event.

Statistical inferences from model-based methods also provide tests of hypotheses, but they provide estimates of parameters in the model and associated confidence intervals and prediction intervals for the response as well. A particular advantage of the logit representation in the logistic regression model is that estimates of odds ratios (Section 3.2.2) may be obtained directly from the parameter estimates.

EXAMPLE 1.2   *Challenger* disaster

To illustrate, the graph in Figure 1.2 is based on a logistic regression model predicting the probability of a failure in one of the O-ring seals used in the NASA space shuttles prior to the disasterous launch of the *Challenger* in January, 1986.[2] The explanatory variable is the ambient temperature at the time of the flight. The sad story behind this data and the lessons to be learned for graphical data display are related in Example 6.5.

Here, we simply note that the fitted model, shown by the solid line in Figure 1.2, corresponds to the prediction equation (with standard errors shown in parentheses),

$$\text{logit(Failure)} = \underset{(3.06)}{5.09} - \underset{(0.047)}{0.116} \text{ Temp}$$

An hypothesis test that failure probability is unassociated with temperature is equivalent to the test that the coefficient for temperature in this model equals 0; this test has a *p*-value of 0.014, which is convincing evidence for rejection. However, the parameter estimate for temperature, -0.116, gives more information. Each 1° increase in temperature decreases the log odds of failure by 0.116, with 95% confidence interval $(-0.208, -0.0235)$. The equivalent odds ratio is $\exp(-0.116) = 0.891$ (0.812–0.977). Equivalently, a 10° *decrease* in temperature corresponds to an odds ratio of a failure of $\exp(10 \times 0.116) = 3.18$, more than tripling the odds of a failure.

When the *Challenger* was launched, the temperature was only 31°. The dashed lines (red) in Figure 1.2 show 95% prediction intervals for failure probability. All previous shuttles (shown by the points in the figure) had been launched at much warmer temperatures, so the prediction interval (the dashed vertical line at the left of the graph) at 31° represents a considerable extrapolation beyond the available data. Nonetheless, the model-building approach does provide such predictions along with measures of their uncertainty. Figure 1.2 is a graph that might have saved lives.   □

Figure 1.2   NASA Space Shuttle O-ring Failure, observed and predicted probabilities

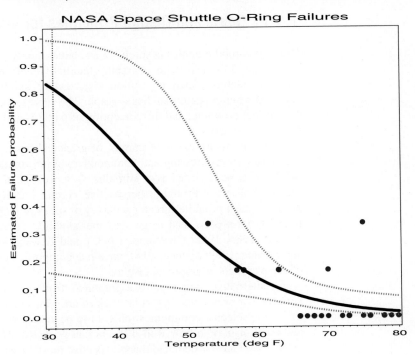

[2]"Risk Analysis of the Space Shuttle: Pre-Challenger Prediction of Failure," vol. 84, no. 408, by Siddhartha R. Dalal, Edward B. Fowlkes, and Bruce Hoadley. Copyright © 1989 by *Journal of the American Statistical Association*. Reprinted by permission of Journal of the American Statistical Association via the Copyright Clearance Center.
Reprinted by permission, *Visual Explanations: Images and Quantities, Evidence and Narrative*, by Edward Tufte, Graphics Press 1997.

An additional advantage of the model-building approach is that it often provides greater flexibility and allows more detailed or specialized descriptions of the relations among variables to be tested. For instance, in square, two-way tables (such as those classifying the occupations of fathers and sons or attitudes of husbands and wives) specialized models that deal with symmetry or forms of lack of symmetry may be fit and tested. Such models are usually of much greater substantive interest than the hypothesis of general association. Similarly, specialized models for ordinal variables allow more detailed tests of the nature of association to be examined. Chapter 4, 6, and 7 illustrate many forms of these specialized models.

1.4   Graphical Methods for Categorical Data

> You can see a lot, just by looking.
>
> Yogi Berra

The graphical methods for categorical data described in this book are in some cases straightforward adaptations of more familiar visualization techniques developed for quantitative data. The graphical principles and strategies, and the relations between the visualization approach and traditional statistical methods are described in *SAS System for Statistical Graphics, First Edition*, Chapter 1, and Cleveland (1993b). Another perspective on visual data display is presented in Section 1.4.1. However, the discrete nature of categorical data implies that some familiar graphical methods need to be adapted, while in other cases, we require a new graphic metaphor for data display. These issues are illustrated in Section 1.4.2.

1.4.1   Goals and Design Principles for Visual Data Display

Designing good graphics is surely an art, but as surely, it is one that ought to be informed by science. In constructing a graph, quantitative and qualitative information is encoded by visual features, such as position, size, texture, symbols, and color. This translation is reversed when a person studies a graph. The representation of numerical magnitude and categorical grouping, and the perception of patterns and their *meanings* must be extracted from the visual display.

There are many views of graphs, of graphical perception, and of the roles of data visualization in discovering and communicating information. On the one hand, a graphical display may be regarded as a "stimulus" — a package of information to be conveyed to an idealized observer. From this perspective, certain questions are of interest: Which form or graphic aspect promotes greater accuracy or speed of judgment (for a specific task or question)? What aspects lead to greatest memorability or impact? Cleveland (Cleveland and McGill, 1984, 1985; Cleveland, 1993a), and Lewandowsky and Spence (Lewandowsky and Spence, 1989; Spence, 1990) have made important contributions to our understanding of these aspects of graphical display.

An alternative view regards a graphical display as an act of communication — like a narrative, or even a poetic text or work of art. This perspective places the greatest emphasis on the selected communication goal to be achieved, and judges the effectiveness of a graphical display in how well it meets that goal. Kosslyn (1985, 1989) and Tufte (1983, 1990, 1997) have articulated this perspective most clearly.

In this view, an effective graphical display, like good writing, requires an understanding of its *purpose* — what aspects of the data are to be communicated to the viewer. In writing, we communicate most effectively when we know our audience and tailor the message appropriately. So too, we may construct a graph in different ways: for personal use, to present at a conference or a meeting of our colleagues, or to publish in a research report or in a communication to a general audience (Friendly, 1991, Chapter 1).

Figure 1.3 shows one type of organization of visualization methods in terms of the primary use or intended communication goal, the functional presentation goal, and the suggested corresponding design principles that are applicable.

Figure 1.3   A taxonomy of the basic functions of data display by intended use and presentation goal

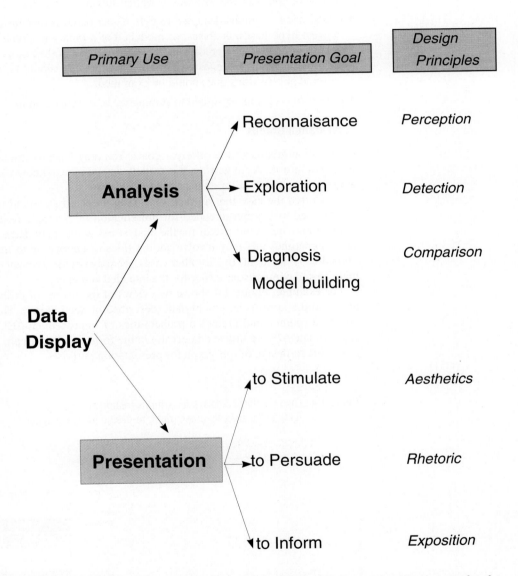

Basic Functions of Data Display

The first distinction identifies *Analysis* or *Presentation* as the primary use of a data graphic (with the understanding that a specific graph may serve both purposes — or, sadly, neither).

Analysis Graphs

Graphs used for data analysis should clearly show the data, but they should also "force us to notice what we never expected to see" (Tukey, 1977, p. vi).

Among graphical methods designed to help study or understand a body of data, it is possible to distinguish those methods designed for different purposes. As suggested in Figure 1.3, each presentation goal is associated with somewhat different design principles.

- *reconnaissance* — a preliminary examination or an overview of a possibly complex terrain. For this goal, we may be willing to sacrifice detail for a wider field of view. For example, with a large, multi-way contingency table, we might want to examine the collection of one-way and two-way marginal subtables visually.

- *exploration* — graphs designed to help detect patterns or unusual circumstances, or to suggest hypotheses, analyses, or models. For a binary response and a number of categorical or quantitative predictors, a collection of smoothed plots of the response against each predictor may suggest important variables that should be included in a model or extreme observations that should be examined.

- *diagnosis* — graphs designed to summarize or critique a numerical statistical summary.

Presentation Graphs

Presentation graphics have different goals. You may want to stimulate, or to persuade, or simply to inform. As in writing, it is usually a good idea to know what it is you want to say with a graph, and to tailor its message to that goal.

It is often the case that a graph originally prepared as an aid to data analysis can be transformed to a graph intended for presentation by a simple re-design. Sometimes this entails removing detail useful for the analyst but which may detract from the major message; sometimes this may involve adding titles or annotation to make the message more immediately apparent. In still other cases, we may decide to change the graphic format to make visual comparisons easier for the intended audience.

For example, Figure 1.4 shows two views of the results of fitting a logistic regression model to the arthritis treatment data (described in Section 6.4). The left panel shows the observed (points) and predicted probabilities of improvement (± 1 standard error, giving approximate 67% confidence intervals) in the form of a line graph. The right panel shows a possible re-design of this graph for presentation purposes.

Figure 1.4   Two graphical displays for arthritis treatment data.
Left: initial analysis graph; right: re-design for presentation.

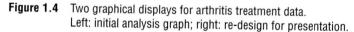
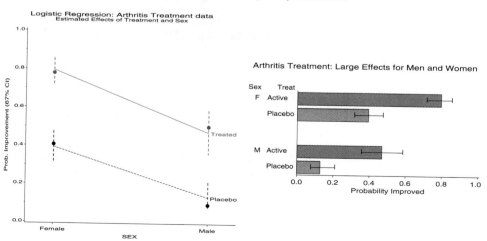

The line graph might be preferred for analysis purposes because it shows (a) the observed and fitted probabilities are quite similar, (b) there is a large effect of both treatment and sex, and (c) the effect of treatment is about the same for both men and women. The presentation version contains the same predicted probabilities and error bars as the original graph, but, for simplicity, omits the observed probabilities. The title explicitly announces the conclusion to be drawn from the graph.

1.4.2   Categorical Data Requires Different Graphical Methods

We will see in Chapters 6 and 7 that statistical models for discrete response data and for frequency data are close analogs of the linear regression and ANOVA models that are used for quantitative data. These analogies suggest that the graphical methods commonly used for quantitative data may be adapted directly to categorical data.

Happily, it turns out that many of the analysis graphs and diagnostic displays (e.g., influence plots, added variable and partial residual plots, etc.), which have become common adjuncts in the analysis of quantitative data, have been extended to generalized linear models including logistic regression and log-linear models.

Unhappily, the familiar techniques for displaying raw data are often disappointing when applied to categorical data. For example, the simple scatterplot is widely used, together with the fitted linear model, to show the relation between quantitative response and predictors. For the arthritis data in case form (Appendix B.1), the analogous plot for a logistic regression model (predicting Pr(Some or Marked) improvement from Age) shown in the left panel of Figure 1.5, is, well, underwhelming. First, the response Improve takes on only the values 0 and 1, and Age (in years) is also discrete, so, many points overplot in this graph.[3] Second, although this graph is enhanced with the curve of predicted probabilities under the fitted model (solid line) and 95% confidence bands (dashed lines), it is hard to appreciate how the data points relate to the fitted model. (Can you see that the probability of improvement increases with age?)

These problems may be reduced to some degree by smoothing and by jiggling the points to avoid overplotting. The right panel of Figure 1.5 shows a modest improvement. Here, the raw observations were offset by stacking down from 1 and up from 0 wherever duplicate observations occurred. In addition, the observations were grouped into tenths by age; the lower boundaries of the age categories are shown by the tick marks on the horizontal scale. The proportion of Improved responses in each age group is then plotted (squares), and

Figure 1.5   Graphical displays for Arthritis treatment data.
Left: raw data with logistic regression on age; right: stacked raw data, logistic regression, and smoothed lowess curve.

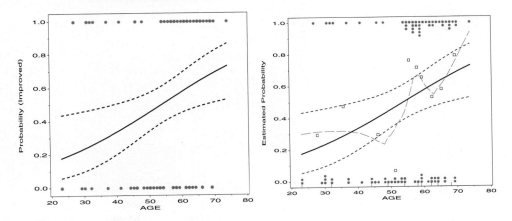

---

[3]Only 51 distinct points are shown for the 84 observations.

a non-parametric (lowess) smoothed curve is added to the plot. Although the smoothed curve is somewhat jagged, we now have a clearer visual impression that the probability of improvement increases with age, and we can see the large number of 1 responses among older people.

In Figure 1.5, the quantitative variable Age supports the use of the scatterplot as the graphic format for visual display. A more essential difference between quantitative data and categorical data arises when all variables are categorical, as in a contingency table like Table 1.2. Then, we find that a different visual representation is more natural and useful (Friendly, 1995, 1997).

For quantitative data, magnitude can be represented by length (in a bar chart) or by position along a scale (dotplots, scatterplots). When the data is purely categorical, design principles of perception, detection, and comparison (Friendly, 1999b) suggest that frequencies are most usefully represented as *areas*. In spite of the fact that (in magnitude estimation tasks) judgments of area are known to be less accurate than those of length (e.g., Cleveland and McGill, 1984), here are two fundamental reasons why area is a preferred visual representation for count data:

- multiplicative relations of probabilities and expected frequencies translate readily into height and width of rectangles, whose area then depicts a cell value.

- a concrete, physical model for categorical data (Friendly, 1995) based on count $\sim$ area yields a surprising range of correct, but novel, interpretations for statistical principles (maximum likelihood), estimation techniques (iterative proportional fitting, Newton–Raphson) and statistical concepts (power, why components of likelihood-ratio G^2 can be negative).

The first reason is illustrated in Figure 1.6, a sieve diagram (Section 3.5) for the Berkeley admissions data, broken down by department. In this display, each box has a height

Figure 1.6   Sieve diagram for Berkeley admissions data. Each box has area proportional to its expected frequency and is cross-ruled with boxes equal to the observed frequency.

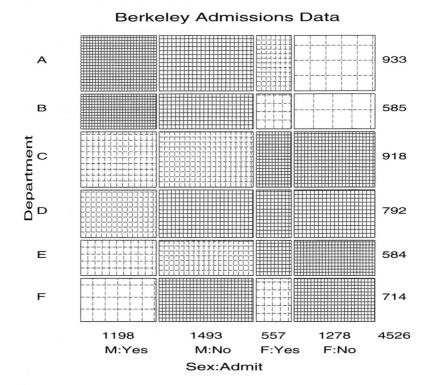

Figure 1.7 Conceptual model for categorical data

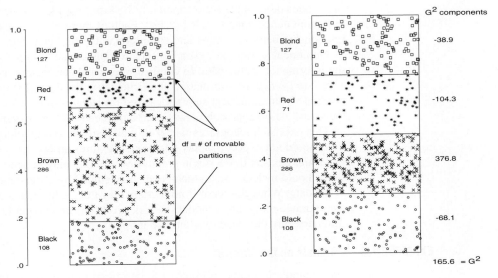

proportional to the marginal total for the corresponding department and a width proportional to the column marginal total, so the area is proportional to the expected frequency under independence. The observed frequency in each cell is shown by the number of cross-ruled boxes, so departures from independence are shown visually as variations in shading density.

The second point is illustrated in Figure 1.7, using data (see Table 3.2) on $n = 592$ individuals classified by hair color. In the conceptual model (Friendly, 1995, Sall, 1991), categorical observations are likened to molecules of an ideal gas confined to chambers separated by movable partitions. In both panels of the figure, the number of symbols in each box exactly equals the number of observations in each hair-color category.

When the location of the partitions are unconstrained, as shown in the left panel of Figure 1.7, the forces balance in each chamber by moving to the positions of minimum potential energy, so that the height of each chamber is $p_i = n_i/n$, which is the maximum likelihood estimate of the probability π_i in each cell.

To test the hypothesis that all hair colors are equally likely, imagine forcing the partitions to move to the positions where $\pi_i = \frac{1}{4}$, as shown in the right panel. The change in energy in each compartment is then $-(\log p_i - \log \pi_i) = -\log(p_i/\pi_i)$, the change in negative log-likelihood. Sum these and multiply by 2 to get the likelihood ratio G^2. This gives a concrete interpretation of G^2 as a measure of the effort to maintain belief in the hypothesis in the face of the data.

This concrete model supplies neat explanations of many other results for categorical data, extends readily to multiway tables, and provides a rationale for the graphic representation of counts by area or by visual density. It also serves as the basis for the mosaic display described in Chapter 4.

1.5   Visualization = Graphing + Fitting + Graphing

> Look here, upon this picture, and on this.
>
> William Shakespeare, *Hamlet*

Statistical summaries, hypothesis tests, and the numerical parameters derived in fitted models are designed to capture a particular feature of the data. An analysis of the data from Table 1.1, for example, shows that 44.5% of male applicants were admitted to Berkeley, compared to 30.4% of female applicants, giving a Pearson chi-square of 92.2 with 1 degree of freedom for association between admission and gender ($p < 0.001$). Expressed in terms of the odds ratio, males were apparently 1.84 times as likely to be admitted as females, with 99% confidence bounds 1.562–2.170. Each of these numbers expresses some part of the relationship between gender and admission in the Berkeley data.

Numerical summaries, even for such a small dataset as this, are designed to compress the information in the data. In contrast, the visualization approach to data analysis is designed to (a) *expose* information and structure in the data, (b) *supplement* the information available from numerical summaries, and (c) *suggest* more adequate models. In general, the visualization approach seeks to serve the needs of both summarization and exposure.

This approach recognizes that both data analysis and graphing are iterative processes. You should not expect that any one model captures all features of the data, any more than you should expect that a single graph shows all that may be seen. In most cases, the initial steps should include some graphical display guided by understanding of the subject matter of the data. What you learn from a graph may then help suggest features of the data to be incorporated into a fitted model. Your desire to ensure that the fitted model is an adequate summary may then lead to additional graphs.

EXAMPLE 1.3   **Lifeboats on the *Titanic***

One example is shown in Figure 1.8, described in more detail in Example 3.18. The left panel shows a trilinear plot of the composition of lifeboats on the *Titanic*. Each point in the plot shows the relative proportions of male passengers and identifies the lifeboats that have 10% or more men, women and children, and men-of-crew reported in each of the 18 lifeboats launched from the port and starboard sides of that ill-fated vessel. Trilinear plots are described in Section 3.8, but essentially, the points near the top apex represent boats that are almost all filled with women and children.

Figure 1.8   Two graphical displays for *Titanic* lifeboat data.
Left: trilinear plot, right: logistic regression.

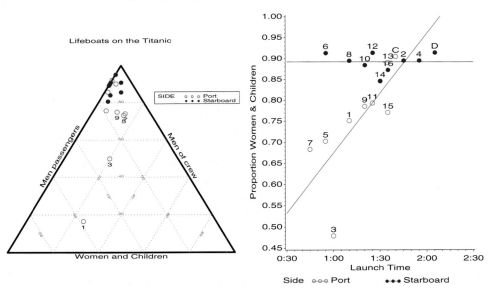

That graph suggested that the procedures for loading the lifeboats might have differed for the port and starboard side of the ship. This led to fitting a logistic regression model to predict the proportion of women and children loaded over a period of time, with separate slopes and intercepts for the port and starboard sides. The panel on the right of Figure 1.8 shows predicted proportions from this model, with simple linear regression lines for the two sides. Even without further details about the data or the analysis, the graph clearly shows that passengers on the two sides of the *Titanic* were subject to different regimes for loading the lifeboats.   □

This interplay between graphing and fitting can be expressed as

$$\textbf{Visualization} = \textbf{Graphing} + \textbf{Fitting} + \textbf{Graphing} + \cdots \ ,$$

where the ellipsis ($\cdots$) reminds us that there are often additional steps.

Sometimes a visualization is sufficiently strong (as, perhaps in Figure 1.4 or in the panel on the right side of Figure 1.8), that hypothesis tests and model parameters serve an ancillary role in understanding the effects in the data. *p*-values are useful in the conventions of scientific communication, but perhaps less convincing evidence than a graph whose conclusions hit you between the eyes (sometimes called the Intraocular Traumatic Test).

In other cases, graphing serves as a supporting member of the data-analytic cast. Model-based methods rely on assumptions about the data. Diagnostic plots for logistic regression (Section 6.6) and log-linear models (Section 7.7) may provide comfort that the assumptions on which these inferences depend are reasonable for the data at hand, or the plots may suggest that some modification of the model would help us to rest more easily.

In any event, it is well to remember that data analysis requires both summarization and exposure, and the needs of both are served by the combination of graphing and fitting.

1.5.1   Static vs. Dynamic Graphics

The confines of a book and of the software that are described here for visualizing categorical data limit this presentation to static displays that are produced by SAS programs. Many of these static graphics are made considerably easier to use and more flexible when you use SAS macros as illustrated in the following chapters and described in Appendix A.

The most productive use of these methods requires the addition of two aspects of interactive graphics that presently are being developed by me (Friendly, 1996) and by others (Theus and Lauer, 1999; Young, 1994).

- The first aspect relates to interactive methods for choosing variables, parameters, and options for analysis and graphical displays. The development tools for this form of interactivity are provided in SAS/AF and most of the macro programs described here may be easily wrapped in an interactive front-end.

- A second aspect of dynamic graphics is related to the ability to interact with multiple, linked views of a dataset, so that, for example, selecting a subset of cases in one view highlights them in all other views. SAS/INSIGHT is a prototype for this type of interaction in SAS software. JMP software provides another route.

I look forward to the possible development of more interactive methods and the extension of multiple, linked data views for categorical data to be used with SAS software. Nevertheless, it is necessary to understand the various forms of graphic displays that are particularly useful for discrete data before learning how to employ them interactively.

Chapter

2

Fitting and Graphing Discrete Distributions

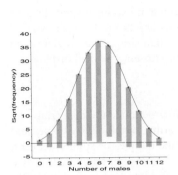

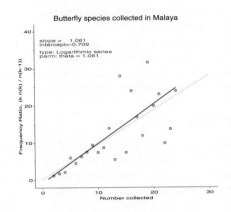

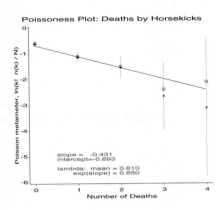

Discrete data often follows various theoretical probability models. Graphic displays are used to visualize goodness-of-fit, to diagnose an appropriate model, and to determine the impact of individual observations on estimated parameters.

2.1 Introduction

Not everything that counts can be counted, and not everything that can be counted counts.

Albert Einstein

Discrete frequency distributions often involve counts of occurrences, such as accident fatalities, words in passages of text, births of twins, events of terrorism or suicide, or blood cells with a specific characteristic. Typically, such data consists of a table that records that the n_k of the observations pertain to the basic outcome value k, $k = 0, 1, \ldots$. For such data, you often want to understand the process that gives rise to these numbers, or to estimate frequencies for outcome values k that you did not observe. Both goals can be approached by examining how closely the data follows a specific discrete probability distribution, such as the Poisson, the binomial, or the geometric distribution.

The properties of some of the most widely used discrete distributions are briefly described in Section 2.2, along with SAS techniques for calculating and visualizing these distributions. Section 2.3 presents theory and visualization techniques related to fitting these distributions to empirical data. In some cases, you may not know *which* discrete distribution should be fit to a specific dataset. Section 2.4 describes a simple graphical method designed to determine an appropriate distribution type. A more robust graphical method for diagnosing whether a specific dataset follows the Poisson distribution is illustrated in Section 2.5. Because the discrete distributions described here are members of a more general, parametric family, the *power series*, these techniques can be applied to all of them. Several SAS macros to simplify the fitting and graphing of discrete distributions are presented throughout this chapter.

The tables described in Example 2.1 through Example 2.5 illustrate several discrete datasets. For data such as this, various discrete distributions can be fit and you can test hypotheses that the fit is reasonably close. However, rather than simply summarizing the goodness-of-fit in a single number, we learn more from well-chosen graphical displays.

EXAMPLE 2.1   Deaths by horse kicks

One of the oldest and best known examples of a Poisson distribution is the data from von Bortkiewicz (1898) about deaths of soldiers in the Prussian army from kicks by horses and mules, as shown in Table 2.1.[1] von Bortkiewicz tabulated the number of soldiers in each of 14 army corps during the 20 years from 1875 to 1894 who died after being kicked by a horse (Andrews and Herzberg, 1985, p. 18). Table 2.1 shows the data used by Fisher (1925) for 10 of these army corps, summed over 20 years, giving 200 'corps-years' observations. In 109 corps-years, no deaths occurred; 65 corps-years had 1 death, etc. The dataset is given more fully in Appendix B.14. The distribution is plotted in Figure 2.1.   □

Table 2.1   Deaths by horse kicks

Number of Deaths (k)	Number of Corps-Years (n_k)
0	109
1	65
2	22
3	3
4	1
	$N = 200$

Figure 2.1   von Bortkiewicz's data

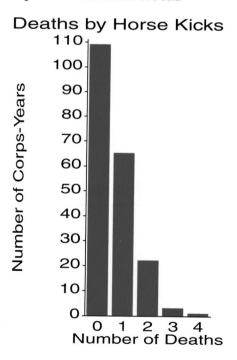

EXAMPLE 2.2   Federalist Papers

In 1787–88, Alexander Hamilton, John Jay, and James Madison wrote a series of newspaper essays to persuade the voters of New York State to ratify the U.S. Constitution. The essays were titled the *Federalist Papers* and all were signed with the pseudonym "Publius." Of the 77 papers published, the author(s) of 65 are known, but *both* Hamilton and Madison later claimed sole authorship of the remaining 12 papers. Mosteller and Wallace (1984) investigated the use of statistical methods to identify authors of disputed works based on the frequency distributions of certain key function words. They concluded that Madison had authored the 12 disputed papers.

Table 2.2 shows the distribution of the occurrence of one of these "marker" words. The word *may* occurs in 262 blocks of text (each about 200 words long) in the *Federalist Papers* and in other essays known to be written by James Madison. In 156 blocks, the word *may* did not occur; it occurred once in 63 blocks, etc. The distribution is plotted in Figure 2.2.

Table 2.2   Number of Occurrences of the word *may* in *Federalist Papers* and essays written by James Madison[2]

Number of Occurrences (k)	Blocks of Text (n_k)
0	156
1	63
2	29
3	8
4	4
5	1
6	1
	N = 262

Figure 2.2   Mosteller & Wallace data

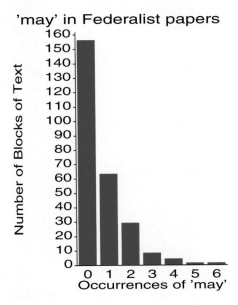

Note that the distributions of these datasets in Figure 2.1 and Figure 2.2 are superficially similar in shape: both have their modes at $k = 0$ and frequencies n_k that steadily decline as k increases. Nevertheless, it turns out, the Horse Kicks data is reasonably well-described by a Poisson distribution, but the Madison data is not (Mosteller and Wallace concluded that a negative binomial distribution provides a better fit).   □

Several other discrete distributions are illustrated by Examples 2.3, 2.4, and 2.5.

EXAMPLE 2.3   Women in queues

Jinkinson and Slater (1981) and Hoaglin and Tukey (1985) give the frequency distribution of the number of females observed in queues of length 10 in a London Underground station. If it is assumed that people line up independently, and that men and women are equally likely to be found in a queue (not necessarily reasonable assumptions), then the number of women out of 10 would have a (symmetric) binomial distribution with parameters $N = 10$

---

[2]*Exploring Data Tables, Trends, and Shapes*, David C. Hoaglin, Frederick Mosteller, and John W. Tukey, Copyright © 1985 John Wiley & Sons, Inc. Reprinted by permission of John Wiley & Sons, Inc.

and $p = \frac{1}{2}$. The frequency distribution shown in Table 2.3 appears systematically asymmetric, as you can see more clearly in the histogram (Figure 2.3). However, there is no real reason to expect that males and females are equally likely to be found in queues in the London underground, so you may be interested in estimating p from the data and determining if a binomial distribution fits.   □

Table 2.3   Number of women in 100 queues of length 10[3]

Number of women (k)	Number of queues (n_k)
0	1
1	3
2	4
3	23
4	25
5	19
6	18
7	5
8	1
9	1
10	0
	N=100

Figure 2.3   Women in queues of length 10

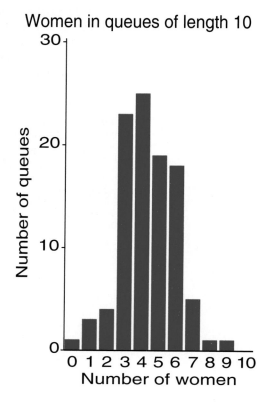

Women in queues of length 10

EXAMPLE 2.4   Weldon's dice

Common examples of binomial distributions involve tossing coins or dice. Perhaps the most industrious dice-tosser of all times, Weldon tallied the results of throwing 12 dice 26,306 times (a task that presumably required a good amount of leisure time). He reported his results in a letter to Francis Galton dated February 2, 1894, in order "to judge whether the differences between a series of group frequencies and a theoretical law . . . were more than might be attributed to the chance fluctuations of random sampling" (Kemp and Kemp, 1991). In his seminal paper, Pearson (1900) used Weldon's data to illustrate the χ^2 goodness-of-fit test, as did Kendall and Stuart (1963, Table 5.1, p. 121). This data is shown here as Table 2.4, in terms of the number of occurrences of either a 5 or a 6 in the throw of 12 dice. If the dice were all identical and perfectly fair (balanced), you would expect that $p = \Pr\{5 \text{ or } 6\} = \frac{1}{3}$ and the distribution of the numbers 5 or 6 would be binomial. A peculiar feature of this data, as presented by Kendall and Stuart, (not uncommon in discrete distributions) is that the frequencies of 10 to 12 successes are grouped together. This grouping must be taken into account in fitting the distribution. The distribution is shown in Figure 2.4.   □

---

[3]*Exploring Data Tables, Trends, and Shapes*, David C. Hoaglin, Frederick Mosteller, and John W. Tukey, copyright © 1985 John Wiley & Sons, Inc. Reprinted by permission of John Wiley & Sons, Inc.

Table 2.4 Frequencies of a 5 or a 6 in throws of 12 dice[4]

Number of 5s or 6s (k)	Frequency (n_k)
0	185
1	1149
2	3265
3	5475
4	6114
5	5194
6	3067
7	1331
8	403
9	105
10+	18
	N=26306

Figure 2.4 Weldon's dice data

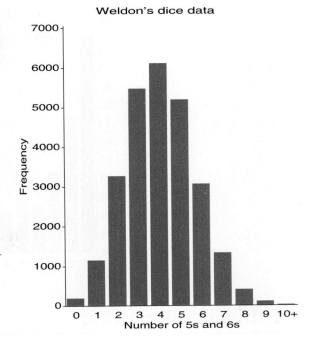

EXAMPLE 2.5   Butterfly species in Malaya

In studies of the diversity of animal species, tokens (individuals) are collected and classified by species. The distribution of the number of species (types), where $k = 1, 2, \ldots$ tokens were collected, forms a kind of type-token distribution. An early example of this kind of distribution was presented by Fisher, et al. (1943). Table 2.5 lists the number of tokens of each of 501 species of butterfly collected in Malaya. There were 118 species for which just a single instance was found, 74 species for which two tokens were found, down to 3 species for which 24 tokens were collected. However, Fisher et al. note that the distribution was truncated at $k = 24$. Type-token distributions are often J-shaped and have a long upper tail, as shown in Figure 2.5.   □

Table 2.5 Number of butterfly species for which k tokens were collected[5]

Number of Tokens (k)	Number of Species (n_k)	Number of Tokens (k)	Number of Species (n_k)
1	118	13	6
2	74	14	12
3	44	15	6
4	24	16	9
5	29	17	9
6	22	18	6
7	20	19	10
8	19	20	10
9	20	21	11
10	15	22	5
11	12	23	3
12	14	24	3
			N = 501

[4]Reprinted with permission from *The American Statistician*. Copyright © 1991 by the American Statistical Association. All rights reserved.
[5]*Exploring Data Tables, Trends, and Shapes*, David C. Hoaglin, Frederick Mosteller, and John W. Tukey, copyright © 1985 John Wiley & Sons, Inc. Reprinted by permission of John Wiley & Sons, Inc.

Figure 2.5   Butterfly species in Malaya

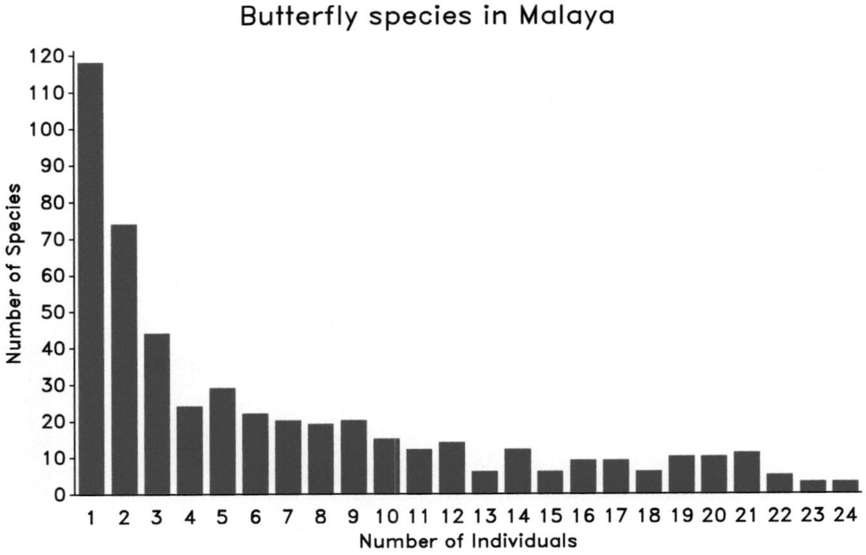

2.2 Discrete Distributions

This section briefly reviews the characteristics of some of the important discrete distributions encountered in practice. For each distribution, properties and generating mechanisms are described, and you see how the distribution parameters can be estimated and how to plot the frequency distribution. For more detailed information about these and other discrete distributions, Johnson, et al. (1992) present the most comprehensive treatment and Zelterman (1999, Chapter 2) gives a concise summary.

2.2.1 The Binomial Distribution

The binomial distribution arises as the distribution of the number of events-of-interest that occur in n independent trials when the probability of the event on any one trial is the constant value $p = $ Pr(event). For example, if 15% of the population has red hair, the number of red-heads in randomly sampled groups of $n = 10$ might follow a binomial distribution, Bin(10, 0.15). Over n independent trials, the number of events k may range from 0 to n; if X is a random variable that has a binomial distribution, the probability that $X = k$ is given by

$$\text{Bin}(n, p) : \Pr\{X = k\} \equiv p(k) = \binom{n}{k} p^k (1-p)^{n-k} \qquad k = 0, 1, \ldots, n \ , \qquad (2.1)$$

where $\binom{n}{k} = n!/k!(n-k)!$ is the number of ways of choosing k out of n. The first three (central) moments of the binomial distribution are (letting $q = 1 - p$),

$$\text{Mean}[X] = np$$

$$\text{Var}[X] = npq$$

$$\text{Skew}[X] = npq(q - p) \ ,$$

so, when $p = .5$, the binomial distribution has its maximum variance and is symmetric.

If you have data in the form of a discrete (binomial) distribution (and n is known), then the maximum likelihood estimator of p can be obtained as

$$\hat{p} = \frac{\bar{x}}{n} = \frac{(\sum_k k \times n_k)/\sum_k n_k}{n} \; ,$$

with sampling variance pq/n.

Calculation and Visualization

In SAS, you can calculate binomial probabilities (Equation 2.1) by using the PROBBNML function and generate random data from a binomial distribution with the RANBIN function or the CALL RANBIN routine. The PROBBNML function, probbnml(p,n,m), calculates the cumulative probabilities, $\sum_{k=0}^{k=m} p(k)$. Therefore, to find individual probability densities, you must subtract successive values for k and $k-1$. In SAS Release 6.12 and more-current versions, the general PDF function directly calculates probability densities for the binomial and most other distributions. For the binomial distribution, it is called as pdf('binomial',m,p,n).

Discrete distributions are easily visualized by plotting the probability density (or expected frequencies in a total sample of a specified size) against the random variable (k), for specific values of the distribution parameters.

For example, assume that 15% of the population has red hair and 35% has brown hair. What are the probabilities that in groups of $n = 10$ people, $k = 0, 1, \ldots, 10$ have red hair or brown hair, respectively? You can calculate these probabilities (and the expected frequencies in 1000 repetitions) in a DATA step as shown in the program that follows this paragraph. The results are shown in Output 2.1. I use macro variables for n and p (in the form of a DO list) so that the same program can be used for any binomial distributions. A complete distribution is generated for each combination of n and p.

```
%let N=10;
%let p=.15, .35;
title "Binomial distributions, N=&N, p=&p";
data binomial;
   reps = 1000;
   drop reps;
   N=&N;
   do p=&p;
      do k=0 to N;
         if k=0
            then prob = probbnml(p, N, 0);
            else prob = probbnml(p, N, k) - probbnml(p, N, k-1);
         freq = reps * prob;
         output;
         end;
      end;
   label freq='Frequency'
      k = 'k';
proc print;
   id p;
   by p;
run;

proc means data=binomial mean var max vardef=weight;
   var k;
   weight prob;
   by p;
```

Output 2.1   Binomial probabilities

```
        Binomial distributions, N=10, p=.15, .35

        P       N       K       PROB          FREQ

      0.15     10       0      0.19687       196.874
               10       1      0.34743       347.425
               10       2      0.27590       275.897
               10       3      0.12983       129.834
               10       4      0.04010        40.096
               10       5      0.00849         8.491
               10       6      0.00125         1.249
               10       7      0.00013         0.126
               10       8      0.00001         0.008
               10       9      0.00000         0.000
               10      10      0.00000         0.000

      0.35     10       0      0.01346        13.463
               10       1      0.07249        72.492
               10       2      0.17565       175.653
               10       3      0.25222       252.220
               10       4      0.23767       237.668
               10       5      0.15357       153.570
               10       6      0.06891        68.910
               10       7      0.02120        21.203
               10       8      0.00428         4.281
               10       9      0.00051         0.512
               10      10      0.00003         0.028
```

Output 2.2   Means and variances for binomial probabilities

```
        Binomial distributions, N=10, p=.15, .35

        Analysis Variable : K k


--------------------------------- P=0.15 ---------------------


            Mean        Maximum        Variance
        -----------------------------------------
         1.5000000     10.0000000      1.2750000
        -----------------------------------------


--------------------------------- P=0.35 ---------------------


            Mean        Maximum        Variance
        -----------------------------------------
         3.5000000     10.0000000      2.2750000
        -----------------------------------------
```

Notice that in the PROC MEANS step the option VARDEF=WEIGHT is used to correctly calculate the variance from a grouped frequency distribution, producing the output in Output 2.2. These distributions are shown side-by-side in Figure 2.6. They are plotted by using PROC GCHART with *p* as a group variable.

```
proc gchart data=binomial;
   vbar k /sumvar=freq group=p midpoints=0 to 10
      coutline=black frame raxis=axis1;
   pattern1 v=solid c=gray c0;
   axis1 order=(0 to 350 by 50);
run; quit;
```

Figure 2.6   Binomial distributions for *n* = 10 trials

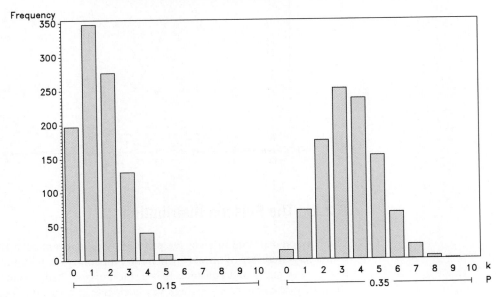

Alternatively, you may prefer to plot such distributions as frequency polygons or as needle graphs by using PROC GPLOT. For example, Figure 2.7 shows frequency polygons for the binomial distributions Bin(10, *p*) with *p* = 0.15(0.20)0.75, obtained by running the binomial DATA step with

```
%let p=.15 to .75 by .20;
```

The PROC GPLOT step (excluding statements for symbols, axes, and the legend) is

```
proc gplot data=binomial;
   plot freq * k = p / frame vminor=1 hminor=0 ... ;
```

Figure 2.7   Binomial distributions for $n = 10$ trials, as frequency polygons

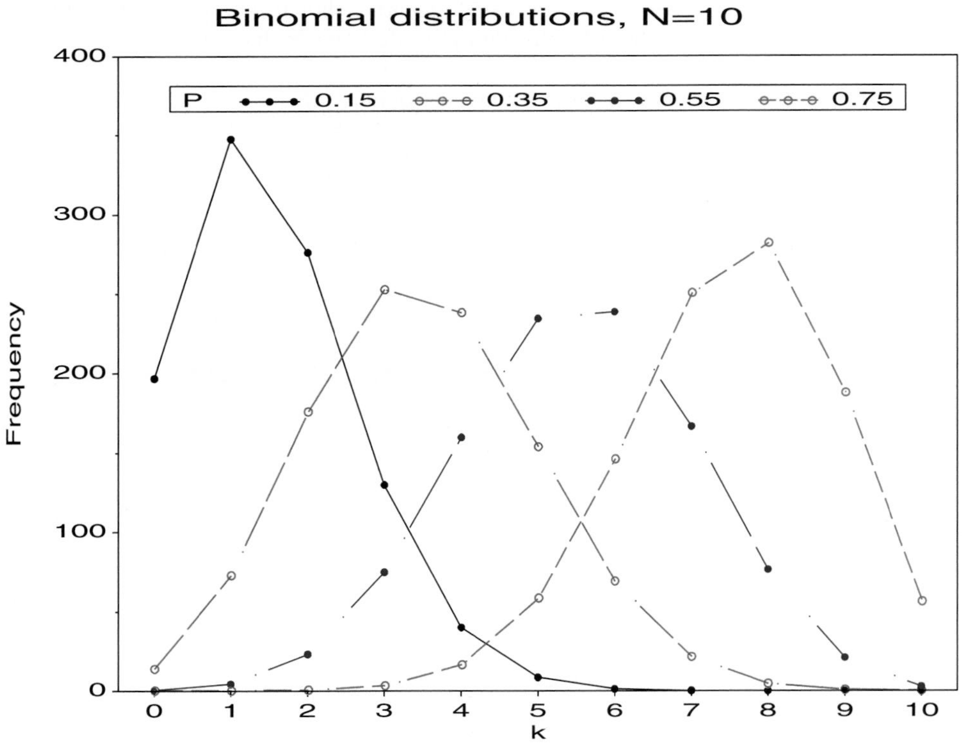

2.2.2   The Poisson Distribution

The Poisson distribution gives the probability of an event occurring $k = 0, 1, 2, \ldots$ times over a large number of "trials", when the probability, p, that the event occurs on any one trial is very small and constant; hence, the Poisson distribution is usually applied to the study of rare events, such as highway accidents at a specific location, deaths from horse kicks, or defects in a well-controlled manufacturing process.

For the Poisson distribution, the probability function is

$$\text{Pois}(\lambda) : \Pr\{X = k\} \equiv p(k) = \frac{e^{-\lambda}\,\lambda^k}{k!} \qquad k = 0, 1, \ldots \tag{2.2}$$

where the parameter λ turns out to be the mean of the distribution. The first three (central) moments of the Poisson distribution are, in fact, all equal to λ.

$$\text{Mean}[X] = \lambda$$

$$\text{Var}[X] = \lambda$$

$$\text{Skew}[X] = \lambda$$

So, the mean and variance of the Poisson distribution are always the same. This property is sometimes used to identify a distribution as Poisson. For the binomial distribution, the mean (Np) is always greater than the variance (Npq); for other distributions (negative binomial and geometric), the mean is less than the variance.

The maximum likelihood estimator of the parameter λ in Equation 2.2 is the mean of the distribution

$$\hat{\lambda} = \bar{x} = \frac{\sum_k k\, n_k}{\sum_k n_k} \enspace.$$

Therefore, the expected frequencies can be estimated by substituting the sample mean into Equation 2.2. Moreover, Poisson variables have a nice reproductive property: if $X_1, X_2, \ldots X_m$ are independent Poisson variables with the same parameter λ, then their sum, $\sum X_i$ is a Poisson variate with parameter $m\lambda$; if the Poisson parameters differ, the sum is still Poisson with parameter $\sum \lambda_i$.

EXAMPLE 2.6   UK soccer scores

Table 2.6 shows the distributions of goals scored by the 20 teams in the 1995/96 season of the Premier League of the UK Football Association as presented by Lee (1997).[6] Over a season, each team plays each other team exactly one time, so the total number of games is $20 \times 19 = 380$. Because there may be an advantage for the home team, the goals scored have been classified in the table as Home-Team goals and Away-Team goals.

Table 2.6   Goals scored by Home and Away teams in 380 games in the Premier Football League, 1995/96 season

Home-Team Goals	Away-Team Goals					Total
	0	1	2	3	4+	
0	27	29	10	8	2	76
1	59	53	14	12	4	142
2	28	32	14	12	4	90
3	19	14	7	4	1	45
4+	7	8	10	2	0	27
Total	140	136	55	38	11	380

If we assume that in any small interval of time there is a small, constant probability that the Home team or the Away team may score a goal, the distributions of the goals scored by Home teams (the row totals in Table 2.6) may be modeled as $\text{Pois}(\lambda_H)$, and the distribution of the goals scored by Away teams (the column totals) may be modeled as $\text{Pois}(\lambda_A)$.

If the number of goals scored by the Home and Away teams are independent[7], you would expect that the total number of goals scored in any game would be distributed as $\text{Pois}(\lambda_H + \lambda_A)$. These totals are shown in Table 2.7. As a preliminary check of the distributions for the Home-Team and Away-Team goals, you can determine if the means and variances are reasonably close to each other. If so, then the TOTAL (goals) variable should also have a mean and variance equal to the sum of those statistics for the Home-Team and Away-Team goals.

Table 2.7   Total goals scored in 380 games in the Premier Football League, 1995/96 season

Total goals	0	1	2	3	4	5	6	7
Number of games	27	88	91	73	49	31	18	3

---

[6]Lee (1997, p. 16) apparently has the Home and Away labels reversed in his table. The row and column labels in Table 2.6 show the means 1.48 for Home teams and 1.06 for Away teams. The raw data was verified from data listed at `http://users.aol.com/mabstabs/soccer.html`

[7]This question is examined visually in Chapter 4 (Example 4.2) and Chapter 5 (Example 5.10), where we find that the answer is "basically, yes."

The following statements read the data from Table 2.6, calculate the TOTAL goals, and find the distribution of TOTAL goals shown in Table 2.7. The PROC MEANS step produces the mean and variance of each variable, as shown in Output 2.3.

```
title 'UK Soccer scores 95/96 season';
data soccer;
    input away @;
    do home = 0 to 4;
        total = home+away;
        input freq @;
        output;
        end;
datalines;
0    27 29 10  8  2
1    59 53 14 12  4
2    28 32 14 12  4
3    19 14  7  4  1
4     7  8 10  2  0
;
proc freq;
    weight freq;
    tables total;
run;

proc means mean var vardef=weight;
    var away home total;
    weight freq;
```

Output 2.3 UK Soccer data, assessing Poissonness

```
               UK Soccer scores 95/96 season                    2

            Variable          Mean         Variance
            ------------------------------------------
            AWAY          1.0631579       1.1696953
            HOME          1.4868421       1.3129848
            TOTAL         2.5500000       2.6106579
            ------------------------------------------
```

The means are all approximately equal to the corresponding variances. More to the point, the variance of the TOTAL score is approximately equal to the sum of the individual variances. Also, note that there does appear to be an advantage for the Home team of nearly half a goal.   □

Calculation and Visualization

Poisson probabilities may be calculated by using the POISSON function, which is called as poisson(lambda, m) for a distribution that has the mean lambda. This also returns cumulative probabilities, $\sum_{k=0}^{k=m} p(k)$, which must be differenced to calculate the probability of exactly m events. The PDF function, called as pdf('poisson', m, lambda), calculates these densities directly. Random data from a Poisson distribution may be obtained by using the CALL RANPOI routine.

The following DATA step illustrates the use of the PDF function to calculate Poisson frequencies for the distributions with means (λ) 2 and 5, for $k = 0, 1, \ldots, 12$.

```
%let N=12;
%let lambda = 2, 5;
title "Poisson distributions, lambda=&lambda, k=0..&N";
data poisson;
   reps = 1000;
   drop reps;
   N=&N;
   do lambda=&lambda;
      do k=0 to N;
         prob = pdf('poisson', k, lambda);
         freq = reps * prob;
         output;
         end;
      end;
   label freq='Frequency'
         lambda='Lambda'
         k = 'k';
```

These distributions are shown in Figure 2.8. They are plotted by using PROC GCHART as shown earlier for the binomial distribution.

Figure 2.8   Poisson distributions with $\lambda = 2$ and 5. The vertical lines show the mean of each distribution; the horizontal lines show the standard deviation.

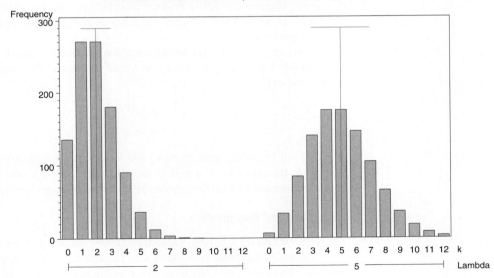

2.2.3   The Negative Binomial Distribution

The negative binomial distribution is a type of waiting-time distribution. One form of the negative binomial distribution (also called the Pascal distribution) arises when a series of Bernoulli trials is observed with the constant probability p of some event, and you ask how many trials it takes to observe n events. The probability function with parameters n

(an integer, $0 < n < \infty$) and p ($0 < p < 1$) gives the probability that k non-events (failures) are observed before the nth event (success), and can be written

$$\text{NBin}(n, p) : \text{Pr}\{X = k\} \equiv p(k) = \binom{n + k - 1}{k} p^n (1 - p)^k \qquad k = 0, 1, \ldots, \infty \quad (2.3)$$

The moments of the negative binomial distribution are

$$\text{Mean}[X] = nq/p$$

$$\text{Var}[X] = nq/p^2$$

$$\text{Skew}[X] = \frac{2 - p}{\sqrt{nq}} \ ,$$

where $q = 1 - p$.

A more general form of the negative binomial distribution allows n to take non-integer values and to be an unknown parameter. In this case, the combinatorial coefficient, $\binom{n+k-1}{k}$ in Equation 2.3 is calculated by using the gamma function, $\Gamma(\bullet)$, a generalization of the factorial for non-integer values, defined so that $\Gamma(x + 1) = x!$ when x is an integer. Then the probability function in Equation 2.3 becomes

$$\text{Pr}\{X = k\} \equiv p(k) = \frac{\Gamma(n + k)}{\Gamma(n)\Gamma(k + 1)} p^n (1 - p)^k \qquad k = 0, 1, \ldots, \infty \ . \qquad (2.4)$$

In this form, the negative binomial distribution is frequently used as an alternative to the Poisson distribution when the assumptions of the Poisson (constant probability and independence) are not satisfied, or when the variance of the distribution is greater than the mean (termed **overdispersion**). Greenwood and Yule (1920) developed the negative binomial distribution as a model for accident proneness or susceptibility of individuals to repeated attacks of disease. They assumed that, for any individual, the number of accidents or disease occurrences has a Poisson distribution with parameter λ_i. If individuals vary in proneness, so that the λ_i have a gamma distribution, the resulting distribution is the negative binomial.

When both n and p are treated as unknown parameters, maximum likelihood estimators are available but involve complex non-linear equations. The simpler method of moments estimators are

$$\hat{p} = \bar{x}/s^2$$

$$\hat{n} = \bar{x}^2/(s^2 - \bar{x}) \ ,$$

where $\bar{x}$ and s^2 are the sample mean and variance of the observed distribution. Note that if $s^2 < \bar{x}$, the estimate of n will be negative and that of p will be greater than 1, so the negative binomial distribution should be considered inappropriate.

Calculation and Visualization

The SAS PROBNEGB function calculates negative binomial cumulative probabilities for integer values of the number-of-successes parameter, n. To calculate probabilities for individual values of k, it is necessary to compute the difference between successive values $k-1$ and k, as with the binomial and Poisson distribution functions; or use the PDF function, called as pdf('negbinomial', k, p, n). For non-integer values of n, it is necessary to calculate the probabilities directly by using Equation 2.4. Random values from a negative binomial distribution may be obtained by calculating the probabilities, $p(k), k = 0, 1, \ldots$ and using these with the RANTBL function.

Figure 2.9 shows negative binomial distributions for the number of trials to observe $n = 2$ or $n = 4$ successes with $p = .2, .3, .4$, and with values of k from 0 to 20. The vertical line in each panel marks the location of the mean; the horizontal line shows the range of one standard deviation about the mean.

Figure 2.9   Negative binomial distributions for the number of trials to observe $n = 2$ or $n = 4$ successes

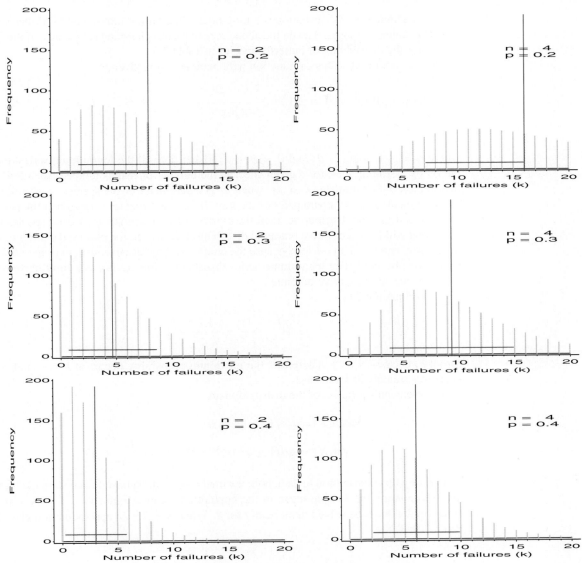

2.2.4   The Geometric Distribution

The special case of the negative binomial distribution when $n = 1$ is a geometric distribution. A series of independent trials are observed and the number of non-events (failures) preceding the first successful event are counted. The probability that there will be k failures before the first success is given by

$$\text{Geom}(p) : \Pr\{X = k\} \equiv p(k) = p(1 - p)^k \qquad k = 0, 1, \dots . \tag{2.5}$$

For this distribution the central moments are

$$\text{Mean}[X] = 1/p$$

$$\text{Var}[X] = (1 - p)/p^2$$

$$\text{Skew}[X] = (2 - p)/\sqrt{1 - p}$$

2.2.5   The Logarithmic Series Distribution

The logarithmic series distribution is a long-tailed distribution introduced by Fisher, et al. (1943) in connection with data on the abundance of tokens classified by species, of the type shown for the distribution of butterfly species in Table 2.5.

The probability distribution function with parameter θ is given by

$$\text{LogSer}(\theta) : \Pr\{X = k\} \equiv p(k) = \frac{\theta^k}{-(k \log(1 - \theta))} = \alpha\theta^k / k \qquad k = 1, 2, \ldots, \infty \; ,$$

$$(2.6)$$

where $\alpha = -1/\log(1 - \theta)$ and $0 < \theta < 1$. Fisher derived the logarithmic series distribution by assuming that, for a given species, the number of tokens trapped has a Poisson distribution with parameter $\lambda = \gamma t$, where γ is a parameter of the species (susceptibility to entrapment) and t is a parameter of the trap. If different species vary so that the parameter γ has a gamma distribution, then the number of representatives of each species that is trapped will have a negative binomial distribution. However, the observed distribution is necessarily truncated on the left because the number of species never caught (where $k = 0$) cannot be observed. The logarithmic series distribution thus occurs as a limiting form of the zero-truncated negative binomial.

From Equation 2.6,

$$\frac{p(k + 1)}{p(k)} = \frac{k\theta}{k + 1} < 1 \; ,$$

for all k, because $\theta < 1$. Therefore, the maximum probability occurs at $k = 1$ and $p(k)$ decreases steadily as k increases.

The mean and variance of the distribution are

$$\text{Mean}[X] = \alpha\theta/(1 - \theta) \equiv \mu \tag{2.7}$$

$$\text{Var}[X] = \alpha\theta(1 - \alpha\theta)/(1 - \theta)^2 = \mu(\frac{1}{1 - \theta} - \mu)$$

In fitting this distribution to data, both the method of moments and maximum likelihood involve equating the sample mean to the population mean in Equation 2.7, a non-linear equation that must be solved numerically for θ. When $\bar{x} < 25$, an approximation given by Birch (1963),

$$\hat{\theta} \approx 1 - \frac{1}{1 + [(\frac{5}{3} - \frac{1}{16} \log \bar{x})(\bar{x} - 1) + 2] \log \bar{x}} \; .$$

Another useful unbiased approximation is based on the proportion of observations at $k = 1$.

$$\hat{\theta} \approx 1 - \frac{n_1/N}{\bar{x}}$$

2.2.6   Power Series Family

I mentioned earlier that the Poisson distribution was unique among all discrete (one parameter) distributions, in that it is the only one whose mean and variance are equal (Kosambi, 1949). The relation between mean and variance of discrete distributions also provides the basis for integrating them into a general family. All of the discrete distributions described in this section are, in fact, special cases of a family of discrete distributions called the

Power Series distributions by Noack (1950) and defined by

$$p(k) = a(k)\theta^k / f(\theta) \qquad k = 0, 1, \ldots \ ,$$

with parameter $\theta > 0$, where $a(k)$ is a coefficient function that depends only on k, and $f(\theta) = \sum_k a(k)\theta^k$ is called the series function. The definitions of these functions are shown in Table 2.8.

Table 2.8   The Power Series family of discrete distributions

Discrete Distributions	Probability function, $p(k)$	Series parameter, θ	Series function, $f(\theta)$	Series coefficient, $a(k)$
Poisson	$e^{-\lambda}\lambda^k / k!$	$\theta = \lambda$	e^θ	$1/k!$
Binomial	$\binom{n}{k} p^k (1-p)^{n-k}$	$\theta = p/(1-p)$	$(1+\theta)^n$	$\binom{n}{k}$
Negative binomial	$\binom{n+k-1}{k} p^n (1-p)^k$	$\theta = (1-p)$	$(1-\theta)^{-k}$	$\binom{n+k-1}{k}$
Geometric	$p(1-p)^k$	$\theta = (1-p)$	$(1-\theta)^{-k}$	1
Logarithmic series	$\theta^k / [-k \log(1-\theta)]$	$\theta = \theta$	$-\log(1-\theta)$	$1/k$

These relations among the discrete distributions provide the basis for graphical techniques for diagnosing the form of discrete data described later in this chapter (see Section 2.5.5).

2.3   Fitting Discrete Distributions

Often, interest is focused on how closely such data follows a specific distribution, such as the Poisson, binomial, or geometric distribution. Usually, this is examined by using a classical (Pearson) goodness-of-fit chi-square test,

$$\chi^2 = \sum_{k=1}^{K} \frac{(n_k - N\hat{p}_k)^2}{N\hat{p}_k} \sim \chi^2_{(K-s-1)} \ , \qquad (2.8)$$

where there are K frequency classes, s parameters have been estimated from the data, and $\hat{p}_k$ is the estimated probability of each basic count, under the null hypothesis that the data follows the chosen distribution. An alternative test statistic is the likelihood-ratio G^2 statistic

$$G^2 = \sum_{k=1}^{K} n_k \log(n_k / N\hat{p}_k) \ , \qquad (2.9)$$

when the $\hat{p}_k$ are estimated by maximum likelihood, which also has an asymptotic $\chi^2_{(K-s-1)}$ distribution. *Asymptotic* means that these are large sample tests. A common rule-of-thumb is that all expected frequencies should exceed 1 and that fewer than 20% should be less than 5.

For the Horse-Kicks data, the mean is $122/200 = .610$. The calculation of Poisson probabilities (PHAT), expected frequencies, and contributions to χ^2 (Equation 2.8) are shown next.

k	nk	p	phat	exp	chisq
0	109	0.545	0.54335	108.670	0.00100
1	65	0.325	0.33144	66.289	0.02506
2	22	0.110	0.10109	20.218	0.15705
3	3	0.015	0.02056	4.111	0.30025
4	1	0.005	0.00313	0.627	0.22201
	===			=======	=======
	200			199.915	0.70537 $\sim$ χ^2 (3)

In this case, the χ^2 shows an exceptionally good (perhaps unreasonably good?) fit. In the word-frequency example (Example 2.2), the fit of the Poisson is not close at all. However, even a close fit may show something interesting, if we know how to look at it; conversely, it is useful to know why or where the data differs from a chosen model.

2.3.1 The GOODFIT Macro

The GOODFIT macro (Appendix A.9) carries out Pearson χ^2 and likelihood-ratio goodness-of-fit tests for the uniform, binomial, Poisson, negative binomial, logarithmic series, and geometric distributions, as well as any discrete (multinomial) distribution whose probabilities you can specify. The data may consist of individual observations on a single variable or of a grouped frequency distribution in the form shown in Table 2.1. The parameter(s) of the distribution can be specified as constants or can be estimated from the data.

The macro parameters are described in Appendix A.9. We illustrate its use in Example 2.7 and Example 2.8.

EXAMPLE 2.7 **Weldon's dice**

The data from Table 2.4 can be fit to a binomial distribution as shown in the program that follows. Note that, because the frequencies have been grouped for 10–12 successes, it is necessary to (a) input frequencies for all values of $k = 0, \ldots, 12$ by using missing values for the frequencies beyond $k = 10$; (b) specify sumat=10 in the macro call.

```
title "Weldon's dice data";
data dice;
   do k=0 to 12;
      input freq @@;
      output;
      end;
   label k='Number of 5s and 6s'
      freq='Frequency';
   datalines;
185  1149  3265  5475  6114  5194  3067  1331  403  105  18  .  .
;
proc print;
   id k;
   sum freq;
run;

title2 'Fit Binomial(12,1/3)';
%goodfit(data=dice,    var=k, freq=freq, dist=binomial, sumat=10,
   parm=.333333);

title2 'Fit Binomial(12,p)';
%goodfit(data=dice,    var=k, freq=freq, dist=binomial, sumat=10);
```

The first call to the GOODFIT macro fits the binomial distribution with parameter $p = \frac{1}{3}$ (assuming the dice to be fair) and produces the results shown in Output 2.4 and Output 2.5. The χ^2 statistics indicate that the fit is poor, and the pattern of residuals suggests that $p > \frac{1}{3}$ (the observed frequencies for larger values of k are all greater than the expected frequencies).

Output 2.4   Fitting Binomial$(12, \frac{1}{3})$ to Weldon's dice data: Observed and fitted frequencies (rounded)

```
                        Weldon's dice data
                      Fit Binomial(12,1/3)


    K      FREQ      PHAT         EXP         CHI         DEV

    0       185     0.00771      202.75     -1.24662     -5.8224
    1      1149     0.04624     1216.50     -1.93536    -11.4537
    2      3265     0.12717     3345.38     -1.38965    -12.6018
    3      5475     0.21195     5575.62     -1.34751    -14.1213
    4      6114     0.23845     6272.56     -2.00205    -17.6941
    5      5194     0.19076     5018.04      2.48395     18.9213
    6      3067     0.11127     2927.19      2.58419     16.9175
    7      1331     0.04769     1254.51      2.15967     12.5522
    8       403     0.01490      392.03      0.55391      4.7158
    9       105     0.00331       87.12      1.91582      6.2614
   10        18     0.00054       14.31      0.97689      2.8759
            =====   =======     ========
           26306   1.00000     26306.00
```

Output 2.5   Fitting Binomial$(12, \frac{1}{3})$ to Weldon's dice data: Goodness-of-fit tests

```
                        Weldon's dice data
                      Fit Binomial(12,1/3)


   Goodness-of-fit test for data set DICE

   Analysis variable:      K Number of 5s and 6s
   Distribution:           BINOMIAL
   Specified Parameters:   p = .333333


   Pearson chi-square    = 35.498479274
   Prob > chi-square     = 0.0001026185


   Likelihood ratio G2   = 35.10741191
   Prob > chi-square     = 0.000119703


   Degrees of freedom    = 10
```

The second call to the GOODFIT macro allows the parameter p to be estimated from the data, giving $\hat{p} = .3377$, and produces the results shown in Output 2.6 and Output 2.7. The fit is much better — in fact, it is quite satisfactory. So, Weldon's dice differed minutely from being absolutely fair, but with over 26,000 tosses, it is easy to detect the difference.   □

Output 2.6   Fitting Binomial(12,p) to Weldon's dice data: Observed and fitted frequencies (rounded)

```
                        Weldon's dice data
                        Fit Binomial(12,p)


    K       FREQ       PHAT         EXP        CHI         DEV

    0        185      0.00712     187.42     -0.17697    -2.1941
    1       1149      0.04359    1146.71      0.06770     2.1423
    2       3265      0.12224    3215.62      0.87084     9.9759
    3       5475      0.20775    5465.03      0.13493     4.4685
    4       6114      0.23832    6269.37     -1.96222   -17.5172
    5       5194      0.19442    5114.38      1.11338    12.6680
    6       3067      0.11565    3042.21      0.44953     7.0562
    7       1331      0.05054    1329.51      0.04093     1.7282
    8        403      0.01611     423.66     -1.00385    -6.3482
    9        105      0.00365      96.00      0.91820     4.3372
   10         18      0.00061      16.10      0.47259     2.0020
             =====    =======    ========
            26306     1.00000   26306.00
```

Output 2.7   Fitting Binomial(12,p) to Weldon's dice data: Goodness-of-fit tests

```
                        Weldon's dice data
                        Fit Binomial(12,p)


    Goodness-of-fit test for data set DICE

    Analysis variable:      K Number of 5s and 6s
    Distribution:           BINOMIAL
    Estimated Parameters:   p = 0.3377


    Pearson chi-square    = 8.1803084987
    Prob > chi-square     = 0.5160827001


    Likelihood ratio G2   = 8.1851945733
    Prob > chi-square     = 0.5155963302


    Degrees of freedom    = 9
```

EXAMPLE 2.8 **Federalist Papers**

The data on the occurrences of the word *may* in Madison's *Federalist Papers* (Table 2.2) is fit to both the Poisson and Negative binomial distributions, as shown in Output 2.8 and Output 2.9. In each case, the parameters are estimated from the data. The results for the Poisson distribution appear in Output 2.8 and Output 2.9. The results for the Negative binomial distribution appear in Output 2.10 and Output 2.11.

```
%include catdata(madison);
%goodfit(data=madison, var=count, freq=blocks, dist=poisson);

%goodfit(data=madison, var=count, freq=blocks, dist=negbin);
```

Output 2.8 Fitting the Poisson(λ) to the *Federalist Papers* data: Observed and fitted frequencies (rounded)

```
              Instances of 'may' in Federalist papers


   COUNT     BLOCKS      PHAT        EXP        CHI         DEV

     0        156      0.51867    135.891    1.72499     6.56171
     1         63      0.34050     89.211   -2.77509    -6.62056
     2         29      0.11177     29.283   -0.05231    -0.75056
     3          8      0.02446      6.408    0.62890     1.88423
     4          4      0.00401      1.052    2.87493     3.26912
     5          1      0.00053      0.138    2.31948     1.98992
     6          1      0.00006      0.015    8.01267     2.89568
             ======    =======    =======
              262      0.99999    261.998
```

Output 2.9 Fitting the Poisson(λ) to the *Federalist Papers* data: Goodness-of-fit tests

```
              Instances of 'may' in Federalist papers


       Goodness-of-fit test for data set MADISON

       Analysis variable:        COUNT Number of Occurrences
       Distribution:             POISSON
       Estimated Parameters:     lambda = 0.6565


       Pearson chi-square     = 88.92304707
       Prob > chi-square      = 0

       Likelihood ratio G2    = 25.243121314
       Prob > chi-square      = 0.0001250511

       Degrees of freedom     = 5
```

Output 2.10 Fitting the Negative binomial(n, p) to the *Federalist Papers* data: Observed and fitted frequencies

COUNT	BLOCKS	PHAT	EXP	CHI	DEV
0	156	0.59047	154.702	0.10434	1.61446
1	63	0.25343	66.398	-0.41706	-2.57290
2	29	0.09826	25.743	0.64188	2.62853
3	8	0.03674	9.625	-0.52374	-1.72003
4	4	0.01348	3.532	0.24905	0.99777
5	1	0.00489	1.281	-0.24862	-0.70425
6	1	0.00176	0.461	0.79297	1.24381
	======	=======	=======		
	262	0.99902	261.743		

Output 2.11 Fitting the Negative binomial(n, p) to the *Federalist Papers* data: Goodness-of-fit tests

```
Goodness-of-fit test for data set MADISON

Analysis variable:       COUNT Number of Occurrences
Distribution:            NEGBIN
Estimated Parameters:    n, p = 1.2397, 0.6538


Pearson chi-square    = 1.6237622915
Prob > chi-square     = 0.8045151082

Likelihood ratio G2   = 1.9839511084
Prob > chi-square     = 0.7387108792

Degrees of freedom    = 4
```

2.3.2 Plots of Observed and Fitted Frequencies

Plots of the observed and fitted frequencies can help to show both the shape of the theoretical distribution we have fitted and the pattern of any deviations between our data and theory.

Figure 2.10(a) shows the fit of the Poisson distribution to the *Federalist Papers* data, using one common form of plot that is sometimes used for this purpose. In this plot, observed frequencies are shown by bars, and fitted frequencies are shown by points that are connected by a smooth (spline) curve.

Such a plot, however, is dominated by the largest frequencies, making it hard to assess the deviations among the smaller frequencies. To make the smaller frequencies more visible, Tukey (1977) suggests plotting the frequencies on a square-root scale, which he calls a *rootogram*, as shown in Figure 2.10(b). An additional improvement is to move the rootogram bars so their tops are at the expected frequencies, which gives a *hanging rootogram*, Figure 2.10(c). This has the advantage of making it easier to judge the

pattern of departures against the horizontal reference line at 0, instead of against the curve.
A final variation is to emphasize the differences between the observed and fitted frequencies by drawing the bars to show the gaps between the 0 line and the (observed-expected)
difference, as shown in Figure 2.10(d).

These plots are produced by the ROOTGRAM macro using the (default) OUT=FIT dataset
from the GOODFIT macro, as shown in the following statements:

```
title "Instances of 'may' in Federalist papers" ;
%include catdata(madison);
%goodfit(data=madison, var=count, freq=blocks, dist=poisson, out=fit);

title;
%rootgram(data=fit, var=count, obs=blocks, btype=0, func=none);   /* a */
%rootgram(data=fit, var=count, obs=blocks, btype=0);              /* b */
%rootgram(data=fit, var=count, obs=blocks);                       /* c */
%rootgram(data=fit, var=count, obs=blocks, btype=dev);            /* d */
```

Figure 2.10   Plots of observed and fitted frequencies for the *Federalist Papers* data, Poisson model.
Each panel shows the fitted frequencies as a smooth curve and observed frequencies
as a bar. Panel (a), raw frequencies; panels (b), (c), and (d), on a square-root scale to
emphasize smaller frequencies. Panel (c) is a hanging rootogram in which observed,
fitted differences can be judged relative to the horizontal line. Panel (d) shows only the
difference between the observed and fitted frequencies.

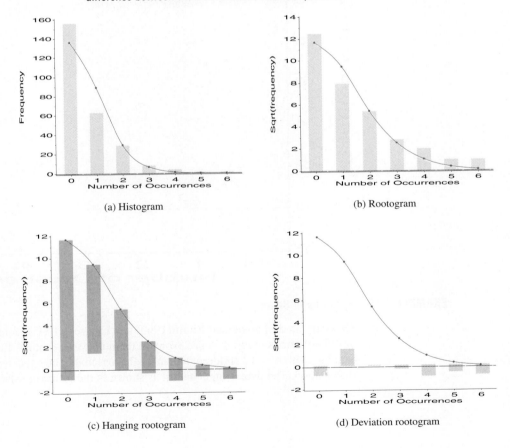

2.3.3   The ROOTGRAM Macro

The ROOTGRAM macro (Appendix A.26) displays observed and fitted frequencies for a dataset in any of the forms shown in Figure 2.10. The input dataset is usually of the form of the output OUT= dataset produced by the GOODFIT macro.

EXAMPLE 2.9   Federalist Papers

We have seen that the negative binomial produces a better fit to the *Federalist Papers* data. The hanging rootogram (Figure 2.11), produced by the following statements, is characteristic of a decent fit.

```
%include catdata(madison);
%goodfit(data=madison, var=count, freq=blocks, dist=negbin, out=fit2);
%rootgram(data=fit2, var=count, obs=blocks, btype=dev);
```

Figure 2.11   Hanging rootogram for the data in the *Federalist Papers*, Negative binomial model

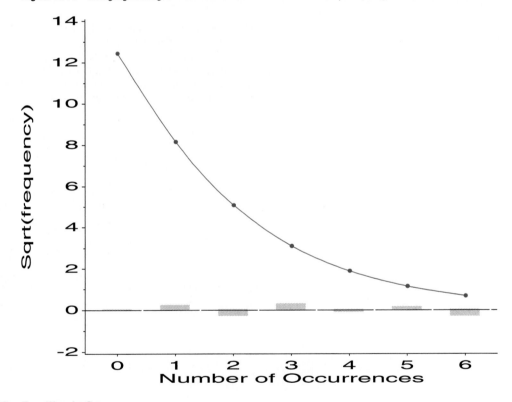

EXAMPLE 2.10   Families in Saxony

Geissler, cited in Sokal and Rholf (1969) and Lindsey (1995), tabulated a huge dataset on sex distributions in families in Saxony in the nineteenth century. Included were $N = 6115$ families with $n = 12$ children, which might reasonably be expected to follow a Bin$(12,p)$ distribution. The data is input and fit as shown in the following statements:

```
title 'Number of males in 6115 families in Saxony';
data saxony;
   do males = 0 to 12;
      input families @;
      output;
      end;
   label males='Number of males'
      families='Number of families';
datalines;
3   24   104   286   670   1033   1343 1112   829   478   181   45   7
;

%goodfit(data=saxony, var=males, freq=families, dist=binomial);

title;
%rootgram(data=fit, var=males, obs=families, exp=exp);
```

The fitted distribution, using the estimated proportion of males, $p = .5192$ is shown in Output 2.12; the goodness-of-fit tests shown in Output 2.13 indicate that the fit of the Binomial is not good. The hanging rootogram in Figure 2.12 shows why — there is a systematic pattern of deviations from the Binomial, which produces fitted frequencies too high in the middle and too small in the tails. The lack of fit might be ascribed to violations of the assumptions — a constant probability of a male birth over a long time span is a good possibility.[8]   □

Output 2.12   Fit of the Binomial(12, p) to the Families in Saxony data: Observed and fitted frequencies (rounded)

	Number of males in 6115 families in Saxony				1
MALES	FAMILIES	PHAT	EXP	CHI	DEV
0	3	0.00015	0.93	2.14028	2.6474
1	24	0.00198	12.09	3.42580	5.7373
2	104	0.01174	71.80	3.79963	8.7782
3	286	0.04227	258.48	1.71205	7.6080
4	670	0.10271	628.06	1.67371	9.3076
5	1033	0.17747	1085.21	-1.58490	-10.0930
6	1343	0.22359	1367.28	-0.65661	-6.9372
7	1112	0.20697	1265.63	-4.31841	-16.9649
8	829	0.13970	854.25	-0.86380	-7.0526
9	478	0.06705	410.01	3.35761	12.1108
10	181	0.02172	132.84	4.17896	10.5829
11	45	0.00427	26.08	3.70417	7.0061
12	7	0.00038	2.35	3.03687	3.9112
	========	=======	=======		
	6115	1.00000	6115.00		

---

[8]Lindsey (1995, p. 131) fits a double binomial model with one extra parameter and achieves a much better fit, but this too shows significant lack of fit—not surprising considering the enormous sample size.

Output 2.13   Fit of the Binomial(12, *p*) to the Families in Saxony data: Goodness-of-fit tests

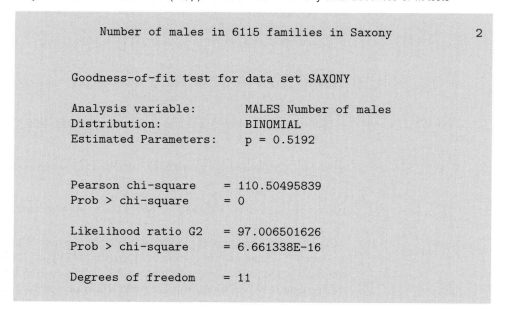

```
              Number of males in 6115 families in Saxony            2


      Goodness-of-fit test for data set SAXONY

      Analysis variable:        MALES Number of males
      Distribution:             BINOMIAL
      Estimated Parameters:     p = 0.5192


      Pearson chi-square     = 110.50495839
      Prob > chi-square      = 0

      Likelihood ratio G2    = 97.006501626
      Prob > chi-square      = 6.661338E-16

      Degrees of freedom     = 11
```

Figure 2.12   Hanging rootogram for Saxony families, Binomial(12, *p*) model. The systematic pattern of deviations shows that the Binomial model is not completely adequate for this data.

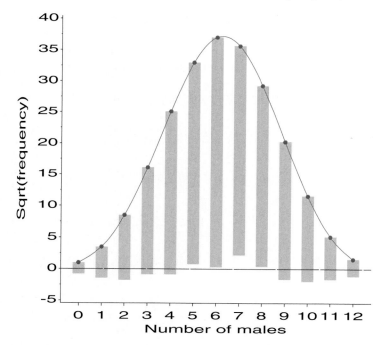

2.3.4   Maximum Likelihood Estimation

Section 2.2 describes the common discrete distributions, their probability functions, and sample estimates. Here, we consider the general case. Suppose we have a multinomial sample of K groups, with frequencies of n_k in group k, and $\sum_k n_k = N$. Suppose, further, that we have a probability model that specifies the probability, $\pi_k(\boldsymbol{\theta})$, $k = 1, 2, \ldots, K$, of an observation in group k, where $\boldsymbol{\theta}$ is a vector of $s \geq 0$ parameters of the distribution and $\sum_k \pi_k(\boldsymbol{\theta}) = 1$.

The likelihood $\mathcal{L}$ is the probability of the data as a function of the parameters,

$$\mathcal{L}(\boldsymbol{\theta}) = n! \prod_{k=1}^{K} \frac{\pi_k(\boldsymbol{\theta})^{n_k}}{n_k!}$$

We can determine the value(s) of $\boldsymbol{\theta}$ that maximize $\mathcal{L}$ by maximizing the log-likelihood,

$$\ell(\boldsymbol{\theta}) \equiv \log \mathcal{L}(\boldsymbol{\theta}) = \log n! + \sum_{k=1}^{K} n_k \log \pi_k(\boldsymbol{\theta}) - \sum_{k=1}^{K} \log n_k! \qquad (2.10)$$

The maximum likelihood estimate (MLE) of $\boldsymbol{\theta}$ will be the value $\hat{\boldsymbol{\theta}}$, which is the solution of the estimating equations

$$\frac{\partial \log \mathcal{L}(\boldsymbol{\theta})}{\partial \theta_i} = 0 \qquad i = 1, 2, \ldots s$$

For example, for the geometric distribution with probability function (Equation 2.5), the log-likelihood is

$$\ell(\boldsymbol{\theta}) = n \log \theta + \sum_{k=1}^{K} (n_k - 1) \log(1 - \theta)$$

which gives the estimating equation

$$\frac{\partial \ell(\theta)}{\partial \theta} = \frac{(\sum_k n_k) - n}{1 - \theta} + \frac{n}{\theta} = 0$$

whose solution is $\hat{\theta} = 1/\bar{k}$. The fitted probabilities under the geometric model are then $\pi_k(\hat{\theta}) = (1 - \hat{\theta})^{k-1}\hat{\theta}$.

Having found the maximum likelihood estimate of the parameters, the likelihood ratio goodness-of-fit G^2 statistic compares the maximized value of the log-likelihood to the maximized log-likelihood of an unrestricted model where the probabilities are only constrained so that $\sum_k \pi_k = 1$. In this case, there are $s = 0$ parameters, and we symbolize the log-likelihood by $\ell(\boldsymbol{\theta}_0) \equiv \ell(\boldsymbol{\pi})$. For a multinomial sample, this is

$$\ell(\boldsymbol{\theta}_0) = \log n! + \sum_{k=1}^{K} n_k \log \pi_k - \sum_{k=1}^{K} \log n_k! \qquad (2.11)$$

Maximizing Equation 2.11 subject to $\sum_k \pi_k = 1$ gives $\hat{\pi}_k = n_k/N$. The likelihood ratio statistic is

$$G^2 = -2 \log \left[\frac{\mathcal{L}(\boldsymbol{\theta}_0)}{\mathcal{L}(\boldsymbol{\theta})} \right] = 2[\ell(\boldsymbol{\theta}) - \ell(\boldsymbol{\theta}_0)] = 2 \sum_{k=1}^{K} n_k \log \left(\frac{n_k}{N \pi_k(\hat{\theta})} \right) \qquad (2.12)$$

which follows an asymptotic chi-square distribution with $K - 1 - s$ df.

2.3.5   Fitting Discrete Distributions as Loglinear Models

In Section 2.2.6, I describe how the common discrete distributions are all members of the general Power Series family. Another general family of distributions, the exponential family, includes most of the common continuous distributions: the normal, gamma, expo-

nential, and others, and is the basis of the class of generalized linear models fit by PROC
GENMOD.

Lindsey and Mersch (1992) and Lindsey (1995, 6.1) have shown how various discrete
(and continuous) distributions can be fit to frequency data by using Poisson log-linear models available in PROC GENMOD. The uniform, geometric, binomial, and Poisson distributions
can all be fit easily in this way. A clear advantage is that this method gives estimated standard errors for the distribution parameters, as well as estimated confidence intervals for
fitted probabilities.

The essential idea is that, for frequency data, any distribution in the exponential family
can be represented by a linear model for the logarithm of the cell frequency, with a Poisson
distribution for errors, which is known as a "Poisson log-linear regression model". These
models have the form

$$\log(N\pi_k) = \text{offset} + \beta_0 + \beta^{\mathsf{T}} S(k) \; ,$$

where $S(k)$ is a vector of 0 or more sufficient statistics for the canonical parameters of the
exponential family distribution, and the offset term is a value that does not depend on the
parameters. Table 2.9 shows the sufficient statistics and offsets for several discrete distributions. See Lindsey and Mersch (1992) for more details and definitions for the double-
binomial distribution.

Table 2.9 Poisson log-linear representations for some discrete distributions

Distribution	Sufficient statistics	Offset
Geometric	k	
Poisson	k	$-\log(k!)$
Binomial	k	$\log \binom{n}{k}$
Double binomial	$k, -k\log(k/n - k)$	$\log \binom{n}{k}$

EXAMPLE 2.11   Families in Saxony

The binomial distribution and the double binomial can both be fit to frequency data as a
Poisson regression by using $\log \binom{n}{k}$ as an offset. Only results for the binomial model are
shown here.

```
*-- calculate offset variables for binomial and double binomial;
data saxony;
   set saxony;
   logkn = log( gamma(12+1) / (gamma(males+1) * gamma(12-males+1)) );
   if 0 < males < 12
      then ylogity = -males * log(males/(12-males));
      else ylogity = 0;

 *-- fit binomial (12,p);
proc genmod data=saxony;
   model families = males /
      dist=poisson offset=logkn obstats ;

 *-- fit double binomial (12,p, psi);
proc genmod data=saxony;
   model families = males ylogity /
      dist=poisson offset=logkn obstats ;
```

The goodness-of-fit tests shown in Output 2.14 are equivalent to the same tests calculated directly by the GOODFIT macro and shown in Output 2.13. The parameter estimate for MALES, $\beta_1 = 0.0769$ is actually estimating the logit of p, $\log p/(1-p)$, so the inverse transformation gives $\hat{p} = \frac{\exp(\beta_1)}{1+\exp(\beta_1)} = 0.5192$, as before. The fitted frequencies shown in Output 2.15, which are specified by the OBSTATS option in the MODEL statement, are the same as those shown in Output 2.12. The standard error for MALES, $s_{\beta_1} = 0.0074$, could also be transformed back to the probability scale in the same way.   □

Output 2.14   Fit of the Binomial(12, p) to the Families in Saxony data: Goodness-of-fit tests

```
                Number of males in 6115 families in Saxony

                        The GENMOD Procedure

                          Model Information

       Description                 Value           Label

       Data Set                    WORK.SAXONY
       Distribution                POISSON
       Link Function               LOG
       Dependent Variable          FAMILIES        Number of families
       Offset Variable             LOGYN
       Observations Used           13



                 Criteria For Assessing Goodness Of Fit

           Criterion            DF        Value       Value/DF

           Deviance             11       97.0065        8.8188
           Scaled Deviance      11       97.0065        8.8188
           Pearson Chi-Square   11      110.5050       10.0459
           Scaled Pearson X2    11      110.5050       10.0459
           Log Likelihood        .    34664.4556          .



                   Analysis Of Parameter Estimates

       Parameter   DF    Estimate    Std Err   ChiSquare   Pr>Chi

       INTERCEPT    1     -0.0695     0.0478     2.1173    0.1456
       MALES        1      0.0769     0.0074   108.3195    0.0001
       SCALE        0      1.0000     0.0000        .         .

   NOTE:  The scale parameter was held fixed.
```

Output 2.15   Fit of the Binomial(12, *p*) to the Families in Saxony data: Observed and fitted frequencies

Number of males in 6115 families in Saxony						
MALES	FAMILIES	PRED	STD	LOWER	UPPER	RESCHI
0	3	0.93	0.047778	0.85	1.02	2.14028
1	24	12.09	0.040707	11.16	13.09	3.42580
2	104	71.80	0.033773	67.20	76.72	3.79963
3	286	258.48	0.027079	245.11	272.56	1.71205
4	670	628.06	0.020860	602.89	654.27	1.67371
5	1033	1085.21	0.015691	1052.34	1119.10	-1.58490
6	1343	1367.28	0.012901	1333.14	1402.29	-0.65661
7	1112	1265.63	0.013995	1231.39	1300.83	-4.31841
8	829	854.25	0.018288	824.17	885.42	-0.86380
9	478	410.01	0.024129	391.07	429.87	3.35761
10	181	132.84	0.030646	125.09	141.06	4.17896
11	45	26.08	0.037488	24.23	28.07	3.70417
12	7	2.35	0.044505	2.15	2.56	3.03687

2.4   Diagnosing Discrete Distributions: Ord Plots

Ideally, the general form chosen for a discrete distribution should be dictated by substantive knowledge of a plausible mechanism for generating the data. When such knowledge is lacking, however, you may not know which distribution is most appropriate for a specific set of data. In these cases, the question is often turned around, so that a distribution that fits well is looked for, and then you try to understand the mechanism in terms of aspects of the underlying probability theory (independent trials, rare events, waiting-time to an occurrence, and so forth).

Although it is possible to fit each of several possibilities, the summary goodness-of-fit statistics can easily be influenced by one or two disparate cells or additional (ignored or unknown) factors. One simple alternative is a plot suggested by Ord (1967) that may be used to diagnose the form of the discrete distribution. Ord shows that a linear relationship of the form

$$\frac{k \, p(k)}{p(k-1)} = a + b k \; , \tag{2.13}$$

holds for each of the Poisson, binomial, negative binomial, and logarithmic series distributions, and these distributions are distinguished by the signs of the intercept *a* and slope *b*, as shown in Table 2.10. The slope *b* in Equation 2.13 is 0 for the Poisson, negative for the binomial, and positive for the negative binomial and logarithmic series distributions; the latter two are distinguished by their intercepts.

Thus, a plot of $k \, n_k / n_{k-1}$ against *k*, if linear, is suggested as a means to determine which of these distributions to apply. The values of the slope and intercept provide rough estimates of the distribution parameters.

Table 2.10   Diagnostic slope and intercept for four discrete distributions. The ratios kn_k/n_{k-1} plotted against k should appear as a straight line, whose slope and intercept determine the specific distribution.

Slope (b)	Intercept (a)	Distribution (parameter)	Parameter estimate
0	+	Poisson (λ)	$\lambda = a$
$-$	+	Binomial (n, p)	$p = b/(b-1)$
+	+	Negative binomial (n,p)	$p = 1 - b$
+	$-$	Log. series (θ)	$\theta = b$
			$\theta = -a$

Fitting the Line

One difficulty in applying this technique is that the number of points (distinct values of k) in the Ord plot is often small, and the sampling variances of $k\, n_k/n_{k-1}$ can vary enormously. A little reflection indicates that points where n_k is small should be given less weight in determining the slope of the line (and, therefore, determining the form of the distribution). In the small number of cases I've tried, I have found that using a weighted least squares fit of $k\, n_k/n_{k-1}$ on k, using weights of $w_k = \sqrt{n_k - 1}$, produces reasonably good[9] automatic diagnosis of the form of a probability distribution, but this choice is surely open to further study.

EXAMPLE 2.12   Deaths by horse kicks

The table below shows the calculations for the horse kicks data, with the ratio $k\, n_k/n_{k-1}$ labeled y. The weighted least squares line, with weights w_k, has a slope close to zero, indicating the Poisson distribution. The estimate $\lambda = a = .656$ compares favorably with the MLE, $\lambda = 0.610$ and the value from the Poissonness plot, shown in the following section.

```
        Ord Plot: Deaths by Horse Kicks


    k      n_k     n_{k-1}      w_k          y

    0      109        .       10.3923        .          -- Weighted LS --
    1      65        109       8.0000      0.5963       slope = -0.034
    2      22         65       4.5826      0.6769       inter = 0.656
    3       3         22       1.4142      0.4091
    4       1          3       0.0000      1.3333
```

EXAMPLE 2.13   *Federalist Papers*

For the word-frequency data, the slope is positive, so, either the negative binomial or the log series is possible. The intercept is essentially 0, which is ambiguous. However, the logarithmic series requires $b \approx -a$, so the negative binomial is a better choice. Mosteller and Wallace did, in fact, find a reasonably good fit to this distribution.

---

[9]This definition implies that frequencies of $n_k = 1$ are ignored in fitting the line.

Instances of 'may' in *Federalist Papers*

k	n_k	n_{k-1}	w_k	y	
0	156	.	12.4499	.	-- Weighted LS --
1	63	156	7.8740	0.4038	slope = 0.424
2	29	63	5.2915	0.9206	inter = -0.023
3	8	29	2.6458	0.8276	
4	4	8	1.7321	2.0000	
5	1	4	0.0000	1.2500	
6	1	1	0.0000	6.0000	

Plots of data fitting four different discrete distributions are shown in Figure 2.13, using the data previously examined in this chapter. In each case, the slope and intercept of the weighted least squares line correctly identify the distribution. □

Figure 2.13 Ord plots for four discrete distributions. Each panel shows the least squares line (dotted, black) and the weighted least squares line (solid, red). The slope and intercept of the weighted least squares line are used to identify the type of the distribution.

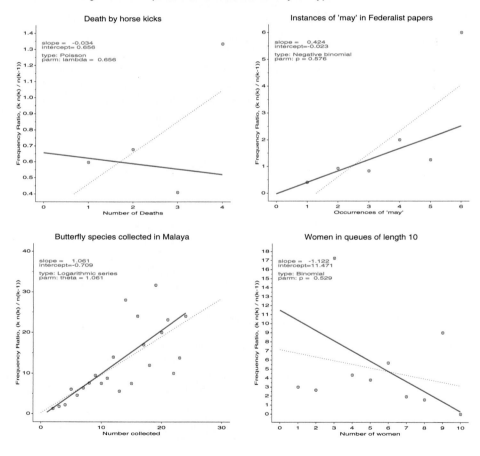

Drawbacks

Using a single plot to determine one of four common discrete distributions is advantageous, but our enthusiasm should be limited by several weaknesses in this method:

- The Ord plot lacks resistance because a single discrepant frequency affects the points for both k and $k + 1$.
- The sampling variance of $k\, n_k / n_{k-1}$ fluctuates widely (Hoaglin and Tukey, 1985; Jinkinson and Slater, 1981). The use of weights w_k helps but is purely a heuristic device.

ORDPLOT Macro

These plots are produced by the ORDPLOT macro (Appendix A.19). For the horse kicks data, the plot in Figure 2.13 is produced by using the macro call

```
%ordplot(data=horskick,
         count=Deaths, freq=corpsyrs);
```

The FREQ parameter specifies the name of the basic frequency variable (k), and the COUNT parameter specifies the associated count, n_k.

2.5 Poissonness Plot

The Poissonness plot (Hoaglin, 1980) is designed as a plot of some quantity against k, so that the result will be points along a straight line when the data follows a Poisson distribution. When the data deviates from a Poisson, the points are curved. Hoaglin and Tukey (1985) develop similar plots for other discrete distributions, including the binomial, negative binomial, and logarithmic series distributions.

2.5.1   Features of the Poissonness Plot

The Poissonness plot has the following advantages:

- *Resistance*: a single discrepant value of n_k affects only the point at value k. (In the Ord plot it affects each of its neighbors.)
- *Comparison standard*: An approximate confidence interval can be found for each point, which indicates its inherent variability and helps to judge whether each point is discrepant.
- *Influence*: Extensions of the method result in plots that show the effect of each point on the estimate of the main parameter of the distribution (λ in the Poisson).

2.5.2   Plot Construction

Assume, for some fixed λ, each observed frequency, n_k, equals the expected frequency, $m_k = N p_k$. Then, setting $n_k = N p_k = N e^{-\lambda} \lambda^k / k!$ and taking logs of both sides gives

$$\log(n_k) = \log N - \lambda + k \log \lambda - \log k!$$

which can be rearranged to

$$\log\left(\frac{k!\, n_k}{N}\right) = -\lambda + (\log \lambda)\, k \ . \tag{2.14}$$

The left side of Equation 2.14 is called the ***count metameter*** and is denoted $\phi(n_k) = \log_e(k!\,n_k/N)$. Hence, plotting $\phi(n_k)$ against k should give a line $\phi(n_k) = a + bk$ that has

- slope = $\log \lambda$
- intercept = $-\lambda$

when the observed frequencies follow a Poisson distribution. If the points in this plot are close enough to a straight line, then an estimate of λ may be obtained from the slope b of the line, and $\hat{\lambda} = e^b$ should be reasonably close in value to the MLE of λ, $\hat{\lambda} = \bar{x}$. In this case, we might as well use the MLE as our estimate.

Leveled Plot

If we have a preliminary estimate λ_0 of λ, we can use this to give a new plot where the reference line is horizontal, which makes comparison of the points with the line easier. In this leveled plot the vertical coordinate $\phi(n_k)$ is modified to

$$\phi'(n_k) = \phi(n_k) + \lambda_0 - k \log \lambda_0 \ .$$

When the data follows a Poisson distribution with parameter λ, the modified plot will have

- slope = $\log \lambda - \log \lambda_0 = \log(\lambda/\lambda_0)$
- intercept = $\lambda_0 - \lambda$

In the ideal case, where our estimate of λ_0 is close to the true λ, the line will be horizontal at $\phi' = 0$. The modified plot is especially useful in conjunction with the confidence intervals for individual points, as described in the next section.

Confidence Intervals

When 1 or 2 points deviate from an otherwise nearly linear relation, it is helpful to determine whether the discrepancy is consistent with chance variation. Also, we must recognize that classes that have small frequencies n_k are less precise than classes that have large frequencies. Hoaglin and Tukey (1985) develop approximate confidence intervals for $\log m_k$ for each point in the Poissonness plot. These confidence intervals are calculated as

$$\phi\left(n_k^*\right) \pm h_k$$

where the count metameter function is calculated by using a modified frequency n_k^* defined as

$$n_k^* = \begin{cases} n_k - .8n_k - .67 & n \geq 2 \\ 1/e & n = 1 \\ \text{undefined} & n = 0 \end{cases}$$

and h_k is the half-width of the 95% confidence interval,

$$h_k = 1.96 \frac{\sqrt{1 - \hat{p}_k}}{[n_k - (.25\hat{p}_k + .47)\sqrt{n_k}]^{1/2}}$$

and $\hat{p}_k = n_k/N$.

2.5.3   The POISPLOT Macro

The POISPLOT macro (Appendix A.21) performs the calculations and produces the plots for all examples shown in this section. The input data should contain a basic count variable (corresponding to k) and a frequency variable (corresponding to n_k) of the form shown in Table 2.1 on page 18.

EXAMPLE 2.14   **Deaths by horse kicks**

A Poissonness plot is produced for the Horse Kicks data by using the POISPLOT macro with the following statements:

```
title 'Poissoness Plot: Deaths by Horsekicks' ;
data horskick;
    input deaths corpsyrs;
    label deaths='Number of Deaths'
        corpsyrs='Number of Corps-Years';
    datalines;
    0   109
    1    65
    2    22
    3     3
    4     1
;
%poisplot(data=horskick, count=Deaths,freq=corpsyrs);
```

The calculations for the Poissonness plot, including confidence intervals, are shown below for the Horse Kicks data. The macro produces the plot shown in Figure 2.14. The fitted least squares line has a slope of -0.431, which indicates $\lambda = e^{-0.431} = 0.65$. This compares well with the MLE, $\lambda = \bar{x} = 0.61$.

Figure 2.14   Poissonness plots for the Horse Kicks data. The data fits the Poisson distribution reasonably well.

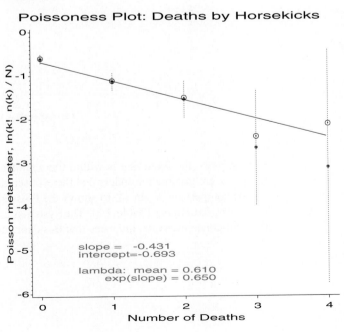

k	nk	$\phi(n_k)$ Y	CI center	CI width	Confidence Int lower	upper
0	109	-0.607	-0.617	0.130	-0.748	-0.487
1	65	-1.124	-1.138	0.207	-1.345	-0.931
2	22	-1.514	-1.549	0.417	-1.966	-1.132
3	3	-2.408	-2.666	1.318	-3.984	-1.348
4	1	-2.120	-3.120	2.689	-5.809	-0.432

The leveled Poissonness plot shown in Figure 2.15 is produced by the following %POISPLOT statement that specifies LAMBDA=.610:

```
title;
%poisplot(data=horskick, count=Deaths, freq=corpsyrs,
        lambda=.610, plot=dist);
run;
```

Figure 2.15   Leveled Poissonness Plot for the Horse Kicks data.

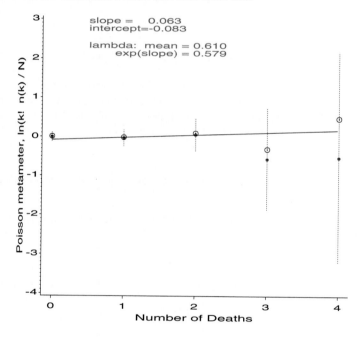

In both plots, the fitted line is within the confidence intervals; the widths of the intervals for $k > 2$ are graphic reminders that these observations have relatively low precision.

For comparison, Figure 2.16 shows the Poissonness plot for the occurrences of *may* in the *Federalist Papers* (Table 2.2). The systematic curvature in the plot, judged relative to the confidence intervals, indicates that this data does not follow a Poisson distribution.   □

Figure 2.16   Poissonness plot for the data from the *Federalist Papers*. The systematic curvature in the plot indicates that this data does not follow a Poisson distribution.

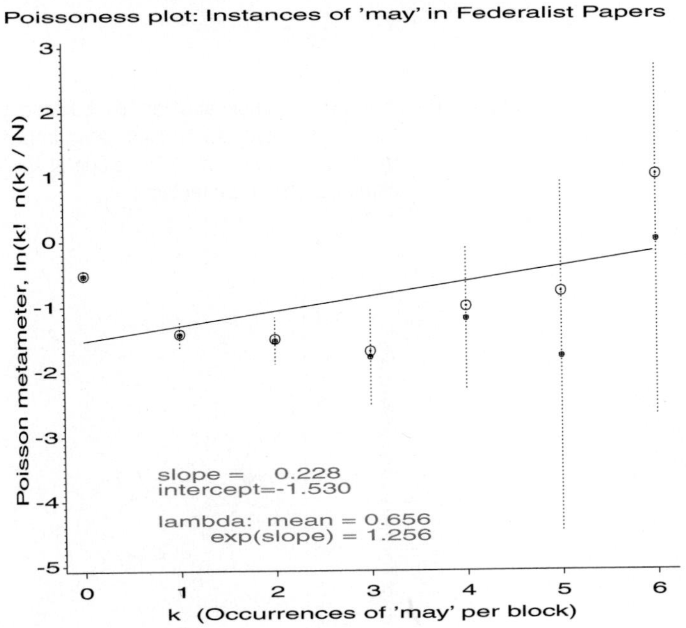

Poissoness plot: Instances of 'may' in Federalist Papers

2.5.4   Leverage and Influence

In standard models for quantitative data, common diagnostic techniques attempt to estimate the effect that each observation has upon the parameter estimates. For linear models, these techniques include measures of **leverage**, the potential that an observation has to influence our results (due to its location on the predictors); and **influence**, the actual effect this observation has on parameter estimates and fitted values.

For discrete distributions, Hoaglin and Tukey (1985) derive measures, which are similar in spirit. However, these measures are based on the change in the estimate of λ at each value of k that would be required to make the observed count metameter $\phi(n_k^*)$ equal to its fitted value $\phi(m_k(\lambda_0))$, which is calculated by using a contemplated or an estimated λ_0.

For the Poisson distribution, analysis by Hoaglin and Tukey leads to the relation

$$\log \frac{\phi(n_k^*)}{\phi(m_k(\lambda_0))} = (\lambda - \lambda_0)\left(\frac{k}{\lambda_0} - 1\right) \ . \tag{2.15}$$

Equation 2.15 is a line through the origin that has the slope equal to $(\lambda - \lambda_0)$. By analogy with least squares regression through the origin (where leverage is proportional to x), Hoaglin and Tukey refer to $(k/\lambda_0) - 1$ as the leverage of point k.

Their parameter-change plot shows each observation in the discrete distribution as a point that has a vertical coordinate proportional to $\log[\phi(n_k^*)/\phi(m_k(\lambda_0))] = \log(\phi(n_k^*)) - \log \phi(m_k(\lambda_0))$ and a horizontal coordinate proportional to $k/\lambda_0 - 1$. In this plot (see Figure 2.17), the slope of a line from the origin to a point shows the change in the Poisson parameter $\lambda - \lambda_0$, which is indicated by that point. The horizontal coordinate is proportional to the potential of that observation to affect the Poisson parameter λ.

An alternative version of this plot, more in the spirit of the influence plots for log-linear models and logistic regression, which are described later in this book, plots the parameter change $\lambda - \lambda_0$ directly on the vertical axis against the same horizontal leverage value, and uses a bubble whose size represents influence as the plotting symbol.

The parameter-change plot and the influence plot are produced by using the POISPLOT macro and including the keyword INFL in the PLOT= parameter (i.e., PLOT=DIST INFL gives all plots). For the Horse Kicks data, these plots are shown in Figure 2.17 and Figure 2.18.

Figure 2.17   Parameter-change plot for the Poisson parameter, fitting the Horse Kicks data. The horizontal coordinate of each point is proportional to the potential of that observation to affect the value of λ. The slope of the line through the origin is proportional to the change in the count metameter.

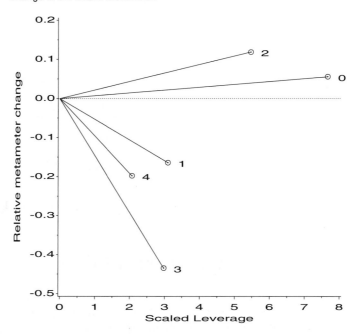

Figure 2.18   Influence plot for the Poisson parameter, fitting the Horse Kicks data. The ordinate shows the indicated change in λ directly, and the bubble size is proportional to influence.

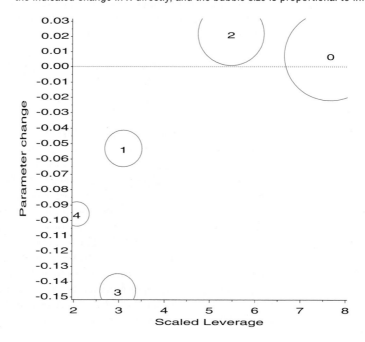

Figure 2.17 shows that the point that corresponds to $k = 0$ has the greatest leverage but influences λ very little. The point for $k = 3$ has only moderate leverage, but it has the greatest impact on the Poisson parameter. Figure 2.15 shows that the circle symbol for $\phi(n_k^*)$ at $k = 3$ is furthest from the line. Figure 2.18 shows that this point indicates a λ value about 0.15 smaller than the estimated value.

2.5.5   Plots for Other Distributions

As described in Section 2.2.6, the binomial, Poisson, negative binomial, geometric, and log series distributions are all members of the general Power Series family of discrete distributions. For this family, Hoaglin and Tukey (1985) develop similar plots of a count metameter against k, which appear as a straight line when a data distribution follows a specified family member.

The distributions that can be analyzed in this way are shown in Table 2.11, with the interpretation given to the slope and intercept for each case. For example, for the Binomial distribution, a "binomialness" plot is constructed by plotting $\log n_k^*/N\binom{n}{k}$ against k. If the points in this plot approximate a straight line, the slope is interpreted as $\log(p/(1-p))$, so the binomial parameter p may be estimated as $p = e^b/(1 + e^b)$.

Table 2.11   Plot parameters for five discrete distributions. In each case the count metameter, $\phi(n_k^*)$ is plotted against k, yielding a straight line when the data follows the given distribution.

Distribution	Probability function, $p(k)$	Count metameter, $\phi(n_k^*)$	Theoretical Slope (b)	Theoretical Intercept (a)
Poisson	$e^{-\lambda}\lambda^k/k!$	$\log(k!n_k^*/N)$	$\log(\lambda)$	$-\lambda$
Binomial	$\binom{n}{k}p^k(1-p)^{n-k}$	$\log\left(n_k^*/N\binom{n}{k}\right)$	$\log\left(\frac{p}{1-p}\right)$	$n\log(1-p)$
Negative binomial	$\binom{n+k-1}{k}p^n(1-p)^k$	$\log\left(n_k^*/N\binom{n+k-1}{k}\right)$	$\log(1-p)$	$n\log(p)$
Geometric	$p(1-p)^k$	$\log\left(n_k^*/N\right)$	$\log(1-p)$	$\log(p)$
Logarithmic series	$\theta^k/[-k\log(1-\theta)]$	$\log\left(kn_k^*/N\right)$	$\log(\theta)$	$-\log(-\log(1-\theta))$

Source: adapted from Hoaglin and Tukey (1985), Table 9-15.

Unlike the Ord plot, a different plot is required for each distribution because the count metameter $\phi(n_k)$ differs from distribution-to-distribution. Moreover, systematic deviation from a linear relationship does not indicate which distribution provides a better fit. However, the attention to robustness, and the availability of confidence intervals and influence diagnostics make this a highly useful tool for visualizing discrete distributions.

2.5.6   DISTPLOT Macro

The DISTPLOT macro (Appendix A.6) carries out the analysis and produces overall distribution plots and influence plots for the members of the Power Series distributions shown in Table 2.11. As with the GOODFIT macro, values for parameters for a specified distribution may be supplied in the PARM parameter.

When the value of the distribution parameter is not supplied, the macro produces the overall distribution plot whose slope b (and intercept a) are used to find graphical estimates of the parameter. For most distributions, the available MLE or moments estimates given in Section 2.2 are also calculated and displayed in the plot. When the value of the distribution parameter is supplied, a leveled plot is produced that has graphical parameter estimates adjusted for the leveling.

EXAMPLE 2.15   Families in Saxony

The analysis in Example 2.10 and Example 2.11 of the Saxony data shows that the distribution of male children had slightly heavier tails than the binomial. You can see this even more clearly in the distribution diagnostic plot produced by the DISTPLOT macro. For a binomial distribution, we might call this a "binomialness plot".

Figure 2.19 is produced by using the statement

```
%distplot(data=saxony, count=males, freq=families, dist=binomial);
```

Again, the systematic curvature of the points indicates the inadequacy of the binomial, and the widths of the intervals around the points show that the two extreme points are of limited reliability. Comparing this plot with the hanging rootogram (Figure 2.12), you see that heavy-tailed distributions tend to curve upwards. You also see that the estimate of $p = \exp(b)/[1 + \exp(b)]$ from the slope of the fitted line is quite close to the maximum likelihood estimate.   □

Figure 2.19   Binomialness plot for the distribution of males in Saxony families

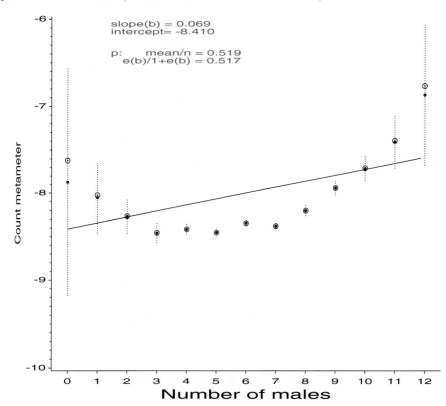

2.6 Chapter Summary

- Discrete distributions typically involve basic *counts* of occurrences of some event that occurs with varying frequencies.

- The most commonly used discrete distributions include the binomial, Poisson, negative binomial, geometric, and logarithmic series distributions. Happily, these are all members of a family called the Power Series distributions. Methods of fitting an observed dataset to any of these distributions are described and implemented in the GOODFIT macro.

- After fitting an observed distribution, it is useful to plot the observed and fitted frequencies. Several ways of making these plots are described and implemented in the ROOTGRAM macro.

- A graphical method for identifying which discrete distribution is most appropriate for a specific set of data involves plotting ratios kn_k/n_{k-1} against k. These plots are constructed by the ORDPLOT macro.

- A more robust plot for a Poisson distribution involves plotting the count metameter $\phi(n_k)$ against k, which gives a straight line (whose slope estimates the Poisson parameter) when the data follows a Poisson distribution. This plot provides robust confidence intervals for individual points and provides a means to assess the influence of individual points on the Poisson parameter. These plots are provided by the POISPLOT macro.

- The ideas behind the Poissonness plot can be applied to the other discrete distributions, as implemented in the DISTPLOT macro.

Chapter

3

2-Way Contingency Tables

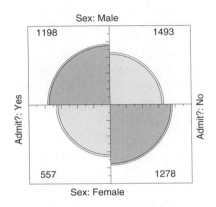

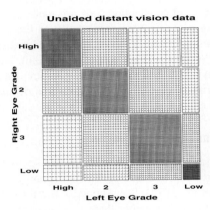

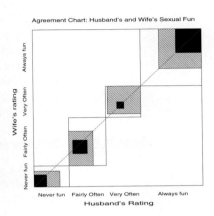

The analysis of two-way frequency tables concerns the association between two variables. Different specialized displays are focused on visualizing an odds ratio (2×2 tables), or the general pattern of association, or the agreement between row and column categories.

3.1 Introduction

> If you choose to represent the various parts in life by holes upon a table, of different shapes, some circular, some triangular, some square, some oblong, and the persons acting these parts by bits of wood of similar shapes, we shall generally find that the triangular person has got into the square hole, the oblong into the triangular, and a square person has squeezed himself into the round hole.
>
> Sydney Smith, 1771–1845, *Sketches of Moral Philosophy*

Most methods of statistical analysis are concerned with understanding relationships among variables. With categorical variables, these relationships are usually studied from data that has been summarized by a ***contingency table***, giving the frequencies of observations cross-classified by two or more such variables.

This chapter presents methods for understanding the association between two categorical variables. Some simple examples are also presented that involve a third, stratifying variable, when you want to determine if the relationship between two primary variables is the same or different for all levels of the stratifying variable. Methods for fitting models and displaying associations for 3-way and larger tables are described in Chapter 4.

In Section 3.2, I describe briefly some methods for testing whether an association exists between two variables, and some methods for quantifying the strength of this association. In Section 3.3, I extend these ideas to situations where the relationship between two variables is of primary interest, but there are one or more background variables to be controlled.

The main emphasis, however, is on graphical methods that help to describe the nature of an association between variables. Section 3.4 presents the fourfold display, designed to portray the odds ratio in 2×2 tables or a set of k such tables. Sieve diagrams (Section 3.5) and association plots (Section 3.6) are more general methods for depicting the pattern of associations in any 2-way tables. When the row and column variables represent the classifications of different raters, specialized measures and visual displays for inter-rater agreement (Section 3.7) are particularly useful. Another specialized display, the trilinear plot (Section 3.8) is designed for three-column frequency tables or compositional data. In order to clarify some of the distinctions that occur in contingency table analysis, I begin with several examples.

EXAMPLE 3.1   Berkeley admissions

Table 3.1 shows aggregate data about applicants to graduate school in 1973 for the six largest departments at Berkeley. The applicants are classified by admission status and gender (Bickel et al., 1975). See Appendix B.2 for the complete data set. For such data, you might want to study whether there is an association between admission and gender. Are male (or female) applicants more likely to be admitted? The presence of an association might be considered as evidence of sex bias in admission practices.

Table 3.1 is an example of the simplest kind of contingency table, a 2×2 classification of individuals according to two dichotomous (binary) variables. For such a table, the question of whether there is an association between admission and gender is equivalent to asking if the proportions of males and females who are admitted to graduate school are the same, or whether the difference in proportions of males and females admitted is 0.   □

Table 3.1   Admissions to Berkeley graduate programs

	Admitted	Rejected	Total
Males	1198	1493	2691
Females	557	1278	1835
Total	1755	2771	4526

Although the methods for quantifying association in larger tables can be used for 2×2 tables, there are specialized measures (described in Section 3.2) and graphical methods for these simpler tables.

It is frequently useful to make a distinction between ***outcome*** (or response) variables and possible ***explanatory*** (or predictor) variables. In Table 3.1, it is natural to consider admission as the outcome, and gender as the explanatory variable. In other tables, no variable may be clearly identified as *the* outcome, or there may be several response variables.

EXAMPLE 3.2   Hair color and eye color

Table 3.2 shows data collected by Snee (1974) on the relationship between hair color and eye color among 592 students in a statistics course (Appendix B.3). Neither hair color nor eye color is considered to be a response in relation to the other; the interest here is whether an association exists between them. Hair color and eye color have each been classified into four categories. Although the categories used are among the most common, they are not the only categories possible.[1] Everyday observation suggests that there probably is an association between hair color and eye color. Tests and measures of associations for larger tables are described in Section 3.2.3.   □

Table 3.2   Hair-color and Eye-color data[2]

Eye Color	Hair Color				Total
	Black	Brown	Red	Blond	
Green	5	29	14	16	64
Hazel	15	54	14	10	93
Blue	20	84	17	94	215
Brown	68	119	26	7	220
Total	108	286	71	127	592

Table variables can be treated simply as unordered ***nominal*** variables or as ***ordinal*** variables, where the categories are ordered according to some underlying dimension. For example, the categories of hair color or eye color are typically considered to be nominal categories; however, they might arguably be considered to be ordered from light to dark. When the variables are ordinal, more sensitive and therefore more powerful tests of association can be used.

If, as is suspected, hair color and eye color are associated, it would be interesting to understand *how* they are associated. The graphical methods described later in this chapter help reveal the pattern of associations present.

EXAMPLE 3.3   Arthritis treatment

The data in Table 3.3 compares the results of an active treatment for rheumatoid arthritis to the results of a placebo (Koch and Edwards, 1988). The outcome reflects whether individuals showed no improvement, some improvement, or marked improvement. Here, the outcome variable is an ordinal one, and it is probably important to determine if the relation between treatment and outcome is the same for males and females. The complete dataset is given in Appendix B.1.

Table 3.3   Arthritis treatment data

Treatment	Sex	Improvement			Total
		None	Some	Marked	
Active	Female	6	5	16	27
	Male	7	2	5	14
Placebo	Female	19	7	6	32
	Male	10	0	1	11
Total		42	14	28	84

---

[1] If students had been asked to write down their hair and eye colors, it is likely that many more than four categories of each would appear in a sample of nearly 600.

[2] Reprinted with permission from *The American Statistician*. Copyright © 1974 by the American Statistical Association. All rights reserved.

Table 3.3 is, of course, a 3-way table that contains the variables Treatment, Sex, and Improvement. If the relation between treatment and outcome is the same for both genders, an analysis of a Treatment-by-Improvement table (collapsed over sex) could be carried out. Otherwise, you could perform separate analyses for men and women, or treat the combinations of Treatment and Sex as four levels of a "population" variable that give a 4×3 2-way table. These simplified approaches ignore certain information that is available in an analysis of the full 3-way table. □

3.2 Tests of Association for 2-Way Tables

3.2.1 Notation and Terminology

To establish notation, let $N = \{n_{ij}\}$ be the observed frequency table of variables A and B with r rows and c columns, as shown in Table 3.4. In the table that follows, a subscript is replaced by a plus sign (+) when it is summed over the corresponding variable, so $n_{i+} = \sum_j n_{ij}$ gives the total frequency in row i, $n_{+j} = \sum_i n_{ij}$ gives the total frequency in column j, and $n_{++} = \sum_i \sum_j n_{ij}$ is the grand total; for convenience, n_{++} can also be symbolized by n.

Table 3.4 The $r \times c$ contingency table

Row Category	Column category 1	2	$\cdots$	c	Total
1	n_{11}	n_{12}	$\cdots$	n_{1c}	n_{1+}
2	n_{21}	n_{22}	$\cdots$	n_{2c}	n_{2+}
$\vdots$	$\vdots$	$\vdots$	$\cdots$	$\vdots$	$\vdots$
r	n_{r1}	n_{r2}	$\cdots$	n_{rc}	n_{r+}
Total	n_{+1}	n_{+2}	$\cdots$	n_{+c}	n_{++}

When each observation is randomly sampled from a population and classified into two categorical variables, A and B, you refer to the **joint distribution** of these variables, and let $\pi_{ij} = \Pr(A = i, B = j)$ denote the probability that an observation is classified in row i, column j (or cell (ij)) in the table. Corresponding to these population joint probabilities, the cell proportions $p_{ij} = n_{ij}/n$ give the sample joint distribution.

The row totals n_{i+} and column totals n_{+j} are called marginal frequencies for variables A and B, respectively. These totals describe the distribution of each variable and *ignore* the other. For the population probabilities, the **marginal distributions** are defined analogously as the row-and-column totals of the joint probabilities, $\pi_{i+} = \sum_j \pi_{ij}$, and $\pi_{+j} = \sum_i \pi_{ij}$. The sample marginal proportions are, correspondingly, $p_{i+} = \sum_j p_{ij} = n_{i+}/n$, and $p_{+j} = \sum_i p_{ij} = n_{+j}/n$.

When one variable (the column variable B, for example) is a response variable, and the other (A) is an explanatory variable, it is most often useful to examine the distribution of the response B for *each* level of A separately. These distributions define the **conditional distributions** of B, given the level of A, and are defined for the population as $\pi_{j|i} = \pi_{ij}/\pi_{i+}$.

These definitions are illustrated in Output 3.1. For the Berkeley data, Table 3.1 shows the joint frequencies, n_{ij}, and the joint sample percentages, $100 \times p_{ij}$, in the first two rows within each table cell. The third row in each cell (Row pct) gives the conditional percentage of admission or rejection, $100 \times p_{j|i}$, for males and females separately. The row and the column labeled Total give the marginal frequencies, n_{i+} and n_{+j}, and the marginal percentages, p_{i+} and p_{+j}.

Output 3.1   Admission to Berkeley graduate programs: joint, marginal, and conditional percents

```
                    TABLE OF GENDER BY ADMIT

        GENDER      ADMIT

        Frequency|
        Percent  |
        Row Pct  |Admitted|Rejected|  Total
        ---------+--------+--------+
        Male     |   1198 |   1493 |   2691
                 |  26.47 |  32.99 |  59.46
                 |  44.52 |  55.48 |
        ---------+--------+--------+
        Female   |    557 |   1278 |   1835
                 |  12.31 |  28.24 |  40.54
                 |  30.35 |  69.65 |
        ---------+--------+--------+
        Total       1755     2771     4526
                    38.78    61.22   100.00
```

3.2.2   2 × 2 Tables

The 2 × 2 contingency table of applicants to Berkeley graduate programs in Table 3.1 may be regarded as an example of a ***cross-sectional study***. The total of $n = 4,526$ applicants in 1973 has been classified by both gender and admission status. Here, you would probably consider the total n to be fixed, and the cell frequencies n_{ij}, $i = 1, 2$; $j = 1, 2$ would then represent a single ***multinomial sample*** for the cross-classification by two binary variables, with probabilities cell p_{ij}, $i = 1, 2$; $j = 1, 2$ such that

$$p_{11} + p_{12} + p_{21} + p_{22} = 1 \ .$$

The basic null hypothesis of interest for a multinomial sample is that of independence. Are admission and gender independent of each other?

Alternatively, if you consider admission to be the response variable and gender to be an explanatory variable, you would treat the numbers of male and female applicants as fixed and consider the cell frequencies to represent two independent ***binomial samples*** for a binary response. In this case, the null hypothesis is described as that of homogeneity of the response proportions across the levels of the explanatory variable.

Odds and Odds Ratios

Measures of association are used to quantify the strength of association between variables. Among the many measures of association for contingency tables, the ***odds ratio*** is particularly useful for 2 × 2 tables and is a fundamental parameter in several graphical displays and models that are described later. Other measures of strength of association for 2 × 2 tables are described in Stokes et al. (1995, Chapter 2) and Agresti (1996, Section 2.2).

For a binary response, where the probability of a "success" is π, define the *odds* for a success as

$$\text{odds} = \frac{\pi}{1 - \pi} \ .$$

Hence, odds $= 1$ corresponds to $\pi = 0.5$; success and failure are equally likely. When success is more likely than failure, $\pi > 0.5$, and the odds > 1 (for instance, when $\pi = 0.75$, odds $= .75/.25 = 3$), so a success is three times as likely as a failure. When failure is more likely, $\pi < 0.5$, and the odds < 1 (for instance, when $\pi = 0.25$, odds $= .25/.75 = \frac{1}{3}$).

The odds of success thus vary multiplicatively around 1. Taking logarithms gives an equivalent measure that varies additively around 0, called the *log odds* or *logit*:

$$\text{logit}(\pi) \equiv \log(\text{odds}) = \log\left(\frac{\pi}{1-\pi}\right) \ .$$

The logit is symmetric about $\pi = 0.5$, in that $\text{logit}(\pi) = -\text{logit}(1-\pi)$.

A binary response for two groups gives a 2×2 table, with Group as the row variable, for example. Let π_1 and π_2 be the success probabilities for Group 1 and Group 2. The *odds ratio* is just the ratio of the odds for the two groups:

$$\text{odds ratio} \equiv \theta = \frac{\text{odds}_1}{\text{odds}_2} = \frac{\pi_1/(1-\pi_1)}{\pi_2/(1-\pi_2)} \ .$$

Like the odds itself, the odds ratio is always non-negative, between 0 and ∞. When $\theta = 1$, the distributions of success and failure are the same for both groups (so $\pi_1 = \pi_2$); there is no association between row and column variables, or the response is independent of group. When $\theta > 1$, Group 1 has a greater success probability; when $\theta < 1$, Group 2 has a greater success probability.

Similarly, the odds ratio may be transformed to a log scale in order to give a measure that is symmetric about 0. The *log odds ratio*, symbolized by ψ, is just the difference between the logits for Groups 1 and 2:

$$\text{log odds ratio} \equiv \psi = \log(\theta) = \log\left[\frac{\pi_1/(1-\pi_1)}{\pi_2/(1-\pi_2)}\right] = \text{logit}(\pi_1) - \text{logit}(\pi_2) \ .$$

Independence corresponds to $\psi = 0$, and reversing the rows or columns of the table merely changes the sign of ψ.

For sample data, the *sample odds ratio* is the ratio of the sample odds for the two groups:

$$\hat{\theta} = \frac{p_1/(1-p_1)}{p_2/(1-p_2)} = \frac{n_{11}/n_{12}}{n_{21}/n_{22}} = \frac{n_{11}n_{22}}{n_{12}n_{21}} \ . \tag{3.1}$$

I described the odds ratio for a sampling context of independent binomial samples, but actually, the odds ratio is an appropriate measure of strength of association for all the standard sampling schemes because it treats the variables symmetrically. It does not matter whether the row or column variable is the response, or whether both variables are treated as responses. Other measures of strength of association, not described here, *do* distinguish between explanatory and response variables.

The sample estimate $\hat{\theta}$ in Equation 3.1 is the maximum likelihood estimator of the true θ. The sampling distribution of $\hat{\theta}$ is asymptotically normal as $n \to \infty$, but may be highly skewed in small to moderate samples. Consequently, inference for the odds ratio is more conveniently carried out in terms of the log odds ratio, whose sampling distribution is more closely normal, with mean $\psi = \log(\theta)$, and asymptotic standard error (ASE):

$$\text{ASE}_{\log(\theta)} \equiv \hat{s}(\hat{\psi}) = \left\{\frac{1}{n_{11}} + \frac{1}{n_{12}} + \frac{1}{n_{21}} + \frac{1}{n_{22}}\right\}^{1/2} = \left\{\sum\sum n_{ij}^{-1}\right\}^{1/2} \tag{3.2}$$

A large-sample $100(1-\alpha)\%$ confidence interval for $\log(\theta)$ may therefore be calculated as $\log(\theta) \pm z_{1-\alpha/2}\, \text{ASE}_{\log(\theta)}$, where $z_{1-\alpha/2}$ is the cumulative normal quantile with $1 - \alpha/2$ in the lower tail. Confidence intervals for θ itself are obtained by exponentiating the end points of the interval for $\log(\theta)$.

However, $\hat{\theta}$ is 0 or ∞ if any $n_{ij} = 0$. Haldane (1955) and Gart and Zweiful (1967) showed that improved estimators of θ and $\psi = \log(\theta)$ are obtained by replacing each n_{ij}

with $[n_{ij} + \frac{1}{2}]$ in Equations 3.1 and 3.2. This adjustment is preferred in small samples, and it is required if any zero cells occur. In large samples, the effect of adding 0.5 to each cell becomes negligible.

EXAMPLE 3.4   Berkeley admissions

Odds ratios and many other measures of association that are not described here are produced with `PROC FREQ` when you specify the `MEASURES` option in the `TABLES` statement. For the Berkeley admissions data, the frequency table in Output 3.1 and the various measures of association are produced by these statements:

```
%include catdata(berkeley);

proc freq data=berkeley order=data;
   weight freq;
   tables gender*admit / nocol measures;
   format admit admit. gender $sex.;
```

The odds ratio is displayed, in a section of the output labeled "Estimates of the Relative Risk", as the value associated with a Case-Control study. This portion of the output is shown in Output 3.2. The value $\hat{\theta} = 1.84 = (1198 \times 1278)/(557 \times 1493)$ indicates that males are nearly twice as likely to be admitted as females. I describe a visualization method for odds ratios in 2×2 tables in Section 3.4 and return to the Berkeley data in Example 3.8. See Stokes et al. (1995, Sections 2.4 and 2.5) for discussion of relative risk and other measures of association in 2×2 tables. □

Output 3.2   Admission to Berkeley graduate programs: Odds ratio and relative risk

```
         Estimates of the Relative Risk (Row1/Row2)


                                                    95%
        Type of Study          Value       Confidence Bounds
        -------------------------------------------------------

        Case-Control           1.841       1.624       2.087
        Cohort (Col1 Risk)     1.467       1.352       1.591
        Cohort (Col2 Risk)     0.797       0.761       0.834
```

3.2.3   Larger Tables: Overall Analysis

For two-way tables, overall tests of association can be carried out using `PROC FREQ`. If the table has more than two factors (as in the Arthritis Treatment data), the other factors are ignored (and collapsed) if not included in the `TABLES` statement. This simplified analysis may be misleading if the excluded factors interact with the factors used in the analysis.

EXAMPLE 3.5   Arthritis treatment

Because the main interest is in the relation between Treatment and Outcome, an overall analysis (which ignores Sex) could be carried out using `PROC FREQ` as shown in the next program.

```
title 'Arthritis Treatment: PROC FREQ Analysis';
data arth;
   input sex$ treat$ @;
   do improve = 'None  ', 'Some', 'Marked';
      input count @;
      output;
      end;
datalines;
Female  Active    6  5  16
Female  Placebo  19  7   6
Male    Active    7  2   5
Male    Placebo  10  0   1
;
*-- Ignoring sex;
proc freq data=arth order=data;
   weight count;
   tables treat * improve / cmh chisq nocol nopercent;
   run;
```

Output 3.3   Arthritis treatment data, overall analysis

```
              Arthritis Treatment: PROC FREQ Analysis                    1

                     TABLE OF TREAT BY IMPROVE

           TREAT      IMPROVE

           Frequency|
           Row Pct  |None    |Some    |Marked  |  Total
           ---------+--------+--------+--------+
           Active   |    13 |     7 |    21 |     41
                    | 31.71 | 17.07 | 51.22 |
           ---------+--------+--------+--------+
           Placebo  |    29 |     7 |     7 |     43
                    | 67.44 | 16.28 | 16.28 |
           ---------+--------+--------+--------+
           Total         42      14      28       84


                STATISTICS FOR TABLE OF TREAT BY IMPROVE


       Statistic                     DF      Value       Prob
       ------------------------------------------------------
       Chi-Square                     2     13.055      0.001
       Likelihood Ratio Chi-Square    2     13.530      0.001
       Mantel-Haenszel Chi-Square     1     12.859      0.000
       Phi Coefficient                       0.394
       Contingency Coefficient               0.367
       Cramer's V                            0.394

       Sample Size = 84
```

In this analysis, note that

- TREAT and IMPROVE are both character variables, which PROC FREQ orders alphabetically (i.e., Marked, None, Some) by default. Because I want to treat the IMPROVE variable as ordinal, I used ORDER=DATA in the PROC FREQ statement to have the levels of IMPROVE ordered by their order of appearance in the dataset.
- The CHISQ option gives the usual χ^2 tests (Pearson, Fisher's, etc.). The CMH option requests the Cochran-Mantel-Haenszel tests, including specialized tests for ordinal variables.

The output, shown in Output 3.3, begins with the frequency table and includes row percentages. The row percentages show a clear effect of treatment: for people given the Active treatment, 51% showed Marked improvement; among those given the Placebo, 67% showed no improvement.

The results for the CHISQ option are also shown in Output 3.3. All tests show a significant association between Treatment and Outcome.   □

3.2.4   Tests for Ordinal Variables

For $r \times c$ tables, different tests are applicable depending on whether either or both of the row and column variables are ordinal. Tests that take the ordinal nature of a variable into account are provided by the CMH option in the TABLES statement. These tests are based on assigning numerical scores to the table categories; the default (table) scores treat the levels as equally spaced. They generally have higher power when the pattern of association is determined by the order of an ordinal variable.

For the arthritis data, these tests (CMH option) give the output shown in Output 3.4.

Output 3.4   Arthritis treatment data, overall analysis

```
               Arthritis Treatment: PROC FREQ Analysis                  2

               SUMMARY STATISTICS FOR TREAT BY IMPROVE



       Cochran-Mantel-Haenszel Statistics (Based on Table Scores)

       Statistic   Alternative Hypothesis    DF      Value     Prob
       ------------------------------------------------------------
           1        Nonzero Correlation        1     12.859    0.000
           2        Row Mean Scores Differ      1     12.859    0.000
           3        General Association         2     12.900    0.002


       Total Sample Size = 84
```

The three types of tests differ in the types of departure from independence that they are sensitive to:

- **General Association**. When *both* the row and column variables are nominal (unordered), the only alternative hypothesis of interest is that there is *some* association between the row and column variables. The CMH test statistic is similar to the (Pearson) Chi-Square and to the Likelihood Ratio Chi-Square in the Statistics table; all have $(r-1)(c-1)$ df.

- **Row Mean Scores Differ**. If the column variable is ordinal, assigning scores to the column variable produces a mean for each row. The association between row and column variables can be expressed as a test of whether these means differ over the rows of the table, with $r-1$ df. This is analogous to the Kruskal-Wallis nonparametric test (ANOVA based on rank scores).

- **Nonzero Correlation (Linear association)**. When *both* the row and column variables are ordinal, we could assign scores to both variables and compute the correlation (r). The Mantel-Haenszel χ^2 is equal to $(N-1)r^2$, where N is the total sample size. The test is most sensitive to a pattern where the row mean score changes linearly over the rows.

Notes:

- Different kinds of scores can be assigned using the SCORES option in the TABLES statement, but only the relative spacing of the scores is important. The default, SCORES= TABLE uses integer row and column numbers for character variables, and numeric levels (or formatted equivalents) for numeric variables.

- When only one variable is ordinal, make it the *last* one in the TABLES statement because PROC FREQ only computes means across the column variable.

- When there are only $r = 2$ rows (as there are here), the nonzero correlation and the row means tests are equivalent. In a 2×2 table, all three tests are identical.

3.2.5   Sample CMH Profiles

Two contrived examples may make the differences among these tests more apparent. Visualizations of the patterns of association reinforce the aspects to which the tests are most sensitive.

General Association

Table 3.5 exhibits a general association between variables *A* and *B*, but no difference in row means or linear association. The row means are calculated by assigning integer scores, $b_i = i$, to the column categories. Figure 3.1(A) shows the pattern of association in this table graphically, as a sieve diagram (described in Section 3.5).

Table 3.5   General pattern of association

	b1	b2	b3	b4	b5	Total	Mean
a1	0	15	25	15	0	55	3.0
a2	5	20	5	20	5	55	3.0
a3	20	5	5	5	20	55	3.0
Total	25	40	35	40	25	165	3.0

Figure 3.1   Sieve diagrams for two patterns of association: (a) General Association and (b) Linear Association. In each figure, cells with greater than expected frequency are shown with solid, blue cross hatching, and the number of boxes is proportional to the observed frequency.

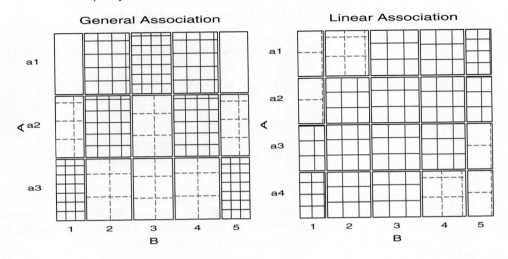

This is reflected in the PROC FREQ output shown in Output 3.5. The chi-square values for nonzero correlation and different row mean scores are exactly zero because the row means are all equal. Only the general association test shows that *A* and *B* are associated.

Output 3.5   General Association example: CMH tests

```
Cochran-Mantel-Haenszel Statistics (Based on Table Scores)

Statistic    Alternative Hypothesis    DF      Value      Prob
-------------------------------------------------------------------
    1        Nonzero Correlation        1      0.000      1.000
    2        Row Mean Scores Differ     2      0.000      1.000
    3        General Association        8     91.797      0.000
```

Linear Association

Table 3.6 contains a weak, non-significant general association, but significant row mean differences and linear associations. Therefore, the unstructured test of general association would lead to the conclusion that no association exists, while the tests that take ordinal factors into account would conclude otherwise. Note that the largest frequencies shift towards lower levels of *B* as the level of variable *A* increases. See Figure 3.1(B) for a visual representation of this pattern.

Table 3.6   Linear pattern of association

	b1	b2	b3	b4	b5	Total	Mean
a1	2	5	8	8	8	31	3.48
a2	2	8	8	8	5	31	3.19
a3	5	8	8	8	2	31	2.81
a4	8	8	8	5	2	31	2.52
Total	17	29	32	29	17	124	3.00

Note that the χ^2 values for the row means and nonzero correlation tests in Output 3.6 are very similar, but the correlation test is more highly significant because it is based on just one degree of freedom.

Output 3.6   Linear Association example: CMH tests

```
        Cochran-Mantel-Haenszel Statistics (Based on Table Scores)

    Statistic    Alternative Hypothesis    DF       Value      Prob
    ---------------------------------------------------------------
        1         Nonzero Correlation        1      10.639     0.001
        2         Row Mean Scores Differ     3      10.676     0.014
        3         General Association       12      13.400     0.341
```

The differences in sensitivity and power among these tests is analogous to the difference between general ANOVA tests and tests for linear trends in experimental designs with quantitative factors: the more specific test has greater power, but it is sensitive to a narrower range of departure from the null hypothesis.

3.3 Stratified Analysis

An overall analysis ignores other variables (like Sex) by collapsing over them. It is possible that the treatment is effective only for one gender, or even that the treatment has opposite effects for men and women.

A stratified analysis:

- controls for the effects of one or more background variables. This is similar to the use of a blocking variable in an ANOVA design.
- is obtained by including more than two variables in the TABLES statement. List the stratification variables *first*. To examine the association between TREAT and IMPROVE, controlling for both Sex and Age (if available):

$$\begin{array}{ccccc} & \overbrace{\text{stratify by}} & & \overbrace{\text{explanatory}} & \overbrace{\text{response}} \\ \text{tables} & \text{age * sex} & * & \text{treat} & * & \text{improve;} \end{array}$$

EXAMPLE 3.6   **Arthritis treatment**

The statements below request a stratified analysis of the arthritis treatment data with CMH tests, controlling for Sex.

```
*-- Stratified analysis, controlling for sex;
proc freq data=arth order=data;
   weight count;
   tables sex * treat * improve / cmh chisq nocol nopercent;
   run;
```

PROC FREQ gives a separate table for each level of the stratification variables (Output 3.7 and Output 3.8), plus overall (partial) tests controlling for the stratification variables (Output 3.9).

Output 3.7   Arthritis treatment data, stratified analysis

```
              Arthritis Treatment: PROC FREQ Analysis          3
              Stratified analysis, controlling for sex

                    TABLE 1 OF TREAT BY IMPROVE
                    CONTROLLING FOR SEX=Female


        TREAT       IMPROVE


        Frequency|
        Row Pct  |None    |Some    |Marked  |  Total
        ---------+--------+--------+--------+
        Active   |     6  |     5  |    16  |    27
                 |  22.22 |  18.52 |  59.26 |
        ---------+--------+--------+--------+
        Placebo  |    19  |     7  |     6  |    32
                 |  59.38 |  21.88 |  18.75 |
        ---------+--------+--------+--------+
        Total         25       12       22       59



                STATISTICS FOR TABLE 1 OF TREAT BY IMPROVE
                     CONTROLLING FOR SEX=Female


        Statistic                    DF     Value        Prob
        ------------------------------------------------------
        Chi-Square                    2    11.296        0.004
        Likelihood Ratio Chi-Square   2    11.731        0.003
        Mantel-Haenszel Chi-Square    1    10.935        0.001
        Phi Coefficient                     0.438
        Contingency Coefficient             0.401
        Cramer's V                          0.438


        Sample Size = 59
```

Note that the strength of association between Treatment and Outcome is quite strong for females (Output 3.7). In contrast, the results for males (Output 3.8) show a not quite significant association, even by the more powerful Mantel-Haenszel test. However, note that there are too few males for the general association χ^2 tests to be reliable (the statistic does not follow the theoretical χ^2 distribution).

The individual tables are followed by the (overall) partial tests of association controlling for Sex, as shown in Output 3.9. Unlike the tests for each stratum, these tests *do not* require large sample size in the individual strata—just a large total sample size. Note that the χ^2 values here are slightly larger than those from the initial analysis that ignored Sex.   □

Output 3.8 Arthritis treatment data, stratified analysis

```
        Arthritis Treatment: PROC FREQ Analysis              4
        Stratified analysis, controlling for sex

              TABLE 2 OF TREAT BY IMPROVE
                 CONTROLLING FOR SEX=Male

        TREAT      IMPROVE

        Frequency|
        Row Pct  |None   |Some   |Marked  | Total
        ---------+-------+-------+--------+
        Active   |     7 |     2 |      5 |    14
                 | 50.00 | 14.29 |  35.71 |
        ---------+-------+-------+--------+
        Placebo  |    10 |     0 |      1 |    11
                 | 90.91 |  0.00 |   9.09 |
        ---------+-------+-------+--------+
        Total           17       2        6      25
           STATISTICS FOR TABLE 2 OF TREAT BY IMPROVE
                    CONTROLLING FOR SEX=Male


    Statistic                      DF      Value      Prob
    --------------------------------------------------------

    Chi-Square                      2      4.907      0.086
    Likelihood Ratio Chi-Square     2      5.855      0.054
    Mantel-Haenszel Chi-Square      1      3.713      0.054
    Phi Coefficient                        0.443
    Contingency Coefficient                0.405
    Cramer's V                             0.443


    Sample Size = 25
    WARNING:  67% of the cells have expected counts less
              than 5. Chi-Square may not be a valid test.
```

Output 3.9 Arthritis treatment data, stratified analysis

```
          Arthritis Treatment: PROC FREQ Analysis            5
          Stratified analysis, controlling for sex

        SUMMARY STATISTICS FOR TREAT BY IMPROVE
                 CONTROLLING FOR SEX


   Cochran-Mantel-Haenszel Statistics (Based on Table Scores)

   Statistic   Alternative Hypothesis     DF      Value      Prob
   -----------------------------------------------------------------

        1       Nonzero Correlation        1      14.632     0.000
        2       Row Mean Scores Differ     1      14.632     0.000
        3       General Association        2      14.632     0.001

  Total Sample Size = 84
```

3.3.1   Assessing Homogeneity of Association

In a stratified analysis, it is often of interest to know if the association between the primary table variables is the same over all strata. For $2 \times 2 \times k$ tables, this question reduces to whether the odds ratio is the same in all k strata, and PROC FREQ computes the Breslow-Day test for homogeneity of odds ratios when you use the measures option in the TABLES statement. PROC FREQ cannot perform tests of homogeneity for larger tables, but these tests can be easily done with the CATMOD procedure.

EXAMPLE 3.7   Arthritis treatment

For the arthritis data, homogeneity means that there is no 3-way Sex * Treatment * Outcome association. That is, the association between Treatment and Outcome (IMPROVE) is the same for both men and women. This hypothesis can be stated as the log-linear model,

$$[\text{SexTreat}] \ [\text{SexOutcome}] \ [\text{TreatOutcome}] \ . \qquad (3.3)$$

This notation (described in Section 7.2) lists only the high-order association terms in a linear model for log frequency. Thus, the model in Equation 3.3 allows associations between Sex and Treatment (e.g., more males get the active treatment), between Sex and Outcome (e.g., females are more likely to show marked improvement), and between Treatment and Outcome, but no 3-way association. In the PROC CATMOD step below, the LOGLIN statement specifies this log-linear model as SEX|TREAT|IMPROVE@2 (where IMPROVE is the Outcome variable), which means "all terms up to 2-way associations."

```
title2 'Test homogeneity of treat*improve association';
data arth;
   set arth;
   if count=0 then count=1E-20;
proc catmod order=data;
   weight count;
   model sex * treat * improve = _response_ /
        ml noiter noresponse nodesign nogls ;
   loglin sex|treat|improve@2 / title='No 3-way association';
run;
   loglin sex treat|improve   / title='No Sex Associations';
```

(Frequencies of 0 can be regarded either as "structural 0s"—a cell that could not occur, or as "sampling 0s"—a cell that simply did not occur. PROC CATMOD treats 0 frequencies as "structural 0s," which means that cells with count = 0 are excluded from the analysis. The DATA step above replaces the one 0 frequency by a small number.)

In the output from PROC CATMOD, shown in Output 3.10, the likelihood ratio χ^2 (the badness-of-fit for the No 3-Way model) is the test for homogeneity across Sex. This is clearly non-significant, so the Treatment-Outcome association can be considered to be the same for men and women.

Note that the associations of Sex with Treatment and Sex with Outcome are both small and of borderline significance. This suggests a stronger form of homogeneity than the log-linear model [Sex] [TreatOutcome], which says that the only association is that between Treatment and Outcome. This model is tested by the second LOGLIN statement given in the previous program, which produced the results shown in Output 3.11. The likelihood ratio test indicates that this model might provide a reasonable fit.   □

Output 3.10   Arthritis treatment data, testing homogeneity

```
             Arthritis Treatment: PROC FREQ Analysis            7
          Test homogeneity of treat*improve association


                        No 3-way association


     MAXIMUM-LIKELIHOOD ANALYSIS-OF-VARIANCE TABLE


       Source               DF    Chi-Square      Prob
       -----------------------------------------------
       SEX                   1        8.02       0.0046
       TREAT                 1        0.42       0.5157
       SEX*TREAT             1        1.62       0.2036
       IMPROVE               2        9.04       0.0109
       SEX*IMPROVE           2        4.12       0.1276
       TREAT*IMPROVE         2       12.85       0.0016


       LIKELIHOOD RATIO      1        0.01       0.9038
```

Output 3.11   Arthritis treatment data, testing homogeneity

```
             Arthritis Treatment: PROC FREQ Analysis            8
          Test homogeneity of treat*improve association


                        No Sex Associations


     MAXIMUM-LIKELIHOOD ANALYSIS-OF-VARIANCE TABLE


       Source               DF    Chi-Square      Prob
       -----------------------------------------------
       SEX                   1        9.06       0.0026
       TREAT                 1        0.02       0.9006
       IMPROVE               2        7.61       0.0223
       TREAT*IMPROVE         2       12.21       0.0022


       LIKELIHOOD RATIO      4        4.60       0.3314
```

3.4   Fourfold Display for 2 × 2 Tables

The *fourfold display* is a relative of the pie chart, designed for the display of 2 × 2 (or 2 × 2 × k) tables (Fienberg, 1975; Friendly, 1994a,c). In this display, the frequency n_{ij} in each cell of a fourfold table is shown by a quarter circle, whose radius is proportional to $\sqrt{n_{ij}}$, so the area is proportional to the cell count. The fourfold display is similar to a pie chart in using segments of a circle to show frequencies. It differs from a pie chart in that it keeps the angles of the segments constant and varies the radius, whereas the pie chart varies the angles and keeps the radius constant.

The main purpose of this display is to depict the sample odds ratio,

$$\hat{\theta} = (n_{11}/n_{12}) \div (n_{21}/n_{22}).$$

An association between the variables ($\theta \neq 1$) is shown by the tendency of diagonally opposite cells in one direction to differ in size from those in the opposite direction, and the display uses color or shading to show this direction. Confidence rings for the observed θ allow a visual test of the hypothesis of independence, $H_0 : \theta = 1$. They have the property that (in a standardized display) the rings for adjacent quadrants overlap *if* the observed counts are consistent with the null hypothesis.

EXAMPLE 3.8   **Berkeley admissions**

Figure 3.2 shows the basic fourfold display for the Berkeley admissions data (Table 3.1). Here, the area of each quadrant is proportional to the cell frequency, shown numerically in each corner. The odds ratio is proportional to the product of the areas shaded dark, divided by the product of the areas shaded light. The sample odds ratio, Odds (Admit|Male) / Odds (Admit|Female), is 1.84 (see Example 3.4), indicating that males were nearly twice as likely to be admitted.

Figure 3.2   Fourfold display for Berkeley admission data, unstandardized

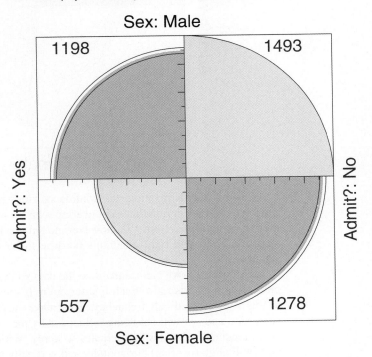

However, it is difficult to make these visual comparisons because there are more men than women, and because the proportions admitted and rejected are unequal. In the unstandardized display the confidence bands have no interpretation as a test of $H_0 : \theta = 1$.

The data in a 2×2 table can be standardized to make these visual comparisons easier. Table 3.7 shows the Berkeley data with the addition of row percentages (which equate for the number of men and women applicants), indicating the proportion of each gender that was accepted and rejected. The table indicates that 44.52% of males were admitted, while only 30.35% of females were admitted. Moreover, the row percentages have the same odds ratio as the raw data: $44.52 \times 69.65/30.35 \times 55.48 = 1.84$. Figure 3.3 shows the fourfold display, where the area of each quarter circle is proportional to these row percentages.

Table 3.7 Admissions to Berkeley graduate programs, frequencies and row percentages

| | Frequencies | | Row Percents | |
	Admitted	Rejected	Admitted	Rejected
Males	1198	1493	44.52	55.48
Females	557	1278	30.35	69.65

Figure 3.3 Fourfold display for Berkeley admission data, genders equated

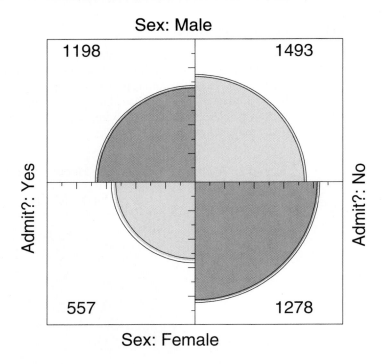

With this standardization, the confidence rings have the property that the confidence rings for each upper quadrant will overlap with those for the quadrant below it if the odds ratio does not differ from 1.0. However, no similar statement can be made about the corresponding left and right quadrants because the overall rate of admission has not been standardized.

As a final step, we can standardize the data so that both table margins are equal, while preserving the odds ratio. Each quarter circle is then drawn to have an area proportional to this standardized cell frequency. This makes it easier to see the association between admission and sex without being influenced by the overall admission rate or by the differential tendency of males and females to apply. With this standardization, the four quadrants will align (overlap) horizontally and vertically when the odds ratio is 1, regardless of the marginal frequencies. The fully standardized display, which is usually the most useful form, is shown in Figure 3.4.

The quadrants in Figure 3.4 do not align and the 99% confidence rings around each quadrant do not overlap, indicating that the odds ratio differs significantly from 1—putative evidence of gender bias. The very narrow width of the confidence rings gives a visual indication of the precision of the data—if we stopped here, we might feel quite confident of this conclusion.   □

Figure 3.4   Fourfold display for Berkeley admission data, genders and admission equated. The area of each quadrant shows the frequency, standardized to equate the margins for sex and admission. Circular arcs show the limits of a 99% confidence interval for the odds ratio.

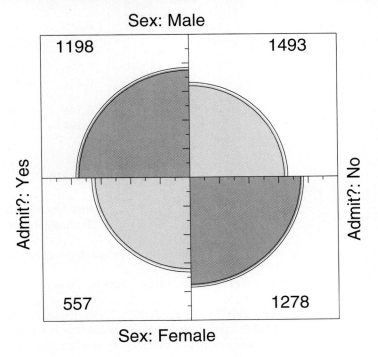

3.4.1   Confidence Rings for Odds Ratio

Confidence rings for the fourfold display are computed from a confidence interval for θ, whose endpoints can each be mapped into a 2×2 table. Each table is then drawn in the same way as the data.

The interval for θ is most easily found by considering the distribution of $\hat{\psi} = \log \hat{\theta}$, whose standard error may be estimated by using Equation 3.2. Then an approximate $1 - \alpha$ confidence interval for ψ is given by

$$\hat{\psi} \pm \hat{s}(\hat{\psi})\, z_{1-\alpha/2} = \{\hat{\psi}_l,\ \hat{\psi}_u\}\ ,$$

as described in Section 3.2.2. The corresponding limits for the odds ratio θ are $\{\exp(\hat{\psi}_l),\exp(\hat{\psi}_u)\}$. For the data shown in Figure 3.4, $\hat{\psi} = \log \hat{\theta} = .6104$, and $\hat{s}(\hat{\psi}) = 0.0639$, so the 99% confidence limits for θ are $\{1.5617, 2.1704\}$.

Now consider how to find a 2×2 table whose frequencies correspond to the odds ratios at the limits of the confidence interval. A table standardized to have equal row and column margins can be represented by the 2×2 matrix with entries

$$\begin{bmatrix} p & (1-p) \\ (1-p) & p \end{bmatrix}\ ,$$

whose odds ratio is $\theta = p^2/(1 - p)^2$. Solving for p gives $p = \sqrt{\theta}/(1 + \sqrt{\theta})$. The corresponding frequencies can then be found by adjusting the standardized table to have the same row and column margins as the data. The results of these computations, which generate the confidence rings shown in Figure 3.4, are shown in Table 3.8.

Table 3.8   Odds ratios and equivalent tables for confidence rings

	Odds Ratio	Standardized Table		Frequencies	
Lower limit	1.562	0.555	0.445	1157.2	1533.8
		0.445	0.555	597.8	1237.2
Data	1.841	0.576	0.424	1198.0	1493.0
		0.424	0.576	557.0	1278.0
Upper limit	2.170	0.596	0.404	1237.8	1453.2
		0.404	0.596	517.2	1317.8

3.4.2   The FOURFOLD Program

Fourfold displays have been implemented by using SAS/IML. The program is described in detail in an article in *Observations* (Friendly, 1994c) and is documented in Appendix A.8 of this book.

FOURFOLD is a SAS/IML module that is called as follows:

```
run fourfold(dim, table, vnames, lnames);
```

where TABLE is the 2×2 (or $2 \times 2 \times k$) frequency table whose dimensions are given by DIM, VNAMES is a character vector that contains the names of the table variables, and LNAMES is a character matrix of the category levels. A variety of options for standardization, shading patterns and colors, confidence rings, etc. are controlled by global variables, as described in Appendix A.8.

To use the program, %INCLUDE the FOURFOLD program within a PROC IML step. Then, enter the observed frequencies in the array TABLE; create the character vector VNAMES, which contains the row and column variable names; and create the two-row character matrix LNAMES, which contains the category labels.

For example, the plots in Figure 3.2 and Figure 3.4 are produced by the statements shown in the following program:

```
goptions hsize=7in vsize=7in;      *-- make plot square;
filename fourfold  'path/to/fourfold.sas';
proc iml;
   %include fourfold;

   *-- Berkeley Admissions data;
   dim = {2 2};
   vnames = {"Admit?" "Sex"};
   lnames = {"Yes" "No",
             "Male" "Female"};

          /* Admit Not */
   table = {1198   1493,
             557   1278};

   patterns={solid solid};
   colors={grayd0 gray80};

   std='MAX';                    /* Figure 3.2 */
   run fourfold(dim, table, vnames, lnames);
```

```
      std='MARG';                  /* Figure 3.4 */
   run fourfold(dim, table, vnames, lnames);
quit;
```

The global variable STD determines the way the table is standardized. STD='MAX' scales the frequencies so that the largest value is 100; STD='MARG' is used to equate the marginal frequencies for the row variable, the column variable, or both (the default). The variable(s) equated are controlled by the global CONFIG variable. For example, to equate the second variable, as in Figure 3.3, specify CONFIG={2}:

```
      std='MARG';
      config={2};                  /* Figure 3.3 (equate gender) */
   run fourfold(dim, table, vnames, lnames);
```

3.4.3   Stratified Analysis for 2 × 2 × *k* Tables

In a $2 \times 2 \times k$ table, the last dimension often corresponds to "strata" or populations, and it is typically of interest to see if the association between the first two variables is homogeneous across strata. For such tables, simply make one fourfold panel for each stratum. The standardization of marginal frequencies is designed to allow easy visual comparison of the pattern of association when the marginal frequencies vary across two or more populations.

The admissions data shown in Figures 3.2, 3.3, and 3.4 were actually obtained from six departments—the six largest at Berkeley (Bickel et al., 1975). To determine the source of the apparent sex bias in favor of males, we make a new plot (Figure 3.5) stratified by department.

Surprisingly, Figure 3.5 shows that, for five of the six departments, the odds of admission are approximately the same for both men and women applicants. Department A appears to differ from the others, with women approximately 2.86 (= (313/19)/(512/89)) times as likely to gain admission. This apparent difference is confirmed by the confidence rings, which in Figure 3.5 are joint 99% intervals for θ_c, $c = 1, \ldots, k$.

This result, which contradicts the display for the aggregate data shown in Figure 3.4, is a nice example of *Simpson's paradox*[3], and it illustrates clearly why an overall analysis of a 3- (or higher-) way table can be misleading. The resolution of this contradiction can be found in the large differences in admission rates among departments. Men and women apply to different departments differentially, and, in this data, women happen to apply in larger numbers to departments that have a low acceptance rate. The aggregate results are misleading because they falsely assume that men and women are equally likely to apply in each field.[4]

A final enhancement of the fourfold display is shown in Figure 3.6. Here, small tick marks are drawn to show the direction of association (positive residuals), and the intensity of the shading colors is varied to distinguish those strata for which the odds ratio differs significantly from 1 at $\alpha = .01$.[5]

---

[3]Simpson's paradox (Simpson, 1951) occurs in a 3-way table, [A, B, C], when the marginal association between two variables, A, B collapsing over C, differs in *direction* from the partial association A, B|C = c_k at the separate levels of C. Strictly speaking, Simpson's paradox would require that for all departments separately the odds ratio, θ_k, is less than 1 (which occurs for Departments A, B, D, and F in Figure 3.5), while in the aggregate data, θ is greater than 1.

[4]This explanation ignores the possibility of structural bias against women, e.g., lack of resources allocated to departments that attract women applicants.

[5]The FOURFOLD program allows these tests to be done either individually or jointly (using a Bonferroni adjustment).

Figure 3.5   Fourfold display of Berkeley admissions, by department. In each panel the confidence rings for adjacent quadrants overlap if the odds ratio for admission and sex does not differ significantly from 1. The data in each panel has been standardized as shown in Figure 3.4.

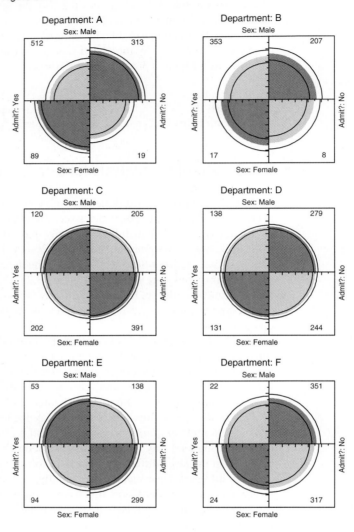

Figure 3.6 Fourfold display of Berkeley admissions, by department, enhanced. Each panel is shaded according to whether or not the odds ratio for admission and sex differs significantly from 1.

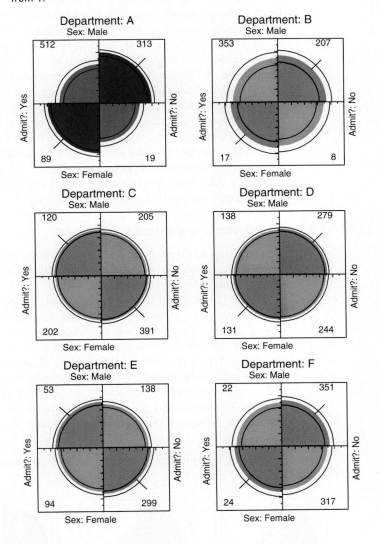

Visualization Principles

An important principle in the display of large, complex datasets is ***controlled comparison***—making comparisons against a clear standard, with other things held constant. The fourfold display differs from a pie chart in that it holds the angles of the segments constant and varies the radius. An important consequence is that we can quite easily compare a series of fourfold displays for different strata because corresponding cells of the table are always in the same position. As a result, an array of fourfold displays serves the goals of comparison and detection better than an array of pie charts. Moreover, it allows the observed frequencies to be standardized by equating either the row or column totals, while preserving the odds ratio. In Figure 3.5, for example, the proportion of men and women and the proportion of accepted applicants in each department were equated visually. This provides a clear standard, which also greatly facilitates controlled comparison.

Another principle is ***visual impact***—distinguishing the important features of the display from the less important (Tukey, 1993). Figure 3.6 distinguishes the one department for which the odds ratio differs significantly from 1 by shading intensity, even though the same information can be found by inspection of the confidence rings.

EXAMPLE 3.9   Breathlessness and wheeze in coal miners

Standardizing a collection of 2×2 tables allows visualizing relations with different factors (row percentages, column percentages, strata totals). Different graphs can speak more eloquently to different questions.

Agresti (1990, Table 7.11) cites data from Ashford and Snowden (1970) on the association between two pulmonary conditions, breathlessness and wheeze, in a large sample of coal miners. The miners are classified into age groups, and the question treated by Agresti is whether the association between these two symptoms is homogeneous across age groups.[6] This question is addressed by displaying the odds ratio in the 2×2 tables with the margins of breathlessness and wheeze equated (i.e., with the default STD='MARG' option), which gives the graph shown in Figure 3.7. Although the panels for all age groups show an overwhelmingly positive association between these two symptoms, one can also see that the strength of this association declines with increasing age.

Figure 3.7   Fourfold display for coal miners data, both margins equated

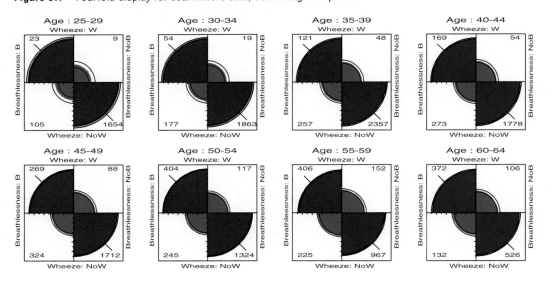

---

[6] A ninth group, aged 20–24, has been omitted from these analyses.

Note that the pattern of change with increasing age is somewhat subtle compared to the dominant positive association within each panel. When the goal is to display how the odds ratio varies with a quantitative factor such as age, it is often better to simply plot the odds ratio directly, as shown in Figure 3.8.

Figure 3.8   Breathlessness and wheeze in coal miners, log odds plot. The smooth curve is a quadratic fit. Vertical bars give individual 95% confidence intervals.

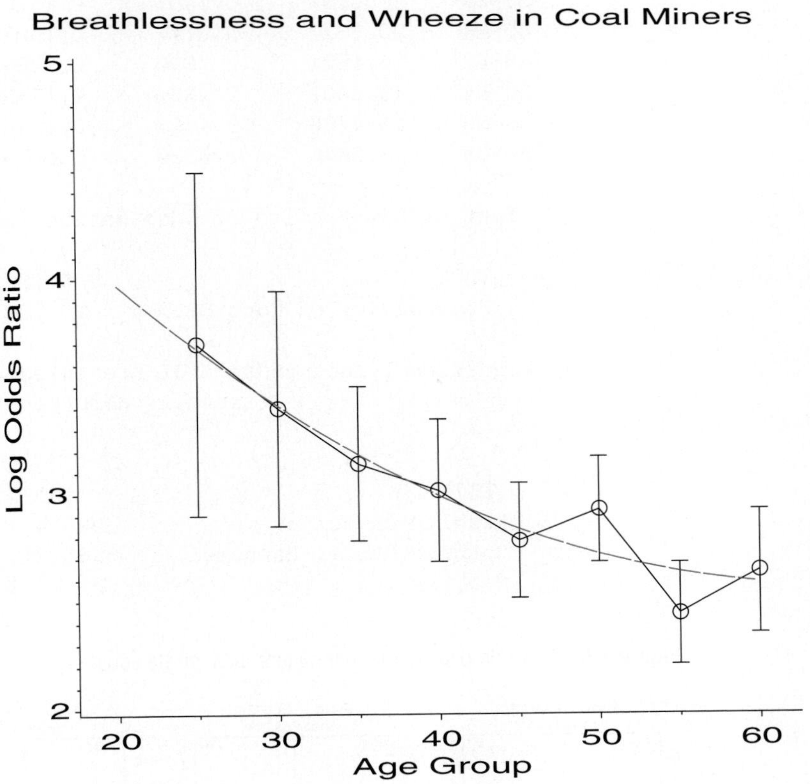

The FOURFOLD program also provides the relevant test statistics, shown in Output 3.12. The test of whether the association is the same over age is a test of the log-linear model [BW][BA][WA] of no 3-way association among the variables Breathlessness, Wheeze, and Age, which is soundly rejected, $G^2(7) = 26.13$.

A more poignant question, however, concerns the prevalence of these two respiratory symptoms among miners and how these change as age increases. The answer is concealed in Figure 3.7 because the proportion of miners with each symptom is equated in each age group. This question can be addressed by standardizing the frequencies to equate the numbers in each stratum (STD='MAX';), which gives the graph shown in Figure 3.9. If age is regarded as reflecting the number of years spent working in coal mines, this figure shows the sad result of such employment: the relative frequency of miners with both symptoms steadily increasing over age. We return to this data in Example 7.14, where we consider a variety of specific logit models for the prevalence of each symptom simultaneously with models for their log odds ratio.   □

Output 3.12   Odds ratios and tests of homogeneity of association for coal miners data

```
            Odds (B|Wheeze) / (B|No Wheeze)

        Odds Ratio    Log Odds    SE(Log)          Z     Pr>|Z|

  25-29    40.2561      3.6953     0.4059      9.1049     0.0000
  30-34    29.9144      3.3983     0.2781     12.2201     0.0000
  35-39    23.1191      3.1407     0.1828     17.1815     0.0000
  40-44    20.3827      3.0147     0.1693     17.8072     0.0000
  45-49    16.1521      2.7820     0.1369     20.3163     0.0000
  50-54    18.6602      2.9264     0.1259     23.2377     0.0000
  55-59    11.4796      2.4406     0.1205     20.2535     0.0000
  60-64    13.9846      2.6380     0.1470     17.9494     0.0000


  Test of Homogeneity of Odds Ratios (no 3-Way Association)

     TEST                        CHISQ      DF     PROB
     Homogeneity of Odds Ratios  26.132      7     0.0005


  Conditional Independence of Breathlessness and Wheeze | Age
                  (assuming Homogeneity)


     TEST                        CHISQ      DF     PROB
     Likelihood-Ratio          2993.411      1     0.0000
     Cochran-Mantel-Haenszel   3266.222      1     0.0000
```

Figure 3.9   Fourfold display for coal miners data, strata equated

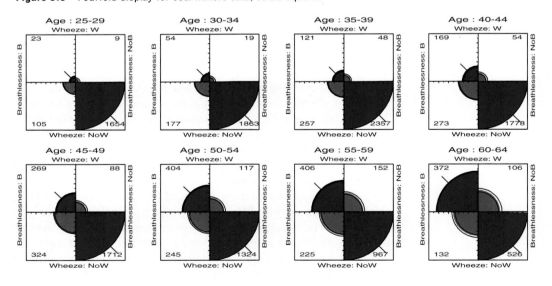

3.5   Sieve Diagrams

> They consider me to have sharp and penetrating vision
> because I see them through the mesh of a sieve.
>
> Kahlil Gibran

For 2- (and higher-) way contingency tables, the design principles of perception, detection, and comparison (see Chapter 1) suggest that we should try to show the observed frequencies in relation to what we would expect those frequencies to be under a reasonable null model—for example, the hypothesis that the row and column variables are unassociated.

To this end, several schemes for graphically representing contingency tables are based on the fact that when the row and column variables are independent, the estimated expected frequencies, m_{ij}, are products of the row and column totals (divided by the grand total).

$$m_{ij} = \frac{n_{i+}n_{+j}}{n_{++}} \ .$$

Then, each cell can be represented by a rectangle whose area shows the cell frequency, n_{ij}, or deviation from independence.

For example, for any 2-way table, the expected frequencies under independence can be represented by rectangles whose widths are proportional to the total frequency in each column, n_{+j}, and whose heights are proportional to the total frequency in each row, n_{i+}; the area of each rectangle is then proportional to m_{ij}. Figure 3.10 shows the expected frequencies for the hair- and eye-color data (Table 3.2).

Figure 3.10   Expected frequencies under independence. Each box has an area equal to its expected frequency, and is cross-ruled proportionally to the expected frequency.

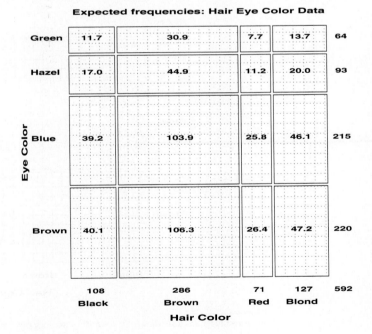

This display simply represents the model (what the frequencies would be if hair color and eye color were independent), not the data. Note, however, that the rectangles are cross-ruled so that the number of boxes in each (counting up the fractional bits) equals the expected frequency with which the cell is labeled, and moreover, the rulings are equally spaced in all cells. Hence, cross-ruling the cells to show the observed frequency would give a data display that implicitly compares observed and expected frequencies.

Riedwyl and Schüpbach (1983, 1994) proposed a ***sieve diagram*** (later called a ***parquet diagram***) based on this principle. In this display, the area of each rectangle is proportional to expected frequency, as shown in Figure 3.10, but observed frequency is shown by the number of squares in each rectangle. Hence, the difference between observed and expected frequency appears as variations in the density of shading. Cells whose observed frequency n_{ij} exceeds the expected m_{ij} appear denser than average. The pattern of positive and negative deviations from independence can be more easily seen by using color—say, red for negative deviations, and blue for positive.[7]

EXAMPLE 3.10 Hair color and eye color

The sieve diagram for hair color and eye color (Table 3.2) is shown in Figure 3.11. The pattern of color and shading shows the high frequency of blue-eyed blonds and people with brown eyes and dark hair. People with hazel eyes are also more likely to have red or brown hair, and those with green eyes more likely to have red or blond hair, than would be observed under independence. □

Figure 3.11 Sieve diagram for hair-color and eye-color data. Observed frequencies are equal to the number of squares in each cell, so departure from independence appears as variations in shading density.

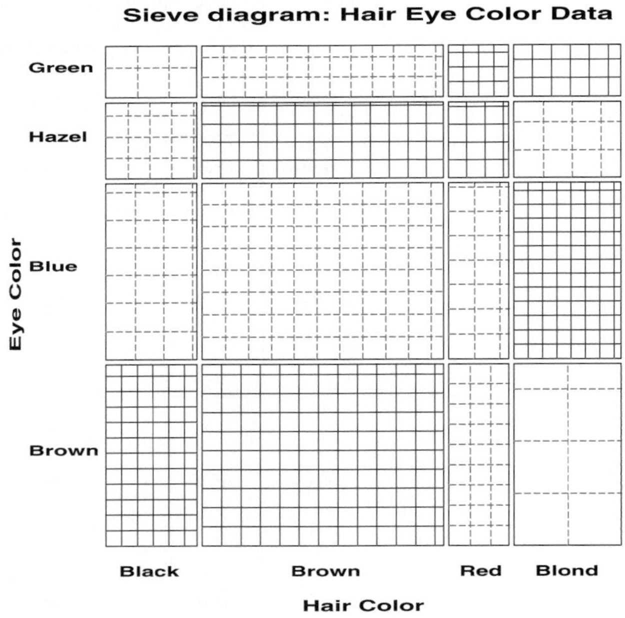

[7]Positive residuals are also shown by solid lines and negative residuals by broken lines, so they may still be distinguished in monochrome versions.

EXAMPLE 3.11   Visual acuity

Figure 3.12 shows the sieve diagram for data on visual acuity in a large sample of women ($n = 7477$), aged 30 through 39, who worked in the U.K. Royal Ordnance factories during World War II (Kendall and Stuart (1961, Table 33.5), Bishop et al. (1975, p. 284)). For each person, unaided distance vision of each eye was measured and categorized into four ordered grades. The data is listed in Appendix B.13.

Figure 3.12   Vision classification data for 7477 women

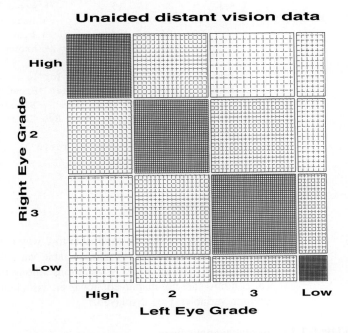

The diagonal cells show the obvious: people tend to have the same visual acuity in both eyes, and there is a strong lack of independence. The off-diagonal cells show a more subtle pattern that suggests symmetry: the cells below the diagonal are approximately equally dense as the corresponding cells above the diagonal. Moreover, the relatively consistent pattern on the diagonals ($\pm 1, \pm 2, \ldots,$) away from the main diagonals suggests that the association may be explained in terms of the *difference* in visual acuity between the two eyes. These suggestions can be tested by fitting intermediate models between the null model of independence (which fits terribly) and the saturated model (which fits perfectly), as we shall see later in this book. For example, a model of quasi-independence (Example 4.3) ignores the diagonal cells and tests whether independence holds for the remainder of the table.   □

3.5.1   The SIEVE Program

Sieve diagrams are implemented as a general module in SAS/IML, because the calculations and graphics are most easily handled by using matrices. The program is documented in Appendix A.27.

To use the program, %INCLUDE the SIEVE program within a PROC IML step. Then enter the observed frequencies in array F; create the character vector VNAMES, which contains the row and column variable names; and create the two-row character matrix LNAMES, which contains the category labels. The sieve diagram is produced with the SIEVE module,

```
run sieve( f, vnames, lnames, title );
```

For example, the sieve diagram in Figure 3.11 for the hair-color and eye-color data is produced by the statements in the program that follows. Note that the graphics options HSIZE and VSIZE should be set to make the plot square.

```
goptions hsize=7in vsize=7in;

filename iml '~/sasuser/iml';
proc iml;
   %include iml(sieve);
   f = {   5   29   14   16 ,        /* green */
          15   54   14   10 ,        /* hazel */
          20   84   17   94 ,        /* blue  */
          68  119   26    7 };       /* brown */

   vnames = {'Eye Color' 'Hair Color'};
   lnames = {'Green' 'Hazel' 'Blue' 'Brown' ,
             'Black' 'Brown' 'Red'  'Blond'};
   title  = 'Sieve diagram: Hair Eye Color Data';
   font='hwpsl011';
   run sieve(f, vnames, lnames, title );
quit;
```

3.5.2   Larger Tables

Sieve diagrams are strictly applicable to 2-way tables. However, larger tables may be displayed by representing two or more table variables interactively along either of the dimensions of a 2-way table. Associations among the variables represented along the rows (or columns) are not displayed; however, associations *between* the row variable(s) and the column variable(s) are displayed.[8]

EXAMPLE 3.12   Berkeley admissions

A sieve diagram may be used to determine if the association between gender and department is the same across departments by structuring the 3-way table as [Department] by [Admission-Sex], which gives the plot shown in Figure 3.13. In terms of the log-linear models discussed in the next chapter, this is equivalent to fitting the model of joint independence, $[D][AG]$.

---

[8]The program fits a model where the row variable(s) are independent of the column variable(s).

Figure 3.13 Sieve diagram for Berkeley admissions data. The display fits a model (homogeneity) in which the combinations of Sex and Admit are jointly independent of Department.

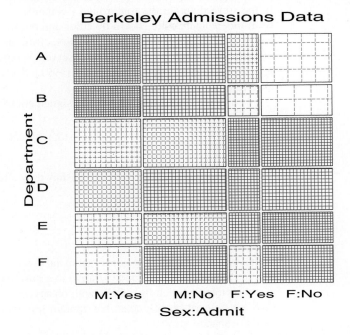

This sieve diagram is produced using the `sieve` module as follows:

```
proc iml;
    %include iml(sieve);

    vnames = {"Department" "Sex:Admit" };
    lnames = { "A" "B" "C" "D" "E" "F",
            "M:Yes" "M:No" "F:Yes"  "F:No" " " " " " "};
            /*    Males         Females   */
    table = { 512   313       89    19,
              353   207       17     8,
              120   205      202   391,
              138   279      131   244,
               53   138       94   299,
               22   351       24   317};

    font='hwpsl009';
    title  = 'Berkeley Admissions Data';
    run sieve(table, vnames, lnames, title );
quit;
```

In this display, the widths of the columns show the greater number of male applicants than female; the greater overall admission rate for males can be seen by comparing the ratios of widths (M:Yes / M:No) to that of (F:Yes / F:No). The marginal frequencies of all applicants to the various departments are shown by the heights of the rectangles in each row. Cells with many small squares (in blue) correspond to those whose observed frequencies are greater than expected under independence. Figure 3.13 shows greater numbers of male applicants in departments A and B (whose overall rate of admission is high) and greater numbers of female applicants in the remaining departments (where the admission rate is low).   □

3.6 Association Plots

In the sieve diagram the foreground (rectangles) shows expected frequencies; deviations from independence are shown by color and density of shading. The association plot (Cohen, 1980; Friendly, 1991) puts deviations from independence in the foreground: the area of each box is made proportional to observed — expected frequency. This graphical method is described in more detail in Friendly (1991), Section 10.2.1, which also lists the program used to produce the association plot.

For a 2-way contingency table, the signed contribution to Pearson χ^2 for cell i, j is

$$d_{ij} = \frac{n_{ij} - m_{ij}}{\sqrt{m_{ij}}} = \text{std. residual}, \qquad \chi^2 = \sum_{ij} (d_{ij})^2$$

In the ***association plot***, each cell is shown by a rectangle:

- (signed) height $\sim d_{ij}$
- width $= \sqrt{m_{ij}}$

so the area of each cell is proportional to the raw residual, $n_{ij} - m_{ij}$. The rectangles for each row in the table are positioned relative to a baseline representing independence ($d_{ij} = 0$) and shown by a dotted line. Cells with observed > expected frequency rise above the line (and are colored black); cells that contain less than the expected frequency fall below it (and are shaded gray).

Figure 3.14 shows the association plot for the hair-color and eye-color data. Note that the residuals in each row tend to increase or decrease systematically in each row, except in the row for hazel eyes.

One virtue of the association plot is that it is quite simple to interpret. Bertin (1981) uses similar graphics to display large complex contingency tables. Like the sieve diagram, however, patterns of association are most apparent when the rows and columns of the display are ordered in a sensible way.

Figure 3.14   Association plot for hair-color and eye-color data

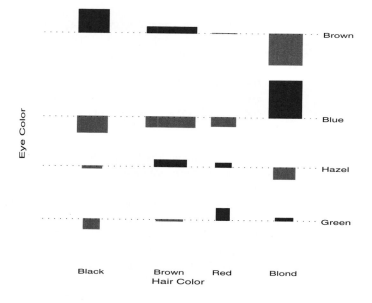

3.7   Observer Agreement

Inter-observer agreement is often used as a method of assessing the reliability of a subjective classification or assessment procedure. For example, two (or more) clinical psychologists might classify patients on a scale with categories of normal, mildly impaired, or severely impaired. Ethologists might classify the behavior of animals in categories of cooperation, dominance, etc.

A contingency table is formed in which the observations represent all individuals who have been rated or classified. The rows of the table refer to the categories used by one observer, and the columns refer to the categories used by another observer. In most cases, the same categories are used by both raters, so the contingency table is square, and the entries in the diagonal cells are the cases where the raters agree.

EXAMPLE 3.13   Sex is fun

Table 3.9 (Agresti (1990, Table 2.10) from Hout et al. (1987)) summarizes the responses of 91 married couples to the questionnaire item

> Sex is fun for me and my partner: (a) never or occasionally, (b) fairly often, (c) very often, (d) almost always.

In each row, the diagonal entry is not always the largest, though it appears that the partners tend to agree more often when either responds "almost always."   □

Table 3.9   Ratings of the questionnaire item "Sex is fun" by husbands and wives. Source: Agresti (1990, Table 2.10) from Hout et al.

| Husband's Rating | Wife's Rating | | | | |
	Never Fun	Fairly Often	Very Often	Almost Always	Total
Never Fun	7	7	2	3	19
Fairly Often	2	8	3	7	20
Very Often	1	5	4	9	19
Almost Always	2	8	9	14	33
Total	12	28	18	33	91

EXAMPLE 3.14   Diagnosis of MS patients

Landis and Koch (1977) gave data on the diagnostic classification of multiple sclerosis (MS) patients by two neurologists, one from Winnipeg and one from New Orleans, who each classified patients from Winnipeg and New Orleans into one of four categories: (a) certain MS, (b) probable MS, (c) possible MS, (d) doubtful, unlikely, or definitely not MS. The data from the 69 patients in the New Orleans sample is shown in Table 3.10.

Table 3.10   Ratings of 69 patients by two neurologists

| New Orleans Neurologist | Winnipeg Neurologist | | | | Total |
	Certain	Probable	Possible	Doubtful	
Certain MS	5	3	0	0	8
Probable MS	3	11	4	0	18
Possible MS	2	13	3	4	22
Doubtful MS	1	2	4	14	21
Total	11	29	11	18	69

There appears to be highest agreement in the Doubtful category, followed by the Probable category. ☐

3.7.1 Measuring Agreement

When assessing the strength of agreement, we usually have a more stringent criterion than when measuring the strength of association, because observers ratings can be strongly associated without strong agreement. For example, one rater could use a more stringent criterion and thus consistently rate subjects one category lower (on an ordinal scale) than another rater. More generally, measures of agreement must take into account the marginal frequencies with which two raters use the categories. If observers tend to use the categories with different frequency, this will affect measures of agreement.

Intraclass Correlation

An analysis of variance framework leads to the **intraclass correlation** as a measure of inter-rater reliability, particularly when there are more than two raters. This approach is not covered here, but various applications are described by Shrout and Fleiss (1979).

Cohen's Kappa

A commonly used measure of agreement, Cohen's kappa (κ) (Cohen, 1960, 1968) compares the observed agreement with the agreement expected by chance if the two observers' ratings were independent. If p_{ij} is the probability that a randomly selected subject is rated in category i by the first observer and in category j by the other, then the observed agreement is the sum of the diagonal entries, $P_o = \sum_i p_{ii}$. If the ratings were independent, this probability of agreement (by chance) would be $P_c = \sum_i p_{i+} p_{+i}$. Cohen's κ is then the ratio of the difference between actual agreement and chance agreement, $P_o - P_c$, to the maximum value this difference could obtain:

$$\kappa = \frac{P_o - P_c}{1 - P_c} \ . \tag{3.4}$$

When agreement is perfect, $\kappa = 1$; when agreement is no better than would be obtained from statistically independent ratings, $\kappa = 0$. κ could conceivably be negative, but this rarely occurs in practice. The minimum possible value depends on the marginal totals.

For large samples (n_{++}), κ has an approximate normal distribution when $H_0 : \kappa = 0$ is true and its standard error (Fleiss, 1973; Fleiss et al., 1969) is given by

$$\hat{\sigma}(\kappa) = \frac{P_c + P_c^2 - \sum_i p_{i+} p_{+i}(p_{i+} + p_{+i})}{n_{++}(1 - P_c)^2} \ .$$

Hence, it is common to conduct a test of $H_0 : \kappa = 0$ by referring $z = \kappa/\hat{\sigma}(\kappa)$ to a unit normal distribution. The hypothesis of agreement no better than chance is rarely of much interest, however. It is preferable to estimate and report a confidence interval for κ.

Weighted Kappa

The original (unweighted) κ counts strict agreement only (the same category is assigned by both observers). A weighted version of κ (Cohen, 1968) may be used when you want to allow for partial agreement. For example, exact agreements might be given full weight, but one-category difference might be given a weight of 1/2. This typically makes sense only when the categories are ordered, as in severity of diagnosis.

Weighted κ uses weights $0 \leq w_{ij} \leq 1$ for each cell in the table, with $w_{ii} = 1$ for the diagonal cells. In this case, P_o and P_c are defined as weighted sums

$$P_o = \sum_i \sum_j w_{ij} p_{ij}$$

$$P_c = \sum_i \sum_j w_{ij} p_{i+} p_{+j}$$

and these weighted sums are used in Equation 3.4.

For an $r \times r$ table, two commonly used patterns of weights are those based on equal spacing of weights (Cicchetti and Allison, 1971) for a near-match, and *Fleiss-Cohen weights* (Fleiss and Cohen, 1972), based on an inverse-square spacing:

$$w_{ij} = 1 - \frac{|i-j|}{r-1} \qquad \text{equal spacing}$$

$$w_{ij} = 1 - \frac{|i-j|^2}{(r-1)^2} \qquad \text{Fleiss-Cohen}$$

By default, PROC FREQ uses the integer (equal) spacing weights. The Fleiss-Cohen weights attach greater importance to near disagreements, as you can see in the 4×4 table that follows. These weights also provide a measure equivalent to the intraclass correlation.

	Integer Spacing				Fleiss-Cohen Weights		
1	2/3	1/3	0	1	8/9	5/9	0
2/3	1	2/3	1/3	8/9	1	8/9	5/9
1/3	2/3	1	2/3	5/9	8/9	1	8/9
0	1/3	2/3	1	0	5/9	8/9	1

Computing Kappa with SAS

In SAS Release 6.10 and later, PROC FREQ provides the κ statistic when you use the AGREE option, as shown in the following example:[9]

```
title 'Kappa for Agreement';
data fun;
   label husband = 'Husband rating'
         wife    = 'Wife Rating';
   do husband = 1 to 4;
   do wife    = 1 to 4;
      input count @@;
      output;
      end; end;
datalines;
   7   7   2   3
   2   8   3   7
   1   5   4   9
   2   8   9  14
;
proc freq;
   weight count;
   tables husband * wife / noprint agree;
run;
```

---

[9]In SAS Version 7 and later PROC FREQ provides the TEST statement using the syntax TEST KAPPA; to test the hypothesis that $\kappa = 0$. You can also request Fleiss-Cohen weights by using the option AGREE (WT=FC) in the TABLES statement. Standard errors, confidence intervals, and test statistics are large-sample (asymptotic) by default. Exact tests are provided by the EXACT AGREE statement in SAS Version 7 and later.

The preceding program produces the output shown in Output 3.1. Simple kappa gives the unweighted value; you can see there is little evidence of agreement beyond chance in husbands' and wives' ratings of their sexual fun. Weighted kappa uses the equal spacing weights, taking into account ratings that "nearly" agree. The weighted sample κ is larger, and the confidence interval does not include 0, so the weighted agreement is significantly greater than chance, though again you see that agreement is relatively small. The test of symmetry (Bowker's test) shown in Output 3.1 tests the null hypothesis that non-agreements are symmetric.

Output 3.1   Sex-is-fun data, agreement analysis

```
                        Kappa for Agreement
              STATISTICS FOR TABLE OF HUSBAND BY WIFE


                        Test of Symmetry
                        ----------------

      Statistic = 3.878          DF = 6          Prob = 0.693


                        Kappa Coefficients
      Statistic        Value     ASE    95% Confidence Bounds
      -----------------------------------------------------------

      Simple Kappa     0.129    0.069     -0.005      0.264
      Weighted Kappa   0.237    0.078      0.084      0.391


      Sample Size = 91
```

3.7.2   Bangdiwala's Observer Agreement Chart

The observer agreement chart by Bangdiwala (1987) provides a simple graphic representation of the strength of agreement in a contingency table and a measure of strength of agreement with an intuitive interpretation.

The agreement chart is constructed as an $n \times n$ square, where n is the total sample size. Black squares, each of size $n_{ii} \times n_{ii}$, show observed agreement. These are positioned within larger rectangles, each of size $n_{i+} \times n_{+i}$, as shown in Figure 3.15. The large rectangle shows the maximum possible agreement, given the marginal totals. Thus, a visual impression of the strength of agreement is given by

$$B_N = \frac{\text{area of dark squares}}{\text{area of rectangles}} = \frac{\sum_i^k n_{ii}^2}{\sum_i^k n_{i+} n_{+i}} \tag{3.5}$$

Partial Agreement

Partial agreement is allowed by including a weighted contribution from off-diagonal cells, b steps from the main diagonal. For a given cell frequency, n_{ij}, a pattern of weights, $w_1, w_2, \ldots, w_b$ is applied to the cell frequencies, as shown here schematically:

$$
\begin{array}{ccccc}
& n_{i-b,i} & & & w_b \\
& \vdots & & & \vdots \\
n_{i,i-b} \cdots & n_{i,i} & \cdots n_{i,i+b} & \quad w_b \cdots\ 1\ \cdots\ w_b \\
& \vdots & & & \vdots \\
& n_{i-b,i} & & & w_b
\end{array}
$$

Figure 3.15   Agreement chart for husbands' and wives' sexual fun. The B_N measure (Equation 3.5) is the ratio of the areas of the dark squares to their enclosing rectangles, counting only exact agreement. $B_N = 0.146$ for this data.

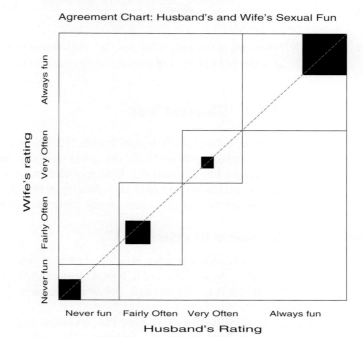

These weights are incorporated in the agreement chart (Figure 3.16) by successively lighter shaded rectangles whose size is proportional to the sum of the cell frequencies, denoted A_{bi}, as shown in Figure 3.15. A_{1i} allows 1-step disagreements, using weights

Figure 3.16   Weighted agreement chart. The B_N^W measure is the ratio of the areas of the dark squares to their enclosing rectangles, weighting cells 1 step removed from exact agreement with $w_1 = 8/9 = .889$. $B_N^W = 0.628$ for these data.

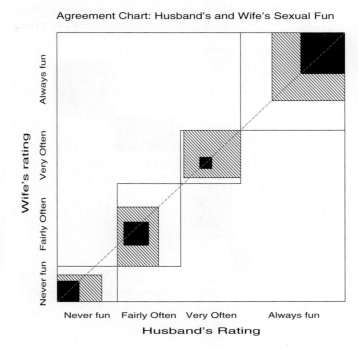

1 and w_1; A_{2i} includes 2-step disagreements, etc. From this, you can define a weighted measure of agreement, analogous to weighted κ.

$$B_N^w = \frac{\text{weighted sum of areas of agreement}}{\text{area of rectangles}} = 1 - \frac{\sum_i^k [n_{i+}n_{+i} - n_{ii}^2 - \sum_{b=1}^q w_b A_{bi}]}{\sum_i^k n_{i+} n_{+i}}$$

where w_b is the weight for A_{bi}, the shaded area b steps away from the main diagonal, and q is the furthest level of partial disagreement to be considered.

3.7.3   Observer Bias

With an ordered scale, it may happen that one observer consistently tends to classify the objects into higher or lower categories than the other. This produces differences in the marginal totals, n_{i+} and n_{+i}. While special tests exist for ***marginal homogeneity***, the observer agreement chart shows this directly by the relation of the dark squares to the diagonal line: when the marginal totals are the same, the squares fall along the diagonal.

EXAMPLE 3.15   **Diagnosis of MS patients**

Table 3.10 shows the classification of 69 New Orleans patients regarding multiple sclerosis diagnosis by neurologists in New Orleans and Winnipeg. The complete dataset, listed in Appendix B.8, also includes 149 Winnipeg patients who were assessed by both neurologists.

It is instructive to compare the agreement charts (Figure 3.17) for the two samples of patients. For both groups of patients, the two intermediate categories lie largely above the line, indicating that the Winnipeg neurologist tends to classify patients into more severe diagnostic categories. The departure from the diagonal is greater for the Winnipeg patients for whom the Winnipeg neurologist very often uses the two most severe diagnostic categories.

□

Figure 3.17   Weighted agreement chart for the MS data. Departure of the middle squares from the diagonal indicates lack of marginal homogeneity.

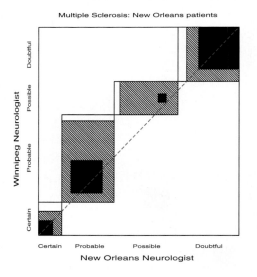
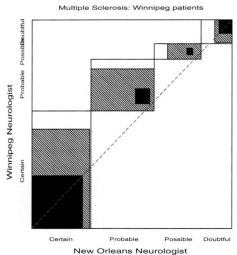

3.7.4 The AGREE Program

The observer agreement charts are produced by the AGREE program, which is listed and described in Appendix A.2. It is written in SAS/IML and is used like the SIEVE program:

```
run agree(table,w, vnames, lnames, title);
```

In addition to the TABLE, VNAMES, and LNAMES arguments, the AGREE module takes a vector W of one or more weights to specify the number of steps of disagreement and the weight to be applied to each. The following statements produce Figure 3.15 and Figure 3.16. In the first call to AGREE, w=1, so only exact agreement is considered; in the second call, w={1 .889}, so 1-step disagreements are given weights of $\frac{8}{9}$.

```
title "Observer Agreement Chart";
proc iml;
   %include iml(agree);
   table =
     { 7    7    2     3,
       2    8    3     7,
       1    5    4     9,
       2    8    9    14 };
   title = "Agreement Chart: Husband's and Wife's Sexual Fun";
   vnames = {"Husband's Rating" "Wife's rating"};
   lnames = {'Never fun' 'Fairly Often' 'Very Often' 'Always fun'} ;
   font = 'hwpsl009';

   w=1;                        /* Figure 3.15 */
   run agree(table, w, vnames, lnames, title);
   w = w || (8/9);            /* Figure 3.16 */
   run agree(table, w, vnames, lnames, title);
   end;
quit;
```

3.8 Trilinear Plots

The **trilinear plot** (also called a *ternary diagram* or *trinomial plot*) is a specialized display for a 3-column contingency table or for three variables whose relative proportions are to be displayed. This display is useful for both frequencies and proportions. For example, individuals might be assigned to one of three diagnostic categories, or a chemical process might yield three constituents in varying proportions, or the division of votes among three parties in a parliamentary election might be examined. Trilinear plots are featured prominently in Aitchison (1986), who describes statistical models for this type of **compositional data**. Upton (1976, 1994) uses them in detailed analyses of spatial and temporal changes in British general elections. Wainer (1996) reviews a variety of other uses of trilinear plots and applies them to aid in understanding the distributions of students' achievement in the National Assessment of Educational Progress, making some aesthetic improvements to the traditional form of these plots along the way.

A trilinear plot displays each observation as a point inside an equilateral triangle whose coordinate corresponds to the relative proportions in each column. The three vertices represent the three extremes when 100% occurs in one of the three columns; a point in the exact center corresponds to equal proportions of $\frac{1}{3}$ in all three columns. For instance, Figure 3.18

shows how three points whose compositions of the three variables A, B, and C are shown as annotations. Note that each apex corresponds to 100% of the labeled variable, and the percentage of this variable decreases linearly along a line to the midpoint of the opposite baseline. The grid lines in the figure show the percentage value along each axis.

Figure 3.18   An illustrative trilinear plot

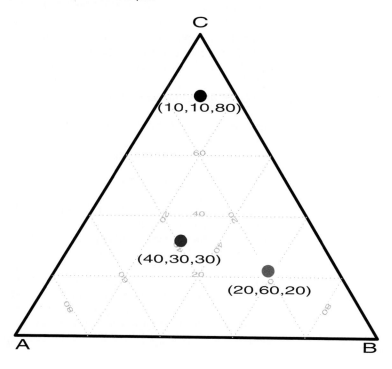

The construction of trilinear plots is described in detail by Fedenczuk and Bercov (1991). In summary, let $P(a, b, c)$ represent the three components normalized so that $a + b + c = 1.0$. If the apex corresponding to Point A in Figure 3.18 is given (x, y) coordinates of $(x_A, y_A) = (0, 0)$, and those at apex B are $(x_B, y_B) = (100, 0)$, then the coordinates of apex C are $(x_C, y_C) = (50, 50\sqrt{3})$. The coordinates (x_P, y_P) of P are then calculated as

$$y_P = c\, y_C$$

$$x_P = y_P \left(\frac{y_C - y_B}{x_C - x_B} \right) + \frac{\sqrt{3}}{2} y_C (1 - a)$$

The figures shown here are produced using the TRIPLOT macro, which is described in Appendix A.30.

EXAMPLE 3.16   Arthritis treatment

In the Arthritis treatment data, our interest is focused on the relative numbers of individuals in the three outcome categories for the four groups defined by the combinations of Treatment and Sex.

Figure 3.19 shows clearly that in both groups given the Active treatment there was a greater proportion of successful outcomes (Some improvement or Marked improvement) than in the Placebo groups. In addition, regardless of treatment, females show greater proportions of successful outcomes than males do.

Figure 3.19   Trilinear plot for Arthritis treatment data

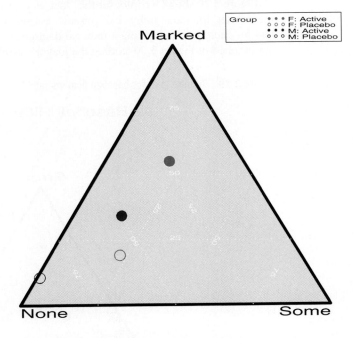

Figure 3.19 is produced by using the `TRIPLOT` macro as follows. For convenience in identifying the Treatment-Sex combinations, these two variables are combined into a single `GROUP` variable, used as the value of the `CLASS=` parameter in the macro call.

```
title 'Arthritis Treatment Data';
data arth;
    input sex $ treat $ @;
    input none some marked;
    length group $10;
    sex = substr(sex,1,1);
    group = trim(sex) || ': ' || treat;
    label group='Group';
datalines;
Female  Active   6  5  16
Female  Placebo  19  7  6
Male    Active   7  2  5
Male    Placebo  10  0  1
;
%triplot(data=arth,
    var=None Some Marked, class=group,
    symht=4,
    symbols=dot circle dot circle,
    colors=red red blue blue,
    backclr=grayd0, backpat=solid,
    gridclr=white, gridby=25);
```

EXAMPLE 3.17   Baseball fielding

The *Baseball dataset* from *SAS System for Statistical Graphics, First Edition*, Section A2.3 (Friendly, 1991), includes data on the salaries and batting-and-fielding performance of 322 Major League players during the 1986 baseball season. Fielding performance includes the number of Errors, Putouts, and Assists made by each player. (*Putouts* occur when a fielder causes an opposing player to be tagged or forced out; *assists* are credited to other fielders involved in making that putout.)

Figure 3.20 shows a triplot for this data. Because of the large number of observations in the dataset, the mean number of putouts, assists, and errors was calculated for each team and for each position, giving a reduced dataset of 169 observations.[10] These observations are graphed in Figure 3.20, coding the player's position by the plotting symbol.

Figure 3.20   Trilinear plot for baseball fielding data

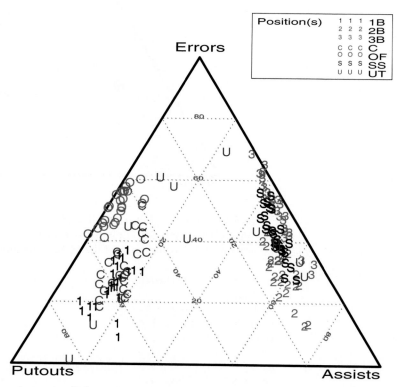

Two main types of players can be distinguished by their relative proportions of putouts and assists: outfielders, catchers, and first basemen contribute to defense primarily in making putouts; other infielders primarily make assists. The utility players (UT) play in a variety of positions and are scattered throughout the plot. Beyond this main observation, you can also see that outfielders and third basemen tend to make more errors than players in other positions.   □

EXAMPLE 3.18   Lifeboats on the *Titanic*

We examine the question of who survived and why in the sinking of the RMS *Titanic* in Section 4.3 (Example 4.5), where we analyze a 4-way table of the 2201 people on board (1316 passengers and 885 crew), classified by Class, Sex, Age, and Survival. A different dataset that sheds some light on the same issues is appropriate here.

After the disaster, the British Board of Trade launched several inquiries, the most comprehensive of which resulted in the *Report on the Loss of the "Titanic" (S.S.)* by Lord Mersey (Mersey, 1912). Section 4 of this document contains a detailed account of the sav-

---

[10]Putouts and assists also occur far more often than errors, so the values of each variable were also first scaled to a common range.

ing and rescue of the passengers and crew who survived. The *Titanic* was outfitted with 20 boats, half on each of the port and starboard sides, of which 14 were large lifeboats with a capacity of 65, two were emergency boats designed for 40 persons, and the remaining four were collapsible boats capable of holding 47—a total capacity of 1178 (considered adequate at that time). Two of the collapsible boats, lashed to the roof of the officers' quarters, were ineffectively launched and utilized as rafts after the ship sank. The report lists the time of launch and the composition of the remaining 18 boats categorized as male passengers, women and children, and "men of crew," as reported by witnesses. The dataset LIFEBOAT (see Appendix B.5) contains the data listed on page 38 of that report.[11]

Of interest here is the composition of the boats by these three categories, and by whether the boats were launched from the port or starboard side. The data is represented in a trilinear display using the statements shown in the following program. The parameter IDSUBSET = MEN>.1 is used to label only boats in which the proportion of male passengers exceeded 10%. (The values of variables have been scaled to sum to 1.0 for each observation at the time the IDSUBSET parameter is used.) The LABLOC=0 parameter is used to label the axes at the value corresponding to 0% rather than at the vertex (LABLOC=100) as in the earlier plots.

```
legend1  position=(top right inside) across=1
    offset=(0,-25pct) mode=share frame;
%triplot(data=lifeboat,
    var=Crew Men Women,
    id=boat, class=side,
    legend=legend1, labloc=0,
    idht=1.7, symht=1.7,
    idsubset=men>.1,
    symbols= circle dot, colors=red blue);
```

Figure 3.21 Lifeboats on the *Titanic*, showing the composition of each boat. Boats with more than 10% male passengers are labeled.

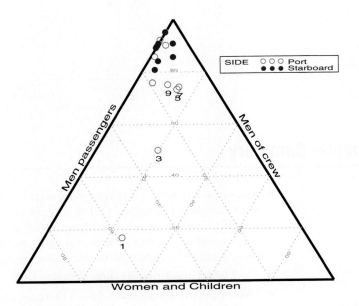

---

[11] The data lists a total of 854 in 18 boats, although only 712 were, in fact, saved. Mersey notes "it is obvious that these figures are quite unreliable." Allowing for 60 people rescued from the water, only 652 could have left in the boats (Mersey, 1912, p. 39). An alternative dataset, LIFEBOA2, is presented in Appendix B.5, based on more conservative and historically accurate information.

The result (shown in Figure 3.21) makes it immediately apparent that the composition of many of the boats launched from the port side differed substantially from that of the remaining boats, whose passengers were almost entirely women and children. Boat 1 had only 20% (2 out of 10) women and children, and the percentage for boat 3 was only 50% (25 out of 50).

The triplot scales the numbers for each observation to sum to 1.0, so differences in the total number of people on each boat cannot be seen in Figure 3.21. The total number of people reported loaded is plotted against launch time in Figure 3.22, with a separate regression line fit to the data for the port and starboard sides. It seems clear that the rescue effort began in panic on the port side, with relatively small numbers of people loaded, and, from Figure 3.21, small proportions of women and children. But the loading regime improved steadily over time. The procedures began more efficiently on the starboard side and the number of people loaded increased only slightly, though still with large variability from boat to boat.   □

Figure 3.22 Lifeboats on the *Titanic*, showing the number of people loaded on each boat. Regression lines for each side indicate a difference in regimes for the port and starboard sides.

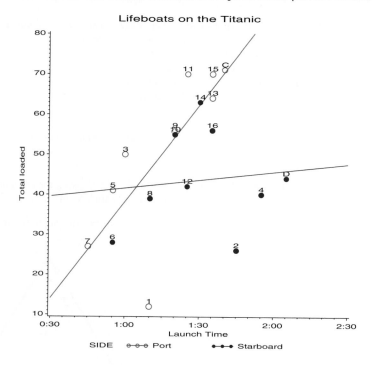

3.9 Chapter Summary

- A *contingency table* gives the frequencies of observations cross-classified by two or more categorical variables. Different types of variables may be distinguished, such as response, explanatory, and stratifying variables. With such data, we are typically interested in testing whether associations exist, quantifying the strength of association, and understanding the nature of the association among these variables.

- 2×2 tables may be easily summarized in terms of the odds ratio or its logarithm.

- Tests of general association between two categorical variables are most typically carried out using the Pearson's chi-square or likelihood-ratio tests provided by PROC FREQ. Stratified tests controlling for one or more background variables, and tests for ordinal categories are provided by the Cochran-Mantel-Haenszel tests.

- For 2×2 tables, the fourfold display provides a visualization of the association between variables in terms of the odds ratio. Confidence rings provide a visual test of whether the odds ratio differs significantly from 1. Stratified plots for $2 \times 2 \times k$ tables are also provided by the FOURFOLD program.

- Sieve diagrams and association plots provide other useful displays of the pattern of association in $r \times c$ tables.

- When the row and column variables represent different observers rating the same subjects, interest is focused on agreement rather than mere association. Cohen's κ is one measure of strength of agreement. The observer agreement chart provides a visual display of how the observers agree and disagree.

- Another specialized display, the trilinear plot, is useful for three-column frequency tables or compositional data.

Chapter

4 Mosaic Displays for *n*-Way Tables

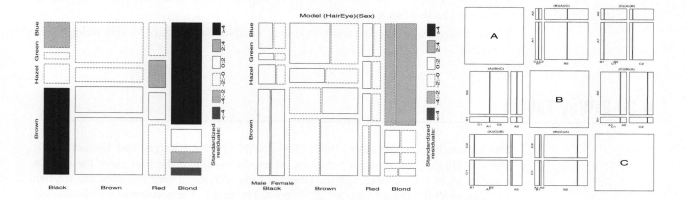

Mosaic displays help to visualize the pattern of associations among variables in 2-way and larger tables. Extensions of this technique can reveal partial associations and marginal associations and shed light on the structure of log-linear models themselves.

4.1   Introduction

> Little boxes, little boxes, little boxes made of ticky-tacky;
> Little boxes, little boxes, little boxes all the same.
> There are red ones, and blue ones, and green ones, and yellow ones;
> Little boxes, little boxes, and they all look just the same.

Pete Seeger

In Chapter 3, I describe a variety of graphical techniques for visualizing the pattern of association in simple contingency tables. These methods tend to be specialized, however, for specific shapes and sizes of tables: 2-way (sieve diagram), 2×2 tables (fourfold display), $r \times 3$ tables (trilinear plots), and so on.

This chapter describes the ***mosaic display***, a graphical method that displays the frequencies in a contingency table by a collection of rectangular "tiles" whose size (area) is proportional to the cell frequency. In this respect, the mosaic display is similar to the sieve diagram. However, the mosaic display

- generalizes readily to *n*-way tables. One can usefully examine 3-way, 4-way, and even larger tables, subject, of course, to the limitations of resolution in any graph.
- displays the deviations (residuals) from a given log-linear model that has been fit to the table.
- provides a method for fitting a series of sequential log-linear models to the various marginal totals of an *n*-way table.
- can be used to illustrate the relations among variables that are fitted by various log-linear models.

4.2   2-Way Tables

The mosaic display (Friendly, 1992, 1994b, 1997, 1999a; Hartigan and Kleiner, 1981, 1984) is similar to a grouped bar chart, where the widths of the bars show the relative frequencies of one variable, and the heights of the sections in each bar show the relative frequencies of the second variable, as shown in Figure 4.1. The construction of the mosaic display and what it reveals are most easily understood for 2-way tables.

Figure 4.1   Basic mosaic display for Hair-color and Eye-color data. The area of each rectangle is proportional to the observed frequency in that cell.

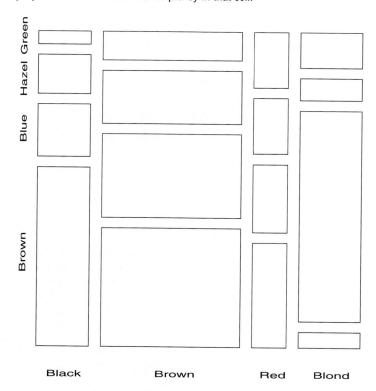

EXAMPLE 4.1   Hair color and Eye color

Consider the data in Table 3.2, which shows the relation between Hair color and Eye color among students in a statistics course. For such a 2-way table, the mosaic display is constructed by first dividing a unit square in proportion to the marginal totals of one variable, for example, Hair color.

For this data, the marginal frequencies and proportions are

	Black	Brown	Red	Blond	TOTAL
Frequencies	108	286	71	127	592
Proportions	0.1824	0.4831	0.1199	0.2145	1.000

These can be shown as the mosaic for the first variable (Hair color), as in Figure 4.2. The rectangular tiles are shaded to show the residuals (deviations) from a particular model, as follows:

- The 1-way table of marginal totals can be fit to a model, in this case, the model that all hair colors are equally probable. This model has expected frequencies $m_i = 592/4$.

Fitted frequencies

Black	Brown	Red	Blond
148.00	148.00	148.00	148.00

- The Pearson residuals from this model, $d_i = (n_i - m_i)/\sqrt{m_i}$, are

Standardized Pearson residuals

Black	Brown	Red	Blond
-3.29	11.34	-6.33	-1.73

and these values are shown by color and shading, as shown in the legend for Figure 4.2. The high positive value for Brown hair indicates that people who have brown hair are much more frequent in this sample than the Equiprobability model would predict.

Figure 4.2   First step in the mosaic display

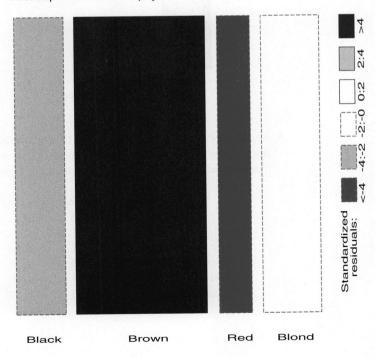

Next, the rectangle for each Hair color is subdivided in proportion to the relative (conditional) frequencies of the second variable, Eye color. This gives the following conditional proportions:

```
                   Marginal proportions
              Brown     Blue     Hazel     Green     TOTAL

     Black   0.6296   0.1852   0.1389   0.0463     1.0
     Brown   0.4161   0.2937   0.1888   0.1014     1.0
     Red     0.3662   0.2394   0.1972   0.1972     1.0
     Blond   0.0551   0.7402   0.0787   0.1260     1.0
```

The proportions in each row determine the heights of the tiles in the second mosaic display, as shown in Figure 4.3.

Figure 4.3   Second step in the mosaic display. Each rectangle for hair color is subdivided in proportion to the frequencies of eye color.

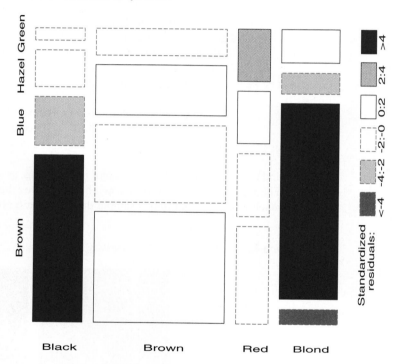

- Again, the cells are shaded in relation to standardized residuals, $d_{ij} = (n_{ij} - m_{ij})/\sqrt{m_{ij}}$, from a model. For a 2-way table, the model shows that Hair color and Eye color are independent in the population from which this sample was drawn.

```
              Standardized Pearson residuals
              Brown     Blue     Hazel     Green

     Black    4.40    -3.07    -0.48    -1.95
     Brown    1.23    -1.95     1.35    -0.35
     Red     -0.07    -1.73     0.85     2.28
     Blond   -5.85     7.05    -2.23     0.61
```

- Thus, the two tiles that are deep blue in color correspond to the two cells (Black, Brown) and (Blond, Blue) whose residuals are greater than $+4$. This indicates a much greater frequency in those cells than would be found if Hair color and Eye color were independent. The tile that is deep red in color (Blond, Brown) corresponds to the largest residual, -5.85, which indicates that this combination is extremely rare under the hypothesis of independence.

- The overall Pearson χ^2 statistic is just the sum of squares of the residuals.   □

Shading Levels

The default shading patterns for the tiles are based on standardized residuals that exceed the values 2 and 4 in absolute value.[1] Because the standardized residuals are approximately unit-normal $N(0, 1)$ values, this corresponds to highlighting cells whose residuals are *individually* significant at approximately the .05 and .0001 levels, respectively. The purpose of highlighting cells, however, is not to provide tests of significance, but to draw attention to the *pattern* of departures of the data from the assumed model. In any case, the number and values of these cutoffs can be easily set by the user by using the SHADE parameter.

To provide some redundancy when color figures are reproduced in black and white, cells with positive residuals are outlined with solid (blue) lines, while cells with negative residuals are outlined with broken (red) lines. Cells whose absolute residuals are less than the smallest shading level are unfilled. For good-fitting models, it is sometimes useful to distinguish between near-0 residuals and small, non-significant residuals. In color figures, near-0 cells are outlined in solid black; the threshold is determined by the FUZZ parameter.

Interpretation

To interpret the association between Hair color and Eye color, consider the pattern of positive (blue) and negative (red) tiles in the mosaic display. Positive values indicate cells whose observed frequency is substantially greater than would be found under independence; negative values indicate cells that occur less often than under independence.

This interpretation is enhanced by re-ordering the rows or columns of the 2-way table so that the residuals have an opposite-corner pattern of signs. This usually helps interpret any systematic patterns of association in terms of the ordering of the row and column categories. For this data, this is achieved by re-ordering the Eye colors, as shown in Figure 4.4. Note that, in this re-arrangement, both Hair color and Eye color are ordered from dark to light. (In general, the levels of a factor may be re-ordered by arranging them according to their scores on the first (largest) correspondence analysis dimension (Friendly, 1994b)). The re-ordered residuals are

Standardized Pearson residuals

	Brown	Hazel	Green	Blue
Black	4.40	-0.48	-1.95	-3.07
Brown	1.23	1.35	-0.35	-1.95
Red	-0.07	0.85	2.28	-1.73
Blond	-5.85	-2.23	0.61	7.05

---

[1] In datasets that have very large total frequency, most models may fit poorly and have large residuals. In such cases (e.g., Example 5.5), it is often useful to define more shading levels to make finer distinctions. In Example 5.5, we use SHADE={2 4 8} to set three levels of shading.

Figure 4.4   Two-way mosaic, re-ordered. Deviations from independence are shown by color and shading. The two levels of shading density correspond to standardized deviations greater than 2 and 4 in absolute value. This form of the display generalizes readily to multi-way tables.

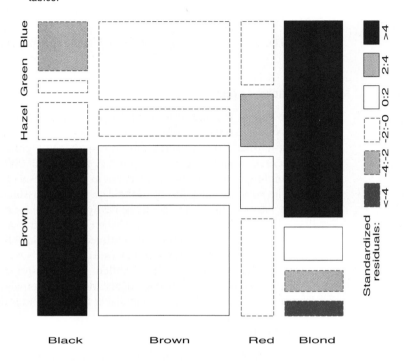

Thus, the mosaic shows that the association between Hair color and Eye color is essentially that

- people with dark hair tend to have dark eyes
- those with light hair tend to have light eyes
- people with red hair do not quite fit this pattern.

4.2.1 Software for Mosaic Displays

Mosaic displays are implemented as a collection of modules (the MOSAICS.SAS program) written in SAS/IML that are used within a PROC IML step, as described in Appendix A.16. The program is designed so that the frequency table and its associated factor levels and variable names may be entered directly by using SAS/IML statements, or (using the READTAB module) may be input from a SAS dataset in the form produced by PROC FREQ. Using the MOSAICS.SAS program within a PROC IML step is most flexible, because you can use SAS/IML statements and modules within MOSAICS.SAS to manipulate the frequency table (selecting or re-ordering rows or columns), to specify structural 0s, or to fit specialized models that cannot be fit by other means.

In addition, several SAS macros are provided to simplify the use of the MOSAICS.SAS program. The MOSAIC macro (Appendix A.17) may be used with any SAS dataset in frequency form (e.g., the output from PROC FREQ). It reads the data into SAS/IML and provides basic mosaic displays, mosaics for externally calculated residuals, and partial mosaic displays (Section 4.3.3). The TABLE macro (Appendix A.29) may be used to construct the frequency table, and to collapse or re-code variables. The MOSMAT macro (Appendix A.18) provides mosaic matrices (Section 4.4), an analog of the scatterplot matrix for categorical data.

The following examples illustrate the use of SAS/IML for basic mosaic displays. Example 4.2 uses the MOSAIC macro, and Example 4.3 uses PROC IML statements to construct and manipulate the frequency table.

EXAMPLE 4.2   UK Soccer scores

In Example 2.6, we examined the distribution of goals scored by the Home team and the Away team in 380 games in the 1995/96 season by the 20 teams in the UK Football Association, Premier League. The analysis there focused on the distribution of the total goals scored, under the assumption that the number of goals scored by the Home team and the Away team were independent.

Here, that assumption is tested and the simple use of the MOSAIC macro to construct the mosaic display is illustrated. It turns out that independence does, in fact, hold. The resulting graph also illustrates a typical pattern shown under independence.

In the following program, the DATA step SOCCER reads the data from Table 2.6 in the same way as in Example 2.6, producing a dataset that has the frequency variable FREQ and the factor variables HOME and AWAY. The MOSAIC macro reads this dataset into SAS/IML and runs the MOSAICS.SAS module. The PLOTS=2 parameter causes the program to display only the mosaic plot for the 2-way table.

```
title 'UK Soccer scores 95/96 season';
data soccer;
    input home @;
    do away = 0 to 4;
        total = home+away;
        input freq @;
        output;
        end;
datalines;
0    27 29 10  8  2
1    59 53 14 12  4
2    28 32 14 12  4
3    19 14  7  4  1
4     7  8 10  2  0
;
%mosaic(data=soccer, var=Home Away, count=freq, plots=2, htext=2);
```

The printed output (not shown) gives the Pearson χ^2 as 18.7 with 16 df, indicating that Home and Away goals are independent. Figure 4.5 shows the mosaic display. The tiles in each row are approximately the same height, and all the tiles except one are unshaded.

The one exception is for the situation where the Home team scores 4 or more goals, and the Away team scores 2 goals, which occurs more often than you would expect under independence. This residual ($d_{42} = 3.08$) accounts for nearly half of the overall χ^2. It may or may not be unusual to find one moderately large residual in a 5×5 table. A half-normal plot of the residuals (described in Section 7.7.2), plots the absolute values of residuals against expected values of normal order statistics, with a simulated 95% envelope for residuals from a good-fitting model. This plot (shown in Figure 4.6) suggests that the residual in the (4, 2) cell is large, but not unduly so.   □

Figure 4.5   Mosaic display for UK Soccer scores

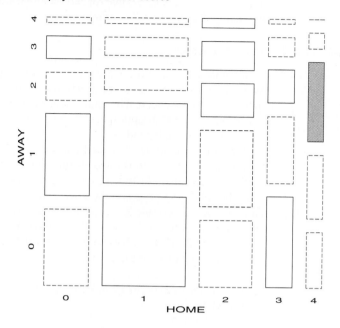

Figure 4.6   Half-normal plot for UK Soccer scores

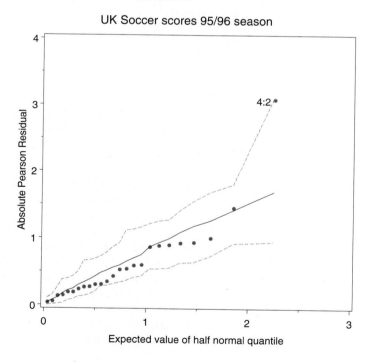

EXAMPLE 4.3   Repeat victimization

Fienberg (1980, Table 2-8) gives the data in Table 4.1 (from Reiss, 1980) about instances of repeat victimization for households in the U.S. National Crime Survey. In this survey, respondents reported all occurrences during the period in question. If a given household reported n such incidents, these led to $n - 1$ tallies in the table, one for each pair of successive victimizations.[2]

Table 4.1   Repeat Victimization Data

Second Victimization	First Victimization							
	Rape	Assault	Robbery	Pickpocket	Personal Larceny	Burglary	Household Larceny	Auto Theft
Rape	26	65	12	3	75	52	42	3
Assault	50	2997	279	102	2628	1117	1251	221
Robbery	11	238	197	40	413	191	206	51
Pickpocket	6	85	36	61	329	102	117	24
Personal Larceny	82	2553	459	243	12137	2649	3757	678
Burglary	39	1083	197	115	2658	3210	1962	301
Household Larceny	48	1349	221	101	3689	1973	4646	367
Auto Theft	11	216	47	38	687	301	391	269

Figure 4.7 shows the 2-way mosaic for a subset of 5 of these crimes (excluding pickpocket, personal larceny, and household larceny). The χ^2 for independence is 3720.2 with

Figure 4.7   Mosaic display for repeat victimization data

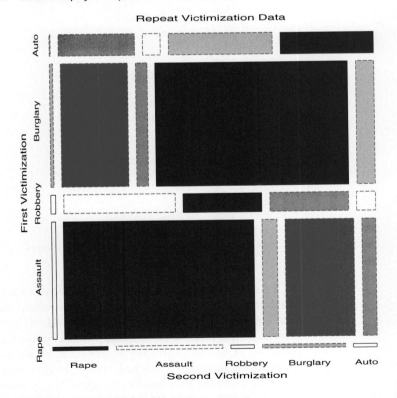

<hr />

[2]The observations are, therefore, not all operationally independent whenever $n > 2$. More detailed analysis would incorporate households in a mixed model; however, that information is unavailable here.

16 df. The association is so strong that three levels of shading were used ($|d_{ij}| \geq 2, 4, 8$). It is at once apparent that individuals tend to be victimized repeatedly in the same way, as shown by the large blocks of positive residuals along the main diagonal.

The following program produces Figure 4.7. The statements in the VICTIMS module define the frequencies in the 8×8 matrix TABLE. The names of the table variables and the names of the factor levels are defined in VNAMES and LNAMES, respectively.

```
goptions vsize=7 in hsize=7 in;
proc iml;

start victims;
    crime = {'Rape' 'Assault' 'Robbery' 'PickPock' 'Pers.Larceny'
             'Burglary' 'Hous.Larceny' 'Auto'};
    levels = {8 8};
    vnames = {'First Victimization' 'Second Victimization'};
    lnames = crime // crime ;
    title  = 'Repeat Victimization Data';
    table = {  26   50   11    6    82    39    48    11,
               65 2997  238   85  2553  1083  1349   216,
               12  279  197   36   459   197   221    47,
                3  102   40   61   243   115   101    38,
               75 2628  413  329 12137  2658  3689   687,
               52 1117  191  102  2649  3210  1973   301,
               42 1251  206  117  3757  1962  4646   391,
                3  221   51   24   678   301   367   269}';
finish;
run victims;

*-- load mosaic modules;
reset storage=mosaic;
load module=_all_;

*-- select subset of rows/cols;
keep = {1 2 3 6 8};
table = table[keep,keep];
lnames = lnames[,keep];
levels = {5 5};

*-- set mosaic global options;
htext = 1.4;
font = 'hwpsl009';
shade = {2 4 8};

plots = {2};
run mosaic(levels, table, vnames, lnames, plots, title);
```

There is more to this story, but it is difficult to see in Figure 4.7, owing to the large differences in the marginal frequencies of the various crimes. Of the crimes shown, Assault and Burglary occur far more often than any others, and they tend to dominate the display. You might ask what the associations would look like if all of these crimes occurred equally often. As in the fourfold display, it is possible to calculate an adjusted table (using iterative proportional fitting) in which both sets of marginal frequencies are equally probable.

In the following program, the statements first re-arrange the rows and columns of TABLE in an order that accounts for the maximum association and gives an opposite-corner pattern to the residuals.[3] The row totals for the crimes are used to construct the ADJUSTED table that has equal marginal frequencies.

```
*-- rearrange rows/cols by CA dim1;
keep = {2 3 1 5 4};
table = table[keep,keep];
lnames = lnames[,keep];

*-- standardize table to equal margins;
avg = table[,+] / levels[1];
newtab = repeat(avg,1,5);
config = {1 2};
call ipf(adjusted, status, levels, newtab, config, table);
title  = 'Repeat Victimization Data, Adjusted to Equal Margins';
lab = crime[keep];
print title, adjusted[r=lab c=lab f=8.2];
plots = 2;
run mosaic(levels, adjusted, vnames, lnames, plots, title);

*-- fit quasi-independence (ignore diagonal cells);
title = 'Repeat Victimization Data, Quasi Independence';
zeros = J(5,5) - I(5);
run mosaic(levels, adjusted, vnames, lnames, plots, title);
quit;
```

Figure 4.8 shows the mosaic for this adjusted table. Now you see that the association among the crimes is consistent with an ordering along a dimension of crimes of violence

Figure 4.8   Mosaic display for the Repeat Victimization Data, margins equated

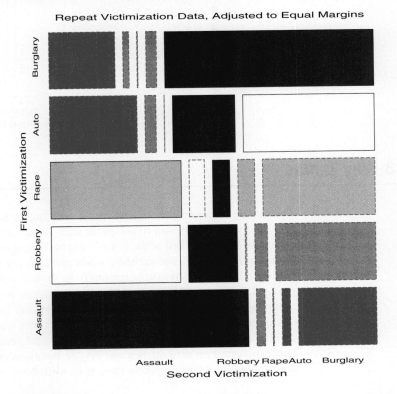

----

[3]This order is found from a correspondence analysis of residuals, using the order of the scores on the dimension that accounts for the largest portion of the association.

vs. crimes against property. Given that someone has been a victim of one type of crime, they are quite unlikely to be a victim of the other type of crime subsequently.

Figure 4.8 is still dominated by the large positive residuals on the diagonal representing the tendency for a person to be victimized twice in the same way. One way to deal with this is to fit a model of *quasi-independence* that ignores the diagonal cells. This is carried out in the last call to MOSAICS. The ZEROS matrix defines a 5 × 5 matrix whose values are 0 on the diagonal and 1 elsewhere; the value 0 indicates that the corresponding value in TABLE is to be ignored.[4] The resulting mosaic is shown in Figure 4.9.   □

Figure 4.9   Repeat victimization data, Quasi Independence

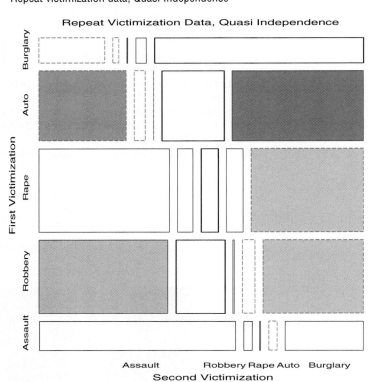

4.3   3-Way Tables

The mosaic display can be extended to 3- and higher-way tables. The relative frequencies of a third variable are used to subdivide each 2-way cell, and so on, recursively.

Imagine that each cell of the 2-way table for Hair color and Eye color is further classified by one or more additional variables—Sex and Level of Education, for example. Then each rectangle can be subdivided horizontally to show the proportion of males and females in that cell, and each of those horizontal portions can be subdivided vertically to show the proportions of people at each educational level in the Hair-Eye-Sex group.

Figure 4.10 shows the mosaic for the 3-way table, with Hair-color and Eye-color groups divided according to the proportions of Males and Females: You see that there is no systematic association between Sex and the combinations of Hair color and Eye color—except among blue-eyed blonds, where there is an overabundance of females.

---

[4]Zero entries cause the corresponding cell frequency to be fitted exactly; 1 degree of freedom is subtracted for each 0. The corresponding tile in the mosaic display is outlined in black.

Figure 4.10   Three-way mosaic display for Hair color, Eye color, and Sex. The categories of Sex are crossed with those of Hair color, but only the first occurrence is labeled. Residuals from the model of joint independence, [*HE*] [*S*] are shown by shading. G^2 = 19.86 on 15 df. The only lack of fit is an overabundance of females among blue-eyed blonds.

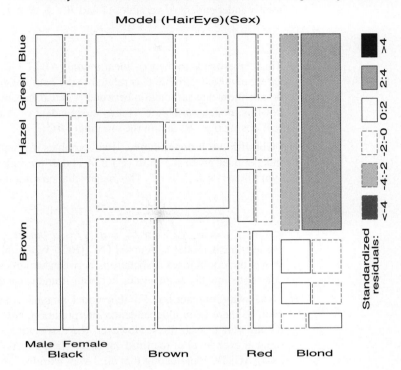

4.3.1   Fitting Models

When three or more variables are represented in the mosaic, you can fit several different models of "independence" and display the residuals from each model. These models are treated as null or baseline models, which may not fit the data particularly well. The deviations of observed frequencies from expected ones, displayed by shading, often suggest terms to be added to an explanatory model that achieves a better fit.

For a 3-way table that contains the variables *A*, *B*, and *C*, some of the hypothesized models that can be fit are described in the sections that follow and are summarized in Table 4.2. Here, I use [ ] notation to list the *high-order terms* in a hierarchical log-linear model; these correspond to the margins of the table that are fitted exactly. The notation [AB][AC], for example, is shorthand for the model

$$\log m_{ijk} = \mu + \lambda_i^A + \lambda_j^B + \lambda_k^C + \lambda_{ij}^{AB} + \lambda_{ik}^{AC} \; ,$$

(as described in Section 7.2) and reproduces the {*AB*} and {*AC*} marginal subtables. Here, $A \perp B$ is read, "*A* is independent of *B*." Table 4.2 also depicts the relations among variables as an association graph, where associated variables are connected by an edge.

Each model fits certain table margins exactly, as shown in Table 4.2; other associations that are present in the data appear in the pattern of residuals.

H_1: **Complete independence.** The model of complete (mutual) independence, symbolized $A \perp B \perp C$, asserts that all joint probabilities are products of the 1-way marginal probabilities:

$$\pi_{ijk} = \pi_{i++} \, \pi_{+j+} \, \pi_{++k} \; ,$$

for all i, j, k in a 3-way table. This corresponds to the log-linear model [A][B][C]. Fitting this model puts all higher terms, and, hence, all association among the variables, into the residuals.

H_2: **Joint independence.** Another possibility is to fit the model in which variable C is jointly independent of variables A and B, $(A, B \perp C)$, where

$$\pi_{ijk} = \pi_{ij+} \, \pi_{++k} \; .$$

This corresponds to the log-linear model [AB][C]. Residuals from this model show the extent to which variable C is related to the combinations of variables A and B, but they do not show any association between A and B because that association is fitted exactly. For this model, variable C is also independent of A and B in the marginal $\{AC\}$ table (collapsing over B) and in the marginal $\{BC\}$.

H_3: **Conditional independence.** Two variables, for example, A and B are conditionally independent given the third (C) if A and B are independent when you control for C, symbolized as $A \perp B \mid C$. This means that conditional probabilities, $\pi_{ij|k}$ obey

$$\pi_{ij|k} = \pi_{i+|k} \, \pi_{+j|k} \; ,$$

where $\pi_{ij|k} = \pi_{ijk}/\pi_{ij+}$, $\pi_{i+|k} = \pi_{i+k}/\pi_{i++}$, and $\pi_{+j|k} = \pi_{+jk}/\pi_{+j+}$. The corresponding log-linear model is denoted [AC][BC]. When this model is fit, the mosaic display shows the conditional associations between variables A and B, controlling for C, but does not show the associations between A and C, or B and C.

H_4: **No 3-way interaction.** For this model, no pair is marginally or conditionally independent, so there is *no* independence interpretation. Nor is there a closed-form expression for the cell probabilities. However, the association between any two variables is the same at each level of the third variable. The corresponding log-linear model formula is [AB][AC][BC], indicating that all 2-way margins are fit exactly and, therefore, are not shown in the mosaic residuals.

Table 4.2   Fitted margins, model symbols, and interpretations for some hypotheses for a 3-way table

Hypothesis	Fitted Margins	Model Symbol	Independence Interpretation	Association Graph
H_1	$n_{i++}, n_{+j+}, n_{++k}$	[A][B][C]	$A \perp B \perp C$	
H_2	n_{ij+}, n_{++k}	[AB][C]	$(A, B) \perp C$	
H_3	n_{i+k}, n_{+jk}	[AC][BC]	$A \perp B \mid C$	
H_4	$n_{ij+}, n_{i+k}, n_{+jk}$	[AB][AC][BC]	-	

For example, with the data from Table 3.2 broken down by sex, fitting the joint-independence model [HairEye][Sex] allows us to see the extent to which the joint distribution of Hair color and Eye color is associated with Sex. For this model, the likelihood-ratio G^2 is 19.86 on 15 df ($p = .178$), indicating an acceptable overall fit. The 3-way mosaic for this model is shown in Figure 4.10. Any other model fit to this table will have the same size tiles in the mosaic because the areas depend on the observed frequencies; the residuals, and, hence, the shading of the tiles will differ. Thus, fitting a conditional independence model, [HairSex][EyeSex] would test whether, given Sex, Hair color and Eye color are independent (probably not a meaningful hypothesis here). This model fits very poorly ($G^2(18) = 156.68$). The mosaic display (Figure 4.11) has a pattern similar to that in the 2-way display (Figure 4.4).

Figure 4.11   Mosaic display for Hair color, Eye color, and Sex. This display shows residuals from the model of conditional independence, [*HS*] [*ES*], $G^2 = 156.68$ on 18 df.

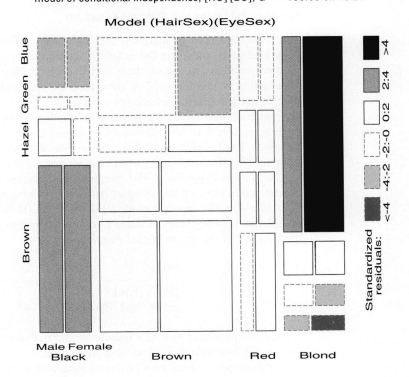

Sequential Plots and Models

The mosaic display is constructed in stages, with the variables listed in a specified order. At each stage, the procedure fits a (sub)model to the marginal subtable defined by summing overall variables not yet entered. For example, for a 3-way table $\{ABC\}$, the marginal subtables $\{A\}$ and $\{AB\}$ are calculated in the process of constructing the 3-way mosaic. The $\{A\}$ marginal table can be fit to a model where the categories of variable A are equiprobable (or some other discrete distribution); the independence model can be fit to the $\{AB\}$ subtable, and so forth.

The series of plots can give greater insight into the relationships among all the variables than a single plot. Moreover, the series of mosaic plots, which fit submodels of joint independence to the marginal subtables, have the special property that they can be viewed as partitioning the hypothesis of mutual independence in the full table.

For example, for the Hair- and Eye-color data, the mosaic displays for the [Hair] [Eye] marginal table (Figure 4.4) and the [HairEye] [Sex] table (Figure 4.10) can be viewed as representing the partition of G^2, as shown here:

Model	df	G^2
[Hair] [Eye]	9	146.44
[Hair, Eye] [Sex]	15	19.86
[Hair] [Eye] [Sex]	24	155.20

This partitioning scheme for sequential models of joint independence extends directly to higher-way tables. The MOSAICS program implements a variety of schemes for fitting a sequential series of submodels, including mutual independence, joint independence, conditional independence, partial independence, and Markov chain models.

Marginal Subtables and Simpson's Paradox

The sequential plots of marginal subtables assume that the (unconditional) relationship among earlier variables in the ordering, ignoring later variables, is the *same* as the (conditional) relationship among these variables controlling for later ones. For example, you assume that Hair color and Eye color have the same relation in the marginal subtable as they do in the subtable for each sex separately.

It is possible, however, for the marginal relations among variables to differ in magnitude, or even in direction, from the relations among those variables controlling for additional variables. The peculiar result that a pair of variables can have a marginal association in a different direction than their partial associations is called ***Simpson's paradox***.

One way to determine if the marginal relations are representative is to fit models of conditional association and compare them with the marginal models. For the Hair-color and Eye-color data, the appropriate model is the model [Hair, Sex] [Eye, Sex], which examines the relation between Hair color and Eye color controlling for Sex. The fit statistic is nearly the same as for the unconditional marginal model:

Model	df	G^2
[Hair] [Eye]	9	146.44
[Hair, Sex] [Eye, Sex]	15	156.68

And, the pattern of residuals is quite similar to that of the [Hair] [Eye] marginal model, so, you can conclude there is no such problem here.

In this section, I describe a variety of models that can be fit to higher-way tables, some relations among those models, and the aspects of lack-of-fit that are revealed in the mosaic displays. The following sections illustrate the process of model fitting, using the mosaic as an interpretive guide to the nature of associations among the variables. In general, you start with a minimal baseline model.[5] The pattern of residuals in the mosaic suggests associations to be added to an adequate explanatory model. As the model achieves better fit to the data, the degree of shading decreases, so you might think of the process of model fitting as "cleaning the mosaic."

4.3.2   Causal Models

This sequence of models of joint independence has another interpretation when the ordering of the variables is based on a set of ordered hypotheses involving causal relationships

---

[5]When the variable R is a response, this normally is the model of joint independence $[E_1 E_2 \ldots] [R]$, where $E_1, E_2, \ldots$ are the explanatory variables.

among variables (Goodman (1973), Fienberg (1980, Section 7.2)). Suppose, for example, that the causal ordering of four variables is $A \rightarrow B \rightarrow C \rightarrow D$, where the arrow means "is antecedent to." Goodman suggests that the conditional joint probabilities of B, C, and D, given A, can be characterized by a set of recursive logit models that treat (a) B as a response to A, (b) C as a response to A and B jointly, and (c) D as a response to A, B, and C. These are equivalent to the log-linear models that we fit as the sequential baseline models of joint independence, namely [A][B], [AB][C], and [ABC][D]. The combination of these models with the marginal probabilities of A gives a characterization of the joint probabilities of all four variables.

EXAMPLE 4.4   Marital status and pre- and extramarital sex

A study of divorce patterns by Thornes and Collard (1979) reported the 2^4 table shown in Table 4.3 (see Appendix B.6 for the SAS dataset). This data was analyzed by Agresti (1990, Section 7.2.4) and by Friendly (1994b), from which this account draws. A sample of about 500 people who had petitioned for divorce and a similar number of married people were asked two questions regarding their pre- and extramarital sexual experience: (1) "Before you married your (former) husband/wife, had you ever made love with anyone else?," (2) "During your (former) marriage (did you) have you had any affairs or brief sexual encounters with another man/woman?" Thus, the table variables are gender (G), reported premarital (P) and extramarital (E) sex, and current marital status (M).

Table 4.3   Marital Status in Relation to Gender and Reported Premarital and Extramarital Sex

Extramarital Sex	Premarital Sex	Gender	Marital Status	
			Divorced	Married
Yes	Yes	Women	17	4
No			54	25
Yes	No		36	4
No			214	322
Yes	Yes	Men	28	11
No			60	42
Yes	No		17	4
No			68	130
Total			494	542

In this analysis, the variables are considered in the order G, P, E, and M. That is, the first stage treats P as a response to G and examines the [Gender][Pre] mosaic to assess whether gender has an effect on premarital sex. The second stage treats E as a response to G and P jointly; the mosaic for [Gender, Pre] [Extra] shows whether extramarital sex is related to either gender or premarital sex. Finally, the mosaic for [Gender, Pre, Extra] [Marital] is examined for evidence of the dependence of marital status on the three previous variables jointly. As noted above, these models are equivalent to the recursive logit models whose path diagram is $G \rightarrow P \rightarrow E \rightarrow M$.[6] The G^2 values for these models are shown

---

[6]Agresti (1990, Section 7.2.4) considers a slightly more complex, but more realistic model, in which premarital sex affects both the propensity to have extramarital sex and subsequent marital status.

next. Here is a breakdown of the G^2 for the model of complete independence fit to the full table.

Model	df	G^2
[G] [P]	1	75.259
[GP] [E]	3	48.929
[GPE] [M]	7	107.956
[G] [P] [E] [M]	11	232.142

The [Gender] [Pre] mosaic is shown in Figure 4.12. The mosaic shows that men are much more likely to report premarital sex than are women; the sample odds ratio is 3.7. We also see that the number of women is about twice as prevalent as the number of men in this sample.

For the second stage, the [Gender, Pre][Extra] mosaic is shown in Figure 4.13. G^2 for the model [GP][E] is 48.93 on 3 df, indicating that extramarital sex depends on gender and premarital sex, jointly.

Figure 4.12 Mosaic display for gender and premarital sexual experience.

Figure 4.13 Mosaic display for the model of joint independence, [GP] [E].

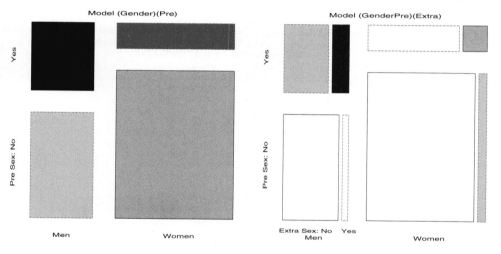

From the pattern of residuals in Figure 4.13, you see that men and women who have reported premarital sex are also far more likely to report extramarital sex. From the marginal totals for the [GP] [E] table, the conditional odds ratio of extramarital sex is 3.61 for men and 3.56 for women. Thus, extramarital sex depends on premarital sex but not on gender.

Figure 4.14 shows the mosaic for the final stage, fitting the model [Gender, Pre, Extra] [Marital]. It shows that marital status depends strongly on gender and premarital and extramarital sex, jointly. Among those reporting no premarital sex (bottom part of Figure 4.14), there is a similar pattern of cell sizes and deviations for marital status in relation to gender and extramarital sex. People who did not report premarital sexual experience are more likely to remain married if they report no extramarital sex and more likely to be divorced if they did. Among those who do report premarital sex (top part of Figure 4.14), there is also a similar pattern of sign of deviations: positive for those who are divorced, negative for those who are married.

The four 2 × 2 blocks in Figure 4.14 show the conditional relation of extramarital sex to marital status. Comparing these, you see that the odds ratios of divorce in relation to reported extramarital sex are considerably larger for men and women who also reported premarital sex. These observations imply the need to incorporate associations [PM] and [EM] of premarital and extramarital sex with marital status, and probably the 3-way asso-

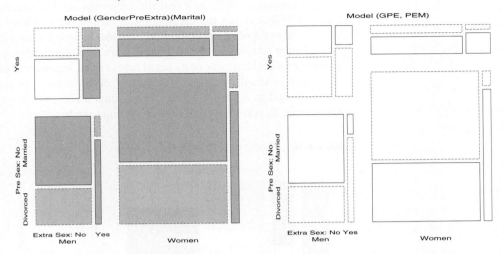

Figure 4.14 Four-way mosaic for the model [GPE] [M]. The pattern of residuals suggests terms to be included in an explanatory model.

Figure 4.15 Four-way mosaic for the model [GPE] [PEM].

ciation [PEM] into an explanatory model. Because this stage considers marital status as a response to gender, premarital sex, and extramarital sex, you would usually fit the $\{GPE\}$ marginal table exactly and consider the models [GEP][PM][EM] or [GPE][PEM] for the complete table.

The model [GPE][PM][EM] does not fit particularly well (this mosaic is not shown here), producing $G^2 = 18.16$ on 5 df ($p = .0028$). The model [GPE][PEM], however, does fit quite well, $G^2 = 5.25$ with 4 df ($p = .26$). The term [PEM] indicates that premarital sex and extramarital sex interact in their effects on marital status: i.e., the effect of extramarital sex on divorce is much greater for those who had no premarital sex than for those who did! The final mosaic for this model (shown in Figure 4.15) still shows some slight structure in the pattern of signs of residuals (compare the blocks for men with those for women), but all residuals are quite small.   □

EXAMPLE 4.5   Survival on the *Titanic*

There have been few marine disasters resulting in the staggering loss of life that occurred in the sinking of the *Titanic* on April 15, 1912 and (perhaps as a result) few that are so widely known by the public. It is surprising, therefore, that neither the exact death toll from this disaster nor the distributions of death among the passengers and crew is widely agreed upon. Dawson (1995, Table 2) presents the cross-classification of 2201 passengers and crew on the *Titanic* by Gender, Age, Survival, and Class (1st, 2nd, 3rd, Crew) as

Table 4.4 Survival on the Titanic

Gender	Age	Survival	Class			
			1st	2nd	3rd	Crew
Male	Adult	Died	118	154	387	670
Female			4	13	89	3
Male	Child		0	0	35	0
Female			0	0	17	0
Male	Adult	Survived	57	14	75	192
Female			140	80	76	20
Male	Child		5	11	13	0
Female			1	13	14	0

shown in Table 4.4 (see also Appendix B.11) and describes his efforts to reconcile various historical sources.[7] Let us see what can be learned from this dataset.

Figure 4.16(a) and Figure 4.16(b) show the 2-way and 3-way plots among the background variables. Figure 4.16(a) shows that the proportion of males decreases with increasing economic class, and that the crew was almost entirely male. The 3-way plot (Figure 4.16(b)) shows the distribution of adults and children among the Class-Gender groups. The residuals display the fit of a model in which Age is jointly independent of the Class-Gender categories. Note that there were no children among the crew, and the overall proportion of children was quite small (about 5%). Among the passengers, the proportion of children is smallest in 1st class, largest in 3rd class. The only large positive residuals correspond to a greater number of children among the 3rd-class passengers, perhaps representing families traveling or immigrating together.

Figure 4.16   *Titanic* data: Background variables

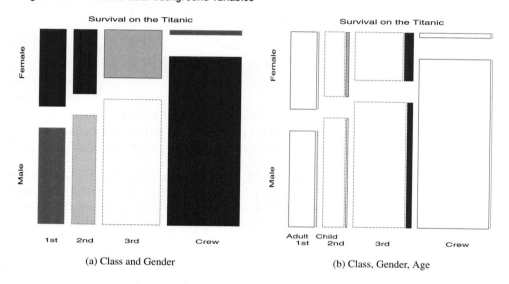

(a) Class and Gender   (b) Class, Gender, Age

Examining the series of mosaics for the variables, ordered by Class, Gender, Age, and Survival, shows the relationships among the background variables and how these are related to survival. The letters C, G, A, S, respectively, are used in Figure 4.17 to refer to these variables.

The 4-way mosaic, shown in Figure 4.17(a), fits the model $[CGA][S]$, which asserts that survival is independent of Class, Gender, and Age. This is the minimal null model when the first three variables are explanatory. It is clear that greater proportions of women survived than men in all classes, but with greater proportions of women surviving in the upper two classes. Among males, the proportion who survived also increases with economic class (towards 1st class). However, this model fits very poorly ($G^2(15) = 671.96$). You can try to fit a more adequate model by adding associations between survival and the explanatory variables.

Adding an association of each of Class, Gender, and Age with Survival amounts to fitting the model [CGA][CS][GS][AS]. That is, each of the three variables (C, G, A) is associated with survival, but they have independent, additive effects. The mosaic for this model is shown in Figure 4.17(b). The fit of this model is much improved ($\Delta G^2(5) = 559.4$) but still does not represent an adequate fit ($G^2(10) = 112.56$). There are obviously interactions among Class, Gender, and Age that impact Survival (some of which we have already noted).

---

[7]Robert J. MacG. Dawson, "The 'Unusual Episode' Data Revisited," *Journal of Statistical Education*, volume 3, number 3. Copyright © 1995. Reprinted by permission of Robert J. MacG. Dawson.

Figure 4.17 *Titanic* data: Class, Gender, Age, and Survival

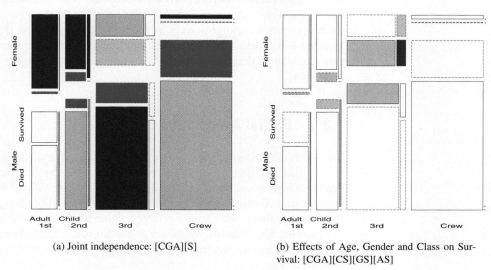

(a) Joint independence: [CGA][S]

(b) Effects of Age, Gender and Class on Survival: [CGA][CS][GS][AS]

Taking the rubric of "women and children first," you next fit the model [CGA][CS][GAS] in which Age and Gender interact in their influence on Survival. The mosaic for this model is shown in Figure 4.18(a). Adding the association of Age and Gender with Survival has improved the model slightly; however, the fit is still not good ($G^2(9) = 94.54$). If you add the interaction of Class and Gender to this (the model [CGA][CGS][GAS]) the likelihood-ratio chi-square is reduced substantially ($G^2(6) = 37.26$), but the lack of fit is still significant.

Finally, you can try a model in which Class interacts with both Age and Gender to give the model [CGA][CGS][CAS], whose residuals are shown in Figure 4.18(b). The likelihood-ratio chi-square is now 1.69 with 4 df—a very good fit, indeed.

Figure 4.18 *Titanic* data: Models with interactions

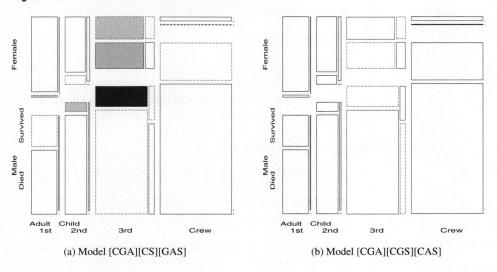

(a) Model [CGA][CS][GAS]

(b) Model [CGA][CGS][CAS]

The implication of these figures is clear. Regardless of Age and Gender, lower economic status was associated with increased mortality; the differences due to Class were moderated, however, by both Age and Gender. Although women on the *Titanic* were, overall, more likely to survive than men, the interaction of Class and Gender shows that women in 3rd class did not have a significant advantage; while men in 1st class did, compared to men in other classes. The interaction of Class and Age is explained by the observation that, while no children in 1st or 2nd class died, nearly two-thirds in 3rd class died; for adults, mortality increases progressively as economic class declines. Hence, although the phrase "women and children first" is mellifluous and appeals to our sense of Edwardian chivalry, a more adequate description might be "women and children (according to class), then 1st-class men."   □

4.3.3   Partial Association

In a 3-way table, it might be that two variables, e.g., A and B, are associated at some levels of the third variable, C, but not at other levels of C. More generally, you might want to explore whether and how the association among two (or more) variables in a contingency table varies over the levels of the remaining variables. The term ***partial association*** refers to the association among some variables within the levels of the other variables.

Consider, for example, the model of conditional independence, $A \perp B \mid C$ for a 3-way table. This model asserts that A and B are independent within *each* level of C. Denote the hypothesis that A and B are independent at level $C(k)$ by $A \perp B \mid C(k)$. Then one can show (Anderson, 1991) that

$$G^2_{A \perp B \mid C} = \sum_{k}^{K} G^2_{A \perp B \mid C(k)} \qquad (4.1)$$

That is, the overall G^2 for the conditional independence model with $(I-1)(J-1)K$ df is the sum of the values for the ordinary association between A and B over the levels of C (each with $(I-1)(J-1)$ df). Thus, (a) the overall G^2 can be broken down into portions attributable to the AB association in the layers of C, and (b) the collection of mosaic displays for the dependence of A and B for each of the levels of C provides a natural visualization of this classification. These displays provide an analog, for categorical data, of the conditioning plot, or ***co-plot***, that Cleveland (1993b) has shown to be an effective display for quantitative data. See Friendly (1999a) for further details.

Mosaic displays for partial association are produced by using the SAS/IML module MOSPART, which is called in a PROC IML step, as follows:

```
run mospart(dim, table, vnames, lnames, title, byvar);
```

where BYVAR specifies the variables that are used to stratify the data. One mosaic is produced for each combination of the levels of BYVAR. In addition, the MOSAIC macro may be used with a BY parameter for the same purpose. The separate plots may be combined into one figure with the PANELS macro, as illustrated in Example 4.6.

EXAMPLE 4.6   **Employment status data**

Data from a 1974 Danish study of 1314 employees who had been laid off is given in Table 4.5 (from Anderson (1991, Table 5.12)). The workers are classified by (a) their employment status on January 1, 1975 (new job or still unemployed) (b) the cause of their layoff (closure, etc. or replacement) (c) the length of their employment at the time they were laid off.

If employment status (variable A) is the response and cause of layoff (B) and length of employment (C) are explanatory, the minimal baseline model is $[A][BC]$, in which employment status is independent of both cause and length of employment. This model fits quite poorly ($G^2(11) = 172.27$). The residuals, shown in Figure 4.19, indicate that workers who were laid off as a result of a closure are more likely to be unemployed, regardless of length of time they were employed. Workers who were replaced, however, apparently are more likely to be employed, particularly if they were employed for three months or more.

Table 4.5   Employment Status Data. Employment status on Jan. 1, 1975, by cause of layoff and length of previous employment at time of layoff for 1314 employees who lost their jobs in Fall 1974 in Denmark (Andersen, 1991).

Employment Status	Cause of Layoff	Length of Employment					
		<1 Mo	1-3 Mo	3-12 Mo	1-2 Yr	2-5 Yr	>5 Yr
NewJob	Closure	8	35	70	62	56	38
Unemployed		10	42	86	80	67	35
NewJob	Replaced	40	85	181	85	118	56
Unemployed		24	42	41	16	27	10

Figure 4.19   Mosaic display for the employment status data, fitting the model of joint independence, $[A][BC]$, $G^2(11) = 172.27$

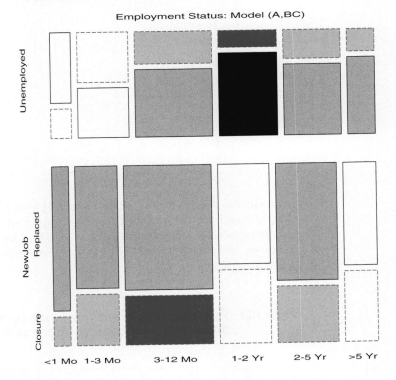

The model of conditional independence, $[AB][BC]$ is interpreted as $A \perp C \mid B$; that is, given the cause of layoff, employment status is independent of length of employment. This model fits far better ($G^2(10) = 24.63$), but the lack of fit is still significant. The residuals, shown in Figure 4.20, suggest that the pattern of association between employment in a new job and length of employment in the previous job is different for replaced workers than for those laid off due to closure.

Figure 4.20   Mosaic display for the employment status data, fitting the model of conditional independence, [AB][BC], $G^2(10) = 24.63$

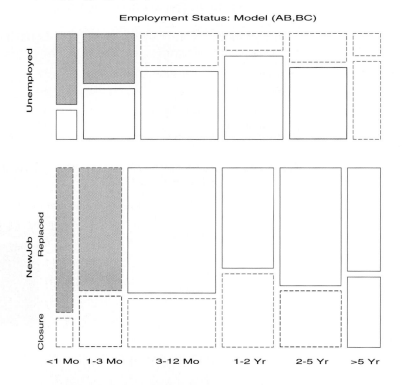

In order to test this notion, we fit the model $[A][C]$ (employment status independent of length) to each subtable separately for the causes of layoff. The mosaic displays for closure and for replacement are shown in Figure 4.21. These are produced with the MOSAICS macro as shown in the program that follows. Using BY=Layoff gives a separate 2-way plot for each cause of layoff.

Figure 4.21   Partial mosaic plots for employment status data. Each panel fits a model of independence between employment status and length of previous job.

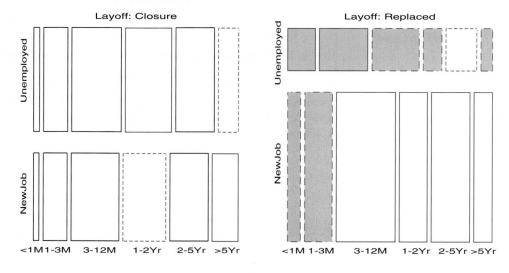

```
title 'Employment status data';
data employ;
    length employed $10;
    input length $ @;
    do layoff ='Closure ', 'Replaced';
        do employed = 'NewJob   ', 'Unemployed';
            input count @;
            output;
            end;
        end;
    input;
datalines;
<1M       8   10    40   24
1-3M     35   42    85   42
3-12M    70   86   181   41
1-2Yr    62   80    85   16
2-5Yr    56   67   118   27
>5Yr     38   35    56   10
;
%gdispla(OFF);
%mosaic(data=employ, vorder=Employed Length Layoff, sort=no,
    by=Layoff, shade=1 2 4, split=H V, fuzz=0.1, htext=2);

%gdispla(ON);
%panels(rows=1, cols=2);
```

The residuals are all quite small when the cause of layoff is a closure, and the $G^2(5) = 1.44$, indicating that the chances of getting a new job are independent of length of employment in this case. On the other hand, when the cause of layoff is a replacement, the $G^2(5) = 23.19$ and the residuals are large, particularly for the first two length-of-employment categories. These two subfigures represent the partition of the G^2 in Equation 4.1.

Model	df	G^2
$A \perp C \mid B_1$	5	1.44
$A \perp C \mid B_2$	5	23.19
$A \perp C \mid B$	10	24.63

The partial mosaic plots in Figure 4.21 show clearly that there is no association between employment status and length of job among workers laid off due to closure. Among replaced workers, those who had been employed less than or equal to three months are likely to remain unemployed, while those with longer job tenure are more likely to have found a new job.

4.4   Mosaic Matrices for Categorical Data

One reason for the wide usefulness of graphs of quantitative data has been the development of effective, general techniques for dealing with high-dimensional datasets. The scatterplot matrix (Friendly (1991), Section 8.3.2) shows all pairwise (marginal) views of a set of variables in a coherent display, whose design goal is to show the interdependence among the collection of variables as a whole. It combines multiple views of the data into a single display, which allows detection of patterns that could not readily be discerned from a series of separate graphs. In effect, a multivariate dataset in p dimensions (variables) is shown as a collection of $p(p - 1)$ two-dimensional scatterplots, each of which is the projection of the cloud of points on two of the variable axes. These ideas can be extended readily to categorical data.

A multi-way contingency table of p categorical variables, $A, B, C, \ldots$, also contains the interdependence among the collection of variables as a whole. The saturated log-linear model, $[ABC \ldots]$ fits this interdependence perfectly but is often too complex to describe or understand. By summing the table over all variables except two, A and B, for example, you obtain a two-variable (marginal) table that shows the bivariate relationship between A and B, which is also a projection of the p-variable relation into the space of two (categorical) variables. If you do this for all $p(p-1)$ unordered pairs of categorical variables and display each two-variable table as a mosaic, you have a categorical analog of the scatterplot matrix, called a ***mosaic matrix***. Like the scatterplot matrix, the mosaic matrix can accommodate any number of variables in principle, but, in practice, the mosaic matrix is limited by the resolution of the display to three or four variables.

Mosaic matrices are produced by using the SAS/IML module MOSMAT, which is called in a PROC IML step, as follows:

```
run mosmat(dim, table, vnames, lnames, plots, title);
```

When there are p variables in TABLE, a set of p^2 plots are produced; these plots include the $p(p - 1)$ pairwise mosaics and a set of p panels that contain the variable names (from VNAMES). After the SAS/IML step, the separate plots may be combined into one figure by using the PANELS macro. The MOSMAT macro provides a simple interface to these steps.

EXAMPLE 4.7   Marital status and pre- and extramarital sex

In Example 4.4, you examined a series of models relating marital status to reported premarital and extramarital sexual activity and gender. Figure 4.22 shows the mosaic matrix for this data, produced by using the following MOSMAT macro:

```
%include catdata(marital);
%mosmat(data=marital, var=Gender Pre Extra Marital,
    vorder=Marital Extra Pre Gender, devtype=LR ADJ);
```

If you view gender, premarital sex, and extramarital sex as explanatory and marital status (divorced vs. still married) as the response, then the mosaics in row 1 (and in column 1)[8] show how marital status depends on each predictor, marginally. The remaining panels show the relations within the set of explanatory variables.

Thus, you see in row 1 and column 4 (1,4) that marital status is independent of gender (all residuals equal 0, here) by design of the data collection. In the (1, 3) panel, we see that reported premarital sex is more often followed by divorce, while non-report is more prevalent among those still married. The (1, 2) panel shows a similar, but stronger relation, between extramarital sex and marriage stability. These effects pertain to the associations of P and E with marital status—the terms [PM] and [EM] in the log-linear model. Earlier, you saw that an interaction of P and E (the term [PEM]) is required to fully account for this data. This effect is not displayed in Figure 4.22.

Among the background variables (the log-linear term [GPE]), the (2, 3) panel shows a strong relation between premarital sex and subsequent extramarital sex, and the (2, 4) and (3, 4) panels show that men are far more likely than women, in this sample, to report premarital sex. Men are also more likely to report extramarital sex.   □

---

[8]Rows and columns in the mosaic matrix are identified as in a table or numerical matrix, with row 1, column 1 in the upper-left corner.

Figure 4.22   Mosaic matrix for marital status data. Each panel shows the marginal relation, fitting an independence model between the row and column variable, collapsed over other variable(s).

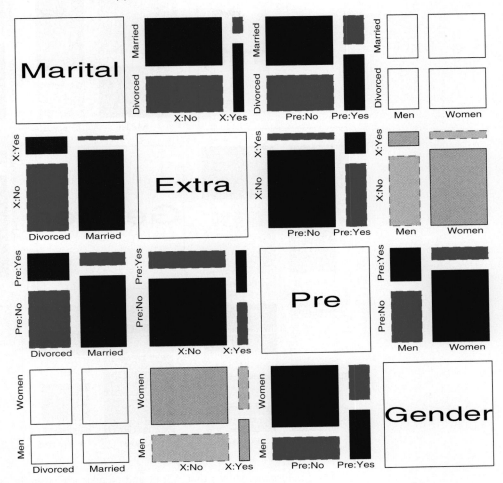

EXAMPLE 4.8   Berkeley admissions

Figure 4.23 shows the pairwise marginal relations among the variables Admit, Gender, and Department in the Berkeley data, which was examined earlier (Example 3.1) in fourfold displays (Figure 3.4 and Figure 3.5). Figure 4.23 is produced by using the MOSMAT macro as shown below. The TABLE macro is first used to re-code the factor variables to more meaningful character labels.

```
%include goptions;
goptions hsize=7 in vsize=7 in;
libname mosaic '~/sasuser/mosaics';

%include catdata(berkeley);
proc format;
   value admit 1="Admit" 0="Reject" ;
   value dept  1="A" 2="B" 3="C" 4="D" 5="E" 6="F";
   value $sex  'M'='Male'   'F'='Female';
%table(data=berkeley, var=Admit Gender Dept, weight=freq, char=Y,
       format=admit admit. gender $sex. dept dept.,
       order=data, out=berkeley);

%mosmat(data=berkeley, vorder=Admit Gender Dept, sort=no, htext=3.5);
```

Figure 4.23   Mosaic matrix of Berkeley admissions, showing bivariate marginal relations.

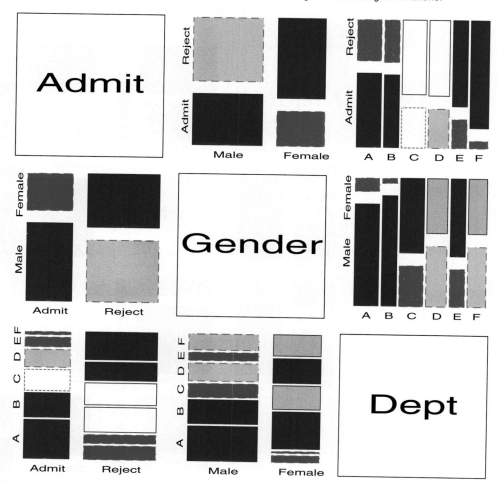

The (2, 1) panel shows that Admit and Gender are strongly associated marginally, as is seen in Figure 3.4, and overall, males are more often admitted. The diagonally-opposite (1, 2) panel shows the same relation, splitting first by Gender.[9]

The (3, 3) panels illuminate the explanation for the paradoxical result (Figure 3.5) that, within all except Department A, the likelihood of admission is equal for men and women, yet, overall, there appears to be a bias in favor of admitting men (Figure 3.4). The (1, 3) and (3, 1) panels show the marginal relation between Admit and Dept; Departments A and B have the greatest overall admission rate, Departments E and F, the least. The (2, 3) panel shows that men apply in much greater numbers to Departments A and B, while women apply in greater numbers to the departments that have the lowest overall rate of admission.

□

---

[9]Note that this is different than just the transpose or interchange of horizontal and vertical dimensions as in the scatterplot matrix, because the mosaic display splits the total frequency, first, by the horizontal variable and, then (conditionally), by the vertical variable. However, the areas of all corresponding tiles are the same in each diagonally opposite pair, as are the residuals shown by color and shading.

4.4.1 Conditional Mosaic Matrices

The marginal relation between each pair of variables in the mosaic matrix need not be shown. A conditional mosaic matrix fits a model of conditional independence between each row and column, controlling for one or more of the other variables. Friendly (1999a) gives further details and describes analogous displays for quantitative data.

EXAMPLE 4.9 Berkeley admissions

For example, Figure 4.24 shows all pairwise *conditional* relations among the variables Gender, Dept, and Admit in the Berkeley data. All panels show the *same* observed frequencies in the 3-way table by the areas of the tiles, but each fits a model of conditional independence between the row-and-column variable, with the remaining variable controlled. Thus, the shading in the (1, 2) and (2, 1) panels shows the fit of the model [Admit, Dept] [Gender, Dept], which asserts that Admit and Gender are independent, given (controlling for) Dept. Except for Department A, this model fits quite well, again indicating lack of gender bias. The (1, 3) and (3, 1) panels show the relation between Admit and Dept controlling for Gender, highlighting the differential admission rates across departments.

Figure 4.24   Conditional mosaic matrix of Berkeley admissions. Each panel shows the conditional relation, fitting a model of conditional independence between the row-and-column variable, controlling for other variable(s).

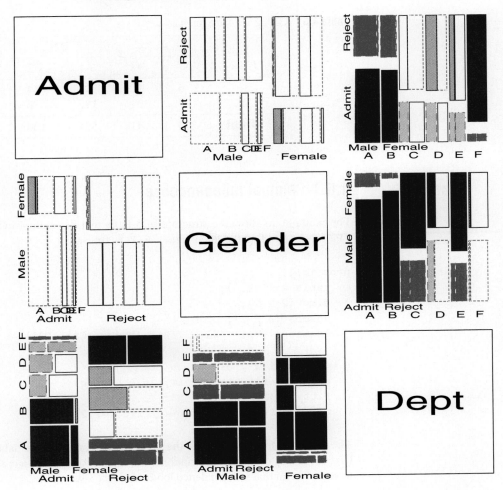

Conditional mosaic matrices are produced with the MOSMAT macro by specifying CONDIT as the FITTYPE parameter. The parameter PLOTS=3 specifies that each panel in the display contains the 3-way mosaic plot for the data.

```
%mosmat(data=berkeley, vorder=Admit Gender Dept, sort=no, htext=3.5,
    plots=3, fittype=CONDIT);
```

□

4.5   Showing the Structure of Log-linear Models

The mosaic display can also be used to illuminate the relations among variables in a contingency table that are represented in various log-linear models, a point described by Theus and Lauer (1999). Each of the model types depicted in Table 4.2 has, in fact, a characteristic shape and structure in a mosaic display. This, in turn, leads to a clearer understanding of the structure that appears in real data when a given model fits, the relations among the models, and the use of mosaic displays.

To show this, we use artificial data for a $2 \times 2 \times 2$ table (Table 4.6). You can force such a table to conform to any log-linear model (e.g., $H_1 - H_4$) simply by finding the expected frequencies under that model and constructing a mosaic depicting the expected frequencies.

Table 4.6   A $2 \times 2 \times 2$ table (artificial data)

C	B1		B2		Total
	A1	A2	A1	A2	
C1	6	10	312	44	372
C2	37	31	192	76	336
Total	43	41	504	120	708

4.5.1   Mutual Independence

For example, to show the structure of a table that fits mutual independence, H_1, use the IPF function to find the fitted values, FIT, as follows:

```
proc iml;
    table = { ... };
    dim= {2 2 2};
    vnames={A B C};
    lnames = {'A1' 'A2',  'B1' 'B2',  'C1' 'C2'};

    config = {1 2 3};
    call ipf(fit,status,dim,table,config);
    fittype='MUTUAL';
    print fittype config[f=4.] fit[f=7.2];
```

The fitted frequencies then have the same 1-way margins as the data shown in Table 4.6, but have no 2-way or higher associations. You then display a mosaic for the *fitted frequencies* to see what mutual independence looks like in a 3-way table.

FITTYPE	CONFIG			FIT			
MUTUAL	1	2	3	34.10	10.04	253.31	74.56
				30.80	9.07	228.79	67.34

What you see in a mosaic display depends, in large measure, on the order in which the table variables are entered. For three variables there are 3! = 6 possible orders; conveniently, they are all shown in the mosaic matrix. In this display, you see the 3-way mosaic (PLOTS=3;) for each pair of variables, using the fitted values as the "data." The following statements produce Figure 4.25:

```
    plots=3;
    title=fittype+'&MODEL';
    space={12 5};
    run mosmat(dim, fit, vnames, lnames, plots, title);
quit;
%panels(rows=3, cols=3, equate=Y, order=down);
```

In this figure, the same data is shown in all the off-diagonal panels and the mutual independence model was fitted in each case, but with the table variables permuted. All residuals are exactly 0 in all cells, by construction. We see that in each view, the four large tiles (corresponding to the first two variables) align, indicating that these two variables are marginally independent. For example, in the (1, 2) panel, *A* and *B* are independent, collapsed over variable *C*.

Figure 4.25   Mosaic matrix for mutual independence. All panels show marginal and conditional independence among all three pairs of variables.

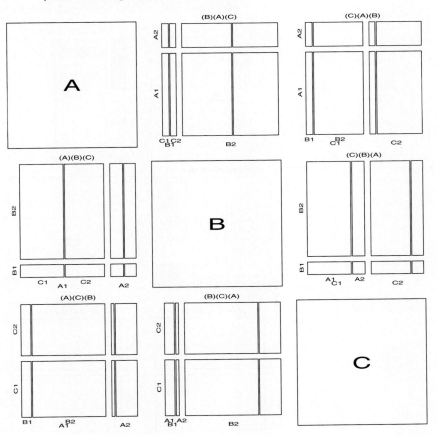

Moreover, comparing the top half to the bottom half in any panel, you see that the divisions by the third variable are the same for both levels of the second variable. In the $(1, 2)$ panel, for example, A and C are independent at $B1$ and also independent at $B2$. This means that A and B are conditionally independent given C ($A \perp B \,|\, C$). Because this holds in all six panels, we see that mutual independence is equivalent to *all pairs* of variables being conditionally independent, given the remaining one ($X \perp Y \,|\, Z$) for all permutations of variables. Figure 4.25 shows what mutual independence means!

4.5.2　Joint Independence

The model of joint independence, $H_2 : (A, B) \perp C$, or equivalently, the log-linear model $[AB][C]$ may be visualized similarly by the mosaic matrix in Figure 4.26, in which the data was replaced by fitted values, under this model.

```
...
config = t({1 2, 3 0});
call ipf(fit,status,dim,table,config);
fittype='JOINT2';
...
```

This model gives these fitted frequencies.

FITTYPE	CONFIG		FIT			
JOINT2	1	3	22.59	21.54	264.81	63.05
	2	0	20.41	19.46	239.19	56.95

Figure 4.26　Mosaic matrix for joint independence. The bottom row shows that A and B are each independent of C, and also conditionally independent of C

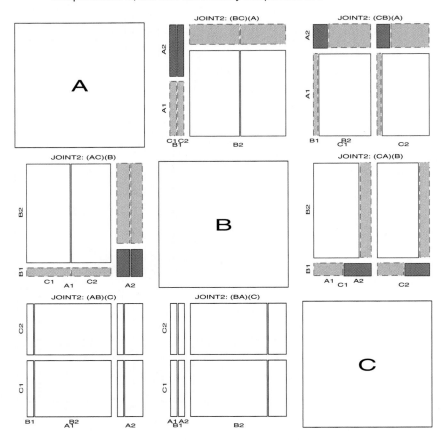

The FITTYPE='JOINT2'; statement specifies that in each panel the fitted model is the model wherein the first and third variable are independent of the second. Now, in Figure 4.26, the same model is fit in both panels in each row, but the second, distinguished variable differs from row to row.

You see in row 3, where C is the second variable, that C is independent of A, and also independent of B, and that these models have residuals equal to 0. The models fit in the other four panels have non-0 residuals. However, the $(1, 2)$ and $(2, 1)$ panels show $B \perp C \mid A$ and $A \perp C \mid B$, respectively, because the top and bottom portions are both divided equally by the third table variable. This relation does not hold, however, in the $(1, 3)$ and $(2, 3)$ panels. Thus, joint independence implies that conditional independence hold as well, but only for the two variables that enter jointly.

The appearance (in the bottom row of Figure 4.26) that A and B are marginally independent is misleading because the AB association is fit exactly in these models. To see the marginal relations under $[AB][C]$ explicitly, you can simply change the PLOTS value to PLOTS=2;, so that the model of (marginal) independence is fit to the first two variables in each panel and only this pair of variables is shown in each panel. This plot appears in Figure 4.27 and clearly shows that A and B are each marginally independent of C, but not of each other.

Figure 4.27   Marginal relations under joint independence. *A* and *B* are each marginally independent of *C*

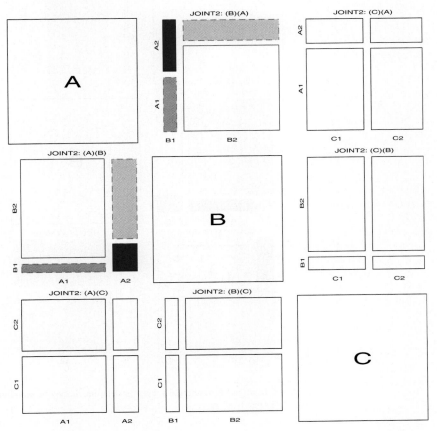

4.5.3 Conditional Independence

For conditional independence, $H_3 : A \perp B \mid C$, or $[AC][BC]$, you can proceed similarly, using

```
config = t({1 2, 2 3});
call ipf(fit,status,dim,table,config);
fittype='CONDIT1';
...
```

to obtain frequencies that fit this model exactly. The resulting 3-way mosaic matrix is shown in Figure 4.28. Now, you see the characteristic signature of conditional independence in the $(1, 3)$ and $(2, 3)$ panels, where A and B are independent at each level of C. But no independence relations appear in the four large blocks of the first two variables in any panel, so no pair of variables is marginally independent.[10]

Figure 4.28 Mosaic matrix for conditional independence

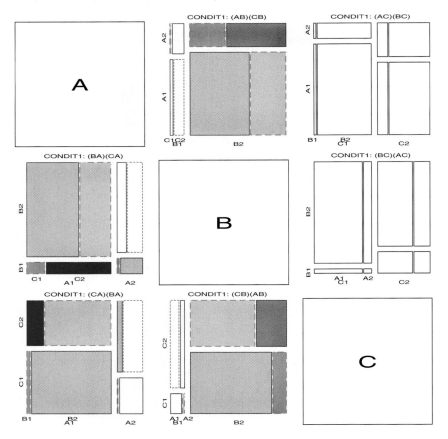

---

[10]In this data, A and B have quite a weak association, as may be seen in the $(1, 2)$ and $(2, 1)$ panels, where the large blocks nearly align.

4.6 Chapter Summary

- The mosaic display depicts the frequencies in a contingency table by a collection of rectangular "tiles" whose area is proportional to the cell frequency. The residual from a specified model is portrayed by shading the tile to show the sign and magnitude of the deviation from the model.

- For 2-way tables, the tiles for the second variable align at each level of the first variable when the two variables are independent (see Figure 4.5).

- The perception and understanding of patterns of association (deviations from independence) are enhanced by re-ordering the rows or columns to give the residuals an opposite-corner pattern.

- For 3-way and larger tables, a variety of models can be fit and visualized. Starting with a minimal baseline model, the pattern of residuals often suggests additional terms which must be added to "clean the mosaic."

- It is often useful to examine the sequential mosaic displays for the marginal subtables that have the variables in a given order. Sequential models of joint independence provide a breakdown of the total association in the full table. They are particularly appropriate when the last variable is a response.

- Partial association, which refers to the associations among a subset of variables within the levels of other variables, may be easily studied by constructing separate mosaics for the subset variables for the levels of the other, "given" variables. These displays provide a breakdown of a model of conditional association for the whole table and serve as an analog of coplots for quantitative data.

- Mosaic matrices, consisting of all pairwise plots of an *n*-way table, provide a way to visualize all marginal, joint, or conditional relations, simultaneously.

- The structural relations among model terms in various log-linear models themselves can also be visualized by mosaic matrices showing the expected, rather than observed, frequencies under different models.

Chapter

5 Correspondence Analysis

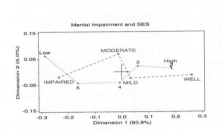
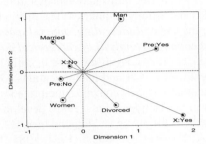
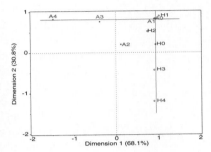

Correspondence analysis (CA) provides visualizations of associations in a 2-way contingency table in a small number of dimensions. Multiple correspondence analysis extends this technique to n-way tables. Other graphical methods, including mosaic matrices and biplots, provide complementary views of log-linear models for 2-way and n-way contingency tables.

5.1 Introduction

Whenever a large sample of chaotic elements are taken in hand and marshaled in the order of their magnitude, an unsuspected and most beautiful form of regularity proves to have been latent all along.

Sir Francis Galton (1822–1911)

CA is an exploratory technique that displays the row and column categories in a 2-way contingency table as points in a graph, so that the positions of the points represent the associations in the table. Mathematically, CA is related to the biplot, to canonical correlation, and to principal components analysis (see Friendly, 1991, Sections 8.7, 9.4, 10.3.) CA finds scores for the row and column categories on a small number of dimensions, which account for the greatest proportion of the χ^2 for association between the row and column categories, just as principal components account for maximum variance. These scores provide a quantification of the categories and have the property that they maximize the correlation between the row-and-column variables. For graphical display, two or three dimensions are typically used to give a reduced rank approximation to the data.

CA has an extensive, multi-national literature. It was re-discovered several times in different fields and different countries. The method, in slightly different forms, is also discussed under the names ***dual scaling***, ***optimal scaling***, ***reciprocal averaging***, ***homogeneity analysis***, and ***canonical analysis of categorical data***.

See Greenacre (1984), Nishisato (1980), Gifi (1981), or Lebart, et al. (1977, 1984) for a detailed treatment of CA and its applications. Greenacre and Hastie (1987) provide an excellent discussion of the geometric interpretation, while van der Heijden and de Leeuw (1985) and van der Heijden, et al. (1989) develop some of the relations between CA and log-linear methods for 3-way and larger tables. CA is usually carried out in an exploratory, graphical way; however, Goodman (1981, 1985, 1986) has developed related inferential models with close links to CA: the *RC* model and the canonical correlation model.

For a 2-way table, the scores for the row categories $X = \{x_{im}\}$ and the column categories $Y = \{y_{jm}\}$ on dimension $m = 1, \ldots, M$ are derived from a (generalized) singular value decomposition of residuals from independence, expressed as $d_{ij}/\sqrt{n}$, to account for the largest proportion of the χ^2 in a small number of dimensions. This decomposition may be expressed as

$$\frac{d_{ij}}{\sqrt{n}} = \frac{n_{ij} - m_{ij}}{\sqrt{n\, m_{ij}}} = \sum_{m=1}^{M} \lambda_m\, x_{im}\, y_{jm} \;, \tag{5.1}$$

where $\lambda_1 \geq \lambda_2 \geq \cdots \geq \lambda_M$, and $M = \min(I - 1, J - 1)$. In M dimensions, the decomposition, as shown in Equation 5.1, is exact. For example, an $I \times 3$ table can be depicted exactly in two dimensions when $I \geq 3$. A rank-d approximation in d dimensions is obtained from the first d terms on the right side of Equation 5.1; the proportion of the Pearson χ^2 accounted for by this approximation is

$$n \sum_{m}^{d} \lambda_m^2 / \chi^2 \;.$$

The quantity $\chi^2/n = \sum_i \sum_j d_{ij}^2/n$ is called the total ***inertia*** and is identical to the measure of association known as Pearson's mean-square contingency, the square of the ϕ coefficient.

Thus, CA is designed to show how the data deviates from expectation when the row and column variables are independent, as in the association plot and mosaic display. However, the association plot and mosaic display depict every *cell* in the table, and for large tables, it may be difficult to see patterns. CA shows only row and column *categories* in the two (or three) dimensions that account for the greatest proportion of deviation from independence. The pattern of the associations is inferred from the positions of the row and column points.

5.2 Simple Correspondence Analysis

5.2.1 Notation and Terminology

Because correspondence analysis grew up in so many homes, the notation, formulae, and terms used to describe the method vary considerably. The notation used here generally follows Greenacre (1984, 1997), as does the documentation in the *SAS/STAT User's Guide, Version 6, First Edition*, Chapter 19, "The CORRESP Procedure."

The descriptions here use the following matrix and vector definitions:

- $N = \{n_{ij}\}$ is the $I \times J$ contingency table with row and column totals n_{i+} and n_{+j}, respectively. The grand total n_{++} is also denoted by n for simplicity.
- $P = \{p_{ij}\} = N/n$ is the matrix of joint cell probabilities or the **correspondence matrix**.
- $r = \sum_j p_{ij} = P1$ is the row margin of P; $c = \sum_i p_{ij} = P^{\mathsf{T}}1$ is the column margin. r and c are called the *row masses* and *column masses*.
- D_r and D_c are diagonal matrices (used as weights) with r and c on their diagonals.
- $R = D_r^{-1}P = \{n_{ij}/n_{+j}\}$ is the matrix of row conditional probabilities or *row profiles*. Similarly, $C = D_c^{-1}P^{\mathsf{T}} = \{n_{ij}/n_{i+}\}$ is the matrix of column conditional probabilities or *column profiles*.

Two types of coordinates, X and Y, for the row and column categories are defined, based on the generalized singular value decomposition of P,

$$P = AD_\lambda B^{\mathsf{T}}$$

where D_λ is the diagonal matrix of singular values $\lambda_1 \geq \lambda_2 \geq \cdots \geq \lambda_M$; A is the $I \times M$ matrix of left singular vectors, normalized so that $AD_r^{-1}A^{\mathsf{T}} = I$; and B is the $J \times M$ matrix of right singular vectors, normalized so that $BD_c^{-1}B^{\mathsf{T}} = I$. Thus, the columns of A and B are orthogonal in the weighted metrics defined by the row and column margins D_r^{-1} and D_c^{-1}, respectively. The two types of coordinates are

principal coordinates The coordinates of the row F and the column G profiles with respect to their own principal axes are defined so that the inertia along each axis is the corresponding singular value λ_i,

$$F = D_r^{-1}AD_\lambda \quad \text{so that} \quad F^{\mathsf{T}}D_rF = D_\lambda \tag{5.2}$$

$$G = D_c^{-1}BD_\lambda \quad \text{so that} \quad G^{\mathsf{T}}D_cG = D_\lambda \tag{5.3}$$

standard coordinates The standard coordinates Φ and Γ are a re-scaling of the principal coordinates to unit inertia along each axis,

$$\Phi = D_r^{-1}A \quad \text{so that} \quad \Phi^{\mathsf{T}}D_r\Phi = I \tag{5.4}$$

$$\Gamma = D_c^{-1}B \quad \text{so that} \quad \Gamma^{\mathsf{T}}D_c\Gamma = I \tag{5.5}$$

These coordinates differ from the principal coordinates in Equations 5.2 and 5.3 simply by the absence of the scaling factors D_λ.

Thus, the weighted average of the squared principal coordinates for the rows or columns on a principal axis equals the squared singular value, λ, for that axis, whereas the weighted average of the squared standard coordinates equals 1. The relative positions of the row or column points along any axis are the same under either scaling, but the distances between points differ because the axes are weighted differently in the two scalings.

5.2.2   Geometric and Statistical Properties

The following summarizes some geometric and statistical properties of the CA solutions, which are useful in interpretation.

nested solutions   Because they use successive terms of the SVD (Equation 5.1), CA solutions are *nested*, meaning that the first two dimensions of a three-dimensional solution are identical to the two-dimensional solution.

centroids at the origin   In both principal coordinates and standard coordinates, the points representing the row and column profiles have their centroids (weighted averages) at the origin. Thus, in CA plots, the origin represents the (weighted) average row profile and column profile.

reciprocal averages   The column scores are proportional to the weighted averages of the row scores, and vice-versa.

chi-square distances   In principal coordinates, the row coordinates can be shown equal to the row profiles $D_r^{-1}P$, rescaled inversely by the square-root of the column masses $D_c^{-1/2}$. Distances between two row profiles, R_i and $R_{i'}$, are most sensibly defined as χ^2 distances, where the squared difference $[R_{ij} - R_{i'j}]^2$ is inversely weighted by the column frequency, to account for the different relative frequency of the column categories. The rescaling by $D_c^{-1/2}$ transforms this weighted χ^2 metric into ordinary Euclidean distance. The same is true of the column principal coordinates.

interpretation of distances   In principal coordinates, the distance between two row points can be interpreted as described under "**chi-square distances**" and so can the distance between two column points. The distance between a row and column point, however, does not have a clear distance interpretation.

residuals from independence   The distance between a row and column point has a rough interpretation in terms of residuals or in terms of the difference between observed and expected frequencies, $n_{ij} - m_{ij}$. Two row (or column) points deviate from the origin (the average profile) when their profile frequencies have similar values. A row point appears near a column point when $n_{ij} - m_{ij} > 0$ and away from that column point when the residual is negative.

Because of these differences in interpretations of distances, there are different possibilities for graphical display. A joint display of principal coordinates for the rows and standard coordinates for the columns (or vice-versa), sometimes called an *asymmetric map*, is suggested by Greenacre and Hastie (1987) and by Greenacre (1989) as the plot with the most coherent geometric interpretation (for the points in principal coordinates) and is widely used in the French literature. The options `PROFILE=ROW` and `PROFILE=COLUMN` in PROC `CORRESP` generate the asymmetric map.

Another common joint display is the *symmetric map* of the principal coordinates in the same plot, produced with the option `PROFILE=BOTH`. In my opinion, this produces better graphical displays, because both sets of coordinates are scaled with the same weights for each axis. Symmetric plots are used exclusively in this book, but that should not imply that these plots are universally preferred. Another popular choice is to avoid the possibility of misinterpretation by making separate plots of the row and column coordinates. The different scalings and the valid distance interpretations for each are described in detail in the Algorithms section in Chapter 19 of the *SAS/STAT User's Guide*.

5.2.3   The CORRESP Procedure

CA is performed by using `PROC CORRESP` in SAS/STAT. `PROC CORRESP` can read the following kinds of input:

- 2-way contingency tables (*contingency table form*) in which the columns are dataset variables (specified in a `VAR` statement), and the rows are observations (labeled by an `ID` variable). In this case, the column variables contain the frequencies in the corresponding cells.

- raw category responses (*case form*) or cell frequencies (*frequency form*) that are classified by two (or more) table variables. In these two cases, the table variables are specified in a `TABLES` statement. When the observations are cell frequencies, the frequency variable can be specified in the `WEIGHT` statement.

   In addition to printed output, the `OUTC=` option in `PROC CORRESP` produces an output dataset that contains the row and column coordinates and other information. In order to understand the relationships among the row and column categories, you can plot the coordinates with `PROC PLOT` or `PROC GPLOT`. `PROC CORRESP` has many options for scaling row and column coordinates and for printing various statistics, which aid interpretation. Example 5.1 illustrates the basic use of `PROC CORRESP`. A macro program `CORRESP`, described in Section 5.2.4, simplifies the analysis and plotting steps.

EXAMPLE 5.1   Hair color and Eye color

The program that follows reads the hair-color and eye-color data into the dataset `HAIREYE` and calls `PROC CORRESP`. This example also illustrates the use of `PROC PLOT` and the Annotate facility with `PROC GPLOT` to produce a labeled display of the CA solution. To input a contingency table in the CORRESP step, the hair colors (columns) are specified by the variables in the `VAR` statement, and the eye colors (rows) are specified by the variable `EYE` in the `ID` statement.

```
data haireye;
    input  EYE $ BLACK BROWN RED BLOND ;
datalines;
        Brown       68      119     26      7
        Blue        20       84     17     94
        Hazel       15       54     14     10
        Green        5       29     14     16
;
proc corresp data=haireye outc=coord short;
    var black brown red blond;
    id eye;
proc print data=coord;
    var _type_ eye dim1 dim2 quality;
```

   The printed output from `PROC CORRESP` is shown in Output 5.1. The section labeled "Inertia and Chi-Square Decomposition" indicates that over 98% of the Pearson χ^2 for association is accounted for by two dimensions, with most of that attributed to the first dimension.

   A plot of the row and column points can be constructed from the `OUTC=` dataset `COORD` specified in the `PROC CORRESP` statement. The variables of interest in this example are shown in Output 5.2. Note that row and column points are distinguished by the variable `_TYPE_`. In this example, the labels for the points are stored in the variable `EYE`.

Output 5.1   Hair-color and Eye-color data, PROC CORRESP printed output

```
                  The Correspondence Analysis Procedure


                  Inertia and Chi-Square Decomposition

Singular   Principal  Chi-
Values     Inertias   Squares  Percents    18   36   54   72   90
                                         ----+----+----+----+----+---
0.45692    0.20877    123.593  89.37%  ************************
0.14909    0.02223     13.158   9.51%  ***
0.05097    0.00260      1.538   1.11%
           -------    -------
           0.23360     138.29  (Degrees of Freedom = 9)


                        Row Coordinates

                             Dim1           Dim2

              Brown        -.492158       -.088322
              Blue        0.547414        -.082954
              Hazel       -.212597        0.167391
              Green       0.161753        0.339040


                      Column Coordinates

                             Dim1           Dim2

              BLACK        -.504562       -.214820
              BROWN        -.148253        0.032666
              RED          -.129523        0.319642
              BLOND       0.835348        -.069579
```

Output 5.2   Hair-color and Eye-color data, OUTC=coord dataset

OBS	_TYPE_	EYE	DIM1	DIM2	QUALITY
1	INERTIA		.	.	.
2	OBS	Brown	-0.49216	-0.08832	0.99814
3	OBS	Blue	0.54741	-0.08295	0.99993
4	OBS	Hazel	-0.21260	0.16739	0.87874
5	OBS	Green	0.16175	0.33904	0.94843
6	VAR	BLACK	-0.50456	-0.21482	0.98986
7	VAR	BROWN	-0.14825	0.03267	0.90633
8	VAR	RED	-0.12952	0.31964	0.94507
9	VAR	BLOND	0.83535	-0.06958	0.99963

The interpretation of the CA results is facilitated by a *labeled* plot of the row-and-column points. Beginning with Release 6.08, points can be labeled in PROC PLOT. The statements below produce a labeled plot. The plot should be scaled so that the number of data units/inch are the same for both dimensions. Otherwise, the distances (and angles) in this plot would not be represented accurately. In PROC PLOT, this is done with the VTOH option, which specifies the aspect ratio (vertical to horizontal) of your printer, together with the HAXIS and VAXIS options.

The VTOH option tries to equate distances between tick marks, so you should specify the same tick increment (e.g., HAXIS=BY XX, VAXIS=BY XX) for both axes. For example, this PROC PLOT step produces the printer plot shown in Output 5.3.

```
proc plot data=coord vtoh=2;
    plot dim2 * dim1 = '*'$ eye / box haxis=by .1 vaxis=by .1;
run;
```

Output 5.3 Labeled printer plot for the Hair-color and Eye-color CA solution

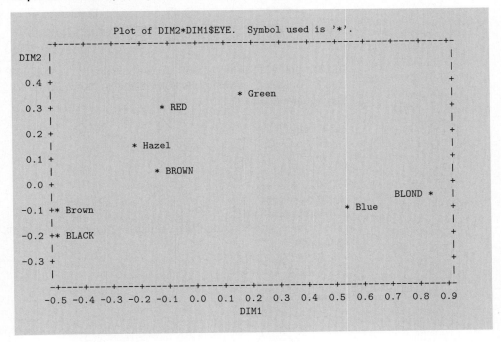

A labeled high-resolution display of the CA solution (Figure 5.1) is constructed with PROC GPLOT by using a DATA step to produce the Annotate dataset LABEL from the COORD dataset. In the PROC GPLOT step, axes are equated with the AXIS statements: the AXIS1 statement specifies a length and a range that are twice the length and range specified in the AXIS2 statement, so that the ratio of data units to plot units is the same in both dimensions. That is, the LENGTH options are set so that

$$\frac{x_{\max} - x_{\min}}{x_{\text{length}}} = \frac{y_{\max} - y_{\min}}{y_{\text{length}}} \,.$$

Alternatively, you may use the EQUATE macro from the SAS Sample Library (see the *SAS/STAT User's Guide*, Chapter 19, Example 3), which calculates the specified lengths from the coordinates, or simply scale the aspect ratio of the plot by using the options

Figure 5.1   CA solution for Hair-color and Eye-color data

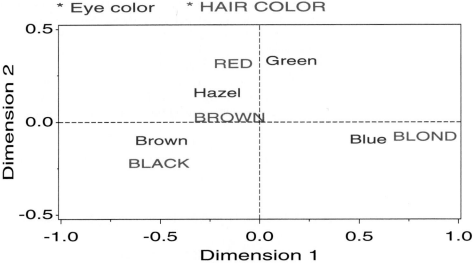

HSIZE= and VSIZE= in the GOPTIONS statement.[1] The CORRESP macro, illustrated in Section 5.2.4, uses a version of the EQUATE macro (Appendix A.31.2) that is modified to scale the plot automatically.

```
data label;
   set coord;
   xsys='2'; ysys='2';
   x = dim1; y = dim2;
   text = eye;
   size = 1.3;
   function='LABEL';
   if _type_='VAR' then color='RED  '; else color='BLUE';
data key;
   xsys='5'; ysys='5';
   length text $12;
   x = 25; y = 77;
   size = 1.4;
   color = 'BLUE ';
   function = 'LABEL    '; text = '* Eye color ' ; output;
   x = 55;
   color = 'RED  ';
   function = 'LABEL    '; text = '* HAIR COLOR' ; output;
data label;
   set key label;
proc gplot data=coord;
   plot dim2 * dim1
       / anno=label frame
         href=0 vref=0 lvref=3 lhref=3
         vaxis=axis2 haxis=axis1
         vminor=1 hminor=1;
   axis1 length=6 in  order=(-1. to 1. by .5)
         label=(h=1.5           'Dimension 1');
```

---

[1]The HSIZE= and VSIZE= options control the entire plot size, including axis labels, titles, and footnotes, so setting these options, while easier, is less exact than setting the axis lengths.

```
axis2 length=3 in  order=(-.5 to .5 by .5)
      label=(h=1.5 a=90 r=0 'Dimension 2');
   symbol v=none;
run;
```
☐

5.2.4 The CORRESP Macro

The steps illustrated in Example 5.1 are not difficult, but it is somewhat tedious to do them repeatedly. The CORRESP macro (documented in Appendix A.5) makes it easy to produce reasonable plots for CA results.

The CORRESP macro

- is designed as a simple macro interface to the CORRESP procedure.

- handles input in either contingency table form (columns specified by the VAR= parameter and rows specified by the ID= parameter), or in frequency or case form (using the TABLES= parameter).

- allows 3-way and larger tables to be analyzed by the "stacking" approach to multi-way tables (as described in Section 5.4) or by the MCA approach.

- optionally produces a labeled printer plot and a high-resolution graphics plot and has many options for controlling the appearance of graphics plots. Axes for high-resolution plots may be equated automatically.

- produces an output dataset (which contains the point coordinates) and an Annotate dataset (which contains point labels) for further plotting or customization.

EXAMPLE 5.2   Mental impairment and parents' SES

Srole, et al. (1978, p. 289) give the data, which is contained in the program that follows, on the mental health status of a sample of 1660 young New York residents in midtown Manhattan, classified by their parents' socio-economic status (SES) (see Appendix B.7).* There are five categories of SES, and mental health is classified in the four categories: Well, Mild symptom formation, Moderate symptom formation, and Impaired. This data has also been analyzed by many authors, including Agresti (1990, Section 8.5.2), Goodman (1979), and Haberman (1979, p. 375).

The statements in the following program read the data in contingency table form with rows identified by the variable SES and the column variables: WELL MILD MODERATE IMPAIRED. These variables are used in the %CORRESP call as the ID= and VAR= parameters, respectively. The graphics output is shown in Figure 5.2.

```
title h=1.5 lspace=3.8in 'Mental Impairment and SES';
data mental;
   input ses $ well mild moderate impaired;
datalines;
High 64    94     58     46
2    57    94     54     40
3    57    105    65     60
4    72    141    77     94
5    36    97     54     78
Low  21    71     54     71
;
axis1 length=3 in  order=(-.15 to .15 by .10)
      label=(h=1.5 a=90 r=0);
axis2 length=6 in  order=(-.30 to .30 by .10)
      label=(h=1.5) offset=(1);
%corresp (data=mental, id=ses, var=Well Mild Moderate Impaired,
      vaxis=axis1, haxis=axis2, htext=1.3, pos=-, interp=join,
      symbols=triangle square);
```

Figure 5.2   CORRESP macro plot for Mental Health data

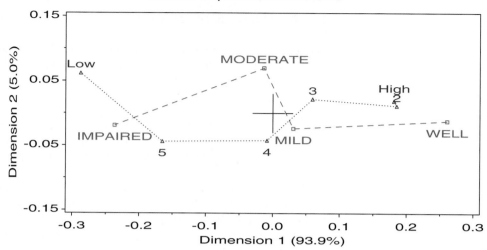

Some of the graphics options for the CORRESP macro are illustrated by the HTEXT= (height of text labels), POS= (position of text labels), INTERP= (point marker interpolation), and SYMBOLS= (point symbols) options. In particular, the option POS=- causes the macro to position the text labels centered above or below the point, depending on whether the y position is positive or negative, as specified by the LABEL macro (see Appendix A.31.6).

The cross at the origin in Figure 5.2 is drawn with equal data units in the x and y direction, and it serves as a guide to whether the axes have been equated. The LENGTH and ORDER values in the AXIS statements shown earlier were determined by inspection after an initial plot.

The plot shows that the association between mental health and parents' SES is almost entirely 1-dimensional, with 94% of the χ^2 (45.98, with 15 df) accounted for by Dimension 1. The diagnostic categories are well-aligned with this dimension and the two intermediate categories are closer on this dimension than the extremes, indicating that their profiles differ little. The SES categories are also aligned with Dimension 1 and approximately equally spaced, with the exception of the highest two categories. Because both row and column categories have the same pattern on Dimension 1, we may interpret the plot as showing that the profiles of both variables are ordered, and their relation can be explained as a positive association between parents' SES and higher mental health status of children.

From a modeling perspective, you might ask how strong is the evidence for the spacing of categories. For example, we might ask whether assigning integer scores to the levels of SES and mental impairment provides a simpler, but satisfactory account of their association. This question is explored in a later chapter (see Example 7.6).   □

EXAMPLE 5.3   Repeat victimization

Example 4.3 presented mosaic displays for the data about repeat victimization. In this example, the CA results are examined and customizing the displays created by the CORRESP macro is illustrated. The following lines create the dataset VICTIMS in contingency table form, where the columns represent the first victimization and the rows represent the second victimization.

```
data victims;
   input crime $ Rape Assault Robbery PickPock PLarceny
              Burglary HLarceny AutoThft;
datalines;
Rape        26   50  11    6    82    39    48    11
Assault     65 2997 238   85  2553  1083  1349   216
Robbery     12  279 197   36   459   197   221    47
PickPock     3  102  40   61   243   115   101    38
PLarceny    75 2628 413  329 12137  2658  3689   687
Burglary    52 1117 191  102  2649  3210  1973   301
Hlarceny    42 1251 206  117  3757  1962  4646   391
AutoThft     3  221  51   24   678   301   367   269
;
```

Because the rows and columns refer to the same crimes (and because the points for the same crime occupy similar positions in the CA map), you might label each crime just once and connect the two points for each crime by a line, as shown in Figure 5.3.

Figure 5.3   2-D CA display for repeat victimization data

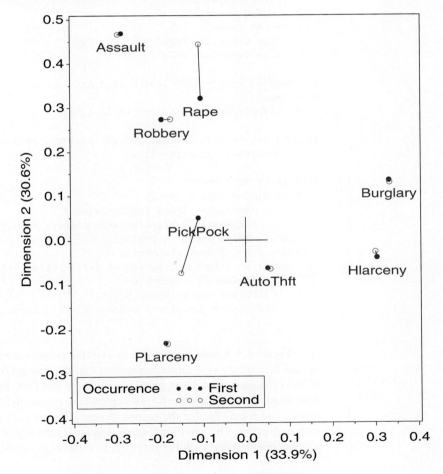

The following program uses the CORRESP macro with the GPLOT=NO parameter, so that no plot is produced; however, the macro still creates the output dataset COORD and the Annotate dataset LABEL used in the GPLOT procedure to produce a customized plot. Lines

joining points for the same crime are created from the COORD dataset, after sorting by
upcase(_name_). The (properly equated) AXIS statements are constructed automatically
by the EQUATE macro.[2]

```
%corresp(data=victims, id=crime,
    var=Rape Assault Robbery PickPock PLarceny Burglary HLarceny AutoThft,
    pos=8, gplot=NO);

*-- Sort crimes by upcase(_name_);
data coord;
    set coord;
    _name_ = upcase(_name_);
proc sort data=coord;
    where (_type_ ^= 'INERTIA');
    by _name_ _type_;

*-- Join first/second occurrence;
data lines;
    set coord(keep=_name_ _type_ dim1 dim2);
    by _name_ _type_;
    xsys='2'; ysys='2';
    x = dim1; y = dim2;
    if first._name_
        then function='MOVE';
        else function='DRAW';

*-- Remove _type_='VAR' labels, and add lines;
data label;
    set label(where=(_type_^='VAR')) lines;

%equate(data=coord, x=dim1, y=dim2, plot=no, vaxis=axis98, haxis=axis99,
    xmextra=1, ymextra=1);

proc gplot data=coord;
    plot dim2 * dim1 = _type_
        / anno=label frame legend=legend1
            vaxis=axis98 haxis=axis99 vminor=1 hminor=1;
    symbol1 h=1.2 v=dot     c=blue;
    symbol2 h=1.2 v=circle c=red;
    legend1 position=(bottom inside left)  offset=(1,2)
        mode=share cborder=blue
        across=1 shape=symbol(6,1.5)
        label=('Occurrence') value=('First' 'Second');
run;
```

In Figure 5.3, it may be seen that most of the points are extremely close for the first and
second occurrence of a crime, indicating that the row profile for a crime is very similar
to its corresponding column profile, with Rape and Pick Pocket as exceptions. The first
dimension appears to contrast crimes against the person (left) with crimes against property
(right), and it may be that the second dimension represents degree of violence associated
with each crime. The latter interpretation is consistent with the movement of Rape towards
a higher position and Pick Pocket towards a lower one on this dimension.   □

---

[2]The EQUATE macro is called by %CORRESP when the HAXIS parameter and the VAXIS parameter are not specified
in the macro call.

5.2.5   Quasi-Independence and Structural Zeros

Incomplete tables can result when particular cells are simply not observed (sampling zeros, e.g., insufficient data collected) or when some combinations of levels cannot logically occur (structural zeros, e.g., pregnant males). Alternatively, in some cases you might want to ignore the data in some cells and fit a quasi-independence model to the remaining cells. This is commonly done with square tables having the same row and column categories, where the dominant diagonal cells cause a global independence model to fail.

Because CA decomposes departures from independence, many of these cases can be handled simply by estimating the expected frequencies that would occur in these cells if the row and column variables were independent, and by replacing the zero, missing, or dominant observed frequencies by their expected values.[3] More general, iterative procedures are discussed by Greenacre (1984, Section 8.5) and by van der Heijden (1987, Chapter 3).

EXAMPLE 5.4   **Repeat victimization**

Example 4.3 also shows a mosaic display (Figure 4.9) for the model of quasi-independence that ignores the diagonal cells in the repeat victimization data. The analysis below gives another view of this model.

The elements in the diagonal cells of the VICTIMS dataset can be replaced by their expected frequencies under independence in the following PROC IML step:

```
proc iml;
    use victims;
    read all var _num_  into table[r=crime c=vars];
    read all var crime into crime;
    close victims;

    exp = table[,+] * table[+,] / table[+,+];
    table = table + diag(vecdiag(exp - table));

    create victims from table[r=crime c=vars];
    append from table[r=crime c=vars];
```

Using the same %CORRESP step and plotting steps, as in Example 5.3 (with a different LEGEND statement), gives the 2-D plot shown in Figure 5.4.

Note that the 2-D solution now accounts for 92% of the remaining association, which now concerns only the cells where the crime differs from the first to the second occurrence. For these cells, the differences between first and second incident are magnified.   □

---

[3]This does not account properly for the loss in degrees of freedom, but significance tests in CA are usually not treated formally. Indeed, the method would be of little interest for data in which independence holds.

Figure 5.4   2-D CA display for repeat victimization data, quasi-independence model, ignoring diagonal cells

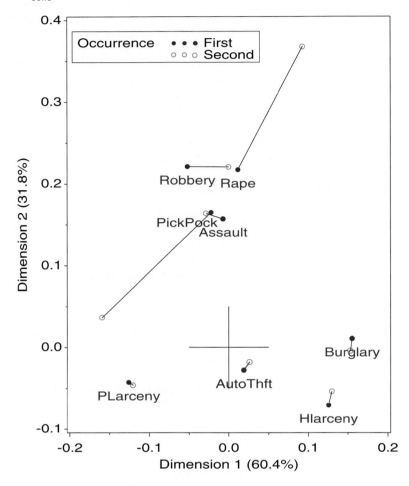

5.3 Properties of Category Scores

This section illustrates several properties of the CA scores by using calculation and visualization.

5.3.1 Optimal Category Scores

The singular values shown in Output 5.1 are the λ_i, in Equation 5.1. They are also the (canonical) correlations between the optimally scaled categories. Thus, if the DIM1 scores for Hair color and Eye color are assigned to the 592 observations in the table, the correlation of these variables would be 0.4569—the largest possible correlation for *any* assignment of scores. The DIM2 scores give a second, orthogonal scaling of these two categorical variables, whose correlation would be 0.1491.

In this sense, CA scores provide an optimal way of transforming categorical water into quantitative wine, hence the name "optimal scaling."

We can illustrate this numerically and visually as follows. If the row scores on Dimension 1 are in the $r \times 1$ vector $\mathbf{x}_1$ and the column scores are in the $c \times 1$ vector $\mathbf{y}_1$, then these scores can be expanded to conform with the $r \times c$ table by forming the appropriate outer product with a unit vector:

$$X_1 = x_1\, \mathbf{1}^\mathsf{T} \qquad \text{and} \qquad Y_1 = \mathbf{1}\, y_1^\mathsf{T}\ .$$

The program that follows uses the SAS/IML PROC IML statement to perform this operation on the COORD dataset and then merges these scores with a reshaped copy of the Hair-color and Eye-color data. The resulting HAIREYE dataset is shown in Output 5.4.

```
*-- Attach X, Y values to eye color, hair color and reshape;
proc iml;
   use coord;
   read all var{dim1 dim2} where (_type_='VAR') into var[r=eye]; hair=eye;
   read all var{dim1 dim2} where (_type_='OBS') into obs[r=eye];

   r = nrow(obs);
   c = nrow(var);
   x1 = obs[,1] * j(1, c);
   x2 = obs[,2] * j(1, c);
   y1 = j(r,1)  * t(var[,1]);
   y2 = j(r,1)  * t(var[,2]);

   hair = repeat( hair, r, 1);
   eye  = shape(repeat( eye, 1,c),r*c, 1);

   create scores var{eye hair x1 y1 x2 y2};
   append;
   quit;

*-- Reshape data to frequency form and merge with scores;
proc transpose data=haireye out=haireye2;
   var BLACK BROWN RED BLOND;
   by eye notsorted;

data haireye2;
   set haireye2;
   rename _name_=hair col1=count;

data scores;
   merge haireye2 scores;

proc print data=scores;
   format x1 x2 y1 y2 7.4;
   id eye hair;

*-- Correlations of scores = singular values;
proc corr data=scores nosimple;
   freq count;
   var x1 x2;
   with y1 y2;
```

The CA scores then serve to quantify the Hair-color and Eye-color categories, producing the maximum possible correlations of $(X1, Y1)$ and $(X2, Y2)$, while all other pairs are uncorrelated. These correlations are shown in Output 5.5. A plot of the optimal scores, using cell frequencies as weights (Figure 5.6), is developed in the next subsection.

Output 5.4   Hair-color and Eye-color data, DIM1, DIM2 scores assigned to Hair-color and Eye-color categories

EYE	HAIR	COUNT	X1	Y1	X2	Y2
Brown	BLACK	68	-0.4922	-0.5046	-0.0883	-0.2148
Brown	BROWN	119	-0.4922	-0.1483	-0.0883	0.0327
Brown	RED	26	-0.4922	-0.1295	-0.0883	0.3196
Brown	BLOND	7	-0.4922	0.8353	-0.0883	-0.0696
Blue	BLACK	20	0.5474	-0.5046	-0.0830	-0.2148
Blue	BROWN	84	0.5474	-0.1483	-0.0830	0.0327
Blue	RED	17	0.5474	-0.1295	-0.0830	0.3196
Blue	BLOND	94	0.5474	0.8353	-0.0830	-0.0696
Hazel	BLACK	15	-0.2126	-0.5046	0.1674	-0.2148
Hazel	BROWN	54	-0.2126	-0.1483	0.1674	0.0327
Hazel	RED	14	-0.2126	-0.1295	0.1674	0.3196
Hazel	BLOND	10	-0.2126	0.8353	0.1674	-0.0696
Green	BLACK	5	0.1618	-0.5046	0.3390	-0.2148
Green	BROWN	29	0.1618	-0.1483	0.3390	0.0327
Green	RED	14	0.1618	-0.1295	0.3390	0.3196
Green	BLOND	16	0.1618	0.8353	0.3390	-0.0696

Output 5.5   Hair-color and Eye-color data, correlations between X1, X2 and Y1 Y2

```
                    Correlation Analysis

         2 'WITH' Variables:  Y1      Y2
         2 'VAR'  Variables:  X1      X2


  Pearson Correlation Coefficients / Prob > |R| under Ho: Rho=0
  / N = 592 / FREQ Var = COUNT


                         X1                X2

            Y1        0.45692           0.00000
                      0.0001            1.0000


            Y2        0.00000           0.14909
                      1.0000            0.0003
```

5.3.2   Simultaneous Linear Regressions

The correlations among the CA scores have yet another interpretation, which gave rise to the first algebraic derivation of the technique (Hirschfeld, 1935) and which today provides an important concept in the Gifi (1990) system of homogeneity analysis.

Consider an arbitrary assignment of scores $X1$ ($Y1$) to the Hair-color and Eye-color categories; for example, $X1$ ($Y1$) = 1, 2, 3, 4 for the categories in alphabetical order. Instead of plotting these scores along a dimension as in Figure 5.1, you plot $Y1$ against $X1$ for all $n = 592$ cases and show the frequency at each discrete point by the area of a bubble symbol, as in Figure 5.5.

Figure 5.5   Plot of arbitrary scores for the row and column categories. The bubble symbols and numbers show the frequency at each point. The red points (solid line) show the means of $Y1 \mid X1$; blue points (dashed line) show the means of $X1 \mid Y1$.

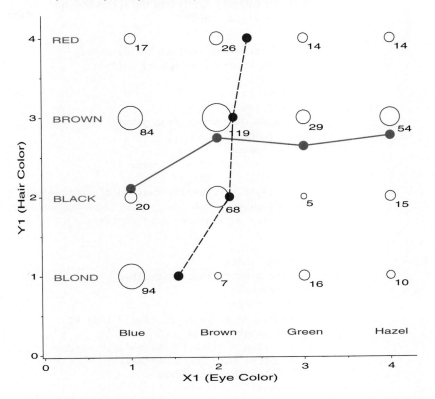

If you carried out a least squares regression of $Y1$ on $X1$, this would be equivalent to finding the weighted mean of $Y1$ for each value of $X1$ and fitting a straight line to these means. Similarly, you could fit a regression of $X1$ on $Y1$, which would be determined by the weighted means of $X1$ for each $Y1$. For the arbitrary scores, the conditional means of $Y1 \mid X1$ have a nonlinear relation to $X1$, and the same is true for the inverse regression of $X1 \mid Y1$, as we see in Figure 5.5.

The question posed by Hirschfeld (1935) was this: Can we find scores a and b for the row and column variables such that *both* regressions are linear? The answer is "Yes!" Indeed, there is one solution for each pair of correspondence analysis scores, a_i and b_i, associated with the singular value λ_i. For a given set of scores, a_i and b_i, the weighted means of the columns are $D_c^{-1}P^{\mathsf{T}}a_i$, and the linear regression on b_i has intercept 0 and slope λ_i,

$$(D_c^{-1}P^{\mathsf{T}})a_i = \lambda_i b_i$$

Similarly, the inverse regression on a_i has intercept 0 and slope $1/\lambda_i$

$$(D_r^{-1}P)b_i = (1/\lambda_i)a_i$$

The choice of the scores associated with the largest singular value, λ_1, makes the slope (equivalently, the correlation) of the regression of $Y1$ on $X1$ as large as possible. Moreover, this choice makes the angle between the two regression lines as small as possible, i.e., the regressions are most collinear (Greenacre, 1984). So, instead of complex, nonlinear relations between the scaled Hair-color and Eye-color variables using arbitrary scores (Figure 5.5), you arrive at simple, linear relations by use of a nonlinear transformation of the arbitrary scores.

You can show these regressions for the first CA dimension in the following program steps, which continue from those shown in Section 5.3.1. Most of the program steps are used to find the means of $Y1 \mid X1$ and $X1 \mid Y1$, and to annotate them on the plot, together with the category labels and the regression line. The plot with both regression lines is shown in Figure 5.6.

```
*-- Annotate the row and column means;
proc means data=scores nway noprint;
   var y1;
   class x1;
   freq count;
   output out=ymeans mean=y1bar;
data ymeans;
   set ymeans;
   retain xsys  ysys '2' size 2;
   x = x1; y = y1bar;
   function = 'symbol'; text='dot'; color='red';  output;

proc means data=scores nway noprint;
   var x1;
   class y1;
   freq count;
   output out=xmeans mean=x1bar;
data xmeans;
   set xmeans;
   retain xsys  ysys '2' size 2 line 4;
   x = x1bar; y = y1;
   function = 'symbol'; text='dot'; color='blue';  output;
   if _n_=1 then function='move';
      else function='draw';
   output;

*-- Annotate the row and column labels;
data label1;
   set scores(keep=eye hair x1 y1);
   where eye='Brown';
   retain xsys ysys '2' color 'red    ' function 'label    ';
   if hair='BROWN' then position='9';
      else position='6';
   x = -.78; y = y1; text = hair;
data label2;
   set scores(keep=eye hair x1 y1);
   where hair='BLACK';
   retain xsys ysys '2' position '5' color 'blue' function 'label    ';
   x = x1; y = -.58; text = eye;

*-- Get slope and intercept of (weighted) regression line;
proc reg data=scores outest=parms noprint;
   model y1 = x1;
   weight count;

data line;
   set parms (keep=x1 intercep);
   drop x1 intercep;
   length text $20;
```

```
*-- Draw (weighted) regression line;
xsys='2'; ysys='2'; color='red    ';
x=-0.65; y = intercep + x1 * x; function='MOVE    '; output;
x= 0.65; y = intercep + x1 * x; function='DRAW    '; output;
x= 0.35; y = intercep + x1 * x; function='LABEL   '; color='black';
angle = atan(x1) * (45/atan(1)); position='2';
text = 'Y1 = 0 + ' || put(x1,6.3) || ' X1';  output;

*-- Combine the annotate data sets;
data labels;
    length text $20;
    set label1 label2 line ymeans xmeans;

proc gplot data=scores;
    bubble y1 * x1 = count /
        blabel bsize=8 bscale=area
        vaxis=axis1 haxis=axis2 hm=2 vm=2 anno=labels;
    axis1 order=(-.6 to .9 by .3) label=(h=1.8 a=90 'Y1 (Hair Color)');
    axis2 order=(-.8 to .7 by .3) label=(h=1.8      'X1 (Eye Color)');
```

Note that the slope of the line for $Y1 \mid X1$ in Figure 5.6 is 0.457, the largest singular value and the largest canonical correlation. If you were to repeat these steps using the CA scores $X2$ and $Y2$ on Dimension 2, you would find another pair of linear regressions with a slope of 0.149 for $Y2 \mid X2$, the second singular value.

Figure 5.6 Simultaneous linear regressions of correspondence analysis scores for Dimension 1. Using the optimal scores makes both regressions linear; choosing the scores associated with the largest singular value makes the two regressions most collinear.

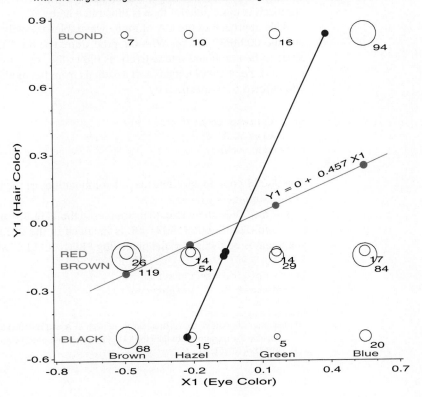

5.4 Multi-Way Tables

A 3- or higher-way table can be analyzed by correspondence analysis in several ways. Multiple correspondence analysis (MCA), described in Section 5.5, is an extension of simple correspondence analysis which analyzes simultaneously all possible 2-way tables contained within a multi-way table. Another approach, described here, is called **stacking**. A 3-way table, of size $I \times J \times K$ can be sliced into I 2-way tables, each $J \times K$. If the slices are concatenated vertically, the result is one 2-way table, of size $(I \times J) \times K$. In effect, the first two variables are treated as a single composite variable with IJ levels, which represents the main effects and the interaction between the original variables that were combined. Van der Heijden and de Leeuw (1985) discuss this use of CA for multi-way tables and show how *each* way of slicing and stacking a contingency table corresponds to the analysis of a specified log-linear model. Like the mosaic display, this provides another way to visualize the relations in a log-linear model.

In particular, for the 3-way table that is reshaped as a table of size $(I \times J) \times K$, the CA solution analyzes residuals from the log-linear model [AB] [C]. That is, for such a table, the $I \times J$ rows represent the joint combinations of variables A and B. The expected frequencies under independence for this table are

$$m_{[ij]k} = \frac{n_{[ij]+} n_{[+]k}}{n} = \frac{n_{ij+} n_{++k}}{n} \tag{5.6}$$

which are the ML estimates of expected frequencies for the log-linear model [AB] [C]. The χ^2 that is decomposed by CA is the Pearson χ^2 for this log-linear model. When the table is stacked as $I \times (J \times K)$ or $J \times (I \times K)$, correspondence analysis decomposes the residuals from the log-linear models [A] [BC] and [B] [AC], respectively. Van der Heijden and de Leeuw (1985) also show how a generalized form of correspondence analysis can be interpreted as decomposing the difference between two specific log-linear models, so their approach is more general than is illustrated here.

This approach to the CA of multi-way tables is easily carried out with `PROC CORRESP` and the `CORRESP` macro. With the procedure, use the `TABLES` statement and list the variables to be combined interactively as either the row or column variables (separated by a comma). For example, the CA of residuals from the model [A B][C] of joint independence (Equation 5.6) is specified by

```
proc corresp cross=row;
   tables A B, C;
   weight count;
```

The `CROSS=` option specifies that all combinations of the levels of A and B define the rows of the contingency table.[4]

For the `CORRESP` macro, the variables in the `TABLES=` parameter are separated by a slash (/),[5] and `CROSS=BOTH|ROW|COL` is included in the `OPTIONS=` parameter. The following statement is equivalent to the preceding `PROC CORRESP` step:

```
%corresp(options=cross=row,
   tables=A B/ C, weight=count);
```

---

[4]If this option is omitted, the separate levels of each of A and B define the table rows.
[5]You can also use a comma, but then the `TABLES=` parameter must be protected with the `%STR()` macro function, e.g., `TABLES=%STR(A B, C)`.

EXAMPLE 5.5   Suicide rates in Germany

In this section, the use of CA for the analysis for 3-way tables is illustrated by using data on suicide rates in West Germany (presented in Table 5.1). The data is classified by Age, Sex, and Method of suicide used. The data from Heuer (1979, Table 1) has been discussed by Friendly (1991, 1994b), van der Heijden and de Leeuw (1985)[6] and others. The original $2 \times 17 \times 9$ table (Appendix B.10) contains 17 age groups from 10 to 90 in 5-year increments and 9 categories of suicide method. To avoid extremely small cell counts and cluttered displays this example uses a reduced table in which age groups are combined into 10-year intervals except for the last interval, which includes ages 70 to 90; the methods "toxic gas" and "cooking gas" were collapsed and the methods "knife" and "other" were deleted, giving the $2 \times 5 \times 6$ table shown in Table 5.1. These changes do not affect the general nature of the data or conclusions drawn from it.

Table 5.1   Suicide data: frequencies of suicide by Age, Sex, and Method (Heuer, 1979)

Sex	Age	Poison	Gas	Hang	Drown	Gun	Jump
M	10-20	1160	335	1524	67	512	189
M	25-35	2823	883	2751	213	852	366
M	40-50	2465	625	3936	247	875	244
M	55-65	1531	201	3581	207	477	273
M	70-90	938	45	2948	212	229	268
F	10-20	921	40	212	30	25	131
F	25-35	1672	113	575	139	64	276
F	40-50	2224	91	1481	354	52	327
F	55-65	2283	45	2014	679	29	388
F	70-90	1548	29	1355	501	3	383

Table 5.2 shows the results of all possible hierarchical log-linear models for the suicide data. It is apparent that none of these models has an acceptable fit to the data. However, given the enormous sample size ($n = 48,177$), even relatively small departures from expected frequencies under any model would appear significant.

Table 5.2   Goodness-of-fit for hierarchical log-linear models for the suicide data

Model	df	L.R. G^2	G.F. χ^2
[M][A][S]	49	10119.60	9908.24
[M][AS]	45	8632.0	8371.3
[A][MS]	44	4719.0	4387.7
[S][MA]	29	7029.2	6485.5
[MS][AS]	40	3231.5	3030.5
[MA][AS]	25	5541.6	5135.0
[MA][MS]	24	1628.6	1592.4
[MA][MS][AS]	20	242.0	237.0

The decision about which variables to combine interactively depends more on which associations are to be displayed and which are to be ignored, rather than on which is the best-fitting model. For example, CA applied to the [AS] by [M] table helps to show the

---

[6]"Correspondence Analysis Used Complementary to Loglinear Analysis," Peter G. M. van der Heijden, *Psychometrika*, Volume 50, Number 4, pp. 429–447. Copyright © 1985 by The Psychometric Society. Reprinted by permission of The Psychometric Society.

nature of the association between Method of suicide and the joint Age-Sex combinations and decomposes the $\chi^2 = 8371$ for the log-linear model [AS] [M]. However, this analysis would ignore the Age-Sex association.

To carry out this analysis with the data in the form of a frequency dataset (with variables AGE, SEX, METHOD, and COUNT), call PROC CORRESP with the following statements:

```
proc corresp data=suicide cross=row short;
   table age sex, method;
   weight count;
run;
```

Or, to perform this analysis and produce the graphical display in Figure 5.7, call the CORRESP procedure as follows:

```
axis1 order=(-.7 to .7 by .7) length=6.5 in label=(a=90 r=0);
axis2 order=(-.7 to .7 by .7) length=6.5 in;
%corresp(data=suicide, tables=%str(age sex, method), weight=count,
        options=cross=row short, vaxis=axis1, haxis=axis2);
```

Figure 5.7   2-D CA solution for the [AS] [M] multiple table of the suicide data

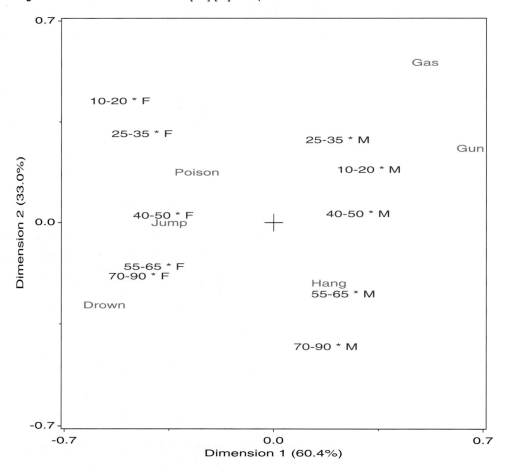

The printed results, shown partially in Output 5.6, indicate that over 93% of the association between the Age-Sex categories and Method of suicide can be represented well in two dimensions.

Output 5.6 Chi-Square decomposition for suicide data

```
                    Inertia and Chi-Square Decomposition

Singular   Principal  Chi-
Values     Inertias   Squares  Percents    12   24   36   48   60
                                        ----+----+----+----+----+---
0.32138    0.10328    5056.91  60.41%  *************************
0.23736    0.05634    2758.41  32.95%  **************
0.09378    0.00879     430.55   5.14%  **
0.04171    0.00174      85.17   1.02%
0.02867    0.00082      40.24   0.48%

           -------    -------
           0.17098    8371.28  (Degrees of Freedom = 45)
```

The plot of the CA scores for the rows (Sex-Age combinations) and columns (Methods) in Figure 5.7 shows residuals from the log-linear model [AS] [M]. Thus, it shows the 2-way associations of Sex × Method, Age × Method, and the 3-way association, Sex × Age × Method that are set to zero in the model [AS] [M]. The possible association between Sex and Age is not shown in this plot.

Dimension 1 in the plot separates males and females. This dimension indicates a strong difference between suicide profiles of males and females. The second dimension is mostly ordered by Age with younger groups at the top and older groups at the bottom. Note also that the positions of the age groups are approximately parallel for the two sexes. Such a pattern indicates that Sex and Age do not interact in this analysis. The relation between the Age-Sex groups and Methods of suicide can be interpreted in terms of similar distance and

Figure 5.8 Mosaic display showing deviations from model [AS] [M]. The methods have been re-ordered according to their positions on Dimension 1 of the CA solution for the [AS] [M] table.

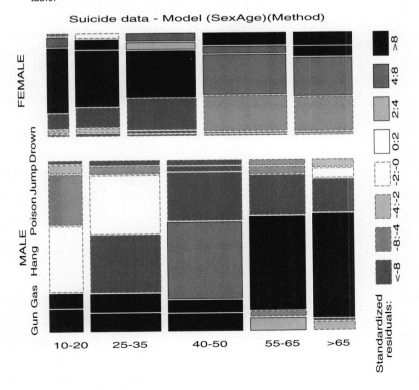

direction from the origin, which represents the marginal row and column profiles. Young males are more likely to commit suicide by using gas or a gun; older males, by hanging; while young females are more likely to ingest some toxic agent and older females, by jumping or drowning.

For comparison, the mosaic display for the [AS] [M] table is shown in Figure 5.8. The methods have been arranged in order of the method scores on the first dimension of the CA solution of Figure 5.7. Figure 5.8 again shows the prevailing use of GUN and GAS among younger males, and their use decreasing with age, whereas the use of HANG increases with age. For females, GUN, GAS, and HANG are used less frequently than would be the case if method were independent of age and sex, whereas, POISON, JUMP, and DROWN occur more often.   □

5.4.1 Marginal Tables and Supplementary Variables

An *n*-way table in frequency form or case form is automatically collapsed over factors that are not listed in the TABLES statement (or in the macro TABLES= parameter). The analysis gives a marginal model for the categorical variables that *are* listed.

The positions of the categories of the omitted variables may nevertheless be recovered, by treating them as supplementary variables. A supplementary variable is ignored in finding the CA solution, but its categories are then projected into that space.

To illustrate, the statement below lists only the AGE and METHOD variables, and therefore, produces an analysis collapsed over SEX. This ignores not only the effect of Sex itself, but also all associations of Age and Method with Sex, which (from Table 5.2) are substantial.

```
%corresp(data=suicide, tables=%str(age, method),  weight=count);
```

This analysis and the graph that is produced do not include category points for SEX, but we may re-do the same analysis including SEX as a supplementary variable as shown next.

```
%corresp(data=suicide, tables=%str(age sex, method), sup=sex,
   weight=count, inc=0.2 0.1, dimlab=Dim);
```

Note that SEX must also be listed among the TABLES= variables.

This analysis produces a $\chi^2(20) = 2917.83$, the same as the Pearson chi-square for the [A] [M] marginal table. The plot (Figure 5.9) is essentially one-dimensional, where Dimension 1 reflects Age most prominently. Comparing this graph with Figure 5.7, you may see that ignoring Sex has collapsed the differences between males and females that

Figure 5.9   Two-dimensional CA solution for the [A] [M] marginal table. Category points for Sex are shown as supplementary points.

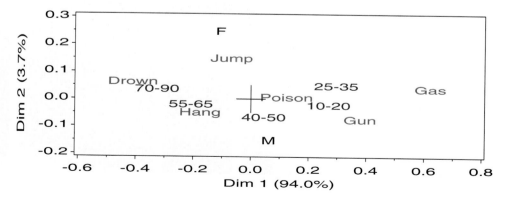

were the dominant feature of the analysis including Sex. However, as in Figure 5.7, the supplementary points for Sex show a greater tendency for females to use JUMP and for males to use HANG or GUN.

5.5 Multiple Correspondence Analysis

Multiple correspondence analysis (MCA) is designed to display the relationships of the categories of two or more discrete variables. Again, there are several complementary ways of defining MCA as an optimal scaling of categorical data. The most typical analysis starts by defining indicator ("dummy") variables for each category and re-expresses the n-way contingency table in the form of a cases-by-variables indicator matrix, $\mathbf{Z}$. Simple correspondence analysis for a 2-way table can, in fact, be derived as the canonical correlation analysis of the indicator matrix. Unfortunately, the generalization to more than two variables follows a somewhat different path, so that simple CA does not turn out to be precisely a special case of MCA in some respects, particularly in the decomposition of an interpretable χ^2 over the dimensions in the visual representation.

Nevertheless, MCA does provide a useful graphic portrayal of the *bivariate* relations among any number of categorical variables, and has close relations to the mosaic matrix (Section 4.4). If its limitations are understood, it may also be helpful in understanding large, multivariate categorical datasets.

5.5.1 Bivariate MCA

For the Hair-color and Eye-color data, the indicator matrix $\mathbf{Z}$ has 592 rows and $4 + 4 = 8$ columns. The columns refer to the eight categories of hair color and eye color and the rows to the students in Snee's 1974 sample. The indicator matrix is shown in Table 5.3, where to save space each combination of hair color and eye color actually corresponds to the

Table 5.3 Indicator matrix for Hair-color and Eye-color data (grouped)

Hair	Eye	n_{ij}	Hair h_1	h_2	h_3	h_4	Eye e_1	e_2	e_3	e_4
BLACK	Brown	68	1	0	0	0	1	0	0	0
BROWN	Brown	119	0	1	0	0	1	0	0	0
RED	Brown	26	0	0	1	0	1	0	0	0
BLOND	Brown	7	0	0	0	1	1	0	0	0
BLACK	Hazel	15	1	0	0	0	0	1	0	0
BROWN	Hazel	54	0	1	0	0	0	1	0	0
RED	Hazel	14	0	0	1	0	0	1	0	0
BLOND	Hazel	10	0	0	0	1	0	1	0	0
BLACK	Green	5	1	0	0	0	0	0	1	0
BROWN	Green	29	0	1	0	0	0	0	1	0
RED	Green	14	0	0	1	0	0	0	1	0
BLOND	Green	16	0	0	0	1	0	0	1	0
BLACK	Blue	20	1	0	0	0	0	0	0	1
BROWN	Blue	84	0	1	0	0	0	0	0	1
RED	Blue	17	0	0	1	0	0	0	0	1
BLOND	Blue	94	0	0	0	1	0	0	0	1
(Totals)		592	220	215	93	64	108	286	71	127

number of repeated rows that are represented by the n_{ij} column. Variable h_1 represents the hair category Black, and Variable e_1 represents the eye category Brown, so the first row of table Table 5.3 corresponds to the 68 people with black hair and brown eyes. The indicator matrix Z thus has 68 identical rows with that response pattern.

Each row of the indicator matrix sums to 2, the number of variables represented, and each category column sums to the marginal total for that category. Note that appropriate subsets of the rows are in a sense synonymous with the column categories. For example, the first four rows of the table are all those with brown eyes, so these rows represent e_1.

If the indicator matrix is partitioned as $Z = [Z_1, Z_2]$, corresponding to the two sets of categories, then the contingency table is given by $N = Z_1^\mathsf{T} Z_2$. In this case, MCA can be described as the application of the simple correspondence analysis algorithm to the indicator matrix Z. This analysis would yield scores for the rows of Z (the cases) and for the columns (the categories). As in simple CA, each row point is the weighted average of the scores for the column categories, and each column point is the weighted average of the scores for the row observations.

Consequently, the point for any category is the centroid of all the observations with a response in that category, and all observations with the same response pattern coincide. As well, the origin reflects the weighted average of the categories for *each* variable. As a result, category points with low marginal frequencies will be located further away from the origin, while categories with high marginal frequencies will be closer to the origin. For a binary variable, the two category points will appear on a line through the origin, with distances inversely proportional to their marginal frequencies.

EXAMPLE 5.6   Hair color and eye color

The analysis of the indicator matrix is provided below for the Hair-color and Eye-color data. MCA is usually carried out more simply through analysis of the "Burt matrix," described in the following subsection.

The indicator matrix may be constructed from the dataset in contingency table form as shown next, using PROC TRANSPOSE and a DATA step to calculate the dummy variables from the original row and column variables.[7]

```
data haireye;
   input  EYE $ BLACK BROWN RED BLOND ;
datalines;
        Brown   68    119    26     7
        Hazel   15     54    14    10
        Green    5     29    14    16
        Blue    20     84    17    94
;
*-- Reshape data to frequency form;
proc transpose data=haireye out=haireye2;
   var BLACK BROWN RED BLOND;
   by eye notsorted;

*-- Create dummy variables;
data haireye2;
   set haireye2 (rename= (_name_=hair col1=count));
   h1 = (hair='BLACK');   h2 = (hair='BROWN');
   h3 = (hair='RED');     h4 = (hair='BLOND');
   e1 = (eye ='Brown');   e2 = (eye ='Hazel');
   e3 = (eye ='Green');   e4 = (eye ='Blue');
```

---

[7]These steps actually create a design matrix, with one observation per category, with the frequencies, n_{ij}, as shown in Table 5.3. In the %CORRESP step, the COUNT variable is used as a weight to reproduce the indicator matrix.

Analysis of the indicator matrix (the dataset `HAIREYE2`) is conveniently carried out with the `CORRESP` macro.

```
axis1 length=6.5 IN order=(-1.2 to 2 by 0.4) label=(a=90);
axis2 length=6.5 IN order=(-1.2 to 2 by 0.4);

%corresp(data=haireye2, id=id, var=h1-h4 e1-e4, weight=count,
    symbols=none dot, pos=5 -, vaxis=axis1, haxis=axis2, anno=labels, gplot=no);
```

Some additional Annotation steps (not shown) to add some lines to the Annotate dataset `LABELS` produces Figure 5.10, in which the row and column points are shown in principal coordinates. Compared with Figure 5.1, the pattern of the hair color and eye color categories is the same in the analysis of the contingency table (Figure 5.1) and the analysis of the indicator matrix (Figure 5.10), except that the axes are scaled differently—the display has been stretched along the second (vertical) dimension. Indeed, it may be shown (Greenacre, 1984) that the two displays are identical, except for changes in scales along the axes. There is no difference at all between the displays in standard coordinates. Greenacre (1984, pp. 130–134) describes the precise relations between the geometries of the two analyses.

Figure 5.10 Correspondence analysis of the indicator matrix **Z** for the Hair-color and Eye-color data. The category points are joined for the Hair-color and Eye-color categories. Observation (row) points are labeled by the subscripts of *h, e*. The dotted line connects those with blond hair.

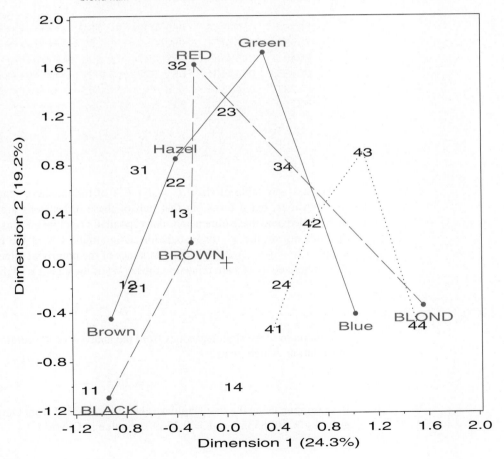

168   *Visualizing Categorical Data*

Figure 5.10 also plots the row points (corresponding to the observations) from this analysis. Each point is labeled by the subscripts, ij, of $h_i e_j$, and actually represents n_{ij} rows from the indicator matrix plotted at the point. For example, the points labeled '41'–'44' represent all the observations with blond hair. There are actually 94 observations at the point '44', representing the blue-eyed blonds. □

A major difference between analysis of the contingency table and analysis of the indicator matrix is in the decomposition of inertia and χ^2 for the dimensions. The inertias for the analysis of the indicator matrix are shown in Output 5.7. Comparing these values with Output 5.1, we see that 6 dimensions are shown in the analysis of the indicator matrix, while only 3 are shown in the analysis of the contingency table. The inertias and χ^2 values differ less dramatically than in Output 5.1, and the inertias sum to exactly 3.0 in the indicator matrix analysis.

Output 5.7   Correspondence analysis output for the indicator matrix of the Hair-color and Eye-color data

```
            The Correspondence Analysis Procedure

            Inertia and Chi-Square Decomposition

Singular   Principal Chi-
Values     Inertias  Squares Percents    5    10   15   20   25
                                        ----+----+----+----+----+---
0.85350    0.72846   862.495  24.28%  **********************
0.75799    0.57454   680.259  19.15%  ******************
0.72491    0.52549   622.177  17.52%  *****************
0.68885    0.47451   561.823  15.82%  ***************
0.65227    0.42546   503.741  14.18%  **************
0.52110    0.27154   321.505   9.05%  ********
           -------          -------
           3.00000            3552 (Degrees of Freedom = 105)
```

For a 2-way table of size $(J_1 \times J_2)$, CA of the indicator matrix produces $J_1 + J_2 - 2$ dimensions, but it turns out that half of these dimensions are artifacts that should be disregarded, and these dimensions correspond to principal inertias $\lambda^2 < \frac{1}{2}$. The total inertia depends not on the χ^2 for association as in simple CA of the contingency table, but is simply $(J_1 + J_2 - 2)/2$. The singular values of the nontrivial dimensions in the analysis of $\mathbf{Z}$ (symbolized as λ_i^Z) are related to those (λ_i) of the analysis of the contingency table by

$$\lambda_i^Z = \{\frac{1}{2}[1 + \lambda_i]\}^{1/2} .$$

We can recover the singular values from the analysis of the contingency table by inverting this relation, which gives

$$\lambda_i = 2(\lambda_i^Z)^2 - 1 . \tag{5.7}$$

For example, using the first singular value, $\lambda_1^Z = 0.8535$ from Output 5.7 (in Equation 5.7) gives $\lambda_1 = 2(0.8535^2) - 1 = 0.4569$, the value in Output 5.1.

5.5.2   The Burt Matrix

The same solution for the category points as in the analysis of the indicator matrix may be obtained more simply from the so-called "Burt matrix" (Burt, 1950),

$$B = Z^\mathsf{T} Z = \begin{bmatrix} N_1 & N \\ N^\mathsf{T} & N_2 \end{bmatrix},$$

where N_1 and N_2 are diagonal matrices containing the marginal frequencies of the two variables (the column sums of Z_1 and Z_2).

The standard coordinates from an analysis of the Burt matrix B are identical to those of Z. The singular values of B are the squares of those of Z; however, the CORRESP procedure compensates by taking the square root, so the same values are printed.

The CORRESP procedure and the CORRESP macro calculate the Burt matrix when the MCA option is used, and the category variables are given in the TABLES= statement. For the Hair-color and Eye-color data, the same category points and inertias found in Example 5.6 are obtained with the following statement, using the table variables HAIR and EYE rather than the indicator variables H1-H4 E1-E4.

```
%corresp(data=haireye2, tables=hair eye, weight=count, options=short mca,
    inc=0.4, xextra=0 1, pos=-, symbols=dot, colors=red);
```

The Burt matrix is symmetric and the rows and columns both refer to the hair, eye categories. Only the column (category) points appear in the output and the plot.

5.5.3   Multivariate MCA

The coding of categorical variables in an indicator matrix provides a direct and natural way to extend this analysis to more than two variables. If there are Q categorical variables, and variable q has J_q categories, then the Q-way contingency table, of size $J = \prod_{q=1}^{Q} J_q = J_1 \times J_2 \times \cdots \times J_Q$, with a total of $n = n_{++\dots}$ observations, may be represented by the partitioned ($n \times J$) indicator matrix $[Z_1 Z_2 \dots Z_Q]$.

Then the Burt matrix is the symmetric partitioned matrix

$$B = Z^\mathsf{T} Z = \begin{bmatrix} N_{[1]} & N_{[12]} & \cdots & N_{[1Q]} \\ N_{[21]} & N_{[2]} & \cdots & N_{[2Q]} \\ \vdots & \vdots & \ddots & \vdots \\ N_{[Q1]} & N_{[Q2]} & \cdots & N_{[Q]} \end{bmatrix},$$

where again the diagonal blocks $N_{[i]}$ contain the one-way marginal frequencies.

Classical MCA (see, e.g., Greenacre (1984), Gower and Hand (1996)) can then be defined as a singular value decomposition of the matrix B, which produces scores for the categories of all variables so that the greatest proportion of the bivariate, pairwise associations in all off-diagonal blocks is accounted for in a small number of dimensions. In this respect, MCA resembles multivariate methods for quantitative data based on the joint bivariate correlation or covariance matrix (Σ), and there is some justification to regard the Burt matrix as the categorical analog of Σ.[8]

There is a close connection between this analysis and the bivariate mosaic matrix described in Section 4.4: The mosaic matrix displays the residuals from independence for each pair of variables, and thus provides a visual representation of the Burt matrix. (The representation would be complete if the one-way margins were drawn in the diagonal cells.)

----

[8]For multivariate normal data, however, the mean vector and covariance matrix are sufficient statistics, so all higher-way relations are captured in the covariance matrix. This is not true of the Burt matrix.

The total amount of shading in all the individual mosaics portrays the total pairwise associations that have been broken down by MCA. See Friendly (1999a) for details.

In Section 5.5.1 the analysis of the indicator matrix or the Burt matrix with $Q = 2$ categorical variables produces twice as many dimensions as the analysis of the equivalent contingency table; but only those whose principal inertias, $(\lambda^Z)^2$, exceed $\frac{1}{2}$ are interesting, the remaining dimensions being artifacts. When there are $Q > 2$ variables represented in the Burt matrix, it may be argued (Greenacre, 1984, 1990) that the interesting dimensions correspond to those with principal inertia $> 1/Q$.

A more serious problem lies in the calculation of total inertia and, therefore, in the chi-square values and corresponding percentages of association accounted for in some number of dimensions. In simple CA, the total inertia is χ^2/n, and it, therefore, makes sense to talk of percentage of association accounted for by each dimension. But in MCA of the Burt matrix (with the square-root fixup provided by the CORRESP procedure), the total inertia is simply $(J - Q)/Q = J/Q - 1$, because that is what the analysis of the equivalent indicator matrix would give. The consequence is that the χ^2 percentages reported by PROC CORRESP are somewhat misleading, and give a rather pessimistic view of the association accounted for in the two (or three) dimensions usually plotted.

To more adequately reflect the percentage of association in MCA, Benzécri (1977) suggested the calculation of

$$(\lambda_i^\star)^2 = \left[\frac{Q}{Q-1} (\lambda_i^Z - (1/Q)) \right]^2$$

as the principal inertia due to the dimensions with $(\lambda^Z)^2 > 1/2$. Benzécri then expresses the contribution of each dimension as $(\lambda_i^\star)^2 / \sum (\lambda_i^\star)^2$, with the summation over only those dimensions with $(\lambda^Z)^2 > 1/2$.

Although this *is* an improvement, it is somewhat *ad hoc* and not totally satisfactory. Greenacre (1988) develops an alternative analysis called joint correspondence analysis (JCA) which fits only the $Q \times (Q-1)/2$ off-diagonal blocks of the Burt matrix. Greenacre (1990) then proposed to define the total inertia as the average inertia in these off-diagonal blocks.[9]

For the interpretation of MCA plots, note the following relations (Greenacre, 1984, Section 5.2):

- The centroid of the categories for each discrete variable is at the origin of the display.
- The inertia that is contributed by a given variable increases with the number of response categories.
- For a particular variable, the inertia that is contributed by a given category increases as the marginal frequency in that category *decreases*.
- The category points for a binary variable lie on a line through the origin. The distance from each point to the origin is inversely related to the marginal frequency.

EXAMPLE 5.7   Survival on the *Titanic*

An MCA analysis of the *Titanic* data is carried out using the MCA option of PROC CORRESP as follows:

```
%include catdata(titanic);
proc corresp data=titanic short mca outc=coords;
   weight count;
   tables age sex class survive;
   run;
```

---

[9] In SAS Release 8, the CORRESP procedure provides the BENZECRI and GREENACRE options, which give more reasonable and useful inertia contributions. One of these options should be used for MCA in the OPTIONS parameter with the CORRESP macro.

Output 5.8 Chi-Square decomposition for *Titanic* MCA

```
              Inertia and Chi-Square Decomposition

  Singular   Principal Chi-
  Values     Inertias  Squares Percents    6   12   18   24   30
                                         ----+----+----+----+----+---
  0.66714    0.44508   4609.06  29.67%  ************************
  0.55231    0.30504   3158.90  20.34%  ****************
  0.50001    0.25001   2588.96  16.67%  *************
  0.45281    0.20504   2123.28  13.67%  **********
  0.42251    0.17852   1848.63  11.90%  **********
  0.34105    0.11632   1204.54   7.75%  ******
             -------   -------
             1.50000   15533.4 (Degrees of Freedom = 81)
```

Output 5.9 Correspondence analysis coordinates for *Titanic* MCA

NAME	QUALITY	DIM1	DIM2	DIST	FACTOR
Adult	0.53947	-0.06783	-0.15332	0.16765	Age
Child	0.53947	1.30180	2.94265	3.21774	Age
1st	0.49259	1.15194	-1.23142	1.68623	Class
2nd	0.07257	0.65126	0.25252	0.69850	Class
3rd	0.54877	0.13060	1.07005	1.07799	Class
crew	0.52193	-0.73694	-0.48273	0.88097	Class
Female	0.67338	1.57479	0.00893	1.57482	Sex
Male	0.67338	-0.42759	-0.00242	0.42759	Sex
Died	0.61980	-0.50948	0.19024	0.54384	Survive
Survived	0.61980	1.06768	-0.39867	1.13968	Survive

The printed output, shown partially in Output 5.8–5.9, suggests that two dimensions accounts for 50% of the total association ($\chi^2(81) = 15533.4$), representing all pairwise interactions among the four factors. As noted earlier, this assessment is highly pessimistic because of the artificial dimensions induced in the MCA solution by the diagonal blocks of the Burt matrix. The suggestion (Greenacre, 1984, p. 145) that we only consider dimensions whose principal inertias exceed $1/Q = 0.25$ suggests that two dimensions are sufficient here.

Figure 5.11 shows the two-dimensional solution. The points for each factor have the property that the sum of coordinates on each dimension, weighted inversely by the marginal proportions, equals zero, so that high frequency categories (e.g., Adult) are close to the origin. The first dimension is perfectly aligned with the Gender factor, and also strongly aligned with Survival. The second dimension pertains mainly to Class and Age effects. If you consider those points that differ the most from the origin, and with similar distance and direction from the origin to the point for Survived, you could conclude that survival was associated with being female or upper class or (to a lesser degree) being a child.

Figure 5.11   *Titanic* data: MCA analysis

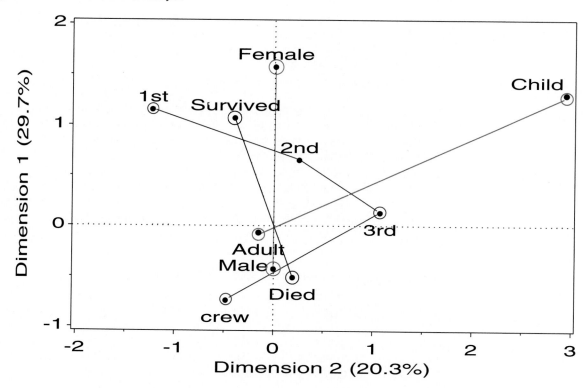

```
data coords;
   set coords;
   where (_type_) = 'VAR';
   keep _name_ factor dim1-dim2 quality dist;
   dist = sqrt(dim1**2 + dim2**2);
   select;
      when (_name_ in ('Adult', 'Child'))    factor = 'Age    ';
      when (_name_ in ('Female', 'Male'))    factor = 'Sex    ';
      when (_name_ in ('Died', 'Survived'))  factor = 'Survive';
      otherwise                              factor = 'Class';
      end;

proc sort;
   by factor;
proc print;
   id _name_;
%label(data=coords, x=dim2, y=dim1, text=_name_,
   pos=-, out=labels);

data labels;
   set labels;
   if text='Male' then do;
      x = x-.3;
      y = y+.2;
      end;
```

```
*-- join pairs of points representing the same variable;
data join;
   set coords;
   by factor;
   length function $8;
   xsys='2'; ysys='2';
   colors='green blue magenta red ';
   if first.factor then g+1;
   color = trim(scan(colors,g));
   x = dim2; y = dim1;
   if first.factor
      then function='move';
      else function='draw';
   output;
   *-- circle proportional to quality;
   size = .5 + 3*quality;
   text = 'circle';
   function = 'symbol';
   output;

data labels;              /* Concatenate the annotate data sets */
   set labels join;

title lspace=3.2in 'Survival on the Titanic';
proc gplot data=coords;
   plot dim1 * dim2
      / frame href=0 vref=0 lvref=34 lhref=34
      vaxis=axis1 haxis=axis2 hm=1 vm=1
      anno=labels;
   symbol1 v=dot h=1;
   axis1 length=4.6in order=(-1 to 2) label=(a=90) ;
   axis2 length=7.65in order=(-2 to 3)  offset=(,.35in);
   label dim1 = 'Dimension 1 (29.7%)'
         dim2 = 'Dimension 2 (20.3%)';
   run;
```

The mosaic matrix in Figure 5.12 may be compared with the results of an MCA analysis of the *Titanic* data. The mosaics in the last row and column show the associations of Class, Age, and Gender with Survival.   □

Figure 5.12   Mosaic matrix of *Titanic* data. Each panel shows the marginal relation, fitting an independence model between the row and column variable, collapsed over other variables.

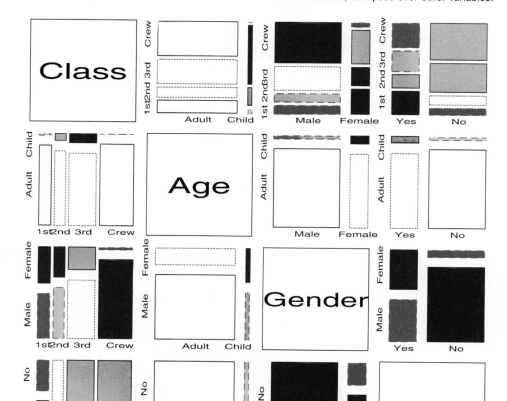

EXAMPLE 5.8   Marital status and pre- and extramarital sex

The data on the relation between marital status and reported premarital and extramarital sex was explored earlier using mosaic displays in Example 4.4 and Example 4.7.

The $2 \times 2 \times 2 \times 2$ table in frequency form can be analyzed as shown below, where the classification variables are GENDER, PRE, EXTRA, and MARITAL.

```
data marital;
   input gender $ pre $ extra $ @;
    pre = 'Pre:' || pre;
    extra = 'X:' || extra;
   marital='Divorced';  input freq @;  output;
    marital='Married';   input freq @;  output;
datalines;
Women  Yes  Yes   17    4
Women  Yes  No    54   25
Women  No   Yes   36    4
Women  No   No   214  322
Men    Yes  Yes   28   11
Men    Yes  No    60   42
Men    No   Yes   17    4
Men    No   No    68  130
;
```

```
proc corresp data=marital mca outc=coords;
    weight freq;
    tables gender pre extra marital;
run;
```

The same analysis, with the addition of the 2-D plot of category scores, would be produced by the CORRESP macro,

```
%corresp(data=marital, tables=gender pre extra marital, weight=freq,
    options=mca short, interp=vec, inc=1, pos=-, symbols=dot);
```

Output 5.10   Chi-Square decomposition for marital status MCA

```
                     Inertia and Chi-Square Decomposition

   Singular  Principal Chi-
   Values    Inertias  Squares Percents    8    16    24    32    40
                                        ----+----+----+----+----+---
    0.62226   0.38721  1796.45  38.72% ************************
    0.50915   0.25923  1202.70  25.92% ****************
    0.43375   0.18814   872.86  18.81% ***********
    0.40672   0.16542   767.47  16.54% *********
              -------   -------
              1.00000  4639.48 (Degrees of Freedom = 49)
```

An enhanced version[10] of this plot is shown in Figure 5.13. The principal inertias, listed in Output 5.10, again suggest that two dimensions are sufficient for this dataset. The positions of the category points on Dimension 1 suggest that women are less likely to have had premarital and extramarital sex and that still being married is associated with the absence of pre- and extramarital sex.

Although two dimensions are probably sufficient for interpreting this data, three-dimensional plots can also be used. When you specify the parameter DIM=3, the CORRESP macro produces a coordinates dataset and an Annotate dataset with three dimensions.[11] It also produces a labeled PROC G3D scatter plot. However, the G3D procedure does not allow axes to be equated, and it is usually necessary to experiment with the ROTATE and TILT options to produce a reasonable display. Therefore, the plot generated by the macro should be considered simply a first approximation.

A three-dimensional MCA solution for the Marital-status data is produced with this statement:

```
%corresp(data=marital, tables=gender pre extra marital, weight=freq, dim=3,
    plotreq=dim1 * dim2 = dim3,
    options=mca short, interp=vec, symbols=dot,
    out=coord, anno=label);
```

---

[10] The size of the bubble symbol surrounding each point is proportional to the quality of the representation in two dimensions.

[11] The first two dimensions are identical to the 2-D solution because of the nested nature of CA and MCA solutions.

Figure 5.13   2-D multiple correspondence analysis display for Marital-status data

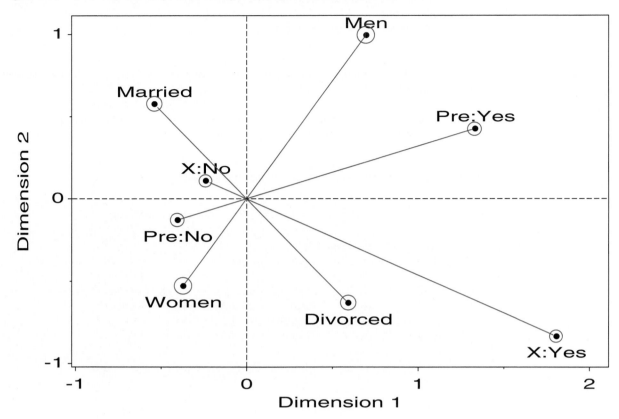

To roughly equate the axes, the initial plot (not shown) was modified by extending the plotting range for all dimensions as shown next. Some additional annotation steps are required (not shown) to produce Figure 5.14. Note that the projections of the points on the Dim1–Dim2 plane is identical to the solution shown in Figure 5.13.

```
data xtra;                  /* Add dummy points to extend X, Y range */
   input dim1-dim3 shapevar $;
datalines;
 2   1  -.6  POINT
-1  -1  -.6  POINT
data coord;
   Set coord xtra;

goptions vsize=6in hsize=8in;
proc g3d data=coord;
   scatter dim1 * dim2 = dim3
     / shape='point' color='green'
       zmin=-0.6 tilt=80 rotate=75 caxis=gray60
       xticknum=2 yticknum=2 zticknum=2 grid
       annotate=label;
```

Figure 5.14   3-D MCA display for marital status data

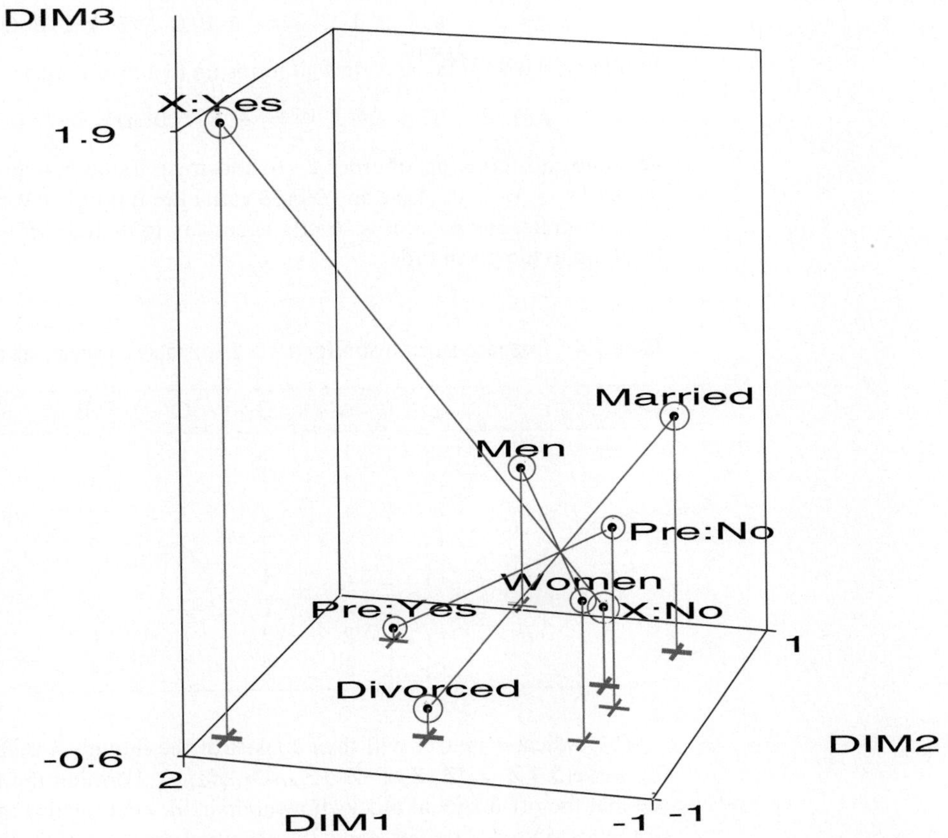

5.6   Extended MCA: Showing Interactions in 2^Q Tables

Earlier in this chapter MCA was explained as a way to depict the relationships among the categories of multiple categorical variables, and the derivation of the method based on the Burt matrix implies that only the relations in the bivariate marginal tables are represented in the displays. This is based on the assumption (Gifi, 1990, Greenacre, 1988) that, as with multivariate normal data, the structural relations among variables are adequately captured by bivariate associations.[12] These developments, and usual practice, have led to the mistaken beliefs that, (a) MCA can *only* represent bivariate (first-order) interactions, (b) MCA can *only* portray the category points of the variables (not their combinations), and (c) associations must be inferred from the relative positions of the category points.

A recent paper by Meulman and Heiser (1997) demonstrates, however, that none of these are necessary consequences of MCA itself. Moreover, for the case of binary variables (a 2^Q table), an odds interpretation of distances between category points leads to simple geometrical patterns in MCA plots.

Their method for including higher-order effects involves adding all cross-terms, up to a given order, to the set of variables in frequency form, which are analyzed by MCA. For

---

[12]Another concern is that higher-way contingency tables may become sparse, resulting in instability in solutions (van der Heijden, 1987).

example, three variables, *A*, *B*, and *C*, generate all interaction terms (using the | syntax of PROC GLM or PROC CATMOD),

$$A \mid B \mid C \iff A\ B\ C\ A*B\ A*C\ B*C\ A*B*C$$

Similarly, the @ syntax specifies all terms up to a given order; for example,

$$A \mid B \mid C \mid D@2 \iff A\ B\ C\ D\ A*B\ A*C\ A*D\ B*C\ B*D\ C*D$$

generates all terms up to order 2. To illustrate, Table 5.4 shows all terms for the 3-way model (A | B | C). Like any CLASS variables, it is only necessary for the variable values to be discrete. However, it is strictly necessary to include *all* terms at the same interaction level, up to the given order.

Table 5.4   Extended factor matrix for a $2 \times 2 \times 2$ table, including all possible cross-classifications

			A	B	C	AB	AC	BC	ABC
a_1	b_1	c_1	1	1	1	1	1	1	1
		c_2	1	1	2	1	2	2	2
	b_2	c_1	1	2	1	2	1	3	3
		c_2	1	2	2	2	2	4	4
a_2	b_1	c_1	2	1	1	3	3	1	5
		c_2	2	1	2	3	4	2	6
	b_2	c_1	2	2	1	4	3	3	7
		c_2	2	2	2	4	4	4	8

The indicator matrix will then consist of the dummy variables for these terms so that for Table 5.4 $\boldsymbol{Z} = [\boldsymbol{Z}_A \boldsymbol{Z}_B \boldsymbol{Z}_C \boldsymbol{Z}_{AB} \boldsymbol{Z}_{AC} \boldsymbol{Z}_{BC} \boldsymbol{Z}_{ABC}]$. Forming the Burt matrix, $\boldsymbol{B} = \boldsymbol{Z}^{\mathsf{T}}\boldsymbol{Z}$, we see that the off-diagonal blocks now contain *all* contingency tables, which can be formed from the original variables (up to the specified order), not just the pairwise bivariate tables. The category points for an MCA solution that is based on this extended $\boldsymbol{Z}$ matrix will then contain, in addition to the usual one-way "main effect" points of the variables themselves, sets of interaction points $((ab)_{ij}, (ac)_{ik}$, and so on) for the various combinations of factors included.

What happens to the category points for these interaction terms in the MCA solution? Meulman and Heiser (1997) demonstrate the remarkable results:

- Distance ratios between sets of interaction points correspond to odds ratios in the higher-order table
- The various independence structures discussed earlier in Table 4.2 give rise to simple configurations of points in the category space.

For simplicity, consider a 2×2 table with cell probabilities p_{ij}. Let z_{ij} refer to the profile coordinate points for the $(ab)_{ij}$ combinations, and let $z_{i\bullet}, z_{\bullet j}$ be the coordinate points for the one-way *A* and *B* effects, respectively. Then, the z_{ij} defines a quadrilateral, and the $z_{i\bullet}$ and $z_{\bullet j}$ are the centroids (weighted by p_{ij}) of the corresponding corners, as shown in Figure 5.15. In this figure, the mass, p_{ij} of each cell point is indicated by its size, and the z points are labeled by their subscripts.

The centroid points are related to the interaction points as (weighted) linear combinations:

$$z_{i\bullet} = \frac{p_{i1}}{p_{i+}} z_{i1} + \frac{p_{i2}}{p_{i+}} z_{i2}$$

$$z_{\bullet j} = \frac{p_{1j}}{p_{+j}} z_{1j} + \frac{p_{2j}}{p_{+j}} z_{2j}$$

Figure 5.15 Category points (z_{ij}) and profile points ($z_{i\bullet}$, $z_{\bullet j}$) in extended MCA representation. Under independence, the lines connecting the profile points are parallel to those connecting corresponding category points.

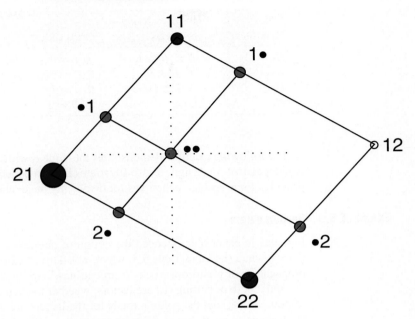

For any edge of the quadrilateral, e.g., z_{i1}, z_{i2}, their centroid is now located on the line between them, so the distances must be additive,

$$d(z_{i1}, z_{i2}) = d(z_{i1}, z_{i\bullet}) + d(z_{i\bullet}, z_{i2})$$

From these relations, Meulman and Heiser (1997) show that:

- Given $A = i$ (or $B = j$), the odds of being in category 1 vs. category 2 of B (or A) are shown in the display by the inverse ratio of their distances to their centroid. For example,

$$\frac{p_{i1}}{p_{i2}} = \frac{d(z_{i2}, z_{i\bullet})}{d(z_{i1}, z_{i\bullet})}$$

- The odds ratio θ has a simple multiplicative relation to these distances among the four corner points and their centroids.

$$\theta = \frac{p_{11}p_{22}}{p_{12}p_{21}} = \frac{d(z_{12}, z_{\bullet2})\, d(z_{21}, z_{\bullet1})}{d(z_{11}, z_{\bullet1})\, d(z_{22}, z_{\bullet2})} \tag{5.8}$$

- Under independence, $\theta = 1$, and Equation 5.8 implies that (a) the corner points form a parallelogram, and (b) the lines connecting the centroids of the same variable (e.g., ($z_{\bullet1}, z_{\bullet2}$)) are parallel to those of their respective category points. These relations of parallelism and additivity are shown in Figure 5.15.

Although this discussion was presented in terms of a 2×2 table, the geometrical relations extend directly to *any* number of binary variables. For a $2 \times 2 \times 2$ table, the models of various types of independence shown in Table 4.2 can all be characterized in terms of the three odds ratios for all pairs of variables and, therefore, in terms of parallelism and additivity of the corresponding pairwise quadrilaterals in the spatial representation. Essentially, each independence relation corresponds to one odds ratio $\theta = 1$, which in turn is shown as one 2-way term whose profile points form a parallelogram, as shown in the following table:

Hypothesis	Independence relations	Odds ratios	Number of parallel 2-way profile sets
H_1	$A \perp B \perp C$	$\theta_{AB} = \theta_{AC} = \theta_{BC} = 1$	3
H_2	$A, B \perp C$	$\theta_{AC} = \theta_{BC} = 1$	2
H_3	$A \perp B \mid C$	$\theta_{AB} = 1$	1
H_4	none	all $\theta \neq 1$	0

The following example demonstrates these ideas with a 2^3 table, where one 2-way term is independent by design. It also illustrates how to generate the interaction variables, and provides some special techniques for displaying the extended MCA solution.

EXAMPLE 5.9   Bartlett's data

In a classic paper that extended the notion of interaction to 3-way tables, Bartlett (1935) gave the data shown in Table 5.5, which was derived from an experiment investigating the propagation of plum root stocks from cuttings.[13] In the $2 \times 2 \times 2$ table, time of planting (T) and length of cutting (L) are factors; whether the cutting was alive or dead (A) was the response. Note that the column totals for the factors are all equal, these having been fixed by the experimental design. Thus, there can be no $T \times L$ marginal association, and interest naturally is focused on the [AT] and [AL] associations. Does time or length affect survival?

Table 5.5   Bartlett's data on propagation of plum root stocks

Alive?	Time of planting				Total
	Now		Spring		
	Length of cutting				
	Long	Short	Long	Short	Total
Alive	156	107	84	31	378
Dead	84	133	156	209	582
Total	240	240	240	240	960

The marginal relations are easily seen in a mosaic matrix, shown in Figure 5.16. Time and Length are independent, but there is a strong [AT] association, with planting now more likely to be successful, and a weaker [AL] association, so that long cuttings are more likely to survive.

---

[13] Reprinted by permission from *Journal of the Royal Statistical Society, Supplement, Series B.* Copyright © 1935 by the Royal Statistical Society.

Figure 5.16   Mosaic matrix for marginal associations in Bartlett's data

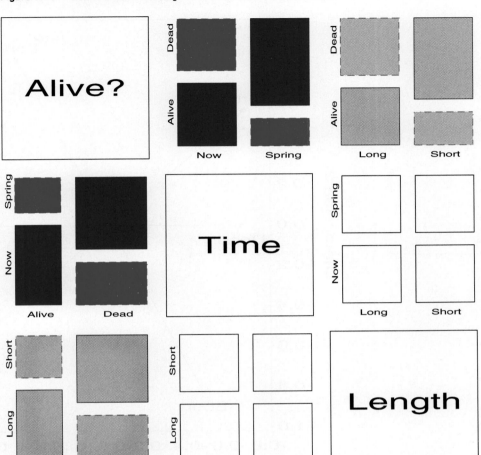

The standard MCA analysis is carried out with the statements below. In the call to the CORRESP macro, the INTERP=VEC parameter draws vectors from the origin to each main category point. The macro produces the graph of the 2D solution shown in Figure 5.17; the principal inertias are shown in Output 5.11.

```
data bartlett;
   do alive='Alive', 'Dead';
      do time='Now   ', 'Spring';
         do Length = 'Long ', 'Short';
            input count @;
            output;
            end;
         end;
      end;
datalines;
 156 107  84  31
  84 133 156 209
;
*-- Ordinary MCA of the three variables;
%corresp(data=bartlett, tables=Alive Time Length, weight=count,
   options=mca short, interp=vec, inc=0.2, pos=-,
   symbols=dot, colors=black, m0=0);
```

Figure 5.17   2-D MCA solution for Bartlett's data

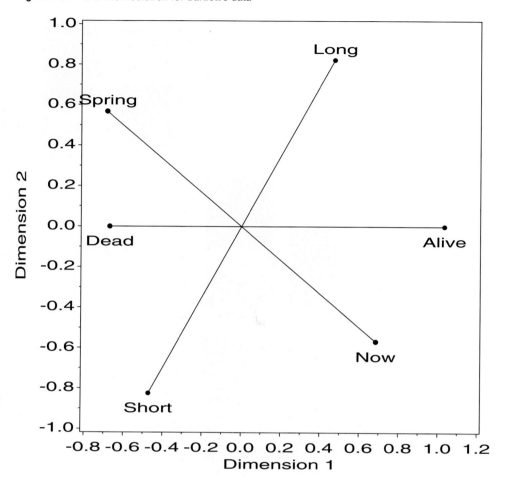

Output 5.11   Chi-Square decomposition for Bartlett's data, MCA

```
                    Inertia and Chi-Square Decomposition

    Singular  Principal  Chi-
    Values    Inertias   Squares Percents    9    18    27    36    45
                                          ----+----+----+----+----+---
    0.67902   0.46107    1457.90  46.11%  *************************
    0.57735   0.33333    1053.99  33.33%  ******************
    0.45342   0.20559     650.08  20.56%  **********

              -------    -------
              1.00000    3161.97  (Degrees of Freedom = 25)
```

The interpretation of Figure 5.17 is quite simple. Dimension 1 is perfectly aligned with the Alive response variable. The associations [AT] and [AL] of Time and Length are shown by their projections (coordinates) on this axis. Time has a stronger association, so its projection on this axis is larger, and planting long cuttings now leads to increased survival. The independence of Time and Length is shown by the nearly right angle between their vectors.[14] Because the second principal inertia in Output 5.11 equals $1/Q = 1/3$ it is not necessary to interpret the second dimension. Note also how the odds are shown by distance ratios in the plot. Both Time and Length have equal marginal frequencies for their two levels (odds = 1), and the ratio of distances to the origin for the levels of both variables equals 1.0. The ratio of distances to the origin for Alive and Dead is inversely related to their marginal frequencies.

The statements shown next illustrate one way to construct the interaction variables representing the first-order associations [AT], [AL], and [TL] and the second-order interaction, [ATL]. Each of the character variables ALIVE, TIME, and LENGTH is used to create a dummy (0/1) variable (A, T, and L, respectively). The interaction terms are then created with binary arithmetic in the DATA step COMBO. A PROC FORMAT step is used to create short character labels for the combinations, to be used in the plots that follow. These labels use an upper-case letter to refer to the first level of each main variable, and a lowercase letter to refer to the second level.

The dataset COMBO that results is shown in Output 5.12. Note that the variables A--ATL are actually numeric, but are printed using their formatted values.[15]

Output 5.12   Dataset COMBO: interactive coding for Bartlett's data, Extended MCA

LENGTH	TIME	ALIVE	COUNT	A	T	L	AT	AL	TL	ATL
Long	Now	Alive	156	A	T	L	AT	AL	TL	ATL
Long	Now	Dead	84	a	T	L	aT	aL	TL	aTL
Long	Spring	Alive	84	A	t	L	At	AL	tL	AtL
Long	Spring	Dead	156	a	t	L	at	aL	tL	atL
Short	Now	Alive	107	A	T	l	AT	Al	Tl	ATl
Short	Now	Dead	133	a	T	l	aT	al	Tl	aTl
Short	Spring	Alive	31	A	t	l	At	Al	tl	Atl
Short	Spring	Dead	209	a	t	l	at	al	tl	atl

```
*-- Formats for higher-order effects;
proc format;
   value a  0='a' 1='A';
   value t  0='t' 1='T';
   value l  0='l' 1='L';

   value at 0='at' 1='aT' 2='At' 3='AT';
   value al 0='al' 1='aL' 2='Al' 3='AL';
   value tl 0='tl' 1='tL' 2='Tl' 3='TL';
   value atl 0='atl' 1='atL' 2='aTl' 3='aTL' 4='Atl' 5='AtL' 6='ATl' 7='ATL';

*-- Code combinations of variables;
data combo;
   set bartlett;

   a = (alive='Alive');
   t = (time='Now');
   l = (length='Long');
```

---

[14]In an equated 3-D representation, they *are* orthogonal.

[15]Because the interaction variables need only be discrete, they could be created more easily, simply by concatenating the main variables, (e.g., AT = ALIVE || TIME;, and so forth). This would produce cluttered displays, however, because each combination is plotted and labeled.

```
at = 2*a + t;
al = 2*a + 1;
tl = 2*t + 1;

atl = 4*a + 2*t + 1;
format a a. t t. l l.  at at.  al al.  tl tl.  atl atl.;
proc print noobs;
```

Applying MCA to this dataset using the main effect variables A T L would produce results identical to Figure 5.17. Adding the three 2-way variables, AT AL TL will add 3×4 category points for the pairwise combinations of these factors. The 3-way variable, ATL, adds an additional 8 category points, representing the individual cells in the table.

The analysis shown below excludes the 3-way ATL terms for simplicity. As long as the terms are added in a balanced way (including all terms of a given order), the positions of points tend to be very similar, whether or not terms of higher-order are included.

```
proc corresp data=combo  mca outc=coords short;
   weight count;
   tables a t l at al tl;* atl;

*-- Identify the size and name of each effect;
data coords;
   set coords;
   where (_type_) = 'VAR';
   drop _type_ inertia contr1--best;
   terms=length(_name_);
   effect = upcase(_name_);
   label dim1 = 'Dimension 1'
         dim2 = 'Dimension 2';
proc sort;
   by terms effect _name_;
proc print;
   id _name_ effect terms;
   var dim1 dim2 mass;
```

Figure 5.18   2-D interaction display for Bartlett's data. Both panels show the same 2-D solution for the MCA analysis, including pairwise interaction effects. In the left panel, points corresponding to the TL association are connected; lines joining the 1-way points are parallel to the sides, showing independence. In the right panel, points for both the AT and AL associations are connected.

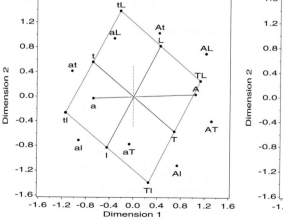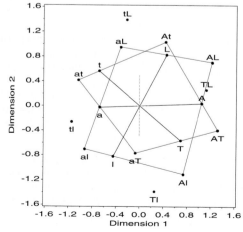

The output dataset COORDS is used to produce the plots shown in Figure 5.18. In order to draw the vectors for the main effect points, and to draw the quadrilaterals for the 2-way terms as in Figure 5.15, variables TERMS and EFFECT are added to the COORDS dataset as shown above.

The following steps construct an Annotate dataset to draw a quadrilateral for each of the AT, AL and TL effects. To do this, it is necessary to extract the DIM1 and DIM2 of the four points for each effect and transpose these to a single observation with variables X1–X4 and Y1–Y4 respectively. The dataset QUADS created here is shown in Output 5.13.

```
*-- Extract x,y coordinates of two-way effects;
proc transpose data=coords(drop=_name_) out=quadx prefix=x;
   where (terms=2);
   var dim1;
   by effect;
proc transpose data=coords(drop=_name_) out=quady prefix=y;
   where (terms=2);
   var dim2;
   by effect;
data quads;
   merge quadx quady;
   drop _name_ _label_;
proc print data=quads;
   format _numeric_ 5.2;
   var x1 y1 x2 y2 x3 y3 x4 y4;
   id effect;

*-- Draw quadrilaterals, connecting points in order 1, 2, 4, 3;
data quads;
   set quads;
   drop x1-x4 y1-y4 i;
   retain xsys ysys '2';
   array xx{*} x1 x2 x4 x3;;
   array yy{*} y1 y2 y4 y3;
   color = scan('blue red green', _n_);
   do i=1 to 4;
      x = xx[i];   y=yy[i];
      if i=1 then function='poly    ';
             else function='polycont';
      output;
      end;
```

Output 5.13   Dataset QUADS, containing the coordinates of the quadrilateral for each 2-way effect

EFFECT	X1	Y1	X2	Y2	X3	Y3	X4	Y4
AL	1.22	0.70	0.74	-1.11	-0.32	0.95	-0.93	-0.71
AT	1.31	-0.40	0.43	1.03	-0.07	-0.77	-1.04	0.42
TL	1.12	0.26	0.25	-1.39	-0.23	1.39	-1.15	-0.26

The following steps complete the custom programming to display the TL effect, with point labels and vectors for the main effects, in the left panel of Figure 5.18.

```
%label(data=coords, out=label, x=dim1, y=dim2, text=_name_, pos=-);

data lines;
   set coords end=eof;
   by terms effect notsorted;
   drop dim1 dim2 quality mass;
   x = dim1;
   y = dim2;
   xsys = '2'; ysys='2';

   if terms = 1  then do;
   color = 'black';
   if mod(_n_,2) = 1
      then do; function='MOVE    '; output; end;
      else do; function='DRAW    '; output; end;
   end;

   if eof then do;
      color='gray'; line=3;
      x=-.5;  y=0;   function='MOVE';  output;
      x=+.5;  y=0;   function='DRAW';  output;
      x= 0 ;  y=-.5; function='MOVE';  output;
      x= 0 ;  y=+.5; function='DRAW';  output;
      end;
run;

*-- Show the Time X Length effect;
data anotes;
   set label lines quads(where=(effect in ('TL')));

proc gplot data=coords;
   plot dim2 * dim1
      / frame vaxis=axis1 haxis=axis2 hm=1 vm=1
      anno=anotes;
   symbol1 v=dot h=1;
   axis1  length=6in order=(-1.6 to 1.6 by .4) label=(a=90);
   axis2  length=6in order=(-1.6 to 1.6 by .4);
run;
```

The right panel of Figure 5.18 is produced using the same PROC GPLOT step, but the Annotate dataset ANOTES is assembled using just the lines to connect the AT and AL points:

```
*-- Show effects on Alive;
data anotes;
   set label lines quads(where=(effect in ('AL' 'AT')));
proc gplot data=coords;
   ...
```

Thus, we see that the independence of Time and Length (by design of the data collection) is characterized by a parallelogram shape for the 2-way points, and by lines joining the A and T 1-way points being parallel to those connecting the 2-way points. Note also that the 1-way points are in essentially the same positions as in Figure 5.17. The quadrilaterals for the AT and AL effects shown in the right panel are not quite parallelograms, however; we could approximate the odds ratio for each of these effects from the cross-product of distances as in Equation 5.8. Finally, because one of the three quadrilaterals shows parallelism, we conclude from Figure 5.18 that the conditional independence model, [AT][AL], holds.

An alternative representation enables us to show the cells instead, corresponding to the ATL terms that were not displayed in Figure 5.18. We form the indicator matrix for the main effects, $Z = [Z_A Z_T Z_L]$, and multiply by a diagonal matrix of the cell frequencies, to give the following:

ID	ALIVE	TIME	LENGTH	COUNT	A1	A2	T1	T2	L1	L2
ATL	Alive	Now	Long	156	156	0	156	0	156	0
aTL	Dead	Now	Long	84	0	84	84	0	84	0
AtL	Alive	Spring	Long	84	84	0	0	84	84	0
atL	Dead	Spring	Long	156	0	156	0	156	156	0
ATl	Alive	Now	Short	107	107	0	107	0	0	107
aTl	Dead	Now	Short	133	0	133	133	0	0	133
Atl	Alive	Spring	Short	31	31	0	0	31	0	31
atl	Dead	Spring	Short	209	0	209	0	209	0	209

Then, a simple correspondence analysis of the variables A1--L2 will have row points corresponding to the cells, and columns for the main effects, which are nearly identical to those from the extended MCA. This analysis produces Figure 5.19 (program steps are not shown to conserve space), where the size of the circle at each point represents the mass (p_{ijk}) of each cell, whose label is the ID variable above. The 2-way points can be added to this representation by including the 2-way indicator matrices, so the matrix diag is analyzed as $(n)[Z_A Z_T Z_L Z_{AT} Z_{AL} Z_{TL}]$. □

Figure 5.19   2-D representation of the cell points in the $2 \times 2 \times 2$ design. The mass (cell proportion) of each point is shown by the size of the circle.

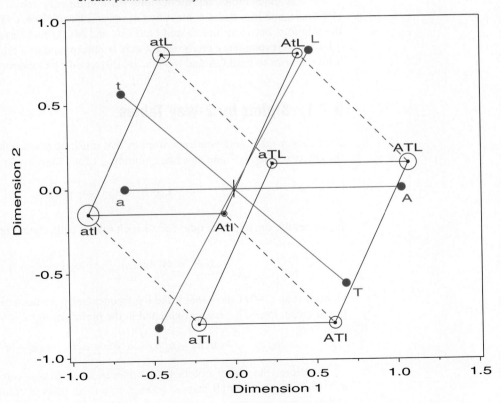

5.7   Biplots for Contingency Tables

Like correspondence analysis, the biplot (Bradu and Gabriel, 1978, Gabriel, 1971, 1980, 1981) is a visualization method that uses the SVD to display a matrix in a low-dimensional (usually two-dimensional) space. They differ in the relationships in the data that is portrayed, however. In correspondence analysis, the *distances* between row points and the *distances* between column points are designed to reflect *differences* between the row profiles and column profiles. In the biplot, on the other hand, row and column points are represented by vectors from the origin, such that the projection (inner product) of the vector $\boldsymbol{a}_i$ for row i on $\boldsymbol{b}_j$ for column j approximates the data element y_{ij},

$$\boldsymbol{Y} \approx \boldsymbol{A}\boldsymbol{B}^\mathsf{T} \iff y_{ij} \approx \boldsymbol{a}_i^\mathsf{T}\boldsymbol{b}_j \ . \tag{5.9}$$

Geometrically, Equation 5.9 may be described as approximating the data value y_{ij} by the projection of the end point of vector $\boldsymbol{a}_i$ on $\boldsymbol{b}_j$ (and vice-versa).

For quantitative data, Bradu and Gabriel (1978) show how the biplot can be used to diagnose additive relations among rows and columns. For example, when a 2-way table is well described by a two-factor ANOVA model with no interaction,

$$y_{ij} = \mu + \alpha_i + \beta_j + \epsilon_{ij}$$

then, the row points, $\boldsymbol{a}_i$, and the column points, $\boldsymbol{b}_j$, will fall on two straight lines at right angles to each other in the biplot. For a contingency table, the multiplicative relations among frequencies under independence become additive relations in terms of log frequency, and Gabriel et al. (1997) illustrate how biplots of log frequency can be used to explore associations in 2-way and 3-way tables.

Several other biplot representations for contingency tables are described by Gabriel (1995a,b), and in a wider context by Gower and Hand (1996). Greenacre (1993) discusses the relations between biplots and both CA and MCA, and shows some conditions under which a correspondence analysis plot may be interpreted as a biplot. More general models, with relations to both CA and biplots, are discussed by Goodman (1986, 1991).

5.7.1   Biplots for 2-Way Tables

For a 2-way table, independence implies that ratios of frequencies should be proportional for any two rows, i, i' and any two columns, j, j'.

$$A \perp B \iff \frac{n_{ij}}{n_{i'j}} = \frac{n_{ij'}}{n_{i'j'}}$$

Equivalently, the log odds ratio for all such sets of cells should be zero:

$$A \perp B \iff \log\theta_{ii',jj'} = \log\left(\frac{n_{ij}n_{i'j'}}{n_{i'j}n_{ij'}}\right) = 0$$

Gabriel et al. (1997) show that if the log frequencies have been centered by subtracting the grand mean, $\log\theta_{ii',jj'}$ is approximated in the biplot (of $\log(n_{ij}) - \overline{\log(n_{ij})}$)

$$\log\theta_{ii',jj'} \approx \boldsymbol{a}_i^\mathsf{T}\boldsymbol{b}_j - \boldsymbol{a}_{i'}^\mathsf{T}\boldsymbol{b}_j - \boldsymbol{a}_i^\mathsf{T}\boldsymbol{b}_{j'} + \boldsymbol{a}_{i'}^\mathsf{T}\boldsymbol{b}_{j'} = (\boldsymbol{a}_i - \boldsymbol{a}_{i'})^\mathsf{T}(\boldsymbol{b}_j - \boldsymbol{b}_{j'}).$$

Therefore, the biplot criterion for independence in a 2-way table is whether $(\boldsymbol{a}_i - \boldsymbol{a}_{i'})^\mathsf{T}(\boldsymbol{b}_j - \boldsymbol{b}_{j'}) \approx 0$ for all pairs of rows, i, i', and all pairs of columns, j, j'. But $(\boldsymbol{a}_i - \boldsymbol{a}_{i'})$ is the vector connecting $\boldsymbol{a}_i$ to $\boldsymbol{a}_{i'}$ and $(\boldsymbol{b}_j - \boldsymbol{b}_{j'})$ is the vector connecting $\boldsymbol{b}_j$ to $\boldsymbol{b}_{j'}$, as shown in Figure 5.20, and the inner product of any two vectors equals zero *if* they are orthogonal.

Figure 5.20   Independence implies orthogonal vector differences in a biplot of log frequency. The line joining a_1 to a_2 represents $(a_1 - a_2)$. This line is perpendicular to the line $(b_1 - b_2)$ under independence.

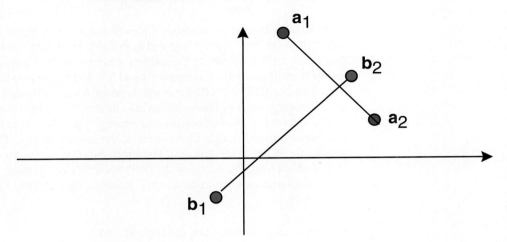

Hence, this criterion implies that all lines connecting pairs of row points are orthogonal to lines connecting pairs of column points, as illustrated in the figure.

Thus, when the entire table exhibits independence, the row points and column points will lie close to two perpendicular lines. Moreover, a two-dimensional biplot will account for nearly all of the variance of the centered log frequencies. When only a subset of the rows and/or columns are independent, the points corresponding to those rows and columns will still lie in orthogonal subspaces, which will be lines or planes depending on whether a 2D or 3D biplot provides an adequate fit. An advantage of this method is that it provides a visual indication of the subsets of rows and columns for which independence does and does not hold.

EXAMPLE 5.10   UK soccer scores

We examined the data on UK soccer scores in Example 4.2 and saw that the number of goals scored by the home and away teams were largely independent (cf. Figure 4.5). This dataset provides a good test of the ability of the biplot to diagnose independence.

The biplot analysis is carried out with an enhanced version of the BIPLOT macro presented in *SAS System for Statistical Graphics, First Edition*, Section 8.7, A1.2. The enhanced version, described in Appendix A.3, provides automatic equating of the axes and labeled plots with a variety of interpolation options.

The statements below read the dataset SOCCER and call the BIPLOT macro. The POWER=0 parameter specifies a $\log_{10}$ transformation of the frequencies contained in the input variables A0–A4. By default, the BIPLOT macro always standardizes the data (after transformation, if any) by removing the grand mean, so the STD=NONE parameter indicates no further standardization is required.

```
title 'UK Soccer scores: Biplot';
data soccer;
    input home $ a0-a4;
datalines;
H0    27 29 10  8  2
H1    59 53 14 12  4
H2    28 32 14 12  4
H3    19 14  7  4  1
H4     7  8 10  2  0
;
```

```
%biplot(data=soccer, var=_num_, id=home,
   std=none, power=0,
   out=biplot, anno=bianno,
   symbols=circle dot, interp=none);
```

By default, the macro produces a plot of the first two biplot dimensions. As with the
CORRESP macro, the axes are equated in this plot by default (when the HAXIS and VAXIS
parameters are not specified). Sometimes, you may wish to inspect an initial plot and then
rescale it, as illustrated in Examples 5.1 and 5.2. The macro also produces an output dataset
of coordinates (OUT=BIPLOT parameter) and an Annotate dataset (ANNO=BIANNO parameter) containing category labels, which may be used for further customization.

The default plot showed that all of the category points, except for A2 and H2, fell along
separate orthogonal straight lines parallel to the coordinate axes. The two biplot dimensions
account for 99.8% of the variance. The statements that follow are used to find the locations
of these lines from the means of the DIM1 and DIM2 coordinates, and to append Annotate
instructions to draw them to the BIANNO Annotate dataset. The PROC GPLOT step produces
Figure 5.21.

```
*-- Find mean coordinates (except A2, H2);
proc means data=biplot noprint;
   where (_name_ not in ('A2', 'H2'));
   var dim1 dim2;
   by _type_;
   output out=means mean=;

*-- Draw lines passing thru the means, parallel to axes;
data lines;
   set means;
   xsys='2'; ysys='2';
   length function color $8;
   if _type_ = 'OBS' then do;
      x = dim1; color='blue';
      y = -1.5; function='move';   output;
      y = +1.0; function='draw';   output;
      end;
   else do;
      y = dim2; color='red';
      x = -1.8; function='move';   output;
      x = +1.5; function='draw';   output;
      end;

*-- Append to annotate data set;
data bianno;
   set bianno lines;

title;
proc gplot data=biplot;
   plot dim2 * dim1 = _type_ /
         anno=bianno frame nolegend
         href=0 vref=0 lvref=34 lhref=34
         vaxis=axis1 haxis=axis2
         vminor=1 hminor=1
         name="soccer3" des="Biplot of log(freq)";
      axis1 order=(-2 to 1) length=4.5in label=(a=90) ;
      axis2 order=(-2 to 2) length=6in;
      symbol1 v=circle c=blue i=none;
      symbol2 v=dot    c=red  i=none;
   run;
```

Figure 5.21   Biplot of UK Soccer scores. Independence is shown when the row and column points lie on orthogonal lines.

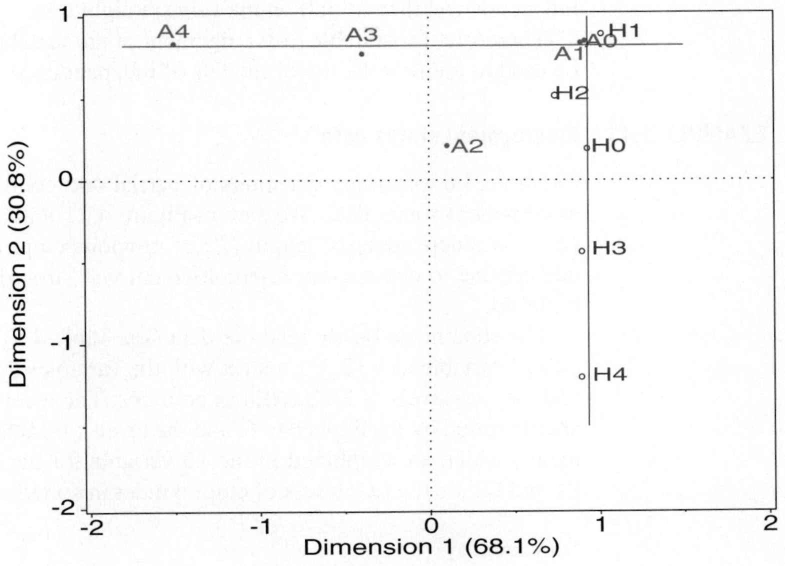

We see that all the A points (except for A2) and all the H points (except for H2) lie along straight lines, and these lines are indeed at right angles, signifying independence. The fact that these straight lines are parallel to the coordinate axes is incidental, and unrelated to the independence interpretation.   □

5.7.2   Biplots for 3-Way Tables

Biplot displays for 3-way tables may be constructed by means of the "stacking" approach that is used in correspondence analysis, described in Section 5.4. That is, a 3-way table, $I \times J \times K$, can be represented (in several ways) as a 2-way table, with two variables combined interactively.

As before, consider a 3-way ABC table structured as $IJ \times K$ so that variables A and B define the rows and variable C defines the columns. (Equivalent results obtain for any permutation of the variables.) Then, a biplot will have row points, $\boldsymbol{a}_{ij}$ and column points $\boldsymbol{b}_k$ that approximate

$$\log(n_{[ij]k}) - \overline{\log(n_{[ij]k})} \approx \boldsymbol{a}_{ij}^{\mathsf{T}}\boldsymbol{b}_k$$

According to the arguments presented in Section 5.7.1, when $\{A, B\} \perp C$ (that is, when the model of joint independence, $[AB][C]$ holds), then the $\boldsymbol{a}_{ij}$ row points will fall on one straight line, and the $\boldsymbol{b}_k$ will fall on another line, perpendicular to the first.

Other configurations of points along lines serve as tests for other models of independence. For example, if, for a given level $j^\star$ of variable B, the points $\boldsymbol{a}_{ij^\star}$ are collinear and orthogonal to the line formed by the $\boldsymbol{b}_k$ of variable C, then *partial independence*, $A \perp C \mid B_{j^\star}$ holds for level $j^\star$. If this is true for all levels of variable B, then A is conditionally independent of C, given B, $\{A \perp C\} \mid B$, or the log-linear model $[AB][CB]$. Thus, for conditional (respectively, partial) independence, the $a_{ij\star}$ points fall on *separate* straight lines orthogonal to the b_k for all (respectively, some) levels of variable B, while for joint independence, they all fall on the *same* straight line.

Therefore, for suitable re-arrangement of the variables into a 2-way table, the biplot can be used to identify the major models of independence.

EXAMPLE 5.11   Employment status data

Example 4.6 examined questions of partial and conditional independence in the Danish employment status data. We saw in Figure 4.21 that whether a worker was re-employed (E) was independent of length (L) of previous employment for those workers that were laid off due to closure, but re-employment was strongly associated for workers who were replaced.

The statements below read the data (see Table 4.5) in frequency form and reshape the COUNT variable as a 12×2 matrix with the variables CAUSE and LENGTH defining the rows and the two levels of EMPLOYED as columns. The levels of length of previous employment are identified by the digits 0 to 6, and the levels of CAUSE by 'C' (closure) and 'R' (replacement), which are combined in the ID variable for the matrix rows. The column variables E1 and E2 are the two levels of employment in sorted order, 'No' and 'Yes'.

```
data employ;
   input length $ @;
   do cause ='Close  ', 'Replace';
      do employed = 'Yes', 'No';
         input count @;
         output;
         end;
      end;
   input;
datalines;
   0    8    10     40    24
   1   35    42     85    42
   2   70    86    181    41
   3   62    80     85    16
   4   56    67    118    27
   5   38    35     56    10
;
*-- Reshape as two column matrix ([CL][E]);
proc sort data=employ;
   by cause length employed ;
proc transpose prefix=e out=employ2;
   var count;
   by cause length;
data employ2;
   set employ2;
   drop _name_;
   id = substr(cause,1,1) || length;

axis1 order=(-2 to 1) length=4.875in
   label=(a=90);
axis2 order=(-2 to 2) length=6.5in;
%biplot(data=employ2, id=id, var=e1 e2,
   std=none, power=0,
   out=biplot, anno=bianno, vaxis=axis1, haxis=axis2,
   symbols=plus triangle, interp=none join);
```

Figure 5.22   Biplot for Employment status data

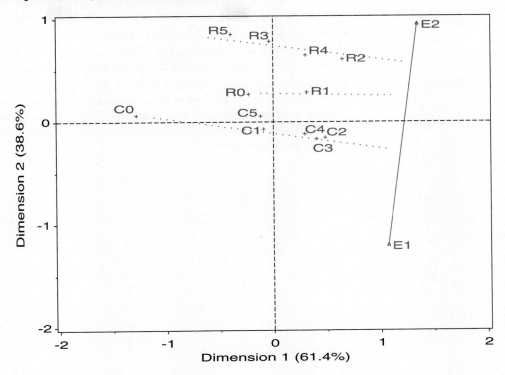

The call to the BIPLOT macro produces Figure 5.22. The line joining E1 and E3 was produced by the INTERP=NONE JOIN parameter. The dotted lines were drawn manually (and therefore approximately) in the Graphics Editor.

We see that the points for closure lie approximately along a line perpendicular to the line for E1-E2, indicating partial independence of employment status and length for the closure workers (points C0-C5). The R points for replaced workers do not all fall on one line, so there is no overall partial independence for these workers; however, for those workers previously employed for three months or more (R2-R5), the points are nearly collinear and orthogonal to E1-E2.   □

5.8   Chapter Summary

- CA is an exploratory technique, designed to show the row and column categories in a 2- (or 3-) dimensional space. These graphical displays, and the various extensions provide ways to interpret the patterns of association and visually explore the adequacy of certain log-linear models.

- The scores assigned to the categories of each variable are optimal in several equivalent ways. Among other properties, they maximize the (canonical) correlations between the quantified variables (weighted by cell frequencies), and make the regressions of each variable on the other variable that is most nearly linear, for each CA dimension.

- Multi-way tables can be analyzed in several ways. In the *stacking* approach, two or more variables are combined interactively in the rows and/or columns of an *n*-way table. Simple CA of the re-structured table reveals associations between the row and column categories but hides associations between the variables that are combined interactively. Each way of stacking corresponds to a specific log-linear model for the full table.

- Multiple correspondence analysis is a generalization of CA to two or more variables based on representing the data as an indicator matrix. The usual MCA provides an analysis of the joint, bivariate relations between all pairs of variables.

- An extended form of MCA provides a means to display higher-order associations among multiple categorical variables. For 2^Q tables composed of Q binary variables, this analysis yields simple geometric relations that may be interpreted in terms of odds ratios.

- The biplot is a related technique for visualizing the elements of a data array by points or vectors in a joint display of their row and column categories. An application of the biplot to contingency table data is described, based on analysis of log frequency. This analysis also serves to diagnose patterns of independence and partial independence in 2-way and larger tables.

6
Logistic Regression

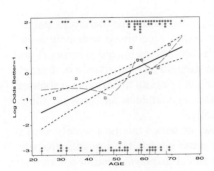 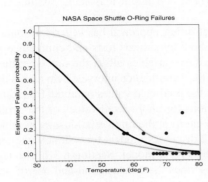 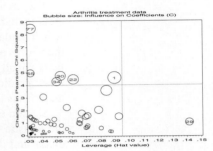

Logistic regression describes the relation between a discrete response, often binary, and a set of explanatory variables. Smoothing techniques are often crucial in visualizations for such discrete data. The fitted model provides both inference and prediction, accompanied by measures of uncertainty. Diagnostic plots help us to detect influential observations that may distort our results.

6.1 Introduction

In scientific thought we adopt the simplest theory which will explain all the facts under consideration and enable us to predict new facts of the same kind. The catch in this criterion lies in the world "simplest."

J. B. S. Haldane, *Possible Worlds*, 1927.

Previous chapters dealt primarily with simple, exploratory methods for studying the relations among categorical variables and with testing hypotheses about their associations through non-parametric tests and with overall goodness-of-fit statistics.

This chapter begins our study of model-based methods for the analysis of discrete data. These models differ from the models examined earlier, primarily in that they consider *explicitly* an assumed probability distribution for the observations, and they make clear distinctions between the systematic component, which is explained by the model, and the random component, which is not. In this chapter, models are considered for a binary response, such as "success" or "failure", or the number of "successes" in a fixed number of "trials", where you might reasonably assume a binomial distribution for the random component.

This model-fitting approach has several advantages. Inferences for the model parameters include both hypothesis tests and confidence intervals. Hypothesis tests help assess which explanatory variables affect the outcome; the size of the estimated parameters and the widths of their confidence intervals help assess the strength and importance of these effects. Finally, the predicted values obtained from the model smooth the discrete responses, allow predictions for unobserved values of the explanatory variables, and provide important means to interpret the fitted relationship, graphically.

Section 6.2 discusses models for a binary response, of which the most widely used is the logistic regression model. Section 6.3 illustrates these models for a quantitative predictor and describes the construction and use of graphical displays. Section 6.4 extends these models to qualitative predictors, and the general, multiple logistic regression model is discussed in Section 6.5. For interpreting and understanding the results of a fitted model, I emphasize plotting predicted probabilities and predicted log odds. Individual observations sometimes exert great influence on a fitted model. Some measures of influence and diagnostic plots are illustrated in Section 6.6. In Section 6.7, I develop several approaches to modeling a multi-category (polytomous) response, and Section 6.8 shows how a classic model for paired comparisons data can be handled by logistic regression. The final section (Section 6.9) illustrates how to calculate and graph statistical power in relation to sample size for two simple cases of logistic regression.

The logistic regression model is also discussed and illustrated using SAS computations in *Logistic Regression Examples Using the SAS System*, Stokes et al. (1995, Chapter 8–9), Allison (1999), and Zelterman (1999, Chapter 3), all of which are useful companions to this book. Agresti (1990), Collett (1991), and Fox (1997) provide a more detailed treatment of the statistical background than I do in this book.

6.2   The Logistic Regression Model

The logistic regression model describes the relationship between a categorical outcome variable, the "response", and a set of explanatory variables. The response variable is often **dichotomous**, although extensions to the model allow multi-category, **polytomous** outcomes, which are discussed in Section 6.7. The explanatory variables may be continuous or (with dummy variables) discrete.

For a binary response, Y, and a continuous explanatory variable, X, you might be interested in modeling the probability of a successful outcome, which is denoted $\pi(x) \equiv \Pr(Y = 1 \mid X = x)$. That is, at a given value $X = x$, you imagine that there is a binomial distribution of the responses, $\mathrm{Bin}(\pi(x), n_x)$.

You might contemplate a simple linear regression model for $\pi(x)$,

$$E(Y) = \pi(x) = \alpha + \beta x \ ,$$

which you could fit by ordinary least squares (PROC REG, for example). However, such a model (called the *linear probability model*), has the serious defect that it yields predicted probabilities $\hat{\pi}(x) < 0$ for sufficiently small x and $\hat{\pi}(x) > 1$ for sufficiently large x (assuming $\beta > 0$).

One way around this difficulty is to re-specify the model so that a transformation of π has a linear relation to x, and that transformation keeps $\hat{\pi}$ between 0 and 1 for all x. A particularly convenient choice gives the linear logistic regression model, which posits a linear relation between the log odds or ***logit*** of this probability and X,

$$\text{logit}[\pi(x)] \equiv \log\left(\frac{\pi(x)}{1-\pi(x)}\right) = \alpha + \beta x \ . \tag{6.1}$$

When $\beta > 0$, $\pi(x)$ and the log odds increase as X increases; when $\beta < 0$, the log odds decrease as X decreases. From Equation 6.1, you see that the odds of a favorable response can be expressed as

$$\text{odds}(Y=1) \equiv \frac{\pi(x)}{1-\pi(x)} = \exp(\alpha+\beta x) = e^\alpha (e^\beta)^x \ , \tag{6.2}$$

a multiplicative model for the odds. So, under the logistic model,

- β is the change in the log odds associated with a unit increase in x. The odds are multiplied by e^β for each unit increase in x.
- α is the log odds at $x = 0$; e^α is the odds of a favorable response at this x-value (which may not have a reasonable interpretation if $X = 0$ is far from the range of the data).

Re-arranging terms in Equation 6.2, the logistic regression model can also be formulated as a direct relationship for the probability of success,

$$\pi(x) = \frac{\exp(\alpha+\beta x)}{1+\exp(\alpha+\beta x)} \ . \tag{6.3}$$

This expression may look complex, but the numerical results are easy to interpret. You will find that it is most convenient for plotting and understanding results from logistic regression to express fitted values on the scale of probabilities.

It might also help to know that, on the scale of probabilities, the slope of the relationship between $\pi(x)$ and x is $\beta\pi(1-\pi)$, so you can also interpret the slope in Equation 6.1 as a change in probability of success for a unit change in x. But the numerical value depends on the probability itself. When $\pi = 0.5$ this expression is at its maximum. However, it doesn't change very much within the range $0.2 < \pi < 0.8$, as you will see in Example 6.1.

EXAMPLE 6.1   Arthritis treatment

In Chapter 3, the data on treatment for rheumatoid arthritis was examined. In addition to Sex and Treatment, the data (see Appendix B.1) contains the age of each patient in this study. Although the response has three categories (None, Some, or Marked improvement), for now, consider whether the patient showed any improvement at all, defining the event Better to mean Some or Marked improvement.

Because Age is continuous, it is difficult to see how the probability of a better response varies with age. Table 6.1 summarizes this data by dividing the patients into 10 decile groups based on age.[1] You see that, for those in the youngest Age Group, the observed $\Pr\{\text{Better}\} = 2/8 = 0.25$, so the odds of a Better response is $0.25/0.75 = \frac{1}{3}$; for those in the 62–63 age range, half improved, so the odds $= 1$. The log odds has the value 0 here. Thus, positive (negative) logits correspond to probabilities greater than (less than) $\frac{1}{2}$.

You can see that the probabilities of a Better response and the Logits tend to increase with age. Thus, we would expect to find $\beta > 0$ in Equation 6.1. Also note that, when the probability is defined as the Observed number divided by the Total in a group, the logit is undefined when the Observed probability is 0 or 1. You can improve on this, as shown in Figure 6.1.

---

[1]The numbers under Total are unequal because of ties.

Table 6.1   Probabilities, Odds, and Logits for the Arthritis Treatment Data

Age Group	Number Better	Total	Observed Pr{Better}	Odds Better	Observed Logit
23 – 31	2	8	0.250	0.333	-1.099
32 – 41	4	9	0.444	0.800	-0.223
44 – 48	2	8	0.250	0.333	-1.099
49 – 53	0	7	0.000	0.000	.
54 – 57	9	12	0.750	3.000	1.099
58 – 58	2	3	0.667	2.000	0.693
59 – 61	7	11	0.636	1.750	0.560
62 – 63	4	8	0.500	1.000	0.000
64 – 67	5	9	0.556	1.250	0.223
68 – 74	7	9	0.778	3.500	1.253

Figure 6.1 shows a plot of the (0/1) variable BETTER against Age. (The programming for such plots is described in Section 6.3.2.) Also shown is the predicted probability from a logistic regression (solid blue curve) and the upper and lower 95% confidence band for this predicted probability (dashed blue curves). For comparison, we also show the result of a linear regression of the (0/1) variable on age (red line) and its 95% confidence band. The two sets of curves are fairly similar, except in the extremes.

Figure 6.1   Arthritis treatment data, linear and logit regressions on age. The curves on this plot show predicted probabilities of improvement and 95% confidence bands. The points on this plot show the observations. Except in the extremes, the linear and logistic models give very similar predicted values; the confidence bounds differ more.

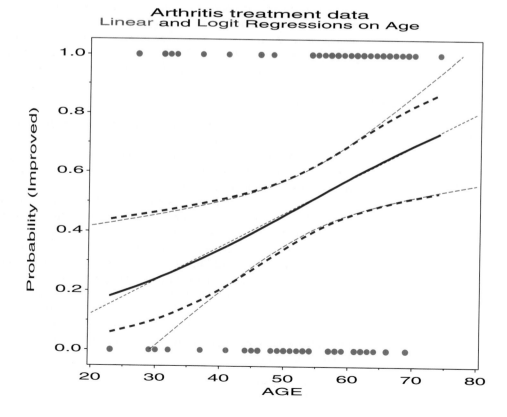

The relevant portion of the output is shown next. The parameter estimates are $\alpha = -2.642$ and $\beta = 0.0492$. So, the estimated odds of a Better response are multiplied by $e^{\beta} = \exp(0.0492) = 1.05$ for each one year increase in age. Equivalently, you can think of this as a 5% increase per year (using $100(e^{\beta} - 1)$ to convert). Over ten years, the odds are multiplied by $\exp(10 \times 0.0492) = 1.64$, a 64% increase.

Analysis of Maximum Likelihood Estimates

Variable	DF	Parameter Estimate	Standard Error	Wald Chi-Square	Pr > Chi-Square	Standardized Estimate	Odds Ratio	
INTERCPT	1	-2.6421	1.0732	6.0611	0.0138	.	.	
AGE	1	0.0492	0.0194	6.4733	0.0110	0.346714	1.050	☐

6.2.1   Plotting a Discrete Response: The LOGODDS Macro

It is sometimes difficult to understand how a binary response can give rise to a smooth, continuous relationship between the predicted response and an explanatory variable, particularly when the predictor is continuous. Thus, in Figure 6.1 you can see the (0/1) responses and the fitted relation, but it takes some effort to see that the observation points determine that relation. Another problem is that the Age variable is not strictly continuous—it was recorded in whole years—so there may be considerable overplotting of the observation points in such a graph.

It is helpful, therefore, to plot the observed sample logits or sample probabilities against X, together with the observations (in a way that avoids overplotting), and the fitted relationships, as is done in Figure 6.2. You can group the observations into multiple intervals, as in Table 6.1, and let n_i denote the number of observations in the ith interval, of which y_i are successful events.

Then, the observed probability is $p_i = y_i/n_i$ in interval i, and the sample logit is $\log[p_i/(1 - p_i)] = \log[y_i/(n_i - y_i)]$. But as you see in Table 6.1, the logit is not defined when $y_i = 0$ or when $y_i = n_i$. You get around this difficulty by substituting the *empirical logit*,

$$\log\left(\frac{y_i + \frac{1}{2}}{n_i - y_i + \frac{1}{2}}\right) ,$$

which is also a less biased estimator of the true logit. Analogously, in a plot of probabilities against X, use the adjusted value $(y_i + \frac{1}{2})/(n_i - y_i + \frac{1}{2})$.

An alternative to grouping the observations into fixed intervals is to imagine a sliding window, wide enough to contain a given fraction, f of the points, moving from left to right across the plot. At each position of the window, calculate a smoothed, locally weighted average of the binary y values within the window by using the *lowess* scatterplot smoothing algorithm (Cleveland, 1979) (without robustness iterations). This gives a smooth, nonparametric regression for $\hat{p}_i$, advocated by Landwehr, et al. (1984) and Fowlkes (1987). Copas (1983) discusses methods based on kernel density estimation for smoothing binary data.

These plots are produced by the LOGODDS macro documented in Appendix A.15. Both plots in Figure 6.2 are produced by the following program:

```
%include data(arthrit);
data arthrit;
   set arthrit;
   format better outcome.;
%logodds(data=arthrit, x=age, y=Better, ncat=10, smooth=0.5);
```

Figure 6.2   Empirical log odds and probability plots for Arthritis Treatment Data. The observed responses are plotted as stacked points at the top and bottom of the figures. The squares show the empirical sample logits and the analogous adjusted sample probabilities.

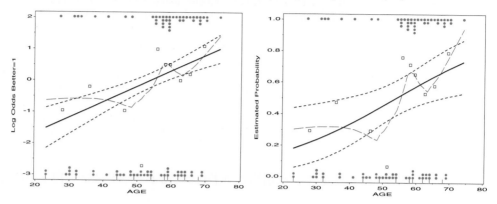

The LOGODDS macro assumes a quantitative predictor and groups the observations into the number of intervals specified by the NCAT= parameter. The lower limits of the intervals are shown by the short vertical lines above the horizontal axis. When the SMOOTH= parameter is specified, the LOWESS macro (Friendly, 1991, Appendix A1.9) uses that value as the smoothing parameter f, and the smoothed nonparametric curve is drawn on the probability plot. With moderate sample sizes, as we have here, the lowess curve can be quite variable, and, of course, ignores other explanatory variables.

Note that the fitted regression relation is linear on the scale of log odds (Equation 6.1) but (slightly) non-linear on the scale of probabilities (Equation 6.3). Because most people find it easier to interpret probabilities than log odds, it is often useful to make a single plot showing *both* scales.

6.2.2   Plotting a Discrete Response: Easy Smoothing with PROC GPLOT

For large datasets, extensive computations are required to calculate the lowess curve because a weighted least squares regression is performed for each observation.[2] A simple alternative, which is often sufficient, is to use the SM*nn* spline smoother provided by the INTERPOL option in the SYMBOL statement. Example 6.2 illustrates this technique and the importance of smoothing.

EXAMPLE 6.2   Survival on the *Titanic*

The *Titanic* data, discussed in Example 4.5, included all passengers and crew, but categorized AGE as either child or adult. The data used here lists 1313 passengers by name and includes the actual age for 633 of them. This data was derived from the "Encyclopedia Titanica" Web site (Hind, 1997). The data is based on the Passenger List of the *Titanic*, originally published by Findlay (1986) and updated by members of various *Titanic* historical societies and internet collaborators who study the sinking of the *Titanic*. We examine here the relation of sex and class to the actual age for the passengers.

The dataset TITANIC2 contains the variables SEX, CLASS, AGE, BOAT, NAME, and the 0/1 variable SURVIVED. A simple, but effective plot of survival probability against age

---

[2]In SAS software Version 7 and higher, the LOWESS macro uses the LOESS procedure to perform the calculations and avoids this difficulty. In earlier versions of SAS, use the STEP= parameter for large datasets. The STEP= parameter sets a step size for successive x values. When STEP>1, the macro performs the regression at every STEP[th] value of x and uses predicted values from that regression for intermediate points.

for men and women is produced simply by plotting SURVIVED * AGE = SEX, using INTERPOL=SM70 in the SYMBOL statement. The numeric value in SM*nn* establishes the relative weighting of criteria for approximating the points vs. smoothness, with larger values giving a smoother curve. For binary responses, values in the range 50–90 appear to work reasonably well.

The following statements produce the left panel in Figure 6.3. (The DATA step LABEL, which produces labels for the curves, is not shown to conserve space.) Similar statements that plot SURVIVED * AGE = CLASS produce the graph shown in the right panel of Figure 6.3.

```
proc sort data=titanic2;
   by age;

proc gplot data=titanic2;
   where (age^=.);
   plot survived * age = sex /
      anno=label vm=1 hm=1 vaxis=axis1 haxis=axis2 nolegend frame;
   symbol1 i=sm70 v=square   h=1.9 c=red;
   symbol2 i=sm70 v=triangle h=1.9 c=blue;
   axis1 order=(0 to 1 by .2) label=(a=90) offset=(3) value=(h=1.6);
   axis2 offset=(3) value=(h=1.6);
```

Figure 6.3   Survival probability vs. age by sex, and by class for passengers on the *Titanic* whose age is recorded. Plot symbols show the individual observations. These graphs are misleading because the effects of sex vary with class.

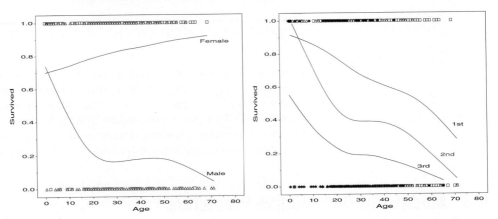

The actual binary responses, shown by the plotting symbols at 0 and 1, are not very informative here because age is also discrete (recorded to the nearest year) and many points are overplotted. Jittering the points would help somewhat but would introduce some bias in the smoothing. The smoothed curves are highly suggestive, however, and give a much more detailed view than our earlier analyses based on the binary age classification.

For females, probability of survival increases steadily with age. For males, however, the probability of survival drops precipitously with age, levels off through middle age, then declines again for the oldest men. The smoothed curves in the right panel show similar cubic trends with age for passengers in 2nd and 3rd class.

It is tempting to speculate that these cubic curves reflect preferential treatment toward boys and greater chivalry, or perhaps decreased will to survive, on the part of older men. Such speculations would be dead wrong, however, because they falsely assume that sex and class do not interact, and that the distributions of age (as recorded in this data) are roughly the same for all sex–class groups.

You can see that both assumptions are wrong by making separate graphs for men and women. These graphs, shown in Figure 6.4, are drawn using a BY statement and smoothing with the SM interpolation method.

```
goptions hby=0;
proc gplot data=titanic2 uniform;
   where (age^=.);
   plot survived * age = class /
      anno=label vm=1 hm=1 vaxis=axis1 haxis=axis2 nolegend frame;
   by sex;
   symbol1 i=sm70 v=square   h=1.9 c=blue;
   symbol2 i=sm70 v=triangle h=1.9 c=red;
   symbol3 i=sm70 v=star     h=1.9 c=black;
```

Figure 6.4   Survival probability vs. age by SEX–CLASS, for passengers on the *Titanic*

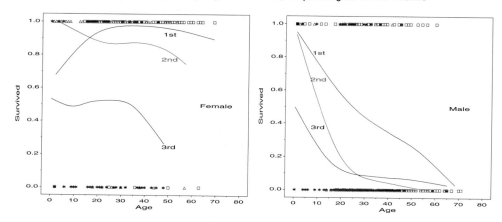

From Figure 6.4, it appears that survival of women actually decreases with age in 2nd and 3rd class; the increasing overall curve for women in Figure 6.3 is due to the greater prevalence of older women in 1st class, who were more likely to survive. Among men, it now appears that survival decreases approximately linearly in 1st class and much more sharply in the other classes. However, you must remember that you are simply smoothing raw data here; an adequate fitted model generally provides better smoothing and simplification. □

6.3   Models for Quantitative Predictors

Logistic regression models may use quantitative predictors or discrete predictors, or a mixture of both, just as in ordinary regression models. Here, I describe the basic theory and visualization steps for quantitative predictors, and extend these ideas to discrete explanatory variables in Section 6.4.

6.3.1   Fitting Logistic Regression Models

The parameters in logistic regression models are usually estimated by maximum likelihood. Because the response variable, Y, takes on only two values, you can take these values as 1 and 0 with probabilities π and $1 - \pi$, respectively. Then the probability distribution for case i can be represented simply as

$$p(y_i) \equiv \Pr(Y_i = y_i) = \pi_i^{y_i} (1 - \pi_i)^{1-y_i} .$$

Assuming the cases are independent, the joint probability of the n observations $y_1, y_2, \ldots, y_n$ is the product of these probabilities over all cases,

$$p(y_1, y_2, \ldots, y_n) = \prod_{i=1}^{n} \pi_i^{y_i} (1 - \pi_i)^{1-y_i} = \prod_{i=1}^{n} \left(\frac{\pi_i}{1 - \pi_i} \right)^{y_i} (1 - \pi_i) .$$

Substituting for π_i from Equation 6.3, you can express the likelihood of the data as a function of the model parameters,

$$\mathcal{L}(\alpha, \beta) = \prod_{i=1}^{n} [\exp(\alpha + \beta X_i)]^{y_i} [1 + \exp(\alpha + \beta X_i)]^{-1} . \qquad (6.4)$$

The maximum likelihood estimates are the values of α and β, which maximize $\mathcal{L}(\alpha, \beta)$, but it is simpler to maximize $\log \mathcal{L}$, which has its maximum at the same values. Taking derivatives of $\log \mathcal{L}$ with respect to α and β gives the estimating equations (in matrix form)

$$X^{\mathsf{T}} y = X^{\mathsf{T}} \hat{p} , \qquad (6.5)$$

where $X = [1, x]$, and $\hat{p}_i = \exp(\hat{\alpha} + \hat{\beta} x_i)/(1 + \exp(\hat{\alpha} + \hat{\beta} x_i))$. This is analogous to the linear model estimating equations in ordinary least squares regression, $X^{\mathsf{T}} y = X^{\mathsf{T}} \hat{y}$, where $\hat{y} = X \hat{\beta}$, and $\hat{\beta} = (X^{\mathsf{T}} X)^{-1} X^{\mathsf{T}} y$. The two equations expressed by Equation 6.5 have no analytic solution, but they may be solved numerically or by iteratively reweighted least squares.

EXAMPLE 6.3   Arthritis treatment

It is also straightforward to calculate the values of $\log \mathcal{L}$ in Equation 6.4 for a grid of values of (α, β) and plot the log likelihood surface as a contour plot or 3-D plot. For example, the DATA step in the next program calculates the log likelihoods over all observations in the arthritis data for a range of α (B0) and β (B1) determined from the parameter estimates $\pm$ two standard errors found in Example 6.4 (see Output 6.1). The contour plot, shown in Figure 6.5, has its maximum value $\log \mathcal{L} = -54.58$ at the value $(\hat{\alpha}, \hat{\beta}) = (-2.64, 0.05)$. From this, $-2 \log \mathcal{L} = 109.16$ is the value displayed for -2 LOG L in Output 6.1 for the intercept and covariates.

Figure 6.5   Contour plot of log likelihood for the Arthritis data

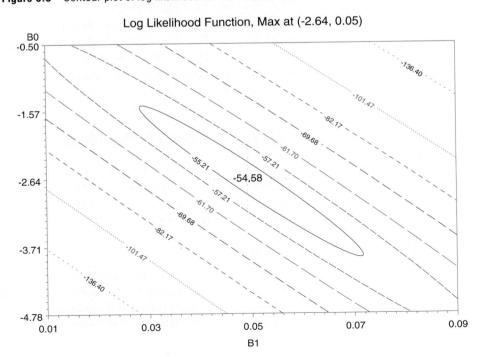

```
data maxlike;
   keep b0 b1 loglike;
   do b0=(-2.64 - 2*1.07) to (-2.64 + 2*1.07) by (1.07/50);
      do b1=(0.05 - 2*0.02) to (0.05 + 2*0.02) by (0.02/50);
         loglike=0;
         do i=1 to n;
            set arthrit point=i nobs=n;
            phat = exp(b0+b1*age)/(1+exp(b0+b1*age));
            loglike = loglike + (better * log(phat))
                                  + ((1-better) * log(1-phat));
         end;
      output;
      end;
   end;
stop;
```

This contour plot of the log likelihood function shows something that is not apparent from the usual printed output: The contours of equal log likelihood have a pronounced negative slope, so an increase in β may be compensated for by a decrease in α without changing the value of $\log \mathcal{L}$ appreciably. Also, the innermost ellipse (corresponding to the largest absolute contour value) is relatively wide along its major axis, reflecting the fact that the precision of these estimates is not extremely high. Increasing the sample size would result in tighter estimates of the slope and intercept. This is the visual representation of the information presented in the covariance matrix of the parameter estimates.   □

Logistic regression models can be fit using PROC LOGISTIC, PROC CATMOD, PROC GENMOD and SAS/INSIGHT. The examples in this chapter mainly illustrate the use of PROC LOGISTIC because it provides the widest range of diagnostics and other facilities for these models.

The input dataset for PROC LOGISTIC can be in one of three forms:

frequency form is used with grouped data, as in a contingency table. For a binary response, there are two observations per group, which correspond to the levels of the response and a variable that contains the frequency for that group. A FREQ statement is used to provide the frequency variable.

events/trial form is also used with grouped binomial data. There is one observation per group: one variable gives the number of events, and a second variable gives the number of trials. A FREQ statement is also used in this situation.

case form is used when there is one observation per case. This form is usually required when there are quantitative predictors.

6.3.2   Plotting Predicted Probabilities

PROC LOGISTIC calculates predicted logits (Equation 6.1) and predicted probabilities (Equation 6.3) for each observation. These results may be saved in an output dataset from which plots can be made. The plots, often supplemented by standard errors or confidence bands for these predictions, provide a visual means to interpret the prediction equations.

EXAMPLE 6.4   Arthritis treatment

This example illustrates the use of PROC LOGISTIC to fit a logistic regression model with a quantitative predictor. It also describes the steps required to plot the observed binary response together with fitted probabilities and confidence intervals. I use the Arthritis Treatment Data and describe how Figure 6.1 was produced.

The following DATA step creates the dataset ARTHRIT in case form. The dichotomous response BETTER is created from the actual outcome variable IMPROVE, which has values 0, 1, 2 corresponding to None, Some, or Marked improvement.

```
data arthrit;
   input id treat$ sex$ age improve @@ ;
   better  = (improve > 0);           /* Dichotomous response   */
   _treat_ = (treat ='Treated') ;     /* Dummy var for treatment */
   _sex_   = (sex = 'Female');        /*          and sex        */
   datalines ;
57 Treated Male    27 1    9 Placebo Male    37 0
46 Treated Male    29 0   14 Placebo Male    44 0
77 Treated Male    30 0   73 Placebo Male    50 0
   ... (observations omitted)
56 Treated Female 69 1   42 Placebo Female 66 0
43 Treated Female 70 1   15 Placebo Female 66 1
                         71 Placebo Female 68 1
                          1 Placebo Female 74 2
;
```

By default, PROC LOGISTIC orders the response values in *increasing* order and sets up the model so that it is predicting the probability of the *smallest* ordered value Pr{better=0}. This means it would be modeling the probability of No improvement here. The DESCENDING option (available in SAS beginning with Release 6.08) reverses this order so that predicted results will be for Pr{better=1}.

```
proc logistic nosimple descending;
   model  better = age / lackfit;
   output out=results p=predict l=lower u=upper;
```

Alternatively, you can use the ORDER option, or, with the default ORDER=FORMATTED, you can create a user-format for the 0/1 values of the response, so that the first (smallest) formatted value corresponds to the event that you want. In the format OUTCOME created with PROC FORMAT, the value IMPROVED conveniently comes first alphabetically and, therefore, is the predicted event.

```
proc format;
   value outcome 0 = 'not improved'
                 1 = 'improved';
proc logistic nosimple;
   format better outcome.;
   model  better = age / lackfit;
   output out=results p=predict l=lower u=upper;
```

In the printed output (Output 6.1), the Response Profiles show that the response values are ordered as specified.

The OUTPUT statement shown in the preceding PROC LOGISTIC step produces the output dataset RESULTS, which contains the predicted probability of improvement (PREDICT) and the 95% confidence limits (LOWER, UPPER) for these observations. The first few observations from the dataset RESULTS are shown in Output 6.2. There is one observation per case because the input data is in case form.

The plot shown in Figure 6.1 is produced as an overlay plot by the PROC GPLOT step shown in the following program. Three SYMBOL statements are used to plot point symbols for the observed response BETTER and interpolated lines for the predicted probabilities of improvement and confidence limits. The linear regression lines (and its confidence limits) in the figure are produced using the INTERP=RLCLM on the SYMBOL1 statement.

Output 6.1   Arthritis treatment data: Logistic regression on age

```
                         The LOGISTIC Procedure

Data Set: WORK.ARTHRIT
Response Variable: BETTER
Response Levels: 2
Number of Observations: 84
Link Function: Logit


                         Response Profile

                    Ordered
                    Value   BETTER            Count

                      1   improved             42
                      2   not improved         42


      Model Fitting Information and Testing Global Null Hypothesis BETA=0

                                      Intercept
                        Intercept        and
     Criterion            Only        Covariates    Chi-Square for Covariates

     AIC                 118.449       113.164           .
     SC                  120.880       118.025           .
     -2 LOG L            116.449       109.164       7.285 with 1 DF (p=0.0070)
     Score                  .             .          7.010 with 1 DF (p=0.0081)


                  Analysis of Maximum Likelihood Estimates

                  Parameter Standard    Wald      Pr >     Standardized    Odds
     Variable DF  Estimate   Error   Chi-Square Chi-Square   Estimate     Ratio

     INTERCPT 1   -2.6421   1.0732    6.0611     0.0138          .           .
     AGE      1    0.0492   0.0194    6.4733     0.0110       0.346714     1.050
```

Output 6.2   Arthritis treatment data: RESULTS dataset (partial)

```
                         Arthritis treatment data

     ID    AGE    IMPROVE    BETTER         PREDICT    LOWER     UPPER

     57     27       1       improved       0.21209   0.08047   0.45297
      9     37       0       not improved   0.30579   0.16660   0.49256
     46     29       0       not improved   0.22902   0.09378   0.46024
     14     44       0       not improved   0.38341   0.25624   0.52881
     77     30       0       not improved   0.23783   0.10112   0.46397
     73     50       0       not improved   0.45522   0.34216   0.57308
     17     32       2       improved       0.25615   0.11725   0.47166
            ....
```

```
proc sort data=results;
   by age;
proc gplot data=results;
   plot better * age = 1
        predict * age = 2
        upper * age = 3
        lower * age = 3
        / frame overlay vaxis=axis1 vm=1 hm=1;
   axis1 label=(a=90) offset=(3) order=(0 to 1 by .2);
   symbol1 v=dot h=1.4 i=rlclm l=2 c=green ci=red;
   symbol2 v=none   i=join l=1  w=3 c=blue;
   symbol3 v=none   i=join l=20 w=3 c=blue;
   label better='Probability (Improved)';
   format better 4.1;
   title2  c=red 'Linear' c=black ' and ' c=blue 'Logit '
           c=black 'Regressions on Age';
run;
```

The model fitting tests in Output 6.1 (Chi-Square for Covariates and the Wald test for AGE) test whether age adds significantly to predicting the outcome. This is a different question than whether the model is adequate—usually provided by a ***lack-of-fit test***, which compares the given model to the saturated model. However, with binary data in case form, the usual lack-of-fit tests do not apply. The LACKFIT option in the MODEL statement requests a lack-of-fit test proposed by Hosmer and Lemeshow (1989). This test divides subjects into 10ths, based on their ordered predicted probabilities. Then, it computes a χ^2 from the observed and expected frequencies in these ten groups. The results from this test (shown in Output 6.3) do not reject the fit of the simple one-variable model; however, the relatively small p-value suggests that the model might be improved.   □

Output 6.3   Arthritis treatment data: Goodness-of-fit test

| | | Hosmer and Lemeshow Goodness-of-Fit Test | | | |
| | | BETTER = improved | | BETTER = not improved | |
Group	Total	Observed	Expected	Observed	Expected
1	8	2	1.76	6	6.24
2	9	4	2.65	5	6.35
3	8	2	3.27	6	4.73
4	10	1	4.81	9	5.19
5	9	8	4.78	1	4.22
6	11	7	6.18	4	4.82
7	7	4	4.16	3	2.84
8	8	4	4.96	4	3.04
9	8	6	5.26	2	2.74
10	6	4	4.16	2	1.84

Goodness-of-fit Statistic = 13.354 with 8 DF (p=0.1002)

EXAMPLE 6.5   Challenger disaster

The space shuttle *Challenger* exploded 73 seconds after take-off on January 28, 1986. Subsequent investigation determined that the cause was failure of the O-ring seals used to isolate the fuel supply from burning gases. The story behind the *Challenger* disaster is, perhaps, the most poignant missed opportunity in the history of statistical graphics. It may be heartbreaking to find out that some important information was there, but the graph maker missed it.

Engineers from Morton Thiokol, manufacturers of the rocket motors, had been worried about the effects of unseasonably cold weather on the O-ring seals and recommended aborting the flight. NASA staff analyzed the data on the relation between ambient temperature and the number of O-ring failures (out of 6), but they had excluded observations where no O-rings failed, believing that they were uninformative. Unfortunately, those observations had occurred when the launch temperature was relatively warm (between 65° and 80°F.) and were indeed informative. The coldest temperature at any previous launch was 53°F; when *Challenger* was launched on January 28, 1986, the temperature was a frigid 31°F.

The data relating O-ring failures to temperature was depicted as shown in Figure 6.6, my candidate for the most misleading graph in history. Examination of this graph seemed to indicate that there was no relation between ambient temperature and failure. Thus, the decision to launch the *Challenger* was made, in spite of the initial concerns of the Morton Thiokol engineers.

Figure 6.6   NASA Space Shuttle pre-launch graph

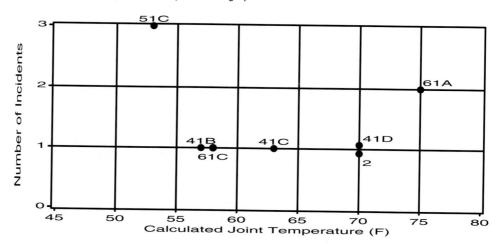

This data has been analyzed extensively (Dalal, et al., 1989; Lavine, 1991). Tufte (1997) gives a thorough and convincing visual analysis of the evidence available prior to the launch. The main goal here is to illustrate predictions from the model for the *Challenger* launch and the graphical display. But, what if the engineers had simply made a better graph? At the least, that would entail (a) drawing a smoothed curve to fit the points (to show the trend), and (b) removing the background grid lines (which obscure the data). Figure 6.7 shows a revised version of the same graph, which should have caused any engineer to conclude that either (a) the data was wrong, or (b) there were excessive risks associated with both high and low temperatures. But it is well known that brittleness of the rubber used in the O-rings is inversely proportional to $(\texttt{temp})^3$, so prudent interest might have focused on the first possibility.

Figure 6.7   NASA Space Shuttle pre-launch graph, revised

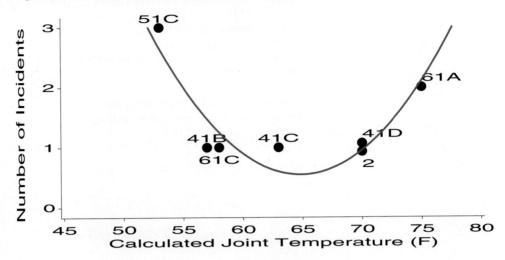

Now, return to the problem of predicting the likelihood of failures at low temperatures. The DATA step in the next program reads the data about the number of O-ring failures and the temperature for the 23 flights for which information was available before the *Challenger* launch. A more detailed dataset, from Dalal, et al. (1989) and Tufte (1997), is given in Appendix B.9.

```
title 'NASA Space Shuttle O-Ring Failures';
data nasa;
   input failures temp @@;
   orings = 6;
   label failures = 'Number of O-ring failures'
      temp = 'Temperature (deg F)';
   datalines;
   2  53    1  57    1  58    1  63
   0  66    0  67    0  67    0  67
   0  68    0  69    0  70    0  70
   1  70    1  70    0  72    0  73
   0  75    2  75    0  76    0  76
   0  78    0  79    0  80
;
```

To obtain predicted probabilities for observations not contained in the original sample, create an additional dataset that contains values for the independent variables in the extrapolation sample, and join these observations to the actual dataset. The response variable FAILURES will be missing for the extrapolation sample.

```
*-- Obtain predicted values for 30-80 degrees;
data temp;
   input temp @@;
datalines;
31 30 35 40 45 50 55 60 65 70 75 80
;
data nasa2;
   set nasa temp;
```

In the PROC LOGISTIC step, I use the *events/trials* syntax to indicate the number of failures and number of trials. (This assumes that O-rings on the same flight fail independently.) The observations in the extrapolation sample are not used in fitting the model, yet the procedure produces predicted probabilities and logits (if the independent variable(s) are non-missing).

```
proc logistic data=nasa2 nosimple;
   model failures/orings = temp ;
      output out=results p=predict l=lower u=upper;
proc print;
```

Output 6.4 indicates that the 12 new observations were not used in the analysis. The odds ratio, 0.891, is interpreted to mean that each increase of 1° in temperature decreases the odds of one O-ring failure by 11%!

Output 6.4   Logistic regression for NASA O-ring data

```
                NASA Space Shuttle O-Ring Failures                      1

                       The LOGISTIC Procedure

Data Set: WORK.NASA2
Response Variable (Events): FAILURES   Number of O-ring failures
Response Variable (Trials): ORINGS
Number of Observations: 23
Link Function: Logit


                            Response Profile

                    Ordered  Binary
                     Value   Outcome     Count

                       1     EVENT          9
                       2     NO EVENT     129

WARNING: 12 observation(s) were deleted due to missing values for
         the response or explanatory variables.


Model Fitting Information and Testing Global Null Hypothesis BETA=0

                              Intercept
                   Intercept     and
    Criterion        Only     Covariates  Chi-Square for Covariates

    AIC              68.540      64.416          .
    SC               71.468      70.271          .
    -2 LOG L         66.540      60.416       6.124 with 1 DF (p=0.0133)
    Score              .           .          6.804 with 1 DF (p=0.0091)


              Analysis of Maximum Likelihood Estimates

            Parameter Standard   Wald        Pr >    Standardized   Odds
    Variable DF Estimate  Error  Chi-Square Chi-Square  Estimate    Ratio

    INTERCPT 1   5.0940   3.0552   2.7798    0.0955        .          .
    TEMP     1  -0.1158   0.0471   6.0491    0.0139     -0.437656   0.891
```

The output dataset RESULTS contains the predicted probability of the failure of a single O-ring at each temperature and upper- and lower-confidence 95% limits for this probability. You can plot the predicted and observed values as shown next. A vertical reference line at 31°F is used to highlight the conditions at the *Challenger* launch.

```
proc sort data=results;
   by predict;
data results;
   set results;
   obs = failures / orings;

proc gplot data=results;
   plot (obs predict lower upper) * temp /
      href=31 lhref=33
      overlay frame vaxis=axis1 vminor=1;
   symbol1 v=dot i=none c=blue h=2;
   symbol2 v=none i=spline c=black w=5;
   symbol3 v=none i=spline c=red l=33 r=2 w=3;
   axis1 label=(a=90 'Estimated Failure probability') offset=(3);
```

The graph is shown in Figure 6.8. There is hardly any data at low temperatures and the width of the confidence band provides an important visual cue to this uncertainty. Nevertheless, the predicted probability of failure per O-ring is uncomfortably high at *all* temperatures below the range of data from previous flights. Would you take a ride on *Challenger* when the weather is cold?   □

Figure 6.8   NASA Space Shuttle O-ring Failure, Observed and Predicted probabilities

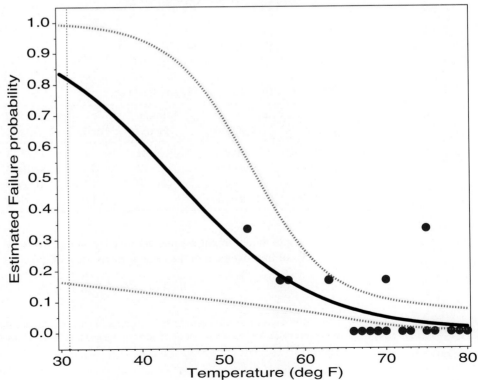

6.4 Logit Models for Qualitative Predictors

Logistic regression can be generalized to include discrete explanatory variables, and such models are often called *logit models*. The main differences (using PROC LOGISTIC) are listed here:

- The data is often entered in frequency form, with one observation per "group", defined by the value(s) of the discrete predictors. With quantitative predictors, the data *must* be entered in case form.
- The discrete predictors must be represented by dummy (0/1) variables for PROC LOGISTIC, so explanatory variables often need to be re-coded.[3]
- The statistics for goodness-of-fit are computed differently.
- The output dataset used for plotting contains one observation per group when the data is in frequency form.

When *all* predictors are discrete, the data actually comprises a contingency table, and there is a close connection between logit models and log-linear models, discussed in Chapter 7. In this case, the methods discussed in that chapter may also be used to analyze the data presented here.

Consider the data that follows, which represents the contingency table for the Arthritis data (Example 3.3) classified by Sex and Treatment, ignoring the Age variable for the moment. For each group, the observed probabilities and logits may be found, as displayed in Table 6.2.

```
                            Improvement
Sex     Treatment    None    Some/Marked    Total

 F       Active        6          21          27
 F       Placebo      19          13          32

 M       Active        7           7          14
 M       Placebo      10           1          11
```

Table 6.2 Arthritis data, by Sex and Treatment

Sex	Treatment	Number Better	Total	Observed Pr{better}	Odds Better	Observed Logit
Female	Active	21	27	0.7778	3.50	1.2529
Female	Placebo	13	32	0.4062	0.68	-0.3797
Male	Active	7	14	0.5000	1.00	0.0000
Male	Placebo	1	11	0.0909	0.10	-2.3026

A simple model might assume additive ("main") effects for Sex and Treatment on the log odds of improvement of the same form as model Equation 6.1.

$$\text{logit}\,(\pi_{ij}) = \alpha + \beta_1 x_1 + \beta_2 x_2 \ . \tag{6.6}$$

---

[3]The GENMOD procedure provides a CLASS statement, so no re-coding is necessary. In Version 8, PROC LOGISTIC now supports CLASS variables. The DUMMY macro (Appendix A.7) can be used to create the dummy variables for PROC LOGISTIC in earlier releases.

In this model,

- x_1 and x_2 are dummy (0/1) variables representing Sex and Treatment, respectively. They are defined as

$$x_1 = \begin{cases} 0 & \text{if male} \\ 1 & \text{if female} \end{cases} \qquad x_2 = \begin{cases} 0 & \text{if placebo} \\ 1 & \text{if active} \end{cases}$$

- α is the log odds of improvement for the baseline group with $x_1 = 0$ and $x_2 = 0$—males who receive the placebo.
- β_1 is the increment in log odds for being female as opposed to male. Therefore, e^{β_1} gives the odds of improvement for females relative to males.
- β_2 is the increment in log odds for being in the active treatment group. e^{β_2} gives the odds of improvement for the active treatment group relative to placebo.

Thus, the parameters defined here are *incremental effects*. The intercept corresponds to a baseline group (males given the placebo); the other parameters are incremental effects for the other groups compared to the baseline group. Thus, when α, β_1, and β_2 have been estimated, the fitted logits and predicted odds are as follows:

Sex	Treatment	Logit	Odds Improved
Female	Active	$\alpha + \beta_1 + \beta_2$	$e^{\alpha+\beta_1+\beta_2}$
Female	Placebo	$\alpha + \beta_1$	$e^{\alpha+\beta_1}$
Male	Active	$\alpha + \beta_2$	$e^{\alpha+\beta_2}$
Male	Placebo	α	e^{α}

In general, there may be multiple explanatory variables, as in multiple regression. A discrete predictor with c categories can be represented by $c - 1$ dummy variables. Interactions between predictors can be included in the model by defining interaction variables as products of the main effect variables, as with PROC REG. For example, the interaction of Sex and Treatment could be included in the model (Equation 6.6) by adding a term $\beta_3 x_3$, where $x_3 = x_1 \times x_2$.[4]

EXAMPLE 6.6 Arthritis treatment

The following DATA step creates a dataset in frequency form named ARTHRIT. The dummy variables _SEX_ and _TREAT_ corresponding to x_1 and x_2 are created with logical assignment statements, as is the dichotomous response variable BETTER.

The first logistic regression model includes effects for Sex and Treatment, specified by the dummy variables in the MODEL statement. Again, the DESCENDING option is used so that predicted results will be for Pr{better=1}.

```
data arthrits;
    input sex$ trtment$ improve$ count;
    _treat_ = (trtment='Active');
    _sex_   = (sex='F');
    better  = (improve='some');
datalines;
F Active  none   6
M Active  none   7
F Active  some  21
```

---

[4]In the current example, this would give a saturated model, which would necessarily fit perfectly. We usually try to obtain the simplest model with an adequate fit.

```
M Active   some   7
F Placebo  none  19
M Placebo  none  10
F Placebo  some  13
M Placebo  some   1
;
proc logistic data=arthrits descending;
   freq count;
   model better = _sex_ _treat_ / scale=none aggregate;
```

The options SCALE=NONE and AGGREGATE provide goodness-of-fit tests for the model. The goodness-of-fit tests are based on the difference between the actual model fitted and the saturated model (containing an interaction of Sex and Treatment, in this example), which would fit perfectly. The results shown in Output 6.5 are produced.

Output 6.5   Arthritis treatment data: Overall tests

```
            Deviance and Pearson Goodness-of-Fit Statistics

                                                        Pr >
        Criterion       DF      Value    Value/DF    Chi-Square

        Deviance        1       0.2776    0.2776       0.5983
        Pearson         1       0.2637    0.2637       0.6076


                    Number of unique profiles: 4

              Testing Global Null Hypothesis: BETA=0

                              Intercept
                  Intercept      and
      Criterion     Only      Covariates   Chi-Square for Covariates

      AIC          118.449     104.222        .
      SC           118.528     104.460        .
      -2 LOG L     116.449      98.222      18.227 with 2 DF (p=0.0001)
      Score           .           .        16.797 with 2 DF (p=0.0002)
```

The chi-square tests for BETA=0 in Output 6.5 test the joint effect of Sex and Treatment. Individual effects in the model are tested by Wald χ^2s, the squared ratio of each parameter divided by its standard error. These tests, in Output 6.6, indicate that both Sex and Treatment effects are highly significant.

Output 6.6   Arthritis treatment data: Parameter estimates

```
               Analysis of Maximum Likelihood Estimates

              Parameter Standard    Wald       Pr >     Standardized   Odds
  Variable DF  Estimate   Error  Chi-Square Chi-Square    Estimate     Ratio

  INTERCPT  1   -1.9037   0.5982   10.1286    0.0015          .           .
  _SEX_     1    1.4687   0.5756    6.5092    0.0107       0.372433     4.343
  _TREAT_   1    1.7817   0.5188   11.7961    0.0006       0.493956     5.940
```

The fitted model,

$$\text{logit}(\pi_{ij}) = -1.90 + 1.47\,\text{sex} + 1.78\,\text{treat} \tag{6.7}$$

is most easily interpreted by considering the odds ratios corresponding to the parameters:

- 1.47 is the increment to log odds of a better outcome for females; the odds ratio $e^{1.47} = 4.34$ indicates that females are 4.3 times as likely to achieve a better outcome than males.
- 1.78 is the increment to log odds for the treatment group; the odds ratio $e^{1.78} = 5.94$ indicates that the treated group is nearly 6 times as likely to achieve a better outcome than the placebo group. □

6.4.1   Plotting Results from PROC LOGISTIC

As we saw in Section 6.3.2, you can save predicted probabilities and fitted logits in an output dataset that can be used for plotting and visualizing the results.

EXAMPLE 6.7   Arthritis treatment

Adding an OUTPUT statement to the PROC LOGISTIC step produces a dataset containing estimated logit values for each group, and corresponding predicted probabilities of improvement and confidence limits (UPPER, LOWER) for these probabilities.

```
proc logistic data=arthrits;
   freq count;
   format better outcome.;
   model better = _sex_ _treat_;
   output out=results p=predict l=lower u=upper xbeta=logit;
proc print data=results;
   id sex trtment; var improve count predict lower upper logit;
   format predict lower upper logit 7.3;
```

The output dataset RESULTS is shown in Output 6.7. There are two observations for each group (for None and Some improvement). The PREDICT variable gives the predicted probability of an improved outcome according to model (Equation 6.7), using the inverse transformation (Equation 6.3) of logit to probability. Note that the fitted statistics are the same for both observations corresponding to each Sex-Treatment combination.

Output 6.7   Arthritis treatment data: RESULTS dataset

SEX	TRTMENT	IMPROVE	COUNT	PREDICT	LOWER	UPPER	LOGIT
F	Active	none	6	0.794	0.620	0.900	1.347
M	Active	none	7	0.470	0.257	0.694	-0.122
F	Active	some	21	0.794	0.620	0.900	1.347
M	Active	some	7	0.470	0.257	0.694	-0.122
F	Placebo	none	19	0.393	0.248	0.560	-0.435
M	Placebo	none	10	0.130	0.044	0.325	-1.904
F	Placebo	some	13	0.393	0.248	0.560	-0.435
M	Placebo	some	1	0.130	0.044	0.325	-1.904

To plot the predicted probabilities of improvement and confidence limits from the RESULTS dataset, select the observations for IMPROVE='SOME'. A plot can be created as a bar chart by using PROC GCHART or as a line graph by using PROC GPLOT. Confidence limits can be added to either by using the SAS/GRAPH Annotate facility. The statements that follow show how a grouped horizontal bar chart (see Figure 6.9) is constructed.

```
data results;
   set results;
   if improve='some';
   label predict='Prob. Improved';
data limits;
   set results;
   xsys='2'; ysys='2';
   midpoint=trtment;
   group=sex; when='A'; position='+';
   x = lower;  function='MOVE   '; output;
   text='|';   function='LABEL  '; output;
   x = upper;  function='DRAW   '; output;
   text='|';   function='LABEL  '; output;

proc gchart data=results;
   hbar trtment / sumvar=predict group=sex gspace=3
                  patternid=midpoint
                  anno=limits
                  raxis=axis1
                  maxis=axis2
                  gaxis=axis3;
   axis1 order=(0 to 1 by .2) minor=none
         label=(h=1.5) value=(h=1.3);
   axis2 label=(h=1.3 'Treat') value=(h=1.1);
   axis3 label=(h=1.3) value=(h=1.2);
   pattern1 v=solid c=cyan;
   pattern2 v=solid c=rose;
```

Figure 6.9   Predicted probabilities of improvement

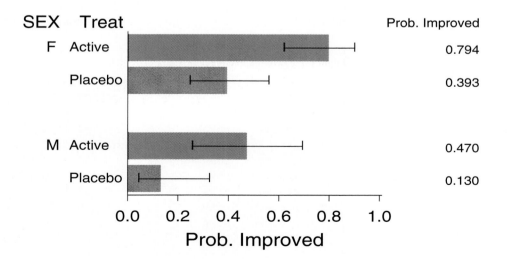

Alternatively, you may prefer a line graph to a bar chart. Figure 6.10 shows one example that has separate lines for the two treatment groups. The observed probabilities of improvement are shown by dots; these values were calculated from the COUNT variable in the RESULTS dataset. The plotting steps are not shown here to conserve space.   □

Figure 6.10   Line graph of observed and predicted probabilities

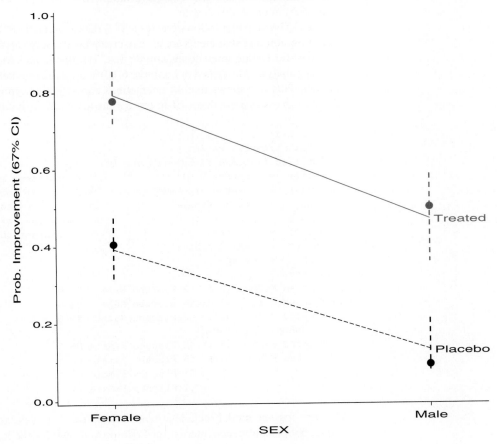

6.5   Multiple Logistic Regression Models

The logistic regression model can be generalized to include an arbitrary number of explanatory variables,

$$\text{logit}(\pi_i) = \alpha + \mathbf{x}_i^\mathsf{T} \boldsymbol{\beta} \tag{6.8}$$
$$= \alpha + \beta_1 x_{i1} + \beta_2 x_{i2} + \cdots + \beta_p x_{ip}$$

The xs can include any of the following sorts of regressors, as in the general linear model:

- **quantitative** variables (e.g., AGE, INCOME)
- **polynomial** powers of quantitative variables (e.g., AGE, AGE^2, AGE^3)
- **transformations** of quantitative variables (e.g., log SALARY)

- **dummy** variables, representing qualitative predictors (e.g., P_1, P_2, P_3 for four political party affiliations)
- **interaction** terms (e.g., SEX × AGE, or AGE × INCOME)

Again, all the regressors in the model must be created explicitly in a DATA step for PROC LOGISTIC.

EXAMPLE 6.8 **Arthritis treatment**

I now combine the analysis of Age (Example 6.4) with that of Sex and Treatment (Example 6.6) in the Arthritis data.

The DATA step that follows creates a SAS dataset named ARTHRIT in case form. As before, programming statements are used to create the dummy variables _SEX_ and _TREAT_. Variables for testing interactions among Sex, Treatment, and Age are also created. A preliminary analysis (described in Example 6.10) is used to test whether any of these variables interact. That test shows that all interactions can safely be ignored in this example. That test also serves as a goodness-of-fit test for the main effects model treated here.

```
data arthrit;
   length treat$7. sex$6. ;
   input id treat$ sex$ age improve @@ ;
   better  = (improve > 0);           /* Dichotomous response    */
   _treat_ = (treat ='Treated') ;     /* Dummy var for Treatment */
   _sex_   = (sex = 'Female');        /*            and Sex       */
   agesex  = age*_sex_ ;              /* Dummy var for testing    */
   agetrt  = age*_treat_;             /*    interactions          */
   sextrt  = _sex_*_treat_;
   age2    = age*age ;
 datalines ;
57 Treated Male   27 1    9 Placebo Male   37 0
46 Treated Male   29 0   14 Placebo Male   44 0
77 Treated Male   30 0   73 Placebo Male   50 0
   ... (observations omitted)
56 Treated Female 69 1   42 Placebo Female 66 0
43 Treated Female 70 1   15 Placebo Female 66 1
                         71 Placebo Female 68 1
                          1 Placebo Female 74 2
```

The next logistic model includes (main) effects for Age, Sex, and Treatment. In this example, both a confidence interval for Pr{Improved} and for the logit ±1s.e. are plotted. To make these intervals roughly comparable, we choose $\alpha = .33$ to give a 67% confidence interval.

```
title2 'Estimated Effects of Age, Treatment and Sex';
proc logistic data=arthrit;
   format better outcome.;
   model  better = _sex_  _treat_  age / lackfit;
   output out=results p=predict l=lower u=upper
                  xbeta=logit stdxbeta=selogit / alpha=.33;
```

The printed results are shown in Output 6.8. The parameter values are similar to those in the earlier examples and have the same interpretations. For example, for AGE, the odds ratio of 1.050 means that the odds of improvement increases 5% per year. Over 10 years, the odds of improvement would be multiplied by $e^{.487} = 1.63$, a 63% increase.

Output 6.8 Arthritis data: Overall tests and parameter estimates

```
                 Testing Global Null Hypothesis: BETA=0
                                  Intercept
                     Intercept      and
        Criterion      Only       Covariates   Chi-Square for Covariates


        AIC          118.449      100.063         .
        SC           120.880      109.786         .
        -2 LOG L     116.449       92.063       24.386 with 3 DF (p=0.0001)
        Score           .            .          22.005 with 3 DF (p=0.0001)


                 Analysis of Maximum Likelihood Estimates
                    Parameter Standard    Wald       Pr >     Standardized   Odds
        Variable DF  Estimate   Error  Chi-Square Chi-Square    Estimate     Ratio
        INTERCPT 1   -4.5033    1.3074   11.8649    0.0006         .           .
        _SEX_    1    1.4878    0.5948    6.2576    0.0124      0.377296     4.427
        _TREAT_  1    1.7598    0.5365   10.7596    0.0010      0.487891     5.811
        AGE      1    0.0487    0.0207    5.5655    0.0183      0.343176     1.050
```

Plots are constructed from the dataset RESULTS. Here are the first few observations.

```
ID    TREAT    AGE   SEX   IMPROVE   PREDICT   LOWER   UPPER   LOGIT   SELOGIT

57   Treated    27   Male      1      0.194    0.103   0.334  -1.427   0.758
 9   Placebo    37   Male      0      0.063    0.032   0.120  -2.700   0.725
46   Treated    29   Male      0      0.209    0.115   0.350  -1.330   0.728
14   Placebo    44   Male      0      0.086    0.047   0.152  -2.358   0.658
   . . .
```

Predicted probabilities and confidence limits are contained in the variables PREDICT, UPPER, and LOWER. Corresponding logit values and their standard errors are contained in the variables LOGIT and SELOGIT. The predicted relations are linear and additive on the logit (log odds) scale according to the model (Equation 6.9), but perhaps more interpretable on the probability scale. One reasonable compromise is to plot the predicted log odds along with an auxiliary scale showing the equivalent probability values.

To show the effects of Sex, Treatment, and Age on improvement (Pr{Better}), separate plots are drawn for each sex, using the statement BY SEX; in a PROC GPLOT step. These plots are shown side by side in Figure 6.11, facilitating their comparison.

Figure 6.11 Estimated logits for Sex, Treatment, and Age. Corresponding probabilities of a "better" response are shown on the scale on the right side.

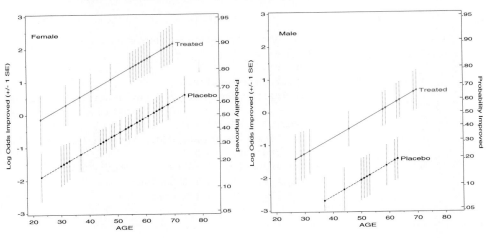

Most of the work consists of drawing the confidence limits with the Annotate facility, but this is worthwhile because it shows the locations and bounds for individual observations. Plots of the predicted probabilities can be made in a similar way using the variables PREDICT, UPPER, and LOWER.

```
proc sort data=results;
   by sex treat age;

data bars;
   set results(keep=sex treat age logit selogit);
   by sex treat;
   length text $8;
   xsys='2'; ysys='2';
   if treat='Placebo' then color='BLACK';
                      else color='RED';
   x  = age; line=33;
   y  = logit+selogit;  function='MOVE    '; output;
   y  = logit-selogit;
   y  = max(-3,y);      function='DRAW    '; output;
   if last.treat then do;
      y = logit;
      x = age+1; position='6';
      text = treat; function='LABEL'; output;
      end;
   if first.sex then do;
      ysys ='1'; y=90;
      xsys ='1'; x=10;
      text = sex; function='LABEL'; output;
      end;
```

The probability scale is constructed using the PSCALE macro (Appendix A.31.8), which produces an Annotate dataset to draw the tick marks and probability values along the right axis. The axis label is drawn by using a TITLE statement that specifies ANGLE=-90.

```
%pscale(anno=pscale);
data pscale;
   set pscale;
   sex = 'Female'; output;
   sex = 'Male  '; output;
proc sort;
   by sex;
data bars;
   set bars pscale;
   by sex;

title ' '
   h=1.5 a=-90 'Probability Improved'
   h=3.5 a=-90 ' ';
goptions hby=0;
proc gplot data=results;
   plot logit * age = treat / vaxis=axis1 haxis=axis2 hm=1 vm=1
                              nolegend anno=bars frame;
   by sex;
   axis1 label=(a=90 'Log Odds Improved (+/- 1 SE)')
         order=(-3 to 3);
   axis2 order=(20 to 80 by 10) offset=(2,6);
   symbol1 v=+ i=join l=3 c=black;
   symbol2 v=$ i=join l=1 c=red;
run;
```

Figure 6.11 provides a clear interpretation for the predicted effects of Age combined with those of Treatment and Sex that you saw earlier. On the logit scale, improvement increases linearly with age. The probability scale enables us to understand the predicted values more readily. For instance, you can see that a 50-year-old woman given the active treatment has a predicted probability of improvement around 0.80, but she has a probability less than 0.40 if given the placebo.

Because the model includes no interaction terms, the fitted lines are parallel for all Treatment–Sex groups, and the effects of all variables are large compared to their standard errors. However, you are only plotting fitted values here and should be cautious until you have tested for interactions among these variables. This interaction is shown in Section 6.5.1 (Example 6.10). □

EXAMPLE 6.9 Survival in the ICU

In this example, some aspects of logistic regression related to model selection and graphical display with a mixture of quantitative and discrete variables are examined. The data is from a study by Lemeshow, et al. (1988) of patients admitted to an intensive care unit at Baystate Medical Center in Springfield, Massachusetts.[5] The goal of this study was to develop a model to predict the probability of survival (up until hospital discharge) of these patients and to study the risk factors associated with ICU mortality. Data for a sample of 200 subjects from this study is given in Hosmer and Lemeshow (1989, Appendix 2), and reproduced in Appendix B.4 in this book.

There are 19 explanatory variables, of which three are quantitative (Age, Systolic blood pressure, and Heart rate), one variable is categorical (Race), and the remaining 15 are binary (many having been dichotomized). Initial model screening was carried out by using the Forward, Backward, and Stepwise procedures using the SELECTION option in the MODEL statement. As in other model selection procedures, it is prudent to regard these simply as "candidate" models, nominated for further attention. The results for the full model with all 19 predictors and for the final selection models are also shown.

Selection	AIC	SC	G^2	Score	df	Variables in Model
Full model	160.78	226.74	79.38	74.74	19	All
Stepwise	149.14	165.63	61.03	62.67	4	Age Cancer Admit Uncons
Forward	149.14	165.63	61.03	62.67	4	Age Cancer Admit Uncons
Backward	144.44	170.83	71.72	70.52	7	Age Cancer Admit Uncons Systolic pH PCO

For the moment, focus on the variables Age, Cancer, Admit (elective vs. emergency admission) and Uncons (stupor or coma at admission). These were nominated by all three procedures and constitute the best model according to the Forward and Stepwise procedures. Estimated coefficients and odds ratios for this model are shown in Output 6.9, which were fit using the statements that follow. The lack-of-fit test (output not shown) gives $\chi^2(8) = 5.081$, $p = 0.74$, showing no evidence of need for a more complex model.

```
%include data(icu);
proc logistic data=icu nosimple order=data;
    model died = age  cancer  uncons admit /
        scale=none aggregate lackfit;
    output out=results p=predict l=lower u=upper / alpha=.33;
```

[5]*Applied Logistic Regression*, David W. Hosmer, Jr. and Stanley Lemeshow, Copyright © 1989 John Wiley & Sons, Inc. Reprinted by permission of John Wiley & Sons, Inc.

Output 6.9   ICU data: Parameter estimates

```
                     Analysis of Maximum Likelihood Estimates

                  Parameter Standard    Wald      Pr >    Standardized   Odds
         Variable DF Estimate  Error  Chi-Square Chi-Square  Estimate    Ratio

         INTERCPT 1   -6.8698  1.3188  27.1341    0.0001                  .
         AGE      1    0.0372  0.0128   8.4751    0.0036    0.411049     1.038
         CANCER   1    2.0971  0.8385   6.2555    0.0124    0.347729     8.143
         UNCONS   1    3.7055  0.8765  17.8734    0.0001    0.539440    40.669
         ADMIT    1    3.1022  0.9186  11.4047    0.0007    0.756716    22.246
```

Because age is continuous, it is sensible to plot predicted results against age, and to construct separate curves according to the combinations of the other risk factors that are present for each case. A composite variable RISK is created combining the values of Cancer, Admit, and Uncons, which all correspond to increased risk of death.

```
data results;
   set results;
   length risk $16;
   if cancer then risk = 'Can';
   if admit  then risk = trim(risk) ||' Emerg';
   if uncons then risk = trim(risk) ||' Uncon';
   if risk =' ' then risk='None';
   risk = left(risk);
   label predict='Estimated Probability of Death';

proc sort;
   by risk age;
```

The following steps create Annotate labels for the risk factors and plot predicted probability of death for each combination, producing the graph in Figure 6.12:

```
data label;
   set results;
   by risk;
   retain xsys ysys '2';
   position ='3';
   if predict>.9 then position='2';
   if last.risk then do;
      x = age;  y=predict;
      function = 'label   ';
      text=risk;
      output;
      end;

proc gplot data=results;
   plot predict * age = risk /
      frame anno=label vaxis=axis1 haxis=axis2 vm=1 hm=1 nolegend;
   axis1 label=(a=90);
   axis2 offset=(,4);
   symbol1 i=join v=square   c=red ci=black;
   symbol2 i=join v=triangle c=red ci=blue;
   symbol3 i=join v=circle   c=red ci=black;
   symbol4 i=join v=dot      c=red ci=blue;
   symbol5 i=join v=plus     c=black;
   symbol6 i=join v=diamond  c=blue ci=blue;
 run; quit;
```

Figure 6.12   ICU Survival data: Predicted probabilities for combinations of risk factors vs. AGE

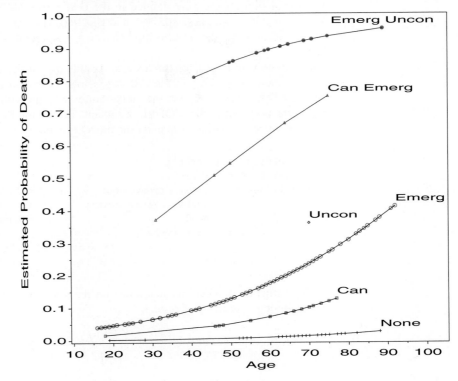

From the graph, it is apparent that mortality increases with age when any of these risk factors are present, particularly when the patient is admitted to Emergency; it is highest when the patient is also unconscious at admission. From the odds ratios (see Output 6.9), notice that the odds of death are increased 40-fold when the patient is unconscious. The graph, however, shows the effects of these risk factors in combination; the points also indicate the number and age distribution of cases that have these combinations.

Before concluding that this model provides an adequate description of the data, you should examine whether any individual cases are unduly influencing the predicted results, and more importantly, the choice of variables in the model. This question is examined in Section 6.6, where this data is used again (Example 6.12).   □

6.5.1   Models with Interaction

The examples for the arthritis data have involved only main effects of Sex, Age, and Treatment. I first illustrate tests for interactions and powers of quantitative variables. Whether interactions are present or not, the plotting of estimated logits or predicted probabilities from PROC LOGISTIC is no more complicated.

In fact, since the predicted probabilities and logits are calculated by the procedure and output to the dataset RESULTS, the results plotted depend *purely* on the MODEL statement. The plotting steps remain the same as used in Figure 6.11, assuming you want to make separate plots for males and females of the Age by Treatment effects. For more complex models, or situations where you want to plot predicted results averaged over some variables, a method for plotting effects from the model coefficients is described in Section 6.5.2.

EXAMPLE 6.10   **Arthritis treatment**

The interaction effects were defined in the DATA step `ARTHRIT` in Example 6.8 as the dummy variables AGESEX, AGETRT, and SEXTRT. The variable AGE2 = AGE**2 can be used to test whether the relationship between age and logit(better) is quadratic rather than linear.

A simple way to test for the need to include *any* of these more complex terms is illustrated here. The `PROC LOGISTIC` step below requests a forward-selection procedure. Setting START=3 requests that the model-building begin with the first three variables (the main effects) listed in the MODEL statement. The option SLENTRY=1 (significance level to enter) forces all variables to enter the model eventually.

```
proc logistic data=arthrit;
   format better outcome.;
   model  better = _sex_ _treat_ age        /* main effects */
                   agesex agetrt sextrt      /* interactions */
                   age2                      /* quadratic age */
         / selection=forward
           start=3                    /* start with main effects */
           slentry=1;                 /* force all terms to enter */
```

The variables included in each model for the selection procedure are listed in a note at the beginning of each set of results:

```
Step  0. The following variables were entered:
         INTERCPT  _SEX_      _TREAT_    AGE
```

Results for this step are identical to those of the main effects model given earlier. Near the end of this step, the residual χ^2 is printed, which corresponds to a joint test for the other four variables. This test is an appropriate test of goodness of fit of the main effects model.

```
Residual Chi-Square = 4.0268 with 4 DF (p=0.4024)
```

Other tests printed show none of the interaction terms is significant individually.   □

6.5.2   Effect Plots from Coefficients

You can also construct plots for a fitted model by calculating the predicted logit values directly from the coefficients for the variables in the model. This method can be used when raw data is not available, or when you want to average over certain effects to present simplified views of a complex model. To illustrate, for the arthritis main effect model, the fitted relationship is

$$\text{logit}(p) = -4.5033 + 1.4878\,\text{sex} + 1.7598\,\text{treat} + 0.0487\,\text{age} \ .$$

With this method, the logit is calculated for each independent variable varied over its range in all possible combinations. Fixing an explanatory variable at its average gives an effects plot for the remaining variables, which is particularly useful when that variable does not interact with others. Fox (1987) explains how this method can be used to construct adjusted effects plots for particular interactions, adjusting for other variables not represented in the plot.

The response can also be graphed on the probability scale by transforming the logit via $p = \exp(\text{logit})/(1 + \exp(\text{logit}))$. For example, the fitted logits and corresponding probabilities for the arthritis data can be calculated in this DATA step:

```
data fitted;
   do _sex_ = 0 to 1;
      do _treat_ = 0 to 1;
         do age = 25 to 75 by 5;
            logit= -4.5033 + 1.4878*_sex_ + 1.7598*_treat_ + 0.0487*age;
            prob = exp(logit) / (1 + exp(logit));
            output;
            end;
         end;
      end;
```

Replacing the outer DO-loop with `_sex_` = $\text{Pr}_{\text{Female}}$ = 59/84 = .702 would give fitted values at the average over sex; using `_sex_` = 1/2 would give fitted values for a population with an equal sex distribution.

EXAMPLE 6.11   **Volunteering for a psychological experiment**

Fox (1987) illustrated this method using data from a study by Cowles and Davis (1987) on the personality factors that predispose people to volunteer for a psychological experiment. In this study, 1,421 university students completed a personality inventory, which contained a 24-item scale of Introversion-Extroversion and a 24-item scale of Stability-Neuroticism, among other measures. They were also asked to indicate their willingness in principle to volunteer for a psychological experiment, which was the response to be explained by the personality variables.

Fox reports the results of a logistic regression fit to this data as

$$\text{logit}(\pi_v) = -2.605 + 0.2472\,\text{Sex} + 0.1668E + 0.1108N - 0.0088552E \times N \quad ,$$

where π_v is the probability of volunteering, Sex is a dummy variable coded 0 for males and 1 for females, E is the Introversion-Extroversion score on a scale of 0–24, and N is the Stability-Neuroticism score, also on a scale of 0–24.

In this model, the positive coefficient for Sex implies that women are more likely to volunteer than men at each combination of extroversion and neuroticism. Because Sex does not interact with either extroversion or neuroticism, you can focus on the relation between the probability of volunteering and the two personality variables. Setting SEX=.5 in the DATA step below generates observations for the adjusted effects in a population equally composed of men and women.[6]

```
data predict;
   array b{0:4} _temporary_ (-2.605  0.2472  0.1668  0.1108 -0.008552);
   do sex = 0 to 1 by .5;
      do neurot = 0 to 24 by 6;
         do extra = 0 to 24 by 6;
            logit = b[0] + b[1]*sex + b[2]*extra + b[3]*neurot
                  + b[4]*extra*neurot;
            prob = exp(logit) / ( 1 + exp(logit) );
            output;
            end;
         end;
      end;
```

---

[6]Alternatively, we could set SEX=0.55, the proportion of women in the sample.

At a given level of Sex, we may graph the fitted probability of volunteering (PROB) against one predictor (extroversion) with separate curves for each level of the other predictor (neuroticism). The graph for the average over Sex is shown in Figure 6.13.

Figure 6.13   Fitted probability of volunteering, controlling for Sex. The effect of Sex is shown at the point where the curves intersect. The vertical lines at other selected combinations of extroversion and neuroticism show individual 50% confidence intervals.

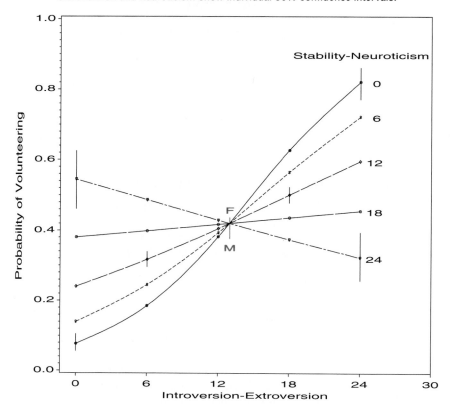

First, you can find the average probability of volunteering by averaging the logits and transforming the average values to the probability scale.

```
proc summary nway data=predict;
   class sex;
   var logit ;
   output out=means mean=;
data means;
   set means;
   drop _type_ _freq_;
   prob = exp(logit) / (1 + exp(logit));
proc print;
```

which produces

OBS	SEX	LOGIT	PROB
1	0.0	-0.50587	0.37616
2	0.5	-0.38230	0.40557
3	1.0	-0.25872	0.43568

The statements below create an Annotate dataset that supplies the labels for the levels of neuroticism in Figure 6.13. The effect of Sex is shown by drawing a vertical line showing the average probability of volunteering for men and for women at the center of the graph.

```
proc format;
   value sex 0='Male'
             .5=' '             /* average */
             1='Female';
data anno;
   set predict;
   by sex neurot;
   xsys='2'; ysys='2';
   length text $22 function color $8;
   position='5';
   if last.neurot then do;
      x=extra+1;
      y=prob;
      text = put(neurot,3.0); function='LABEL'; output;
      end;

   if first.sex then do;
      y=.90;
      x=24; text='Stability-Neuroticism';
      function='LABEL'; output;
      x=2; text=put(sex,sex.);
      function='LABEL'; output;
      if text =' ' then do;
         color = 'red';
         x = 12.956;               * intersection of curves;
         y = 0.43568;              * average prob for females;
         function = 'MOVE '; output;
         text = 'F'; position = '2';
         function = 'LABEL' ; output;
         y = 0.37616;              * average prob for males;
         function = 'DRAW ' ; output;
         text = 'M'; position = '8';
         function = 'LABEL' ; output;
         end;
      end;
```

The graph in Figure 6.13 is the second of three panels (for SEX=0.5) drawn by the PROC GPLOT step below. The other two graphs have the same form, shifted up for females and down for males, as indicated by the vertical bar at the intersection of the curves in Figure 6.13.

```
goptions hby=0;
proc gplot data=predict;
   plot  prob * extra = neurot /
         vaxis=axis1 haxis=axis2 hminor=0
         frame nolegend anno=anno;
   by sex;
   axis1 label=(a=90) order=(0 to 1 by .2);
   axis2 label=(h=1.5 'Introversion-Extroversion')
         order=(0 to 30 by 6)  offset=(3,0);
   symbol1 v=+ i=spline l=1 c=black;
   symbol2 v=* i=spline l=3 c=black;
   symbol3 v=$ i=spline l=5 c=black;
   symbol4 v=- i=spline l=7 c=black;
   symbol5 v=# i=spline l=9 c=black;
```

The interpretation of these results is quite clear from the graph. At low levels of neuroticism, probability of volunteering increases with extroversion, but the slope of this relation decreases as neuroticism increases. (If you want a lot of volunteers in a psychological experiment, look for extroverted non-neurotics.) At the highest levels of neuroticism, probability of volunteering decreases with extroversion.

The error bars shown in Figure 6.13 require the estimated variance-covariance matrix of the coefficients, $\widehat{\mathcal{V}(b)} = (X^\mathsf{T} V X)^{-1}$, in addition to the coefficients themselves. Because the fitted value, $\mathrm{logit}(\pi_i) = x_i^\mathsf{T} b$, is a linear combination of the parameters, its standard error may be calculated as

$$\text{s.e. } \mathrm{logit}(\pi_i) = [x_i^\mathsf{T} \widehat{\mathcal{V}(b)} x_i]^{1/2}$$

An approximate 50% confidence interval for the fitted logit may then be calculated as $\mathrm{logit}(\pi_i) \pm 0.67 \times \text{s.e. } \mathrm{logit}(\pi_i)$, and the end points transformed back to the probability scale.

For example, the DATA step below inputs the coefficients and the estimated variance-covariance matrix in the form it would be produced by PROC LOGISTIC with the options OUTEST=PARMS COVOUT on the PROC statement.

```
data parms;
    input _type_ $ _name_ $ intercep sex extra neurot extneu;
datalines;
PARMS   ESTIMATE  -2.60551   0.24715   0.16682   0.11078  -.0085525
COV     INTERCPT   0.27504  -0.01839  -0.01819  -0.01726   0.0012943
COV     SEX       -0.01839   0.01246   0.00013  -0.00007  -.0000134
COV     INTEXT    -0.01819   0.00013   0.00142   0.00127  -.0001023
COV     NEUROT    -0.01726  -0.00007   0.00127   0.00142  -.0001052
COV     EXTNEU     0.00129  -0.00001  -0.00010  -0.00011   0.0000086
;
```

(If this analysis was carried out using raw data, the OUTEST=PARMS dataset could be used directly.) Calculation of the standard errors and confidence intervals is then done most easily with SAS/IML, as follows:

```
proc iml;
   use parms;
   read var{intercep sex extra neurot extneu} into b where(_type_='PARMS');
   read all var{intercep sex extra neurot extneu} into cov
       where(_type_='COV');
   b = t(b);
   do sex = 0 to 1 by .5;
      do neurot = 0 to 24 by 6;
         do extra = 0 to 24 by 6;
            x = 1 || sex || extra || neurot || extra#neurot;
            logit = x * b;
            selogit = sqrt( x * cov * t(x) );
            prob = exp(logit) / ( 1 + exp(logit) );
            result = result || ( x[,2:4] || logit || selogit || prob );
            end;
         end;
      end;
   ul = result[,4] + .67#result[,5];
   ll = result[,4] - .67#result[,5];
   lower = exp(ll) / ( 1 + exp(ll) );
   upper = exp(ul) / ( 1 + exp(ul) );
   var = {sex extra neurot logit selogit prob lower upper};
   result = result || lower || upper;
   create predict from result[c=var];
   append from result;
quit;
```

The error bars in Figure 6.13 serve notice that the predicted probabilities are most precise for those with average levels of the explanatory variables, as is usual with linear models.

□

6.6   Influence and Diagnostic Plots

In ordinary least-squares (OLS) regression, measures of ***influence*** (leverage, Cook's D, DFBETAs, etc.) help you to determine whether individual cases (or cells in grouped data) have undue impact on the fitted regression model and the coefficients of individual predictors. Analogs of most of these measures have been suggested for logistic regression. Pregibon (1981) provided the theoretical basis for these methods, exploiting the relationship between logistic models and weighted least squares. Some additional problems occur in practical applications to logistic regression because the response is discrete, and because the leave-one-out diagnostics are more difficult to compute.

6.6.1   Residuals and Leverage

As in ordinary least-squares regression, the influence (actual impact) of an observation in logistic models depends multiplicatively on its residual (disagreement between y_i and $\hat{y}_i$) and its leverage (how unusual x_i is in the space of the explanatory variables). The multiplicative definitions imply that a case is influential to the extent that it is poorly fit *and* has unusual values of the predictors.

In logistic regression, the simple raw residual is just $e_i \equiv y_i - \hat{p}_i$, where $\hat{p}_i = \exp(x_i^\mathsf{T} b)/[1 + \exp(x_i^\mathsf{T} b)]$. The Pearson and deviance residuals are more useful for identifying poorly fitted observations, and are components of overall goodness-of-fit statistics. The ***Pearson residual*** is defined as

$$r_i \equiv \frac{e_i}{\sqrt{p_i(1 - p_i)}} \tag{6.9}$$

and the Pearson chi-square is $\chi^2 = \sum r_i^2$. The ***deviance residual*** is

$$g_i \equiv \pm -2[y_i \log p_i + (1 - y_i) \log(1 - p_i)]^{1/2} \tag{6.10}$$

where the sign of g_i is the same as that of e_i. Likewise, the sum of squares of the deviance residuals gives the overall deviance, $G^2 = -2 \log \mathcal{L}(b) = \sum g_i^2$.

When y_i is a binomial count based on n_i trials (grouped data), the Pearson residuals (Equation 6.9) then become

$$r_i \equiv \frac{y_i - n_i p_i}{\sqrt{n_i p_i(1 - p_i)}}$$

with similar modifications made to Equation 6.10.

Leverage measures the *potential* impact of an individual case on the results, which is directly proportional to how far an individual case is from the centroid in the space of the predictors. Leverage is computed as the diagonal elements, h_{ii}, of the "Hat" matrix, H,

$$H = X^\star (X^{\star\mathsf{T}} X^\star)^{-1} X^{\star\mathsf{T}}$$

where $X^\star = V^{1/2} X$, and $V = \text{diag}[\hat{p}(1 - \hat{p})]$. As in OLS regression, leverage values are between 0 and 1, and a leverage value, $h_{ii} > 2(k + 1)/n$ is considered "large"; here, k is the number of predictors, and n is the number of cases. In OLS, however, the hat values depend only on the X's; whereas in logistic regression, they also depend on the dependent variable values and the fitted probabilities (through V). As a result, an observation may be extremely unusual on the predictors, yet not have a large hat value, if the fitted probability is near 0 or 1.

6.6.2 Influence Diagnostics

Influence measures assess the effect that deleting an observation has on the regression parameters, fitted values, or the goodness-of-fit statistics. In OLS regression, these measures can be computed exactly from a single regression. In logistic regression, the exact effect of deletion requires refitting the model with each observation deleted in turn (because the estimating equations (Equation 6.5) are nonlinear), which is a time-intensive computation. Consequently, Pregibon (1981) showed how analogous deletion diagnostics may be approximated by performing one additional step of the iterative procedure.

The simplest measure of influence of observation i is the standardized change in the coefficient for each variable due to omitting that observation, termed **DFBETA**s. From the relation (Pregibon, 1981, p. 716)

$$b - b_{(-i)} = (X^\mathsf{T} V X)^{-1} x_i (y_i - p_i)/(1 - h_{ii}) \ ,$$

the estimated standardized change in the coefficient for variable j is

$$\text{DFBETA}i_j \equiv \frac{b_{(-i)j} - b_j}{\hat{\sigma}(b_j)} \ , \tag{6.11}$$

where $\hat{\sigma}(b_j)$ is the estimated standard error of b_j. With k regressors, there are $k + 1$ sets of DFBETAs, which makes their examination burdensome. Graphical displays ease this burden, as do various summary measures considered below.

The overall influence of observation i on the estimated regression coefficients is assessed by analogs of **Cook's distance**, which measure the difference between b for all the data and $b_{(-i)}$ estimated without observation i. One measure, C_i, is defined as

$$C_i \equiv (b - b_{(-i)})^\mathsf{T} X^\mathsf{T} V X (b - b_{(-i)}) \ ,$$

and calculated as

$$C_i = \frac{r_i^2 h_{ii}}{(1 - h_{ii})^2} \ . \tag{6.12}$$

A second measure, $\overline{C}_i$, is calculated as

$$\overline{C}_i = \frac{r_i^2 h_{ii}}{(1 - h_{ii})} = (1 - h_{ii})C_i \ . \tag{6.13}$$

Because $0 \leq h_{ii} \leq 1$, $\overline{C}_i$ will never be larger than C_i. These measures are referred to by the keywords C and CBAR, respectively, in the OUTPUT statement. Both can be interpreted as squared measures of the change in size of the confidence intervals for all regression coefficients. Rules of thumb for noticeably large values are necessarily only rough indicators, but Johnson (1985) suggests comparing kC_i to a $\chi^2(k)$ distribution.

The Pearson and deviance residuals defined above do not have equal variance, but rather have variance $\approx 1 - h_{ii}$. Studentized versions of both that do have equal variance are obtained by dividing by $\sqrt{1 - h_{ii}}$. For example, the studentized deviance residual (RESDEV) is $g_i^\star = g_i/\sqrt{1 - h_{ii}}$. These are most usefully expressed in squared form as the approximate decrease in the deviance (DIFDEV) and Pearson (DIFCHISQ) χ^2 associated with deleting observation i:

$$\Delta G^2_{(-i)} = \frac{g_i^2}{1 - h_{ii}} \ ,$$

and

$$\Delta \chi^2_{(-i)} = \frac{r_i^2}{1 - h_{ii}} \ .$$

These are both asymptotically distributed as $\chi^2(1)$; so a value exceeding 3.84 (or the rounded value, 4) is worth noticing. They may also be interpreted as indicating how poorly the current model fits observation i.

As with OLS regression, influential observations signal something unusual: extreme (or erroneous) predictor values combined with an ill-predicted response—e.g., someone who died but should have survived (according to the model). They may also signal that some important (perhaps unmeasured) predictor—a lurking variable—has been omitted from the model (Joiner, 1981) or expressed on the wrong scale.

6.6.3   Influence Output from PROC LOGISTIC

All the influence statistics are printed when the INFLUENCE option is used in the MODEL statement. The following example produces these diagnostics for the arthritis data:

```
proc logistic data=arthrit ;
   model better = _sex_ _treat_ _age_ / influence;
```

This produces many pages of output, of the form in Output 6.10, shown for two of the many diagnostic measures. With so much output, it is often difficult to spot unusual observations. A more useful option, IPLOTS, produces index plots of each of the diagnostic measures against the observation index, with the goal of showing which observations stand out from the rest. It is even more useful, I believe, to plot certain diagnostics against each other, including reference lines showing the nominal danger-level for each diagnostic, because they help to pinpoint *why* certain observations are influential. Some examples of these plots are described in the Section 6.6.4.

Output 6.10   Regression diagnostics: Printed output (partial) for arthritis data

```
                        The LOGISTIC Procedure
                        Regression Diagnostics
               Deviance Residual                    Hat Matrix Diagonal

Case                (1 unit = 0.26)                    (1 unit = 0.01)
Number  Value   -8  -4  0 2 4 6 8      Value      0 2 4 6 8   12   16

   1    1.812   | *      |         |   0.089   |               *         |
   2    0.360   |       |*         |   0.031   |    *                    |
   3    0.685   |        |  *      |   0.087   |              *          |
   4    0.425   |        |*        |   0.034   |    *                    |
   5    0.700   |        |  *      |   0.086   |             *           |
   6    0.488   |        |*        |   0.038   |    *                    |
   7    1.703   |  *     |         |   0.084   |             *           |
   8    0.499   |        |*        |   0.039   |    *                    |
   9    1.396   |    *   |         |   0.066   |         *               |
  10    0.511   |        |*        |   0.040   |    *                    |
  11    1.142   |      * |         |   0.064   |          *              |
  12    0.523   |        |*        |   0.041   |    *                    |
  13    1.234   |        |    *    |   0.065   |          *              |
  14    0.599   |        |*        |   0.051   |      *                  |
  15    1.121   |      * |         |   0.065   |          *              |
  16    0.599   |        |*        |   0.051   |      *                  |
  17    1.319   |        |   *     |   0.069   |           *             |
  18    0.640   |       |*         |   0.058   |       *                 |
  19    1.319   |        |   *     |   0.069   |           *             |
  20    0.640   |        |*        |   0.058   |       *                 |
  21    1.340   |        |    *    |   0.070   |           *             |
  22    1.814   | *      |         |   0.061   |        *                |
  23    1.022   |       *|         |   0.070   |           *             |
  24    0.529   |        |*        |   0.060   |        *                |
  25    1.449   |        |    *    |   0.078   |            *            |
  26    0.619   |        |*        |   0.053   |      *                  |
  27    0.909   |       *|         |   0.080   |            *            |
  28    0.619   |        |*        |   0.053   |      *                  |
  29    1.120   |        |   *     |   0.141   |                       *|
  30    1.846   | *      |         |   0.052   |      *                  |
  31    1.309   |        |    *    |   0.092   |                *        |
  32    0.647   |        |*        |   0.050   |      *                  |
  33    0.955   |       *|         |   0.070   |           *             |
  34    1.803   | *      |         |   0.049   |      *                  |
```

6.6.4 Diagnostic Plots of Influence Measures

Plots of the change in χ^2 (DIFCHISQ or DIFDEV) against either leverage or predicted probability are particularly useful for detecting unduly influential cases. These are discrete analogs of plots recommended for linear models by Fox (1991) and Friendly (1991). The estimated overall influence of each case on the estimated coefficients (C_i or $\overline{C}_i$) can be shown in a bubble plot where the plotting symbols are circles proportional to C or CBAR.

Such plots are produced by the INFLOGIS macro, described in Appendix A.12. For example, these statements produce plots of DIFCHISQ against both the predicted probability, PRED (Figure 6.14), and leverage, HAT (Figure 6.15), using bubbles whose area is proportional to C:

```
title 'Arthritis treatment data';
title2 'Bubble size: Influence on Coefficients (C)';
goptions htext=1.6;
%include data(arthrit);
%inflogis(data=arthrit,
    y=better,            /* response    */
    x=_sex_ _treat_ age, /* predictors  */
    id=id,               /* case label  */
    gy=DIFCHISQ,         /* graph ordinate  */
    gx=PRED HAT,         /* graph abscissas */
    lcolor=RED, bsize=14
    );
```

Figure 6.14   Influence plot for arthritis data. Cases with DIFCHISQ > 4 or leverage > $(2k)/n = 0.095$ are labeled as influential, as indicated by the size of the bubble symbol. The systematic pattern shown is inherent in the discrete nature of logistic regression. The most influential observations are usually those with very high or low predicted probabilities.

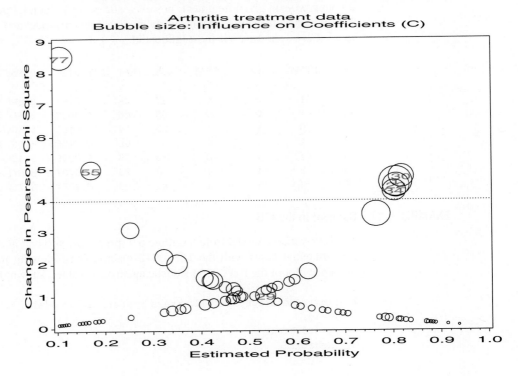

Figure 6.15   Changes in chi-square vs. leverage. The same cases are labeled as in Figure 6.14.

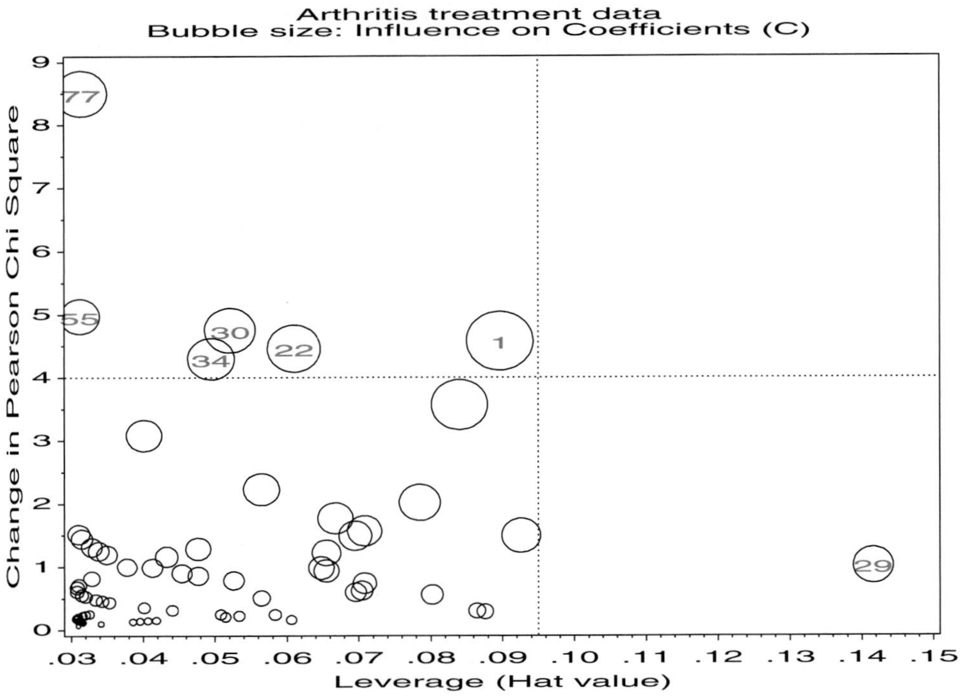

The printed output from the INFLOGIS macro includes a table identifying any observation of high leverage *or* high influence. These observations are also labeled in the graphs. For example, case 29 is of high leverage because she is unusual in terms of the predictors: a young woman given treatment; however, she is not influential in the fitted model. Case 77 is not of high leverage, but is poorly predicted by the model and has a large contribution to χ^2. Case 1, however, is most influential.

CASE	BETTER	_SEX_	_TREAT_	AGE	HAT	DIFCHISQ	DIFDEV	C
1	1	0	1	27	.09	4.5781	3.6953	0.4510
22	1	0	0	63	.06	4.4603	3.5649	0.2898
29	0	1	1	23	.14	1.0183	1.4005	0.1679
30	1	1	0	31	.05	4.7485	3.6573	0.2611
34	1	1	0	33	.05	4.2955	3.4644	0.2236
55	0	1	1	58	.03	4.9697	3.6759	0.1602
77	0	1	1	69	.03	8.4977	4.7122	0.2758

EXAMPLE 6.12   Survival in the ICU

The four-variable model from Example 6.9 (predicting survival in the ICU) was examined for influential cases with the INFLOGIS macro. The following macro call produces an influence plot of the DIFCHISQ statistic against hat values, shown in Figure 6.16:

```
%inflogis(data=icu, y=died, x=age cancer uncons admit,
    id=id,
    gy=difchisq,
    gx=hat);
```

Figure 6.16   ICU Survival data: Influence plot

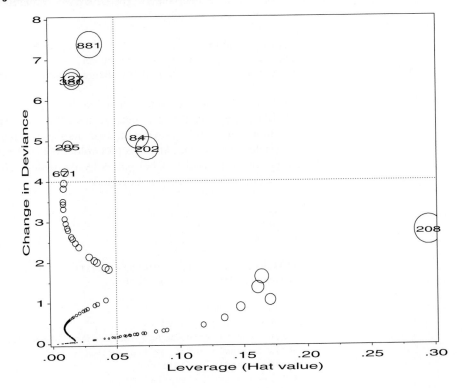

Details for the cases identified in the figure are shown in Output 6.11. None of the cases are particularly influential on the model coefficients overall: the largest C_i is only 1.04. Case 208, with the largest hat value, is unusual on the predictors in this sample: a 70-year-old man without cancer who was admitted on an elective basis (who nonetheless died). On the other hand, case 881, an 89-year-old male who was admitted unconscious as an emergency case, is poorly predicted because he survived. Similarly, two other cases (127, 380) with large $\Delta \chi^2_{(-i)}$ are poorly predicted because they died, although they were young, did not have cancer, and were conscious at admission. From this evidence, we might conclude that none of these cases greatly affects the model, its coefficients, or interpretation.

Output 6.11   ICU data: Influential cases

ID	DIED	AGE	CANCER	UNCONS	ADMIT	HAT	DIFCHISQ	DIFDEV	C
127	Yes	19	No	0	Emergency	.02	21.7188	6.57873	0.37094
380	Yes	20	No	0	Emergency	.02	20.9247	6.49296	0.35586
285	Yes	40	No	0	Emergency	.01	9.9104	4.88418	0.13012
671	Yes	49	No	0	Emergency	.01	7.0743	4.23295	0.07478
208	Yes	70	No	1	Elective	.30	2.4894	2.76148	1.04350
202	Yes	75	Yes	0	Elective	.08	7.8664	4.81787	0.63948
84	No	59	No	1	Emergency	.07	9.0385	5.09973	0.65745
881	No	89	No	1	Emergency	.03	26.5189	7.38643	0.84292

That conclusion might not be warranted without further study, particularly in terms of influence on individual coefficients. The DFBETAs (Equation 6.11) may be obtained in an output dataset as shown below:

```
proc logistic data=icu;
   model died = age admit cancer uncons;
   output out=stats dfbetas=dbint dbage dbadmit dbcancer dbuncons ;
```

Individual DFBETAs are often graphed as *index plots*—that is, for variable j, a plot of DFBETA(i, j) against the case index i. In such plots, it is helpful to label points with large absolute values when (as here) the case number is not meaningful. For example, the following statements produce an index plot of the DFBETA for Age, shown in Figure 6.17. The LABEL macro is used to label points by the patient ID, where the DFBETA value exceeds 0.2 (an arbitrary value) in magnitude.

```
data stats;
   set stats;
   case = _n_;

%label(data=stats, x=case, y=dbage, text=put(id,3.), pos=-,
   subset=abs(dbage)>.2, out=labs);

proc gplot data=stats;
   plot dbage * case = died /
      anno=labs frame nolegend vaxis=axis1 haxis=axis2 vm=1;
   symbol1 i=needle v=dot c=black;
   symbol2 i=needle v=dot c=red;
   axis1 label=(a=90) length=4.5in;
   axis2 offset=(2)  ;
```

Figure 6.17   ICU data: DFBETA index plots for Age and Uncons

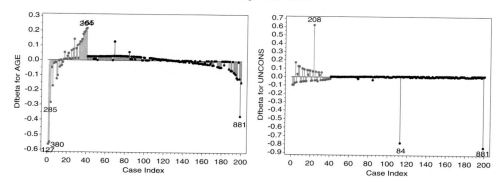

An alternative display, which is often more informative (though possibly more complex), is a scatterplot matrix of the DFBETAs, perhaps with other influence diagnostics as well. The pairwise scatterplots help to highlight observations that are influential on both or only one of each pair of measures. An example is shown in Figure 6.18, which was produced with the SCATMAT macro:

```
%scatmat(data=stats,
   var= dbAge dbAdmit dbCancer dbUncons, group=died,
   symbols=star square,
   plotopt=%str(href=-0.2 0.2 vref=-0.2 0.2 cvref=graya0 chref=graya0));
```

Figure 6.18 ICU Survival data: Scatterplot matrix of DFBETAs. Those who lived are shown by stars, and those who died are shown by squares. The reference lines indicate values of ±0.2 on each statistic.

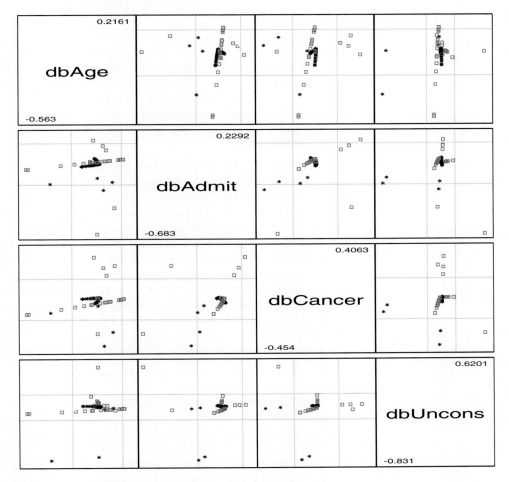

Most of the observations are in the central rectangle, corresponding to small values (< ±0.2) on both measures, but several points stand out on the pairwise combinations. For example, the bottom row and rightmost column (DFBETA for UNCONS) highlight two observations for patients who lived (indicated by stars) whose omission would decrease the coefficient for UNCONS considerably, and one who died whose omission would increase it. Other observations outside the central rectangle might also be investigated. □

6.6.5 Partial Residual and Added-Variable Plots

The graphical methods described in this section are relatively straightforward indicators of the adequacy of a particular model, with a specified set of predictors, each expressed in a given way. More sophisticated methods have also been proposed that focus on the need to include a particular predictor and whether its relationship is linear. These include the *partial residual plot*, *added-variable plot*, and the *constructed variable plot*, which are all analogous to techniques developed in OLS.

Partial Residual Plots

The partial residual plot (Larsen and McCleary, 1972) is designed to show whether a given variable, x_j, included linearly in the model, actually shows a nonlinear relation requiring transformation. As adapted to logistic regression by Landwehr, et al. (1984), the partial residual for variable x_j is defined as

$$r^\star = V^{-1}r + \beta_j x_j = \frac{y - p}{p(1 - p)} \ .$$

The partial residual plot is then a plot of $r^\star$ against x_j, possibly with the addition of a smoothed lowess curve (Fowlkes, 1987) and a linear regression line to aid interpretation. If x_j affects the binary response linearly, the plot should be approximately linear with a slope approximately equal to β_j. A nonlinear plot suggests that x_j needs to be transformed, and the shape of the relation gives a rough guide to the required transformation. For example, a parabolic shape would suggest a term in x_j^2.

Added-Variable Plots

The added-variable plot, developed for generalized linear models by Wang (1985), is a diagnostic plot designed to indicate whether some new regressor, z, should be added to the model that includes other explanatory variables. An overall test could be based on the difference in G^2 for the enlarged model logit$(p) = X\beta + \gamma z$, compared to the reduced model logit$(p) = X\beta$. But the added-variable plot shows whether the evidence for including z is spread throughout the sample or confined to a small subset of observations. The regressor z may be a new explanatory variable or a higher power of a variable already in the model.

The added-variable plot may be constructed by following the logistic regression for the reduced model with the variables in X with one weighted least-squares regression of z on X to find the residual part, $z^\star$, of z not predicted by the previous regressors. Let r be the vector of Pearson residuals from the initial logistic fit of y on the variables in X, and let H and $V = \text{diag}[\hat{p}(1 - \hat{p})]$ be the hat matrix and V matrix from this analysis. Then, the added variable plot is a scatterplot of the residuals r against the z-residuals,

$$z^\star = (I - H)V^{1/2}z \ .$$

The z-residuals are easily calculated as $z_i^\star = (z_i - \hat{z}_i)\sqrt{v_{ii}}$, where $\hat{z}_i$ is the fitted value of z_i in a weighted least-squares regression of z on X using the v_{ii} as weights.

A linear relation in this plot indicates that z should be included in the model, but observations with extreme z-residuals would be highly influential in this decision. A line fitted to this plot should have an intercept approximately zero, and a slope approximating the coefficient γ of z in the full model. Added-variable plots are produced by the ADDVAR macro, described in Appendix A.1 and illustrated in the following example.

EXAMPLE 6.13   Survival in the ICU

In Example 6.9 you saw that the backward selection method nominated three other variables, Systolic, pH, and PCO, in addition to the four variables that have been used throughout. Here, first investigate whether Systolic (blood pressure) should be added to the model that includes Age, Admit, Cancer, and Uncons.

The ADDVAR macro is called as follows to produce Figure 6.19. There is no evidence of a strong linear relation, suggesting that Systolic blood pressure has only a weak relationship to the residual in the current model. The smooth lowess curve suggests that any relationship may be mildly quadratic (though partial residual plots are generally preferable for detecting nonlinearity). The labeled points are those whose studentized Pearson residuals exceed 2 in absolute value.

```
%addvar(data=icu,
    y=Died,                         /* response */
    x=age admit cancer uncons,      /* original predictors */
    z=Systolic,                     /* added variable */
    id=patient,                     /* id variable */
    smooth=0.5);                    /* lowess smoothing fraction */
```

Figure 6.19   ICU data: Added-variable plot for Systolic blood pressure. The solid line shows the weighted least-squares regression of residuals on the Systolic residuals. The broken curve is the lowess smooth.

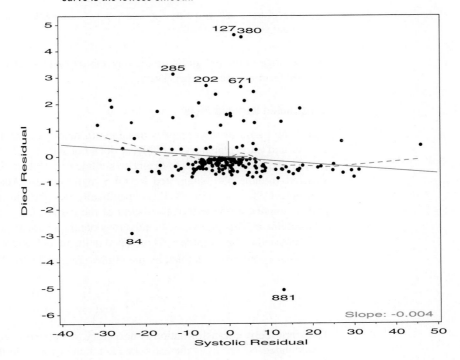

The added-variable plot may also be used to determine if a regressor should be included with an additional polynomial term. For example, you might check to see if Age^2 should be included in the model. The following statements produce Figure 6.20:

Figure 6.20   ICU data: Added-variable plot for Age^2

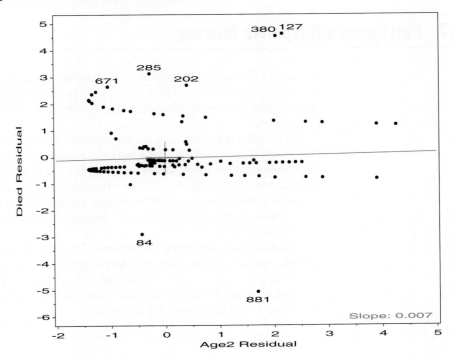

```
data icu;
   set icu;
   age2 = .01 * (age-57.5)**2;

%addvar(data=icu, y=Died,  x=age admit cancer uncons, z=Age2,
   id=patient, smooth=0);
```

The slope of the line in Figure 6.20 is approximately zero, so you can conclude that the squared term in Age is unnecessary. □

Constructed Variable Plots

While the partial residual plot is designed to detect a nonlinear relation between the response and an explanatory variable, it does not indicate the required transformation explicitly and sometimes fails to diagnose nonlinearity (Fienberg and Gong, 1984). The constructed variable plot, suggested for OLS regression by Atkinson (1981) and Cook and Weisberg (1982, Section 2.4.4), is specifically designed to detect nonlinear dependence *and* to suggest a power transformation of the explanatory variable that would make the relation linear. This plot was extended to generalized linear models by Wang (1987).

Suppose that the variable x_j is included in the model, and you are contemplating replacing x_j by a power $x_j^{(\lambda)}$, defined by the family (Box and Cox, 1964)

$$x^{(\lambda)} = \begin{cases} \frac{x^\lambda - 1}{\lambda}, & \lambda \neq 0 \\ \log(x), & \lambda = 0 \end{cases} . \tag{6.14}$$

To determine if a transformation is necessary, the constructed variable, $z_j = b_j x_j \log x_j$ is calculated, where b_j is the estimated coefficient for x_j in the original model. Then the constructed variable plot is just an added-variable plot for z_j.

A linear trend, with a non-zero slope γ, in the constructed variable plot indicates that a transformation of x_j is necessary, and the estimate of the power transformation in Equation 6.14 is $\hat{\lambda} = 1 + \gamma$, usually rounded to the nearest half-integer. The absence of a linear trend means that x_j is linear in the model.

6.7   Polytomous Response Models

When the response, y, takes on $m > 2$ discrete values, there are several ways to model the response probabilities. Let $\pi_{ij} \equiv \pi_j(x_i)$ be the probability of response j for case or group i, given the predictors x_i. Because $\sum_j \pi_{ij} = 1$, only $m - 1$ of these probabilities are required.

The simplest approach uses the ***proportional odds model***, described in Section 6.7.1. This model applies only when the response is ordinal, *and* an additional assumption (the proportional odds assumption) holds. However, if the response is purely nominal (e.g., vote Tory, Liberal, Reform, NDP), or if the proportional odds assumption is untenable, another particularly simple strategy is to fit separate models to a set of $m - 1$ ***nested dichotomies*** derived from the polytomous response (Section 6.7.3). Both of these methods are handled by `PROC LOGISTIC`.

A third strategy, described in Section 6.7.4, is to choose one response category (for example, the last) as the "base category", and model the ***generalized logits*** for each of categories $j = 1, 2, \ldots, (m - 1)$ compared to category m. For example, for a 3-category response, there are 2 generalized logits, $\text{logit}_{i1} = \log(\pi_{i1}/\pi_{i3})$ and $\text{logit}_{i1} = \log(\pi_{i2}/\pi_{i3})$. These models can be fit using `PROC CATMOD`.

6.7.1 Ordinal Response: Proportional Odds Model

The proportional odds model extends logistic regression to handle an ordinal response variable. For example, the response variable IMPROVE in the arthritis data actually has 3 levels, corresponding to None, Some, or Marked improvement.

One way to model this data is to consider two logits for the dichotomies between adjacent categories:

$$L_1 = \log \frac{\pi_{ij1}}{\pi_{ij2} + \pi_{ij3}} = \text{logit (None vs. [Some or Marked])}$$

$$L_2 = \log \frac{\pi_{ij1} + \pi_{ij2}}{\pi_{ij3}} = \text{logit ([None or Some] vs. Marked)}$$

Table 6.3 shows the data and the sample estimates of the adjacent category logits. For example, for males given the active treatment, $L_1 = \log(7/7) = 0$, and $L_2 = \log(9/5) = 0.588$. Consider a linear logistic regression model for each logit:

$$L_1 = \alpha_1 + x_{ij}^{\mathsf{T}} \beta_1 \tag{6.15}$$

$$L_2 = \alpha_2 + x_{ij}^{\mathsf{T}} \beta_2 \tag{6.16}$$

Table 6.3   Arthritis data: Response frequencies and adjacent category logits

Sex	Treatment	Improvement None	Some	Marked	Total	L_1	L_2
F	Active	6	5	16	27	-1.253	-0.375
F	Placebo	19	7	6	32	0.379	1.466
M	Active	7	2	5	14	0.000	0.588
M	Placebo	10	0	1	11	2.302	2.302

The proportional odds assumption is that ***the regression functions are parallel*** on the logit scale, i.e., that $\beta_1 = \beta_2$, as illustrated in Figure 6.21 for a 4-category response.

For the arthritis example, with additive effects for sex and treatment on both log odds, the proportional odds model is

$$L_1 = \alpha_1 + \beta_1 x_1 + \beta_2 x_2 \tag{6.17}$$

$$L_2 = \alpha_2 + \beta_1 x_1 + \beta_2 x_2 \tag{6.18}$$

where:

- x_1 and x_2 are dummy variables representing Sex and Treatment.
- α_1 is the log odds of no improvement (vs. some or marked) for males receiving the placebo.
- α_2 is the log odds of no improvement or some improvement (vs. marked) for males receiving the placebo.
- β_1 is the increment to *both* log odds for being female. Therefore, e^{β_1} gives the odds of improvement for females relative to males.
- β_2 is the increment to both log odds for being in the active treatment group. e^{β_2} gives the odds of improvement for the active treatment group relative to the placebo.

242   *Visualizing Categorical Data*

Figure 6.21   Proportional odds model. The model assumes that the regression functions for different response categories are parallel on the logit scale.

Proportional Odds Model

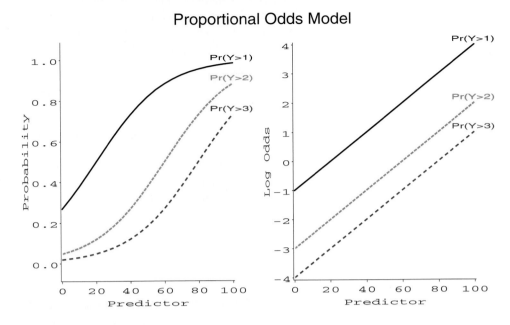

The corresponding models including effects of age, as well as treatment and sex are similar to Equations 6.17 and 6.18, with the addition of a term β_3 age.

6.7.2   Plotting Results from PROC LOGISTIC

Plotting results for the proportional odds model is similar to the earlier examples (e.g., Section 6.3.2) for a binary response variable. The main differences for a polytomous response are listed here:

- The validity of the analysis depends on the correctness of the proportional odds assumption. A test of this assumption appears in the output from PROC LOGISTIC.
- The results from PROC LOGISTIC are cast in terms of predicted probabilities and fitted logits for response *less than* each of the cutpoints. To plot Pr{Improve}, you must reverse the sense of the probabilities and logits.

EXAMPLE 6.14   Arthritis treatment

This example fits the effects of Treatment, Sex, and Age for the proportional odds model with the arthritis data. Note that the dependent variable is IMPROVE, with values 0, 1, and 2.

```
   *-- Proportional Odds Model: Effects of treat, sex and age;
proc logistic data=arthrit nosimple;
   model  improve = _sex_ _treat_ age ;
   output out=results p=predict l=lower u=upper
                     xbeta=logit stdxbeta=selogit / alpha=.33;
```

The response profile, shown in Output 6.12, displays the ordering of the outcome variable. Note that logits are formed from top to bottom, i.e., None vs. Some or Marked, None or Some vs. Marked. The output ("Score test") also shows the proportional odds assumption is reasonable here.

Output 6.12   Proportional odds model: Response profiles and score test

```
                         Response Profile
                  Ordered
                   Value   IMPROVE      Count

                     1        0          42
                     2        1          14
                     3        2          28


          Score Test for the Proportional Odds Assumption

            Chi-Square = 2.4917 with 3 DF (p=0.4768)
```

The parameter estimates for the model (Equations 6.17 and 6.18) appear in Output 6.13. These values relate to the odds of a poorer response (they are all negative).

Output 6.13   Proportional odds model: Parameter estimates

```
                Analysis of Maximum Likelihood Estimates

            Parameter  Standard    Wald       Pr >     Standardized
  Variable    Estimate    Error   Chi-Square  Chi-Square   Estimate

  INTERCP1     3.7837   1.1530    10.7683     0.0010         .
  INTERCP2     4.6827   1.1949    15.3569     0.0001         .
  _SEX_       -1.2517   0.5321     5.5343     0.0186     -0.317412
  _TREAT_     -1.7453   0.4772    13.3770     0.0003     -0.483871
  AGE         -0.0382   0.0185     4.2358     0.0396     -0.268666
```

The output dataset RESULTS contains, for each observation, the predicted probability, Pr{Not Improved} and estimated logit for both types of odds. These are distinguished by the variable _LEVEL_. To plot probabilities for both types of improvement in a single graph, the values of TREAT and _LEVEL_ are combined in a single variable. To plot Pr{Improve}, you must reverse the direction of the variables in a DATA step:

```
data results;
   set results;
   treatl = treat||put(_level_,1.0);
   if _level_=0 then better = (improve > 0);
             else better = (improve > 1);
   *-- Change direction of probabilities & logit;
   predict = 1 - predict;
   lower = 1 - lower;
   upper = 1 - upper;
   logit = -logit;
```

Here are the first few observations in the dataset RESULTS showing these changes:

```
ID   TREAT   SEX IMPROVE _LEVEL_ PREDICT   LOWER   UPPER   LOGIT

57 Treated Male    1       0      0.267   0.417   0.157  -1.008
57 Treated Male    1       1      0.129   0.229   0.069  -1.907
 9 Placebo Male    0       0      0.085   0.149   0.048  -2.372
 9 Placebo Male    0       1      0.037   0.069   0.019  -3.271
46 Treated Male    0       0      0.283   0.429   0.171  -0.932
46 Treated Male    0       1      0.138   0.238   0.076  -1.831
   . . .
```

As in the earlier examples, an Annotate dataset is used to add more descriptive labels and confidence intervals to the plots. (This adds somewhat more work, but I prefer the plots labeled this way, rather than with legends at the bottom.)

```
proc sort data=results;
   by sex treatl age;
data bars;
   set results;
   by sex treatl;
   length text$8;
   xsys='2'; ysys='2';
   if treat='Placebo' then color='BLACK';
                      else color='RED';
   x  = age; line=33;
   *-- plot confidence limits  ;
   y  = upper;  function='MOVE   '; output;
   text='-';    function='LABEL  '; output;
   y  = lower;  function='DRAW   '; output;
   text='-';    function='LABEL  '; output;
   if last.treatl then do;
      y = predict;
      x = age+1; position='C'; size=1.4;
      text = treat; function='LABEL'; output;
      position='F';
      if _level_ = 0
         then text='> None';
         else text='> Some';
      output;
      end;
   if first.sex then do;
      ysys ='1'; y=90;
      xsys ='1'; x=10; size=1.5;
      text = sex; function='LABEL'; output;
      end;
```

The PROC GPLOT step below gives the two plots shown side-by-side in Figure 6.22.

```
goptions hby=0;
proc gplot;
    plot predict * age = treatl / vaxis=axis1 haxis=axis2
                                   nolegend anno=bars    ;
    by sex;
    axis1 label=(h=1.4 a=90 'Prob. Improvement (67% CI)')
          value=(h=1.2) order=(0 to 1 by .2);
    axis2 label=(h=1.4)
          value=(h=1.2) order=(20 to 80 by 10)
          offset=(2,5);
    symbol1 v=+ h=1.4 i=join l=3 c=black;
    symbol2 v=+ h=1.4 i=join l=3 c=black;
    symbol3 v=$ h=1.4 i=join l=1 c=red;
    symbol4 v=$ h=1.4 i=join l=1 c=red;
```

Figure 6.22   Predicted probabilities for the proportional odds model. For each group, the curve labeled >None gives predicted probabilities for a response of Some or Marked improvement; the curve labeled >Some gives that for a response of Marked improvement.

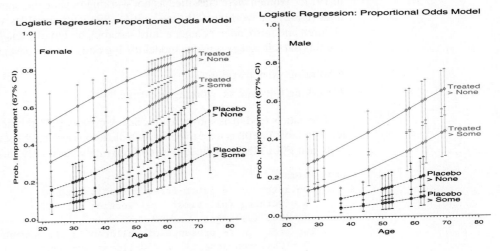

6.7.3   Nested Dichotomies

Nested dichotomies are successive binary partitions of the response categories into nested sets. For the levels of a factor in an ANOVA design, nested dichotomies correspond to orthogonal contrasts (assuming equal ns).

For example, the response categories {1,2,3,4} could be divided first as {1,2} vs. {3,4}, as shown in the left side of Figure 6.23. Then these two dichotomies could be divided as {1} vs. {2}, and {3} vs. {4}. Alternatively, these response categories could be divided as shown in the right side of Figure 6.23: first, {1} vs. {2,3,4}, then {2} vs {3,4}, and finally {3} vs. {4}.

Then,

- Each dichotomy can be fit using the familiar binary-response logistic model.

- When the dichotomies are nested, the $m-1$ models will be statistically independent, so that likelihood-ratio G^2 statistics for overall fit and Wald statistics for individual terms will be additive.

Figure 6.23   Nested dichotomies. The boxes show two different ways a 4-category response can be represented as three nested dichotomies. Adapted from Fox (1997).[7]

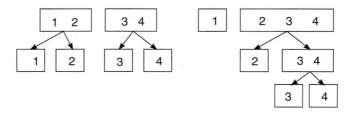

Thus, you can treat the set of $m - 1$ models as a single model for the polytomous response, although you fit them separately for computational purposes. This approach to polytomous responses is described in more detail by Fox (1997).

EXAMPLE 6.15   **Women's labor-force participation**

Fox (1984, 1997) presented survey data on women's labor-force participation in Canada in 1977.[8] Women were classified as not working outside the home (n=155), working part-time (n=42), or working full-time (n=66). Predictor variables were presence/absence of children and husband's income; a third variable, region of Canada, is not considered here. For this data, it makes sense to model the log odds for two nested dichotomies:

- working vs. not working
- working full-time vs. working part-time.

The data is read in as shown below. See Appendix B.16 for the complete dataset. The 3-level variable LABOR is used to define two dichotomous variables, WORKING and FULLTIME. Note that FULLTIME is defined (has non-missing values) only for working women.

```
proc format;
   value labor     /* labor-force participation */
      1 ='working full-time'  2 ='working part-time'
      3 ='not working';
   value kids      /* presence of children in the household */
      0 ='Children absent'  1 ='Children present';
data wlfpart;
   input case labor husinc children region;
   working = labor < 3;
   if working then
      fulltime = (labor = 1);
datalines;
   1  3  15  1  3
   2  3  13  1  3
   3  3  45  1  3
   4  3  23  1  3
   5  3  19  1  3
   ... more data lines ...
```

An initial analysis attempts to fit the proportional odds model, with the 3-level LABOR variable as the response:

```
proc logistic data=wlfpart nosimple;
   model labor  = husinc children ;
   title2 'Proportional Odds Model for Fulltime/Parttime/NotWorking';
```

---

[7] John Fox, *Applied Regression Analysis, Linear Models, and Related Methods*, p. 472, copyright © 1997 by Sage Publications, Inc. Reprinted by permission of Sage Publications.
[8] John Fox, *Applied Regression Analysis, Linear Models, and Related Methods*, p. 451, copyright © 1997 by Sage Publications, Inc. Reprinted by permission of Sage Publications.

However, the proportional odds assumption is rejected by the score test (see Output 6.14).

Output 6.14   Test of the proportional odds assumption

```
           Score Test for the Proportional Odds Assumption

              Chi-Square = 18.5641 with 2 DF (p=0.0001)
```

Hence, you fit models for each of the WORKING and FULLTIME dichotomies. The DESCENDING option is used so that in each case the probability of a 1 response (working or full-time) will be the event modeled.

```
proc logistic data=wlfpart nosimple descending;
    model working = husinc children ;
    output out=resultw p=predict xbeta=logit;
    title2 'Nested Dichotomies';
run;
proc logistic data=wlfpart nosimple descending;
    model fulltime = husinc children ;
    output out=resultf p=predict xbeta=logit;
```

The OUTPUT statements create the datasets RESULTW and RESULTF for plotting the predicted probabilities and logits. The printed output for the working dichotomy is shown (partially) in Output 6.15.

Output 6.15   Women's labor-force data: Analysis of the working/not working dichotomy

```
                            Response Profile
                        Ordered
                          Value   WORKING      Count

                            1        1          108
                            2        0          155


                  Testing Global Null Hypothesis: BETA=0
                                Intercept
                     Intercept     and
     Criterion         Only     Covariates    Chi-Square for Covariates

     AIC              358.151     325.733         .
     SC               361.723     336.449         .
     -2 LOG L         356.151     319.733      36.418 with 2 DF (p=0.0001)
     Score               .           .         35.713 with 2 DF (p=0.0001)


                 Analysis of Maximum Likelihood Estimates

                  Parameter Standard    Wald      Pr >    Standardized   Odds
     Variable DF  Estimate   Error   Chi-Square Chi-Square  Estimate    Ratio

     INTERCPT  1    1.3358   0.3838   12.1165    0.0005         .          .
     HUSINC    1   -0.0423   0.0198    4.5751    0.0324     -0.168541    0.959
     CHILDREN  1   -1.5756   0.2923   29.0651    0.0001     -0.398992    0.207
```

To interpret the parameter estimates, note that the odds ratio of 0.959 for husband's income means a 4% decrease in the odds of working with each \$1,000 increase in husband's income; an additional \$10,000 means a decrease in the odds of working by $e^{-.423} = .655$. Similarly, the effect of having children corresponds to an odds of working of .207 compared to those without children.

The output for the full-time vs. part-time dichotomy is shown in Output 6.16. Note that nonworking women are excluded in this analysis.

Output 6.16   Women's labor-force data: Analysis of the full-time/part-time dichotomy

```
                              Response Profile
                      Ordered
                      Value   FULLTIME      Count

                        1         1           66
                        2         0           42


WARNING: 155 observation(s) were deleted due to missing values for
         the response or explanatory variables.

              Testing Global Null Hypothesis: BETA=0
                                 Intercept
                   Intercept       and
   Criterion         Only       Covariates   Chi-Square for Covariates


   AIC              146.342      110.495          .
   SC               149.024      118.541          .
   -2 LOG L         144.342      104.495      39.847 with 2 DF (p=0.0001)
   Score               .            .         35.150 with 2 DF (p=0.0001)


            Analysis of Maximum Likelihood Estimates


             Parameter Standard    Wald       Pr >     Standardized   Odds
   Variable DF Estimate  Error  Chi-Square Chi-Square    Estimate     Ratio


   INTERCPT 1   3.4778   0.7671   20.5537    0.0001          .          .
   HUSINC   1  -0.1073   0.0392    7.5063    0.0061     -0.424867     0.898
   CHILDREN 1  -2.6515   0.5411   24.0135    0.0001     -0.734194     0.071
```

Thus, the full 3-category response has been fitted by two models:

$$\log\left(\frac{\Pr(\text{working})}{\Pr(\text{not working})}\right) = 1.336 - 0.042\,\text{H\$} - 1.576\,\text{kids} \tag{6.19}$$

$$\log\left(\frac{\Pr(\text{fulltime})}{\Pr(\text{parttime})}\right) = 3.478 - 0.107\,\text{H\$} - 2.652\,\text{kids} \tag{6.20}$$

The second equation gives the predicted log odds for full-time vs. part-time work *conditional* on working.

Because these models are nested, we can add the likelihood ratio or Wald tests across the two models, so the overall test of the hypothesis that neither husband's income nor presence of children predicts working status (the 3-level response) has a $G^2 = 36.42 + 39.85 = 66.27$ on 2+2=4 df ($p < .0001$). Similarly, the hypothesis that husband's income does not predict working status has a Wald-test $G^2 = 4.58 + 7.51 = 12.09$ on 2 df ($p < .001$).

Comparison of the regression coefficients in the two sub-models (in relation to the size of their standard errors) indicates why the proportional odds model was not tenable. The proportional odds model requires that the coefficients for husband's income and children in analogous models of the form shown in Equations 6.15 and 6.16. We can see that both variables have a greater effect on the odds of full-time vs. part-time work than on the odds of working vs. not working.

As usual, these effects can be seen and interpreted more easily in a graph (Figure 6.24). The odds of working outside the home decrease as husband's income increases and when there are children present. However, among working women, the odds of full-time vs. part-time work decrease at a faster rate with husband's income; women with children are less likely to work full-time.

Figure 6.24   Predicted log odds of working vs. not working and of full-time work vs. part-time work

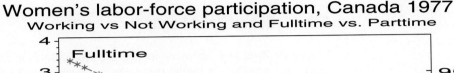

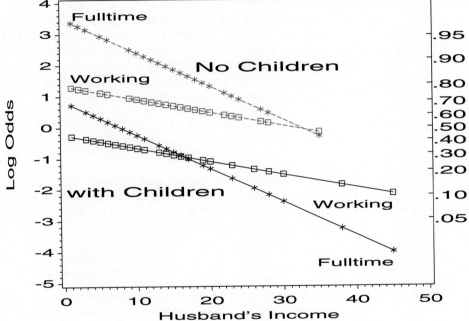

To construct this graph, first join the separate results datasets into one.

```
*-- Merge the results to create one plot;
data both;
   set resultw(in=inw)
       resultf(in=inf);
   if inw then do;
       if children=1 then event='Working, with Children ';
       else event='Working, no Children ';
   end;
   else do;
       if children=1 then event='Fulltime, with Children ';
       else event='Fulltime, no Children ';
   end;
```

Then, you can plot the log odds (or predicted probability) against husband's income, using EVENT to determine the curves to be joined and labeled. (The probability scale is

constructed with the PSCALE macro, and the labels with an Annotate dataset.) These steps
are not similar to those described in Example 6.8 and are shown here:

```
proc gplot data=both;
   plot logit * husinc = event /
        anno=lbl nolegend frame vaxis=axis1;
   axis1 label=(a=90 'Log Odds') order=(-5 to 4);
   title2 'Working vs Not Working and Fulltime vs. Parttime';
   symbol1 v=dot    h=1.5 i=join l=3 c=red;
   symbol2 v=dot    h=1.5 i=join l=1 c=black;
   symbol3 v=circle h=1.5 i=join l=3 c=red;
   symbol4 v=circle h=1.5 i=join l=1 c=black;
```

6.7.4 Generalized Logits

The generalized logit approach models the probabilities of the m response categories directly as a set of $m - 1$ logits. These compare each of the first $m - 1$ categories to the last category, which serves as the baseline. The logits for any other pair of categories can be retrieved from the $m - 1$ fitted ones.

When there are k predictors, $x_1, x_2, \ldots, x_k$, which may be quantitative or categorical, the generalized logit model expresses the logits as

$$L_{jm} \equiv \log \frac{\pi_{ij}}{\pi_{im}} = \beta_{0j} + \beta_{1j} x_{i1} + \beta_{2j} x_{i2} + \cdots + \beta_{kj} x_{ik} \quad j = 1, \ldots, m - 1$$

$$= \boldsymbol{\beta}_j^{\mathsf{T}} \boldsymbol{x}_i \tag{6.21}$$

Thus, there is one set of fitted coefficients, $\boldsymbol{\beta}_j$ for each response category except the last. Each coefficient, β_{hj}, gives the effect, for a unit change in the predictor x_h, on the log odds that an observation belongs to category j, as opposed to category m.

The probabilities themselves are given by

$$\pi_{ij} = \frac{\exp(\boldsymbol{\beta}_j^{\mathsf{T}} \boldsymbol{x}_i)}{\sum_{i=1}^{m} \exp(\boldsymbol{\beta}_j^{\mathsf{T}} \boldsymbol{x}_i)} \ .$$

Parameters in the $m - 1$ equations (Equation 6.21) can be used to determine the parameters or the predicted log odds for any pair of response categories by subtraction. For instance, for an arbitrary pair of categories, a and b, and two predictors, x_1 and x_2,

$$L_{ab} = \log \frac{\pi_{ia}/\pi_{im}}{\pi_{ib}/\pi_{im}}$$

$$= \log \frac{\pi_{ia}}{\pi_{im}} - \log \frac{\pi_{ib}}{\pi_{im}}$$

$$= (\beta_{0a} - \beta_{0n}) + (\beta_{1a} - \beta_{1b})x_{1i} + (\beta_{2a} - \beta_{2b})x_{2i}$$

For example, the coefficient for x_{1i} in L_{ab} is just $(\beta_{1a} - \beta_{1b})$. Similarly, the predicted logit for any pair of categories can be calculated as

$$\hat{L}_{ab} = \hat{L}_{am} - \hat{L}_{bm} \ .$$

The generalized logit model cannot be fit using PROC LOGISTIC, but it can be fit using PROC CATMOD.[9] An output dataset provides all predicted probabilities, and the fitted logits.

---

[9]When one or more of the predictor variables are continuous, however, you may have difficulty due to zero cell frequencies, because PROC CATMOD treats the data as a contingency table. In this case, it may help to reorder the response variable so that the response category with the highest frequency is the last, baseline category. Alternatively, the continuous variable(s) can be collapsed into categories so that populations with zero frequencies do not occur.

EXAMPLE 6.16   Women's labor-force participation

In this example, you fit the generalized logit model to the women's labor force participation data using the statements below. Husband's income is treated as a quantitative variable by declaring it in the DIRECT statement. PROC CATMOD does not provide an overall test of the whole model; however, this can be carried out with a CONTRAST statement to test $H_0 : \boldsymbol{\beta} = 0$.

```
proc catmod data=wlfpart;
   direct husinc;
   model labor = husinc children / noprofile noiter;
   response logits / out=results;
   contrast 'Husinc,Children=0'
      husinc   1,
      children 1;
```

The maximum-likelihood ANOVA table (Output 6.17) shows that there are two parameters fit for each regressor. With a continuous predictor, the likelihood-ratio test of goodness-of-fit, which compares the current model to the saturated model, is unreliable because the contingency table is very sparse.

Output 6.17   Women's labor-force data: Generalized logit model tests

```
               MAXIMUM-LIKELIHOOD ANALYSIS-OF-VARIANCE TABLE

           Source              DF     Chi-Square      Prob
           ---------------------------------------------------
           INTERCEPT            2        15.91       0.0004
           HUSINC               2        12.82       0.0016
           CHILDREN             2        53.98       0.0000

           LIKELIHOOD RATIO    86       138.67       0.0003
```

The table of parameter estimates, shown in Output 6.18, contains the coefficients for the two fitted logits:

$$\log\left(\frac{\Pr(\text{fulltime})}{\Pr(\text{not working})}\right) = 0.7035 - 0.0972\,\text{H\$} + 1.2793\,\text{kids} \qquad (6.22)$$

$$\log\left(\frac{\Pr(\text{parttime})}{\Pr(\text{not working})}\right) = -1.4216 + 0.00689\,\text{H\$} - 0.0107\,\text{kids} \qquad (6.23)$$

The predicted log odds for working full-time as opposed to part-time are given by

$$\log\left(\frac{\Pr(\text{fulltime})}{\Pr(\text{not working})}\right) = 2.1251 - 0.1041\,\text{H\$} + 1.29\,\text{kids} \qquad (6.24)$$

The coefficients in Equations 6.22–6.24 are not directly comparable to those in Equations 6.19 and 6.20 for the nested dichotomies models, because they pertain to different comparisons.

Output 6.18 Women's labor-force data: Generalized logit model parameter estimates

```
          ANALYSIS OF MAXIMUM-LIKELIHOOD ESTIMATES

                                    Standard    Chi-
  Effect          Parameter  Estimate   Error   Square   Prob
  ---------------------------------------------------------------
  INTERCEPT           1       0.7035    0.4140    2.89   0.0892
                      2      -1.4216    0.4528    9.86   0.0017
  HUSINC              3      -0.0972    0.0281   11.98   0.0005
                      4       0.00689   0.0235    0.09   0.7689
  CHILDREN            5       1.2793    0.1811   49.90   0.0000
                      6      -0.0107    0.2345    0.00   0.9635
```

A plot of the predicted probabilities of the three categories of LABOR is easily obtained from the RESULTS dataset produced by PROC CATMOD. This dataset contains both fitted probabilities (_type_='PROB') and fitted logits (_type_='FUNCTION'), so you can select the _type_='PROB' observations with a WHERE statement.

```
proc gplot data=results;
   where (_type_='PROB');
   plot _pred_ * husinc = labor /
      vaxis=axis1 hm=1 vm=1 anno=labels nolegend;
   by children;
   axis1 order=(0 to .9 by .1) label=(a=90);
   symbol1 i=join v=circle   c=black;
   symbol2 i=join v=square   c=red;
   symbol3 i=join v=triangle c=blue;
   label _pred_='Fitted probability';
```

The fitted probabilities are shown in Figure 6.25.

Figure 6.25 Fitted probabilities for the generalized logit model

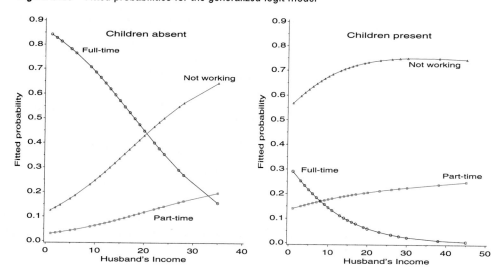

When there are no young children in the home, a woman's probability of not working rises sharply with husband's income, while her probability of working full-time declines sharply, and her probability of working part-time increases modestly. With children present, the direction of these relations with husband's income are the same, but the levels of not working and full-time work are reversed. Plots similar to Figure 6.25 can be produced with the `CATPLOT` macro. These statements would plot predicted probabilities (TYPE=PROB) in the `RESULTS` dataset with separate curves for each working category (CLASS=LABOR), and separate panels for those with and without children (BYVAR=CHILDREN). These plots are not shown to conserve space.

```
axis1 order=(0 to .9 by .1) label=(a=90 'Fitted probability');
axis2 offset=(1,10pct);

%catplot(data=results, x=husinc, y=_pred_, type=PROB,
   class=labor, clfmt=labor.,
   byvar=children, byfmt=kids.);
```

To plot the predicted log odds corresponding to Equations 6.22–6.24 takes slightly more work, because the output dataset from `PROC CATMOD` contains only the first two predicted logits. The following steps calculate the logit for Equation 6.24 from the other two and uses the `CATPLOT` macro to plot the results, as shown in Figure 6.26.

```
proc format;
   value num 1='FT/NW'  2='PT/NW'  3='FT/PT';
data logits;
   set results(rename=(_number_=logit));
   by _sample_;
   format logit num.;
   where (_type_='FUNCTION');
   retain logit1 logit2 se1 se2;
   drop labor logit1 logit2 se1 se2;
   if first._sample_
      then do; logit1 = _pred_; se1=_sepred_; end;
      else do; logit2 = _pred_; se2=_sepred_; end;
   output;
   logit=3;
   _pred_ = logit1 - logit2;
   _sepred_ = sqrt(se1**2 + se2**2);
   if last._sample_ then output;

axis1 label=(a=90 'Fitted Logit') order=(-5 to 4);
%catplot(data=logits, x=husinc, y=_pred_, class=logit,
   byvar=children, byfmt=kids.);
```

Figure 6.26   Fitted log odds for the generalized logit model

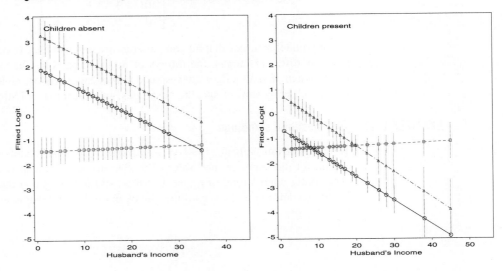

6.8 The Bradley-Terry-Luce Model for Paired Comparisons

The basic methodology of logistic regression finds application in a surprising variety of applications (Strauss, 1992). One example is a model for paired comparisons data proposed by Bradley and Terry (1952), and by Luce (1959) in a more general context. In paired comparisons, K objects are compared in a pairwise manner and the goal is to determine scale values and a ranking of these objects. For example, a market researcher might want to construct a preference ranking for soft drinks among consumers. In other contexts, the objects might be teams or players in a sports league, or they might be sounds of varying intensity or frequency to be judged in a psychophysical experiment.

The Bradley-Terry-Luce (BTL) model assumes that for each object there is a parameter, θ_i, such that the probability of the event $(i > j)$ that object i is preferred to object j is

$$\Pr(i > j) = \frac{\theta_i}{\theta_i + \theta_j} \ . \tag{6.25}$$

Luce's model is more general, and θ_i is interpreted as the probability that object i is ranked first within *any* subset of objects. The BTL model (Equation 6.25) may be cast as a logit model with parameters $\beta_i, = \log \theta_i$ as follows. Substituting $\theta_i = \exp(\beta_i)$ in Equation 6.25 gives

$$\Pr(i > j) = \frac{\exp(\beta_i)}{\exp(\beta_i) + \exp(\beta_j)} = \frac{1}{1 + \exp(\beta_i/\beta_j)} \ . \tag{6.26}$$

But Equation 6.26 is just the inverse logit of θ_i/θ_j. Hence,

$$\text{logit}[\Pr(i > j)] = \log\left(\frac{\Pr(i > j)}{\Pr(j > i)}\right) = \beta_i - \beta_j \tag{6.27}$$

$$= x^{\mathsf{T}}\beta$$

where, $\beta = (\beta_1, \ldots, \beta_K)^{\mathsf{T}}$ and $x = \{x_k\}$ is a vector with $x_k = 1$ if $k = i$, $x_k = -1$ if $k = j$, and 0 otherwise. Thus, Equation 6.27 is a logit model with no intercept, and with a $K(K-1)/2 \times K$ matrix X of explanatory variables whose rows give the items compared in each paired comparison. For $K = 4$ objects, for example, the X matrix is

$$X = \begin{bmatrix} 1 & -1 & 0 & 0 \\ 1 & 0 & -1 & 0 \\ 1 & 0 & 0 & -1 \\ 0 & 1 & -1 & 0 \\ 0 & 1 & 0 & -1 \\ 0 & 0 & 1 & -1 \end{bmatrix} \ .$$

The model assumes that all comparisons are independent. In particular, when items are rated by different judges, the ratings of different pairs by the same judge must also be independent, and all judges are assumed homogeneous. More general versions of the BTL model, allowing subject-specific covariates, are described by Dittrich, et al. (1998).

EXAMPLE 6.17   1987 baseball standings

Table 6.4 (from Agresti (1990, p. 372)) shows the final results from the 1987 baseball season for the teams in the Eastern Division of the American League. Each team played every other team a total of $n_{ij} = 13$ times, so (assuming that the outcome of each game is independent) you can regard the values in the lower triangle as binomial observations, $\text{Bin}(\pi_{ij}, 13)$.

Table 6.4   1987 American League Baseball Results[10]

Winning Team	Losing Team						
	Mil	Det	Tor	NY	Bos	Cle	Bal
Milwaukee	—	7	9	7	7	9	11
Detroit	6	—	7	5	11	9	9
Toronto	4	6	—	7	7	8	12
New York	6	8	6	—	6	7	10
Boston	6	2	6	7	—	7	12
Cleveland	4	4	5	6	6	—	6
Baltimore	2	4	1	3	1	7	—

This example concentrates on fitting the BTL model and graphical displays of the scale values and model diagnostics. A similar example, without graphs, is given in *Logistic Regression Examples Using the SAS System*, Example 19.

The first DATA step below reads the complete data from Table 6.4. In a second step, variables in the array X are created, corresponding to the model matrix in Equation 6.27. The resulting dataset, WINLOSS2, is shown in Output 6.19.

```
title 'Bradley-Terry-Luce Model, 1987 American League, East';
data winloss;
   input t1-t7;
   games=13;
datalines;
  .  7  9  7  7  9 11
  6  .  7  5 11  9  9
  4  6  .  7  7  8 12
  6  8  6  .  6  7 10
  6  2  6  7  .  7 12
  4  4  5  6  6  .  6
  2  4  1  3  1  7  .
;
data winloss2;
   retain i 0 ;
   array team{*} t1-t7;
   array x{*} milwauke detroit toronto new_york boston clevelan baltimor;
   retain milwauke detroit toronto new_york boston clevelan baltimor 0;
   set winloss;
   names='Milwaukee Detroit Toronto New_York Boston Cleveland Baltimore';
   length winner loser $9;
   i+1;
   do j=1 to dim(team);
      if team{j} ne . then do;
         count=team{j};
         x{i}=1;
         x{j}=-1;
         winner = scan(names,i);
         loser  = scan(names,j);
         if i < j then output;
         x{i}=0;
         x{j}=0;
      end;
   end;
   drop i j t1-t7 names;
```

[10]Reprinted by permission of Major League Baseball and Elias Sports Bureau.

Output 6.19   Win-loss data: Set up for fitting BTL model with PROC LOGISTIC

WINNER	LOSER	MILWAUKEE	DETROIT	TORONTO	NEW_YORK	BOSTON	CLEVELAND	BALTIMOR	GAMES	COUNT
Milwaukee	Detroit	1	-1	0	0	0	0	0	13	7
Milwaukee	Toronto	1	0	-1	0	0	0	0	13	9
Milwaukee	New_York	1	0	0	-1	0	0	0	13	7
Milwaukee	Boston	1	0	0	0	-1	0	0	13	7
Milwaukee	Cleveland	1	0	0	0	0	-1	0	13	9
Milwaukee	Baltimore	1	0	0	0	0	0	-1	13	11
Detroit	Toronto	0	1	-1	0	0	0	0	13	7
Detroit	New_York	0	1	0	-1	0	0	0	13	5
Detroit	Boston	0	1	0	0	-1	0	0	13	11
Detroit	Cleveland	0	1	0	0	0	-1	0	13	9
Detroit	Baltimore	0	1	0	0	0	0	-1	13	9
Toronto	New_York	0	0	1	-1	0	0	0	13	7
Toronto	Boston	0	0	1	0	-1	0	0	13	7
Toronto	Cleveland	0	0	1	0	0	-1	0	13	8
Toronto	Baltimore	0	0	1	0	0	0	-1	13	12
New_York	Boston	0	0	0	1	-1	0	0	13	6
New_York	Cleveland	0	0	0	1	0	-1	0	13	7
New_York	Baltimore	0	0	0	1	0	0	-1	13	10
Boston	Cleveland	0	0	0	0	1	-1	0	13	7
Boston	Baltimore	0	0	0	0	1	0	-1	13	12
Cleveland	Baltimore	0	0	0	0	0	1	-1	13	6

The BTL model is fit using the PROC LOGISTIC step below. The options OUTEST and COVOUT create an output dataset containing the estimated β_i parameters and their variance-covariance matrix. A second output dataset containing fitted probabilities and model diagnostic measures is created with the OUTPUT statement. The parameters and their standard errors are shown in Output 6.20. Thus, according to the BTL model (Equation 6.25), the predicted probability that Toronto beats Cleveland would be $\exp(1.294)/(\exp(1.294) + \exp(0.684)) = 0.648$. The squared standard errors are contained along the diagonal of the variance-covariance matrix in the PARM1 dataset. A small SAS/IML step is used to extract the parameter estimates and standard errors.

```
proc logistic data=winloss2 nosimple out=parm1 covout;
  model count/games=milwauke detroit toronto new_york
                boston clevelan baltimor / noint;
  output out=fit prob=prob resdev=resdev c=c;
run;

*-- Extract parameters and standard errors;
proc iml;
  use parm1;
  read all var {_name_} into name where(_type_='COV');
  read all var {milwauke detroit toronto new_york
            boston clevelan baltimor} into parm where(_type_='PARMS');
  read all var {milwauke detroit toronto new_york
            boston clevelan baltimor} into cov where(_type_='COV');
```

```
    stderr = exp(sqrt(vecdiag(cov)));
    parm = exp(t(parm));
    create parms var {name parm stderr};
    append var {name parm stderr};

proc rank data=parms out=parms descending;
    var parm;
    ranks rank;
    label parm='Scale Value'
        rank='Team Rank';
```

Output 6.20   Win-loss data: PROC LOGISTIC output

```
        Model Fitting Information and Testing Global Null Hypothesis BETA=0

                     Without       With
        Criterion    Covariates    Covariates    Chi-Square for Covariates

        AIC          378.458       356.496        .
        SC           378.458       378.153        .
        -2 LOG L     378.458       344.496        33.962 with 6 DF (p=0.0001)
        Score        .             .              32.176 with 6 DF (p=0.0001)


NOTE: The following parameters have been set to 0, since the variables are a
      linear combination of other variables as shown.

      BALTIMOR = -1 * MILWAUKE - 1 * DETROIT - 1 * TORONTO - 1 * NEW_YORK - 1 *
                  BOSTON - 1 * CLEVELAN

                    Analysis of Maximum Likelihood Estimates

                  Parameter Standard    Wald        Pr >      Standardized    Odds
        Variable DF Estimate  Error   Chi-Square Chi-Square    Estimate      Ratio

        MILWAUKE 1   1.5814   0.3433   21.2239    0.0001      0.394584       4.862
        DETROIT  1   1.4364   0.3396   17.8938    0.0001      0.396244       4.206
        TORONTO  1   1.2945   0.3367   14.7839    0.0001      0.376067       3.649
        NEW_YORK 1   1.2476   0.3359   13.7989    0.0002      0.368345       3.482
        BOSTON   1   1.1077   0.3339   11.0070    0.0009      0.321803       3.027
        CLEVELAN 1   0.6839   0.3319    4.2459    0.0393      0.188646       1.981
        BALTIMOR 0   0         .         .          .            .            .
```

The plot of scale values and standard errors shown in Figure 6.27 is produced by the first PROC GPLOT step below. The BARS macro instructs the Annotate dataset to draw the standard error bars, and the LABEL macro produces the team label annotations.

```
%bars(data=parms, var=parm, class=rank, barlen=stderr, baxis=x, barwidth=.1);
%label(data=parms, x=parm, y=rank, text=name, pos=2, yoff=.1, out=_lab_);
data _bars_;
   set _bars_ _lab_;

proc gplot data=parms;
   plot rank * parm /
      anno=_bars_ vaxis=axis1 haxis=axis2 vm=0;
   symbol v=dot color=black h=1.6;
   axis1 label=(a=90) offset=(5);
    axis2 order=(1 to 6) offset=(10,4);
run; quit;

%label(data=fit, x=prob, y=resdev, out=_lab_,
   subset=%str(abs(resdev)>.9),
   text = %str(substr(winner,1,3) || '>' || substr(loser,1,3)));
title;
proc gplot data=fit;
   bubble resdev * prob = c /
      anno=_lab_ bsize=20 bcolor=gray80 vaxis=axis1 vm=1;
   axis1 label=(a=90);
   label prob = 'Estimated Winning Probability';
```

Figure 6.27   Scale values and standard errors for 1987 baseball data

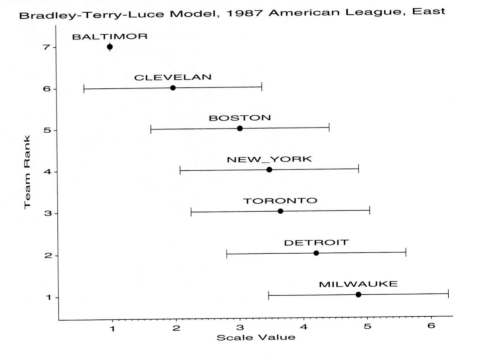

The diagnostic plot shown in Figure 6.28 plots the deviance residual against predicted probabilities. The bubble size is proportional to Cook's distance, C_i. Only one observation has a residual (slightly) greater than 2, and no C_i are excessive, so the BTL model seems to provide a reasonable fit.   □

Figure 6.28 Diagnostic plot for 1987 baseball data

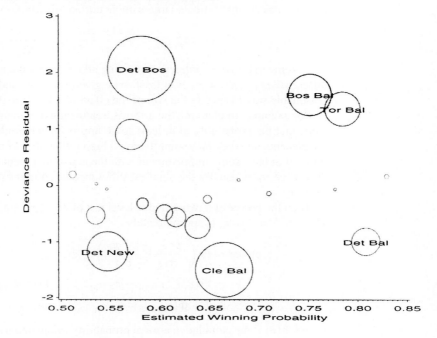

6.9 Power and Sample Size for Logistic Regression

The goal of many studies is to determine if a given predictor X has an effect on a binary outcome variable. In planning such studies it is often crucial to determine the sample size required in order to have a reasonable chance to detect an effect of a given size. Alternatively, if a study failed to detect a significant effect, you might want to determine if no real effect is present, or if the sample size in the study was just insufficient to detect it.

In either case, power and sample size determination requires that you specify the Type I error rate, α, of the test, and the **effect size** you want to detect. In the simple logistic model with one predictor,

$$\log \frac{\pi}{1 - \pi} = \beta_0 + \beta_1 X \ ,$$

the null hypothesis is $H_0 : \beta_1 = 0$, and the size of the effect depends directly on the magnitude of the slope β_1. That is, power increases with $|\beta_1|$, and the sample size required to detect an effect of given size (i.e., reject H_0 at a given α-level) decreases with $|\beta_1|$.

The difficulty in practice is that it is often difficult for the researcher to specify the size of meaningful effect in terms of the slope β_1 of the logistic model. The following section describes two standard situations in which effect size of interest may be specified more simply to determine approximate power or required sample size.

6.9.1 Binary Predictor: Comparing Two Proportions

When there is a single binary predictor (and a binary response), you can take $X = 0$ for Group 1 and $X = 1$ for Group 2, so that β_1 is the log odds of "success" response in Group 2 as compared to Group 1.

But, in this case, the data comprises a 2×2 table, and the test of the logistic model is analogous to a test of the difference of proportions in two independent samples. That is, $H_0 : \beta_1 = 0$ is analogous to the test of $H_0 : \pi_1 = \pi_2$. In this case, the sample difference $p_1 - p_1$ has an approximate large-sample normal distribution, with variance

$$\sigma^2_{p_1-p_2} = \frac{\pi_1(1 - \pi_1)}{n_1} + \frac{\pi_2(1 - \pi_2)}{n_2} \ .$$

Assume that you are interested in being able to reject the null hypothesis when the true difference $|\pi_1 - \pi_2| = \pi_d$ is at least some given value. π_1 and π_2 (or π_1 and π_d) provide a reasonable way to specify the size of the effect of interest in this situation.

For example, in planning the arthritis treatment experiment, the investigators might assume that the probability of at least some improvement would be around $\pi_2 = 0.30$ with the placebo, and they may want to have a high probability of rejecting H_0 when the probability of at least some improvement with the active treatment is $\pi_1 = 0.50$ or greater. The difference π_d is usually the smallest difference of substantive interest. Also assume that $n_1 = n_2$.

Then the power of a two-tailed α-level test of $H_0 : |\pi_1 - \pi_2| = 0$ against the alternative $H_1 : |\pi_1 - \pi_2| = \pi_d$ is approximately

$$\begin{aligned}
\text{power} &= \Pr\left(\frac{|p_1 - p_2| - \pi_d}{\sigma(p_1 - p_2)}\right) \geq z_{1-\alpha/2} \\
&= \Pr[z > z_{1-\alpha/2} - \pi_d\,\sigma_{p_1-p_2}] + \Pr[z < z_{\alpha/2} - \pi_d\,\sigma_{p_1-p_2}] \\
&= 1 - \Phi[z_{1-\alpha/2} - \pi_d\,\sigma_{p_1-p_2}] + \Phi[z_{\alpha/2} - \pi_d\,\sigma_{p_1-p_2}] \quad (6.28)
\end{aligned}$$

where $\Phi(\bullet)$ is the cumulative normal probability calculated by the PROBNORM function. For example, with $\alpha = 0.05$, $\pi_1 = 0.30$, and $\pi_2 = 0.50$, and a sample size of $n = n_1 + n_2 = 80$, Equation 6.28 gives power = 0.462 when $\pi_2 = 0.50$ ($\pi_d = 0.20$) and power = 0.807 when $\pi_2 = 0.60$ ($\pi_d = 0.30$).

It is often more convenient to find the sample size required for a given power. Using $\beta = 1 - \text{power}$ as the probability of a Type II error,[11] the approximate sample size required may be calculated as

$$n_1 = n_2 = \frac{(z_{1-\alpha/2} + z_\beta)^2[\pi_1(1 - \pi_1) + \pi_2(1 - \pi_2)]}{(\pi_1 - \pi_2)^2} \quad (6.29)$$

These calculations (Equations 6.28 and 6.29), along with tabular and graphical displays of power vs. n, are performed by the POWER2X2 macro, described in Appendix A.24. The tabular display is more useful for finding the exact calculated value, while the graphs, as usual, show the overall behavior better.

EXAMPLE 6.18   Arthritis treatment

For the arthritis treatment data, you can perform a power analysis for $\pi_1 = 0.30$ and $\pi_d = 0.2\,(0.1)\,0.4$ with the following statement:

```
%power2x2(p1=.30, diff=.2 to .4 by .1, plot=power * n=diff);
```

By default, the program calculates power for a range of sample sizes, typically 10–200, though any range may be specified with the NMIN parameter and the NMAX parameter.

In addition to printed output (not shown), the macro produces a graph of power against total sample size ($n = n_1 + n_2$) as shown in Figure 6.29. For a desired power of $1 - \beta = 0.80$, the required total sample size is about 80–85 when $\pi_d = 0.3$, but only about 45–50 when $\pi_d = 0.3$. In the data, $p_1 = 28/41 = 0.683$ and $p_2 = 14/43 = 0.325$, so with $n = 83$ there was adequate power.   □

---

[11] Don't confuse $\beta = 1 - \text{power}$ here with the slope, β_1, and intercept, β_0 of the logistic regression model. Both uses are conventional, and there are only a limited number of Greek letters to go around.

Figure 6.29   Power analysis for arthritis treatment data

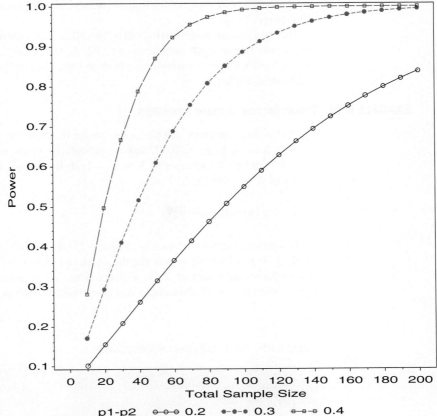

Power for testing two independent proportions
Baseline: p1=.30; p1-p2=.2 to .4 by .1; alpha=.05

6.9.2   Quantitative Predictor

When the predictor is quantitative, a simple method to specify the size of the effect of interest is given by Agresti (1996, p. 131) based on Hsieh (1989). The slope β_1 under an alternative hypothesis may be given in terms of the probabilities, π_1 and π_2 at two points, corresponding to $X = \bar{X}$ and $X = \bar{X} + 1$s.d. From these values, the effect size can be specified in terms of the the odds ratio, $\theta = (p_2/(1 - p_2)) \div (p_1/(1 - p_1))$.

Letting $\psi = \log(\theta)$, Hseih provides the following formula for the approximate sample size n required for a one-tailed test with Type I error rate α and power $= 1 - \beta$:

$$n = \frac{[z_\alpha + z_\beta \exp(-\psi^2/4)]^2(1 + 2p_1\delta)}{p_1\psi^2} \tag{6.30}$$

where

$$\delta = \frac{1 + (1 + \psi^2)\exp(5\psi^2/4)}{1 + \exp(-\psi^2/4)}$$

In multiple logistic regression, larger sample sizes are required to detect the *partial* effect of one variable to the extent that this variable is correlated with other explanatory variables (because holding the other variables fixed then removes some of the effect of the variable of interest). If R^2 is the squared multiple correlation of the target predictor with other predictors in the model, the unique variance of the target variable is $1 - R^2$. To use Equation 6.30 in this situation, let p_1 refer to the probability of the event at the mean level of all predictors, and divide the result of Equation 6.30 by $1 - R^2$. A more comprehensive approach to power analysis for logistic regression with multiple covariates is described by Whittemore (1981).

These calculations are carried out by the POWERLOG macro, described in Appendix A.22. The values of the input parameters P1, P2, ALPHA, POWER, and RSQ, may be supplied as macro arguments or as variable values in an input dataset. Output includes both a table and a graphical display.

EXAMPLE 6.19   Power for one or more predictors

The following statement calculates the power of a test for X_1 when the probability of the event at $X = \bar{X}$ is $p_1 = 0.50$, and the probability of the event is expected to increase to $p_1 = 0.75$ when X increases to $X = \bar{X} + 1$ s.d. By default, the macro calculates power for values of $R^2 = 0(0.2)0.6$.

```
%powerlog(p1=.5, p2=.75);
```

The printed output is shown in Output 6.21. By default, the program uses the statement PLOT N * POWER=RSQ, producing the graph in Figure 6.30. For a given power, the sample size to detect the effect of X_1 is smallest when X_1 is uncorrelated with other predictors. For a given effect size, the sample size is also smallest when $p_1 = 0.50$, as in this example.

$\square$

Output 6.21   Power table from POWERLOG macro

```
            One-tailed test, alpha=.05, p1=.5 p2=.75

     --------------------------------------------------
     |                      |Pr(event) at X-mean+std|
     |                      |-----------------------|
     |                      |         0.75          |
     |                      |-----------------------|
     |                      |  R**2 (X, other Xs)   |
     |                      |-----------------------|
     |                      |  0  | 0.2 | 0.4 | 0.6 |
     |------------------+-----+-----+-----+-----|
     |Power             |     |     |     |     |
     |------------------|     |     |     |     |
     |0.7               |   50|  63|   83|  125|
     |------------------+-----+-----+-----+-----|
     |0.75              |   56|  70|   93|  139|
     |------------------+-----+-----+-----+-----|
     |0.8               |   62|  78|  104|  156|
     |------------------+-----+-----+-----+-----|
     |0.85              |   70|  88|  117|  176|
     |------------------+-----+-----+-----+-----|
     |0.9               |   81| 102|  136|  204|
     --------------------------------------------------
```

Figure 6.30 Sample size display from the POWERLOG macro

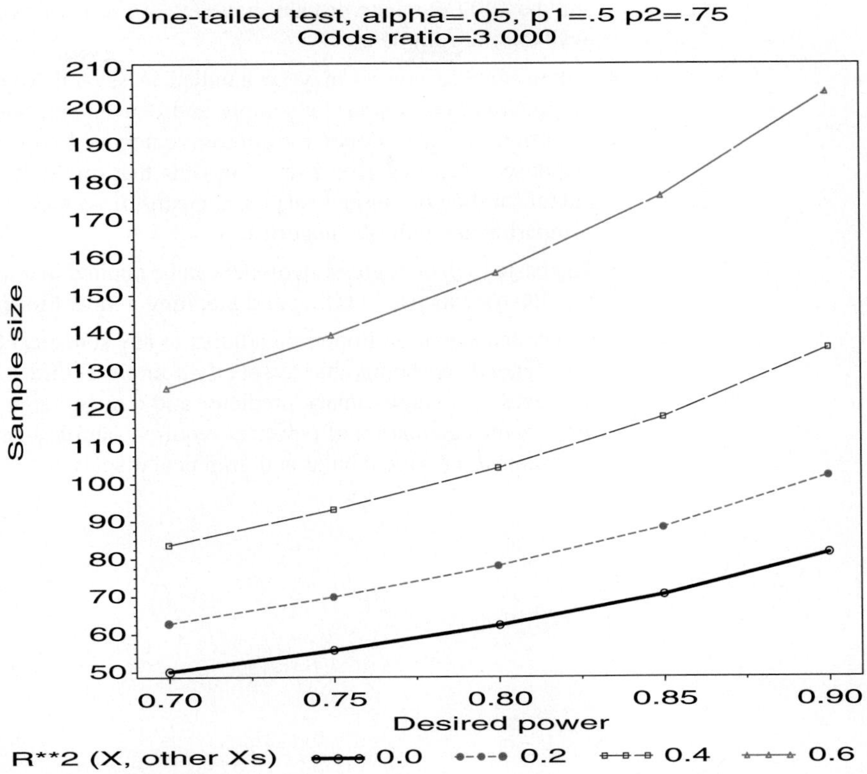

One-tailed test, alpha=.05, p1=.5 p2=.75
Odds ratio=3.000

6.10 Chapter Summary

- Model-based methods for categorical data provide confidence intervals for parameters and predicted values for observed and unobserved values of the explanatory variables. Graphical displays of predicted values help us to interpret the fitted relations and the models.

- The logistic regression model describes the relationship between a categorical response variable, usually dichotomous, and a set of one or more quantitative or discrete explanatory variables. It is conceptually convenient to specify this model as a linear model that predicts the log odds (or logit) of the probability of a success from the explanatory variables.

- The relation between a discrete response and a quantitative predictor may be explored graphically by plotting the binary observations and either the empirical log odds or the equivalent probabilities against the predictor, together with a smoothed curve. The LOGODDS macro provides some useful plots; the SM*nn* spline smoothers, which are available with the SYMBOL statement in PROC GPLOT, provide others.

- For both quantitative and discrete predictors, the results of a logistic regression are most easily interpreted from plots of the predicted probabilities against the predictors (or of log odds with an auxiliary scale of probabilities). Confidence intervals or standard error bars provide a visual indication of the precision of the predicted results.

- When there are multiple predictors, effect plots (Section 6.5.2) provide one method for constructing simplified displays.

- Influence diagnostics assess the impact of individual cases or groups on the fitted model, the predicted values, and the coefficients of individual predictors. The `INFLOGIS` macro and the `ADDVAR` macro produce a variety of useful plots designed to make these methods available for routine use.

- Polytomous responses may be handled in several ways with logistic regression. The *proportional odds model* is simple and convenient, but its validity depends on an assumption of equal slopes for adjacent-category logits. *Nested dichotomies* among the response categories give a set of models that might be regarded as a single, combined model for the polytomous response. *Generalized logits* can be used to construct models comparing any pair of categories.

- The basic logistic regression model can be applied in a wide variety of related situations. We illustrate its use in fitting and graphing a model for paired comparisons.

- Power analysis is an important adjunct to any statistical hypothesis test, but power analysis depends on being able to specify a minimal effect size of substantive interest. For the cases of a single binary predictor and a quantitative predictor (possibly along with others), the calculation of power or required sample size is described, along with macro programs to provide tabular and graphical displays.

Chapter

7 Log-linear and Logit Models

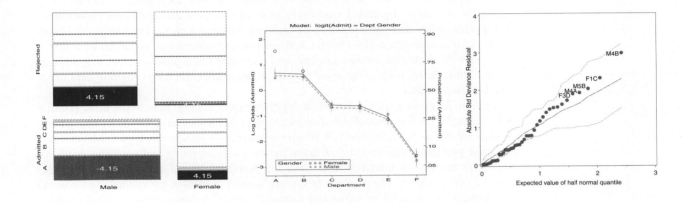

Log-linear models are most easily interpreted through visualizations, including mosaic displays and plots of associated logit models. As with logistic regression, diagnostic plots and influence plots help to assure that the fitted model is an adequate summary of associations among variables.

7.1 Introduction

We share a philosophy about linear algebra: we think basis-free, we write basis-free, but when the chips are down we close the office door and compute with matrices like fury.

Irving Kaplansky, in *Paul Halmos: Celebrating 50 Years of Mathematics*

Log-linear models provide a comprehensive scheme to describe and understand the associations among two or more categorical variables. Whereas logit models focus on the prediction of one response factor, log-linear models treat all variables symmetrically and attempt to model all important associations among them. In this sense, log-linear models are analogous to a correlation analysis of continuous variables, where the goal is to determine the patterns of dependence and independence among a set of variables. Nonetheless, when one variable is indeed a response and the others are explanatory, certain log-linear models are equivalent to logit models for that response.

Chapter 4 and Chapter 5 introduced some aspects of log-linear models in connection with mosaic displays and correspondence analysis. In this chapter, the focus is on fitting and interpreting log-linear models. The usual analyses with PROC CATMOD and PROC GENMOD present the results in terms of tables of parameter estimates. Particularly for larger tables, it becomes difficult to understand the nature of these associations from tables of parameter estimates. Instead, I emphasize plots of observed and predicted probabilities or log odds (when there are one or more response variables), as well as mosaic and other displays for interpreting a given model, and residual and influence plots for model diagnostics. I also illustrate how mosaic displays and correspondence analysis plots may be used in a complementary way to the usual numerical summaries, thereby providing additional insights into the data.

Section 7.2 gives a brief overview of log-linear models in relation to the more familiar ANOVA and regression models for quantitative data. Methods and software for fitting these models are discussed in Section 7.3. When one variable is a response, logit models for that response provide a simpler but equivalent means for interpreting and graphing results of log-linear models, as described in Section 7.4. Another class of simplified models (Section 7.5) occurs when one or more of the explanatory variables are ordinal, and discrete levels might be replaced by numerical values. Section 7.6 presents an extended example illustrating the interplay between model fitting and graphical displays. As in logistic regression models, there are analogs of model diagnostics for log-linear models. These statistics and related visualizations are described in Section 7.7. The final section (Section 7.8) illustrates some more comprehensive log-linear models for two or more response variables.

The models and methods described here attempt to go beyond the typical presentations of log-linear models. That is, the topics and examples in this chapter encompass specialized forms of log-linear models for one response variable, for ordinal explanatory variables, and for multiple response variables. This treatment is perhaps at the expense of more basic models, which were examined in Chapter 4 and Chapter 5 from an exploratory perspective. You may also want to consult *Categorical Data Analysis Using the SAS System*, Chapter 14; Allison (1999, Chapter 10); and Zelterman (1999, Chapters 4–5) for additional examples of fitting and interpretation of log-linear models using SAS, and Agresti (1990, Chapters 6–8) or Christensen (1997) for additional theory and examples.

7.2 Log-linear Models for Counts

Log-linear models have been developed from two formally distinct but related perspectives. The first is a discrete analog of ANOVA models for quantitative data, where the multiplicative relations among joint and marginal probabilities are transformed into an additive one by transforming the counts to logarithms. The second is a discrete analog of regression models, where the log of the cell frequency is modeled as a linear function of predictors.

For a quantitative response variable, the ANOVA and regression approaches are melded into a single *general linear model* by representing discrete predictors as dummy variables or contrasts. The ANOVA and regression perspectives provide interchangeable points of view. Equivalent models can be fit using PROC REG and PROC GLM, although each provides different conveniences for expressing the model in a MODEL statement, for model search, for obtaining separate tests of model terms, diagnostics, and so forth.

Similarly, for contingency table data, log-linear models for nominal variables have a direct relation to ANOVA models, but these models also have a regression interpretation when discrete classification variables are represented by dummy variables. Because the distribution of counts in a multinomial sample over the cells of the contingency table is Poisson, another generalization of log-linear models is to Poisson regression. Here, the log count is modeled as a linear combination of predictors, but with a Poisson distribution for the errors.

The recognition that the general linear model for quantitative data, with normally distributed errors, and similar linear models—such as logistic regression (binomial error distributions), Poisson regression, and so forth—had similar structure led to the development of the ***generalized linear model*** (McCullagh and Nelder, 1989), of which all are special cases. Thus, we can fit log-linear models using PROC CATMOD, which follows the ANOVA approach, or with PROC GENMOD, which follows the GLM approach; each offers somewhat different conveniences for model expression, testing, and diagnostic output.

7.2.1   Log-linear Models as Discrete ANOVA Models

For two discrete variables, A and B, suppose that you have a multinomial sample of n_{ij} observations in each cell i, j of an $I \times J$ contingency table. Let π_{ij} be the joint probabilities in the table, and let $m_{ij} = n_{++}\pi_{ij}$ be the expected cell frequencies under any model. Conditional on the observed total count, n_{++}, each count has a Poisson distribution, with mean m_{ij}. Any log-linear model may be expressed as a linear model for the $\log m_{ij}$. For example, the hypothesis of independence means that the expected frequencies, m_{ij}, follow

$$m_{ij} = \frac{m_{i+} \, m_{+j}}{m_{++}} \; .$$

This multiplicative model can be transformed to an additive (linear) model by taking logarithms of both sides:

$$\log(m_{ij}) = \log(m_{i+}) + \log(m_{+j}) - \log(m_{++}) \; ,$$

which is usually expressed in an equivalent form in terms of model parameters,

$$\log(m_{ij}) = \mu + \lambda_i^A + \lambda_j^B \tag{7.1}$$

where μ is a function of the total sample size; λ_i^A is the "main effect" for variable A, $\lambda_i^A = \log \pi_{i+} - \overline{\log \pi_{i+}}$; and λ_j^B is the "main effect" for variable B, $\lambda_j^B = \log \pi_{+j} - \overline{\log \pi_{+j}}$. In Equation 7.1, there are $1 + I + J$ parameters, but only $(I-1) + (J-1)$ are separately estimable; hence, the same analysis of variance restrictions are usually applied to the parameters: $\sum_i^I \lambda_i^A = \sum_j^J \lambda_j^B = 0$. The main effects in log-linear models pertain to differences among the marginal probabilities of a variable (which are usually not of direct interest).

These sum-to-zero constraints are one way to make the model (Equation 7.1) estimable, but other equivalent restrictions are possible. Setting the last values, λ_I^A and λ_J^B, to zero (as in PROC GENMOD) defines $\lambda_i^A = \log \pi_{i+} - \log \pi_{iJ}$ and $\lambda_j^B = \log \pi_{+j} - \log \pi_{Ij}$ as deviations from the last reference category, but these parameterizations are otherwise identical. [1]

Except for differences in notation, the model (Equation 7.1) is formally identical to the ANOVA main-effects model for a two-factor design:

$$E(y_{ij}) = \mu + \alpha_i + \beta_j$$

---

[1] The actual parameter values differ under different parameterizations, but the *difference* between any pair of parameters, e.g., $\lambda_i^A - \lambda_{i'}^A$, is the same for all parameterizations.

For a 2-way table, a model that *does* allow an association between the variables is the **saturated model**,

$$\log(m_{ij}) = \mu + \lambda_i^A + \lambda_j^B + \lambda_{ij}^{AB} \tag{7.2}$$

where, again, restrictions must be imposed for estimation:

$$\sum_i^I \lambda_i^A = 0, \quad \sum_j^J \lambda_j^B = 0, \quad \sum_i^I \lambda_{ij}^{AB} = \sum_j^J \lambda_{ij}^{AB} = 0 . \tag{7.3}$$

There are $I-1$ linearly independent λ_i^A row parameters, $J-1$ linearly independent λ_j^B column parameters, and $(I-1)(J-1)$ linearly independent λ_{ij}^{AB} association parameters. Again, the model (Equation 7.2) is formally similar to the two-factor ANOVA model with interaction:

$$E(y_{ij}) = \mu + \alpha_i + \beta_j + (\alpha\beta)_{ij}$$

Hence, associations between variables in log-linear models are analogous to interactions in ANOVA models. The use of superscripted symbols ($\lambda_i^A, \lambda_j^B, \lambda_{ij}^{AB}$) rather than separate Greek letters is a convention in log-linear models, and useful mainly for multi-way tables.

Equations 7.1 and 7.2 are examples of **hierarchical models**. This means that the model must contain all lower-order terms contained within any high-order term in the model. Thus, the saturated model (Equation 7.2) contains λ_{ij}^{AB}, and, therefore, must contain λ_i^A and λ_j^B. As a result, hierarchical models may be identified by the shorthand notation that lists only the high-order terms: Equation 7.2 is denoted $[AB]$, while Equation 7.1 is $[A][B]$.

7.2.2   Log-linear Models as Discrete GLMs

In the GLM approach, a log-linear model may be cast in the form of a regression model for $\log m$. One advantage is that models for tables of any size and structure may be expressed in a compact form.

For a contingency table of variables $A, B, C, \ldots$, with $N = I \times J \times K \times \cdots$ cells, let $\mathbf{n}$ denote a column vector of the observed counts arranged in standard order, and let $\mathbf{m}$ denote a similar vector of the expected frequencies under some model. Then, *any* log-linear model may be expressed in the form

$$\log \mathbf{m} = \mathbf{X}\boldsymbol{\beta} ,$$

where $\mathbf{X}$ is a known design or model matrix and $\boldsymbol{\beta}$ is a column vector containing the unknown λ parameters. For example, for a 2×2 table, the saturated model (Equation 7.2) with the usual zero-sum constraints (Equation 7.3) can be represented as

$$\begin{pmatrix} \log m_{11} \\ \log m_{12} \\ \log m_{21} \\ \log m_{22} \end{pmatrix} = \begin{bmatrix} 1 & 1 & 1 & 1 \\ 1 & 1 & -1 & -1 \\ 1 & -1 & 1 & -1 \\ 1 & -1 & -1 & 1 \end{bmatrix} \begin{pmatrix} \mu \\ \lambda_1^A \\ \lambda_1^B \\ \lambda_{11}^{AB} \end{pmatrix}$$

Note that only the linearly independent parameters are represented. $\lambda_2^A = -\lambda_1^A$ because $\lambda_1^A + \lambda_2^A = 0$, and $\lambda_2^B = -\lambda_1^B$ because $\lambda_1^B + \lambda_2^B = 0$, and so forth.

An additional advantage of the GLM formulation is that it makes it easier to express models with ordinal or quantitative variables. PROC GENMOD constructs the model matrix from the terms listed in the MODEL statement. A CLASS variable with K levels gives rise to $K-1$ columns for its main effect and sets of $K-1$ columns in each interaction effect. PROC CATMOD also constructs the model matrix from the effects listed on the MODEL statement and LOGLIN statement, but quantitative variables are treated nominally in models specified in the LOGLIN statement. Models that cannot be expressed using the standard syntax may be represented by entering the model matrix directly.

7.2.3   Log-linear Models for 3-Way Tables

Log-linear models for 3-way contingency tables were described briefly in Section 4.3.1. Each type of model allows associations among different sets of variables, and each has a different independence interpretation, as illustrated in Table 4.2.

For a 3-way table, the saturated model (denoted $[ABC]$) is

$$\log m_{ijk} = \mu + \lambda_i^A + \lambda_j^B + \lambda_k^C + \lambda_{ij}^{AB} + \lambda_{ik}^{AC} + \lambda_{jk}^{BC} + \lambda_{ijk}^{ABC} \ . \tag{7.4}$$

This has all variables associated; Equation 7.4 fits the data perfectly because the number of independent parameters equals the number of table cells. Two-way terms, such as λ_{ij}^{AB}, pertain to the partial association between pairs of factors. The presence of the 3-way term, λ_{ijk}^{ABC}, means that the partial association (conditional odds ratio) between any pair varies over the levels of the third variable.

Omitting the 3-way term gives the model $[AB][AC][BC]$,

$$\log m_{ijk} = \mu + \lambda_i^A + \lambda_j^B + \lambda_k^C + \lambda_{ij}^{AB} + \lambda_{ik}^{AC} + \lambda_{jk}^{BC} \ , \tag{7.5}$$

in which all pairs are conditionally dependent. However, for any pair, the conditional odds ratios are the *same* at all levels of the remaining variable, so this model is often called the **homogeneous association model**.

The interpretation of terms in this model may be illustrated using the Berkeley admissions data (Example 3.8 and Example 3.12), for which the factors are Admit, Gender, and Department, in a $2 \times 2 \times 6$ table. In the homogeneous association model,

$$\log m_{ijk} = \mu + \lambda_i^A + \lambda_j^D + \lambda_k^G + \lambda_{ij}^{AD} + \lambda_{ik}^{AG} + \lambda_{jk}^{DG} \ , \tag{7.6}$$

the λ-parameters have the following interpretations:

- The main effects λ_i^A, λ_j^D, and λ_k^G pertain to differences in the 1-way marginal probabilities. Thus, λ_j^D relates to differences in the total number of applicants to these departments, while λ_k^G relates to the differences in the overall numbers of men and women applicants.

- λ_{ij}^{AD} describes the partial association between admission and department, that is, different admission rates across departments (controlling for gender).

- λ_{ik}^{AG} relates to the association between admission and gender, controlling for department. This term, if significant, might be interpreted as indicating gender-bias in admissions.

- λ_{jk}^{DG}, the association between department and gender, indicates whether males and females apply differentially across departments.

7.3   Fitting Log-linear Models

Fitting a log-linear model is a process of deciding which association terms are significantly different from zero; these terms are included in the model that is used to explain the observed frequencies. Terms that are excluded from the model go into the residual or error term, which reflects the overall badness-of-fit of the model. The usual goal of log-linear modeling is to find a small model (few association terms) that nonetheless achieves a reasonable fit (small residuals).

7.3.1   Goodness-of-Fit Tests

For an *n*-way table, goodness-of-fit tests for a log-linear model attempt to answer the question "How well does the model reproduce the observed frequencies?" To avoid multiple subscripts, let $\boldsymbol{n} = n_1, n_2, \ldots, n_N$ denote the observed frequencies in a table with N cells with corresponding fitted frequencies $\widehat{\boldsymbol{m}} = \widehat{m}_1, \widehat{m}_2, \ldots, \widehat{m}_N$ according to a particular log-linear model. The standard goodness-of-fit statistics are sums over the cells of measures of the difference between the $\boldsymbol{n}$ and $\widehat{\boldsymbol{m}}$. The most commonly used are the familiar Pearson chi-square,

$$\chi^2 = \sum_i \frac{(n_i - \widehat{m}_i)^2}{\widehat{m}_i} \; ,$$

and the likelihood-ratio G^2 or deviance statistic,

$$G^2 = 2 \sum_i n_i \, \log(n_i / \widehat{m}_i) \; . \tag{7.7}$$

Both of these statistics have asymptotic χ^2 distributions when all expected frequencies are large.[2] The (residual) degrees of freedom are the number of cells (N) minus the number of estimated parameters.

In practice, I often find that several models have an acceptable fit or, sadly, that none do (usually because of a large sample size). It is helpful to compare competing models statistically, and two strategies are particularly useful in these cases.

The likelihood-ratio G^2 statistic is unique in that one can compare two ***nested models*** by their difference in G^2 statistics, which has a χ^2 distribution on the difference in degrees of freedom. Two models, M_1 and M_2, are nested when one (for example, M_2) is a special case of the other. That is, model M_2 (with ν_2 residual df) contains a subset of the parameters of M_1 (with ν_1 residual df); the remaining ones are effectively set to zero. Therefore, model M_2 is more restrictive and cannot fit the data better than the more general model M_1, i.e., $G^2(M_2) \geq G^2(M_2)$. The least restrictive of all models, with $G^2 = 0$ and $\nu = 0$ df, is the saturated model for which $\widehat{\boldsymbol{m}} = \boldsymbol{n}$.

Assuming that the less restrictive model M_1 fits, the difference in G^2,

$$\Delta G^2 \equiv G^2(M_2 \mid M_1) = G^2(M_2) - G^2(M_1) \tag{7.8}$$

$$= 2 \sum_i n_i \, \log(\widehat{m}_{i1} / \widehat{m}_{i2}) \tag{7.9}$$

has a chi-squared distribution with df = $\nu_2 - \nu_1$. The last equality (Equation 7.9) follows from substituting in Equation 7.7.

Rearranging terms in Equation 7.8, we see that we can partition the $G^2(M_2)$ into two terms,

$$G^2(M_2) = G^2(M_1) + G^2(M_2 \mid M_1) \; .$$

The first term measures the difference between the data and the more general model M_1. If this model fits, the second term measures the additional lack-of-fit imposed by the more restrictive model. In addition to providing a more focused test, $G^2(M_2 \mid M_1)$ also follows the chi-squared distribution more closely when some $\{m_i\}$ are small (Agresti, 1990, Section 7.7.6).

Alternatively, a second strategy uses other measures that combine goodness-of-fit with model parsimony and may also be used to compare non-nested models. The statistics described below are all cast in the form of badness-of-fit relative to degrees of freedom, so that smaller values reflect "better" models.

---

[2] A wider class of test statistics including χ^2 and G^2 as special cases is described by Cressie and Read (1984) and Read and Cressie (1988). Except in bizarre or borderline cases, all members of this class provide the same conclusions when expected frequencies are at least moderate (all $\widehat{m} > 5$).

The simplest idea (Goodman, 1971) is to use G^2/df (or χ^2/df), which has an expected value of 1 for a good-fitting model. This type of measure is routinely reported by PROC GENMOD.

The *Akaike Information Criterion* (AIC) statistic (Akaike, 1973) is a very general criterion for model selection with maximum likelihood estimation, based on the idea of maximizing the information provided by a fitted model. AIC is defined generally as

$$\text{AIC} = -2 \log \mathcal{L} + 2k$$

where $\log \mathcal{L}$ is the maximized log likelihood; and k is the number of parameters estimated in the model; so better models correspond to *smaller* AIC. For log-linear models, minimizing AIC is equivalent to minimizing

$$\text{AIC}^\star = G^2 - 2\nu$$

where ν is the residual df. This form is easier to calculate by hand from the output of any procedure if AIC is not reported. Christensen (1997, Section IV.8) shows that AIC is a close analog of Mallows (1973) C_p statistic, commonly used for model selection in regression.

A third statistic of this type is the BIC or Schwartz (1978) criterion

$$\text{BIC} = G^2 - \nu \, \log(n)$$

where n is the total sample size. Both AIC and BIC penalize the fit statistic for increasing number of parameters. BIC also penalizes the fit directly with sample size, so it expresses a preference for less complex models than AIC as the sample size increases. But the sample size is fixed for a given multi-way table, so the argument for BIC seems less clear for log-linear models.

Finally, some users are comforted to know that there are analogs in log-linear models of the familiar R^2 and Adjusted R^2 often used to assess the goodness-of-fit of regression and ANOVA models. In these standard linear models, R^2 is defined as

$$R^2 = 1 - \frac{SSE(M_1)}{SSE(M_0)} = \frac{SSE(M_0) - SSE(M_1)}{SSE(M_0)}$$

where $SSE(M_1)$ is the error sum of squares for a model of interest, and $SSE(M_0)$ is the error sum of squares for the smallest null model, usually the model with an intercept only. Hence, R^2 gives the proportion of the variation of the data explained by the model M_1 or, equivalently, the proportion of error removed by the model.

In log-linear models, the deviance G^2 is analogous to the SSE in a classical linear model, and you can define

$$R^2 = 1 - \frac{G^2(M_1)}{G^2(M_0)} = \frac{G^2(M_0) - G^2(M_1)}{G^2(M_0)} \qquad (7.10)$$

For a log-linear model, it usually makes sense to take the null model M_0 as the smallest possible interesting model. For example, in models with one or more response variables, $R_1, \ldots,$ and two or more explanatory variables $E_1, E_2, \ldots,$ the null model is usually $[E_1 E_2 \ldots][R_1] \ldots,$ including the highest-order interaction of the explanatory variables.

As in linear models, the R^2 defined in Equation 7.10 can never decrease as more parameters are fitted (so residual df, ν, decrease). An adjusted R^2, taking model complexity into account, is defined as

$$\text{Adj. } R^2 = 1 - \frac{G^2(M_1)/\nu_1}{G^2(M_0)/\nu_0} \, ,$$

which is the same adjustment used in regression models. The largest value of the adjusted R^2 will occur for the model having the smallest value of G^2/ν.

7.3.2 Software

The SAS System offers a variety of facilities for fitting log-linear models. PROC CATMOD, a very general procedure for categorical data modeling, provides a LOGLIN statement tailored for log-linear models. PROC GENMOD includes log-linear models as a special case of generalized linear models, as a model for log frequency, with a Poisson distribution for errors. In SAS/INSIGHT, the Fit (Y X) menu also fits generalized linear models; for a log-linear model, you select Poisson as the response distribution and Log as the link function on the Method panel. Finally, SAS/IML provides the IPF function, which fits a log-linear model by the method of iterative proportional fitting.

7.3.3 Using PROC CATMOD

For PROC CATMOD, all table variables are considered dependent variables and are treated as discrete factors by default. Thus, for log-linear models, the MODEL statement should specify all contingency table factors in the form A*B*C ... = _RESPONSE_. The _RESPONSE_ keyword indicates that the cell frequencies in the contingency table formed by the variables A, B, C, ... are being modeled. The LOGLIN statement is used to specify the model to be fit. When the data is in frequency form, as is typical, you use a WEIGHT statement to specify the frequency variable giving the cell count.

EXAMPLE 7.1   Berkeley admissions

Data on admission to the six largest graduate departments at Berkeley was examined graphically in Chapter 3 and in Chapter 4. The data is contained in the dataset BERKELEY, listed in Appendix B.2. The log-linear model (Equation 7.6) can be fit to this data with PROC CATMOD as shown here:

```
proc catmod order=data data=berkeley;
   format dept dept. admit admit.;
   weight freq;
   model dept*gender*admit=_response_ /
       ml noiter noresponse nodesign noprofile pred=freq ;
   loglin admit|dept|gender @2 / title='Model (AD,AG,DG)';
run;
```

In the LOGLIN statement, the "bar" notation (ADMIT|DEPT|GENDER @2) means all terms up to 2-way associations. The printed output includes the table-of-fit statistics shown in Output 7.1, which indicates that only the 2-way terms DEPT*ADMIT and DEPT*GENDER are significant. In particular, there is no association between Gender and Admission, controlling for Department.

Several models may be fit within one PROC CATMOD step. We drop the GENDER*ADMIT term in the following model, giving the model fit statistics in Output 7.2.

```
   loglin admit|dept dept|gender / title='Model (AD,DG)';
run;
```

The fit of the model $[AD][DG]$ is not much worse than that of the model $[AD][AG][DG]$. Nevertheless, neither model fits very well, as judged by the likelihood-ratio G^2 statistics. We will see why in the next Example.   □

Output 7.1   Berkeley admissions data: Model [AD] [AG] [DG], fit with PROC CATMOD

```
                        Model (AD,AG,DG)
              MAXIMUM-LIKELIHOOD ANALYSIS-OF-VARIANCE TABLE

          Source             DF    Chi-Square      Prob
          --------------------------------------------------
          ADMIT               1      262.45       0.0000
          DEPT                5      276.37       0.0000
          DEPT*ADMIT          5      534.71       0.0000
          GENDER              1      197.99       0.0000
          GENDER*ADMIT        1        1.53       0.2167
          DEPT*GENDER         5      731.62       0.0000


          LIKELIHOOD RATIO    5       20.20       0.0011
```

Output 7.2   Berkeley admissions data: Model [AD] [DG], fit with PROC CATMOD

```
                        Model (AD,DG)

              MAXIMUM-LIKELIHOOD ANALYSIS-OF-VARIANCE TABLE

          Source             DF    Chi-Square      Prob
          --------------------------------------------------
          ADMIT               1      279.04       0.0000
          DEPT                5      275.86       0.0000
          DEPT*ADMIT          5      623.03       0.0000
          GENDER              1      213.63       0.0000
          DEPT*GENDER         5      763.69       0.0000


          LIKELIHOOD RATIO    6       21.74       0.0014
```

7.3.4   Using PROC GENMOD

With PROC GENMOD, log-linear models are fit directly in the style of Equation 7.6, that is, as a model for the log frequency with a Poisson distribution. Whereas PROC CATMOD assumes that all factor variables are categorical (unless declared as quantitative in a DIRECT statement), PROC GENMOD follows the scheme of PROC GLM, so variables are assumed to be quantitative, unless declared categorical in a CLASS statement.

EXAMPLE 7.2   Berkeley admissions

The homogeneous association model $[AD][GD][AG]$ (Equation 7.6) may be fit as a generalized linear model for log frequency with PROC GENMOD as shown below; this produces the model fit statistics shown in Output 7.3. The Deviance statistic is identical to the likelihood-ratio G^2 shown in Output 7.1. The keywords TYPE3 WALD give Type III Wald tests of individual terms, similar to the maximum likelihood ANOVA table produced by PROC CATMOD.

```
proc genmod data=berkeley;
   class dept gender admit;
   model freq = dept|gender|admit@2 / dist=poisson link=log type3 wald;
```

Output 7.3   Berkeley admissions data: Model [AD] [AG] [DG], fit with PROC GENMOD

```
                       The GENMOD Procedure

                Criteria For Assessing Goodness Of Fit

           Criterion            DF        Value       Value/DF

           Deviance              5      20.2043         4.0409
           Scaled Deviance       5      20.2043         4.0409
           Pearson Chi-Square    5      18.8242         3.7648
           Scaled Pearson X2     5      18.8242         3.7648
           Log Likelihood        .   20503.1035              .


                Wald Statistics For Type 3 Analysis

           Source               DF    ChiSquare   Pr>Chi

           DEPT                  5    276.3530    0.0001
           GENDER                1    197.9725    0.0001
           DEPT*GENDER           5    731.5804    0.0001
           ADMIT                 1    262.4539    0.0001
           DEPT*ADMIT            5    534.7075    0.0001
           GENDER*ADMIT          1      1.5260    0.2167
```

Now fit the model $[AD][GD]$ as shown below. This is the conditional independence model, $A \perp G \mid D$. Because this model does not fit well, the residuals among the observation statistics are obtained with the statement MAKE 'OBSTATS' OUT=OBSTATS;. The factor variables DEPT, GENDER, and ADMIT are merged with the OBSTATS dataset and translated to more meaningful labels. A mosaic display is requested with the MOSAIC macro.

```
proc genmod data=berkeley;
   class dept gender admit;
   model freq = admit|dept gender|dept / dist=poisson obstats residuals;
   make 'obstats' out=obstats;
data obstats;
   merge berkeley obstats;
   D = put(dept, dept.);
   if admit=1
      then A='Admitted';
      else A='Rejected';
   if gender='F'
      then G = 'Female';
      else G = 'Male';

%mosaic(data=obstats, var=A G D, vorder=A G D, count=freq,
   resid=streschi, cellfill=dev, split=H V,
   title=Model: [AdmitDept] [GenderDept]);
```

Figure 7.1   Mosaic display for Berkeley admissions data

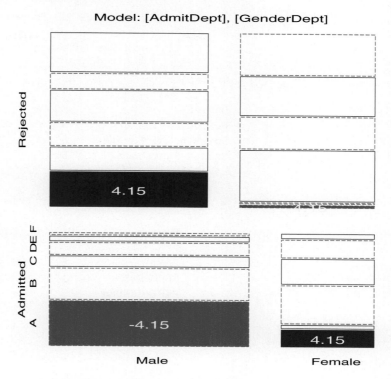

The mosaic display, shown in Figure 7.1, indicates that this model fits well (residuals are small) except in Department A. This suggests a model that allows an association between Admission and Gender in Department A only,

$$\log m_{ijk} = \mu + \lambda_i^A + \lambda_j^D + \lambda_k^G + \lambda_{ij}^{AD} + \lambda_{jk}^{DG} + \delta_{j=1}\lambda_{ik}^{AG} \ , \qquad (7.11)$$

where $\delta_{j=1}$ equals 1 for Department A ($j = 1$) and is zero otherwise. This model asserts that Admission and Gender are conditionally independent, given Department, except in Department A. It has one more parameter than the conditional independence model, $[AD][GD]$. Equation 7.11 may be fit with PROC GENMOD by constructing a variable equal to the interaction of GENDER and ADMIT with a dummy variable having the value 1 for Department A and 0 for other departments.

```
data berkeley;
   set berkeley;
   dept1AG = (gender='F') * admit * (dept=1);

proc genmod data=berkeley;
   class dept gender admit;
   model freq = dept|gender dept|admit dept1AG / dist=poisson type3 wald;
```

The model fit statistics and Type III tests for Equation 7.11 are shown in Output 7.4. This model fits very well indeed. The parameter estimate $\widehat{\lambda}_{ik}^{AG} = 1.052$ may be interpreted as the log odds ratio of admission for females as compared to males in Department A. The odds ratio is $\exp(1.052) = 2.86$, the same as the value calculated from the raw data (see Section 3.4.3).   □

Output 7.4   Berkeley admissions data: Model (Equation 7.11) fit with PROC GENMOD

```
                       The GENMOD Procedure

              Criteria For Assessing Goodness Of Fit

         Criterion            DF        Value      Value/DF

         Deviance              5        2.6815       0.5363
         Scaled Deviance       5        2.6815       0.5363
         Pearson Chi-Square    5        2.6904       0.5381
         Scaled Pearson X2     5        2.6904       0.5381
         Log Likelihood        .    20511.8649          .

               Wald Statistics For Type 3 Analysis

              Source       DF    ChiSquare  Pr>Chi

              DEPT          5     288.4101   0.0001
              GENDER        1     189.3882   0.0001
              DEPT*GENDER   5     514.0723   0.0001
              ADMIT         1     291.1886   0.0001
              DEPT*ADMIT    5     571.3809   0.0001
              DEPT1AG       1      16.0379   0.0001
```

7.3.5 Using SAS/INSIGHT Software

SAS/INSIGHT can be invoked either as a procedure (PROC INSIGHT) or interactively from the Display Manager through menus (Globals->Analyze->Interactive data analysis[3]) or the command line (insight). When you call SAS/INSIGHT as a procedure, you can specify a log-linear model in a FIT statement and obtain printed output from the analysis. When you invoke SAS/INSIGHT interactively, log-linear models may be fit from the Analyze-> Fit (Y X) menu. In either case, you must specify the response distribution to be Poisson, and you must specify the Log link function. In addition, SAS/INSIGHT treats numeric variables as Interval (quantitative) and character variables as Nominal by default. For interactive use, you can change the type of a numeric variable by clicking on the Int button in the spreadsheet window. For procedure use, you must create an equivalent character variable first.

The following statements illustrate the use of SAS/INSIGHT as a procedure, fitting the model in Equation 7.11. First create character variables A, D, and G with DATA step statements. SAS/INSIGHT does not understand "bar" notation, so the model terms must be spelled out.

```
data berkeley;
   set berkeley;
   D = put(dept, dept.);
   if admit=1
      then A='Admitted';
      else A='Rejected';
```

---

[3]In SAS software Version 7 and higher, the menu choices are Solutions->Analysis->Interactive data analysis.

```
    if gender='F'
       then G = 'Female';
       else G = 'Male';
    dept1AG = (gender='F') * admit * (dept=1);

%let _print_=on;
proc insight data=berkeley;
    fit freq = A D A*D G G*D dept1AG / resp=Poisson link=log label=cell;
    tables;
run;
```

SAS/INSIGHT offers far more opportunities for graphic output when used interactively. To
fit a log-linear model, you must select Poisson for the Response Dist. and Log for the Link
Function on the Method panel. A variety of output statistics and residual plots are available
from the Output panel.

Figure 7.2 shows a mosaic display for Admission and Department—obtained from the
menu choices Analyze->Box Plot/Mosiac Plot (Y)—that illustrates how the proportion of
applicants admitted declines across departments (the [*AD*] term). Figure 7.3 shows a plot

Figure 7.2   SAS/INSIGHT mosaic display for Admission and Department

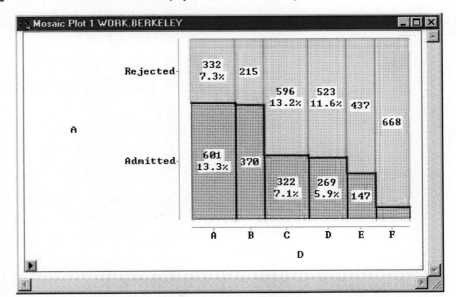

Figure 7.3   SAS/INSIGHT residual plots for model (Equation 7.11)

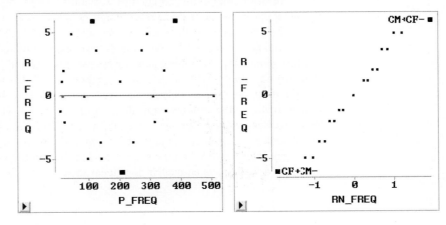

of raw residuals, $(n_{ijk} - \widehat{m}_{ijk})$ against fitted frequencies, and a normal QQ plot of these residuals, with the largest absolute values identified interactively. These residual plots are consistent with an adequate model.

7.4 Logit Models

Because log-linear models are formulated as models for the log (expected) frequency, they make no distinction between response and explanatory variables. In effect, they treat all variables as responses. Logit models, on the other hand, describe how the log odds for one variable depends on other explanatory variables. There is a close connection between the two: When there is a response variable, each logit model for that response is equivalent to a log-linear model. This relationship often provides a simpler way to formulate and test the model, and to plot and interpret the fitted results. The price paid for this simplicity is that associations among the explanatory variables are not expressed in the model.

Consider, for example, the model of homogeneous association—Equation 7.5 for a 3-way table—and let variable C be a binary response. Under this model, the logit for variable C is

$$L_{ij} = \log\left(\frac{\pi_{ij|1}}{\pi_{ij|2}}\right) = \log\left(\frac{m_{ij1}}{m_{ij2}}\right)$$

$$= \log(m_{ij1}) - \log(m_{ij2}) \ .$$

Substituting from Equation 7.5, you find that all terms that do not involve variable C cancel, and you are left with

$$L_{ij} = \log(m_{ij1}/m_{ij2}) = (\lambda_1^C - \lambda_2^C) + (\lambda_{i1}^{AC} - \lambda_{i2}^{AC}) + (\lambda_{j1}^{BC} - \lambda_{j2}^{BC})$$

$$= 2\lambda_1^C + 2\lambda_{i1}^{AC} + 2\lambda_{j1}^{BC} \tag{7.12}$$

because all λ terms sum to zero. To see how these logits depend on A and B, you can replace the λ parameters with new parameters, $\alpha = 2\lambda_1^C$, $\beta_i^A = 2\lambda_{i1}^{AC}$, etc., which express this relation more directly,

$$L_{ij} = \alpha + \beta_i^A + \beta_j^B \ . \tag{7.13}$$

In the logit model (Equation 7.13), the response, C, is affected by both A and B, which have additive effects on the log odds of response category C_1 compared to C_2. The terms β_i^A and β_j^B correspond directly to $[AC]$ and $[BC]$ in the log-linear model (Equation 7.5). The association among the explanatory variables $[AB]$ is assumed in the logit model, but this model provides no explicit representation of that association. The logit model (Equation 7.12) is equivalent to the log-linear model $[AB][AC][BC]$ in goodness-of-fit and fitted values, and parameters in the two models correspond directly.

More generally, when there is a binary response variable, e.g., R, and one or more explanatory variables, $A, B, C, \ldots$, any logit model for R has an equivalent log-linear form. Every term in the logit model, such as β_{ik}^{AC}, corresponds to an association of those factors with R, that is, $[ACR]$ in the equivalent log-linear model. The log-linear model must also include all associations among the explanatory factors, the term $[ABC\ldots]$. Conversely, any log-linear model that includes all associations among the explanatory variables has an equivalent logit form. When the response factor has more than two categories, models for generalized logits have equivalent log-linear form.

EXAMPLE 7.3   Berkeley admissions

The homogeneous association model $[AD][AG][DG]$ did not fit the Berkeley admissions data very well, and we saw that the term $[AG]$ was unnecessary. Nevertheless, it is instructive to consider the equivalent logit model. The features of the logit model that lead to the same conclusions and simplified interpretation from graphical displays are illustrated.

Because Admission is a binary response variable, the model in Equation 7.6 is equivalent to the logit model,

$$\log\left(\frac{m_{\text{Admit}(ij)}}{m_{\text{Reject}(ij)}}\right) = \alpha + \beta_i^{\text{Dept}} + \beta_j^{\text{Gender}} . \tag{7.14}$$

That is, the logit model (Equation 7.14) asserts that Department and Gender have additive effects on the odds of Admission. This model may be fit with PROC CATMOD as shown below, using the variable ADMIT as the response and DEPT and GENDER as predictors. The option ORDER=DATA is used so that PROC CATMOD will form the logit for 'Admitted', the category that appears first in the dataset. The RESPONSE statement is used to create an output dataset containing observed and fitted logits, which are graphed (see Example 7.4) in Figure 7.4.

```
proc catmod order=data
          data=berkeley;
   weight freq;
   response / out=predict;
   model admit = dept gender / ml noiter noprofile ;
```

Output 7.5   Berkeley admissions data: Fit statistics and parameter estimates for the logit model (Equation 7.14)

```
                      CATMOD PROCEDURE

        MAXIMUM-LIKELIHOOD ANALYSIS-OF-VARIANCE TABLE

          Source          DF    Chi-Square      Prob
          ------------------------------------------------
          INTERCEPT        1       262.49      0.0000
          DEPT             5       534.78      0.0000
          GENDER           1         1.53      0.2167

          LIKELIHOOD RATIO 5        20.20      0.0011


           ANALYSIS OF MAXIMUM-LIKELIHOOD ESTIMATES

                                    Standard    Chi-
       Effect      Parameter  Estimate  Error   Square    Prob
       -----------------------------------------------------------
       INTERCEPT       1      -0.6424   0.0397   262.49   0.0000
       DEPT            2       1.2744   0.0723   310.82   0.0000
                       3       1.2310   0.0856   206.98   0.0000
                       4       0.0118   0.0714     0.03   0.8687
                       5      -0.0202   0.0729     0.08   0.7815
                       6      -0.4649   0.0898    26.79   0.0000
       GENDER          7      -0.0499   0.0404     1.53   0.2167
```

The model fit statistics and parameter estimates for the model (Equation 7.14) are shown in Output 7.5. Note that the likelihood-ratio G^2 for this model is the same as that for the log-linear model $[AD][AG][DG]$ shown in Output 7.1 and in Output 7.3. The Wald χ^2 values for DEPT and GENDER in Output 7.5 are similar to the χ^2 values for the association of each of these with ADMIT in the log-linear model.

As in logistic regression models, parameter estimates may be interpreted as increments in the log odds, or $\exp(\beta)$ may be interpreted as the multiple of the odds associated with the explanatory categories. Because PROC CATMOD uses zero-sum constraints, $\sum \beta_i^{\text{Dept}} = 0$ and $\sum \beta_j^{\text{Gender}} = 0$, the parameters for the last level of any factor is found as the negative of the sum of the parameters listed.

Thus, $\beta_1^{\text{Gender}} = -0.0499$ is the increment to the log odds of Admission for men,[4] and, therefore, $\beta_2^{\text{Gender}} = +0.0499$ for women. Overall, but controlling for Department, women were $\exp(2 \times 0.0499) = 1.105$ times as likely to be admitted to graduate school than male applicants in 1973. The logit parameters for DEPT in Output 7.5 decrease over Departments A–E; the value for Department F is $-(1.274 + 1.231 + \cdots - 0.465) = -2.032$. These values correspond to the decline in the fitted logits over Department as shown in Figure 7.4.

Logit models are easier to interpret than the corresponding log-linear models because there are fewer parameters, and because these parameters pertain to the odds of a response category rather than to cell frequency. Nevertheless, interpretation is often easier from a graph than from the parameter values.   □

7.4.1   Plotting Results for Logit Models

Logit models may also be interpreted through plots of observed and fitted values, either in terms of the logit for one response category or in terms of the equivalent response probability. Plots of log odds generally have a simpler, additive form, such as the parallel curves in Figure 7.4, but the effects may be easier to understand in terms of probabilities. As with logistic regression models, both goals may often be achieved by plotting on the logit scale and adding a second vertical axis showing the corresponding probabilities. These plots are similar to those described in Section 6.3 and Section 6.4, but the plotting steps differ because the output information from PROC CATMOD is structured differently from that provided by PROC LOGISTIC.

Such plots are facilitated by the CATPLOT macro (Appendix A.4). The macro uses the output dataset produced with the OUT= option in the RESPONSE statement. This dataset normally contains both logit values and probability values, and either type may be plotted with observed and fitted values and optional confidence intervals. A utility macro, PSCALE (Appendix A.31.8), may be used to add a probability scale to a plot of log odds.

EXAMPLE 7.4   Berkeley admissions

The output dataset PREDICT from the logit model, ADMIT = DEPT GENDER, for the Berkeley data is shown partially in Output 7.6. Each of the 2×6 samples defined by the explanatory factors DEPT and GENDER gives rise to three observations: two response probabilities and one logit, distinguished by the variable _TYPE_.

---

[4] β_1^{Gender} refers to men, the first level of GENDER to appear in the BERKELEY dataset, because ORDER=DATA was used in the PROC CATMOD statement.

Output 7.6 Output dataset PREDICT from the logit model for Berkeley admissions (partial)

DEPT	GENDER	ADMIT	_TYPE_	_OBS_	_PRED_	_SEPRED_
A	Male		FUNCTION	0.492	0.582	0.069
A	Male	Admit	PROB	0.621	0.642	0.016
A	Male	Reject	PROB	0.379	0.358	0.016
A	Female		FUNCTION	1.544	0.682	0.099
A	Female	Admit	PROB	0.824	0.664	0.022
A	Female	Reject	PROB	0.176	0.336	0.022
B	Male		FUNCTION	0.534	0.539	0.086
B	Male	Admit	PROB	0.630	0.631	0.020
B	Male	Reject	PROB	0.370	0.369	0.020
B	Female		FUNCTION	0.754	0.639	0.116
B	Female	Admit	PROB	0.680	0.654	0.026
B	Female	Reject	PROB	0.320	0.346	0.026
....						

The statements below draw the plot of observed and predicted logits (_type_= 'FUNCTION') shown in Figure 7.4. The PSCALE macro constructs an Annotate dataset that draws the probability values on the right vertical axis in the plot. The label for this axis is specified in the TITLE statement, with an angle A=-90, meaning the right-hand side and rotated 90°. By default, the macro uses the AXIS and SYMBOL statements defined before the macro call. Separate curves are drawn for each level of the CLASS=GENDER variable. The values of the CLASS variable may be labeled in the plot or supplied in a LEGEND statement. The parameter Z=1.96 specifies the multiple of the standard error of the fitted logit (_SEPRED_) used to draw the error bars in the plot, giving (asymptotic) 95% individual confidence intervals.

```
%pscale(lo=-4, hi=3, anno=pscale, prob=%str(0.05,.1,.25,.5,.75,.9));

title h=1.6 'Model:  logit(Admit) = Dept Gender'
        a=-90 'Probability (Admitted)'
     h=3.5 a=-90 ' ';
legend1 position=(bottom inside left)  offset=(4,3)
        mode=share cborder=blue across=1
        shape=symbol(6,1.5) label=('Gender')
        value=(c=black 'Female'
               c=red   'Male');
axis1 order=(-3 to 2) offset=(4)
     label=(a=90 'Log Odds (Admitted)');
axis2 label=('Department') offset=(4);
symbol1 i=none v=circle h=1.7 c=black;
symbol2 i=none v=dot    h=1.7 c=red  ;
%catplot(data=predict,
   xc=dept, y=_obs_, class=gender,
   type=FUNCTION,
   z=1.96, anno=pscale, legend=legend1);
```

The effects seen in our earlier analyses (Examples 4.8 and 4.9) may all be observed in this plot. The effect of Gender is shown by the constant separation between the two curves. From the plot you can see that this effect is very small and nonsignificant (compared with the error bars). If the gender effect were omitted from the model, the fitted logits would be the same for men and women applying to each Department, and would plot as a curve parallel to, but in between, the two shown in the graph. Most of the observed points are quite close to their predicted values, except in Department A, where the probability of

Figure 7.4 Observed (points) and fitted (lines) log odds of admission in the logit model corresponding to [AD][AG][DG]. The error bars show individual 95% confidence intervals around each fitted logit.

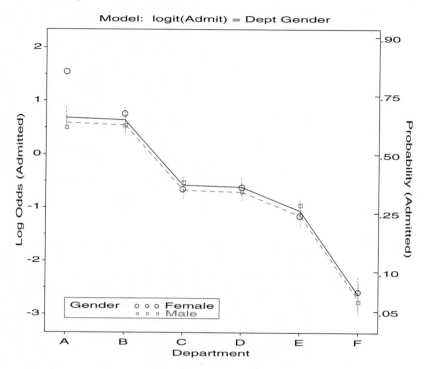

admittance for women is substantially greater than that for men. Example 7.2 dealt with this by allowing one extra parameter for an association between admission and gender in Department A, giving the log-linear model (Equation 7.11).

You can see what this model "looks like" by recasting it in logit form. The log-linear model (Equation 7.11) has an equivalent logit formulation, which also adds a 1 df term for an effect of Gender in Department A,

$$L_{ij} = \alpha + \beta_i^{\text{Dept}} + \delta_{j=1}\beta^{\text{Gender}} \ . \tag{7.15}$$

This model can be fit with PROC CATMOD as shown below. The association term between Admission and Gender for Department A (dept1AG) is fit as a DIRECT variable. The GENDER variable is not included in the MODEL statement, so it must be listed in the POPULATION statement. Because the CATPLOT macro uses the values in the output dataset, the plotting step is unchanged.

```
data berkeley;
   set berkeley;
   dept1AG = (gender='F') * (dept=1);

proc catmod order=data
            data=berkeley;
   weight freq;
   population dept gender;
   direct dept1AG;
   response / out=predict;
   model admit = dept dept1AG / ml noiter noprofile ;
%catplot(data=predict, xc=dept, class=gender, type=FUNCTION,
   z=1.96, legend=legend1);
```

Figure 7.5 Observed and fitted logits for the model in Equation 7.11

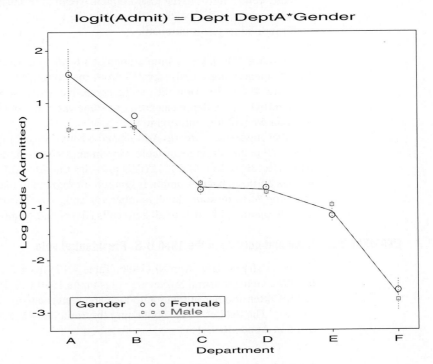

The resulting plot for this model is shown in Figure 7.5. The graph gives a visual interpretation of the model (Equation 7.11) and its logit form (Equation 7.15): No effect of Gender on Admission, except in Department A, where the extra parameter allows perfect fit. □

7.4.2 Zero Frequencies

Cells with frequencies of zero create problems for log-linear and logit models. For log-linear models, most of the derivations of expected frequencies and other quantities assume $n_{ijk\cdots} > 0$. In logit models, the observed log odds (e.g., for a 3-way table), $\log(n_{ij1}/n_{ij2})$, will be undefined if either frequency is zero.

Zero frequencies may occur in contingency tables for two different reasons:

Structural zeros (also called *fixed zeros*) occur when it is impossible to observe values for some combinations of the variables. For example, suppose that you have three different methods of contacting people at risk for some obscure genetically inherited disease: newspaper advertisement, telephone campaign, and radio appeal. If each person contacted in any way is classified dichotomously by the three methods of contact, there can never be a non-zero frequency in the 'No-No-No' cell.[5]

Sampling zeros (also called *random zeros*) occur when the total size of the sample is not large enough in relation to the probabilities in each of the cells to assure that someone will be observed in every cell. For example, in a European survey of religious affiliation and occupation, you may not observe any Muslim vineyard-workers in France, although

---

[5]Yet, if you fit an unsaturated model, expected frequencies can be estimated for all cells and provide a means to estimate the total number at risk in the population. See Lindsey (1995, Section 5.4).

such individuals surely exist. Even when zero frequencies do not occur, tables with many cells relative to the total frequency tend to produce small expected frequencies in at least some cells, which tends to make the χ^2 statistics for model fit and Wald statistics for individual terms unreliable.

PROC CATMOD takes a simple approach to distinguishing these two cases: Cells with zero frequency are simply deleted from the contingency table, and thus are treated as structural zeros. To avoid this, some corrective action is needed. One solution (for sampling zeros) is to collapse categories of some variables, but we are often loath to do this for fear that we will lose information.

Other suggestions are: (a) Add a small positive quantity (0.5 is usually recommended) to every cell in the contingency table (Goodman, 1970), as is done in calculating empirical log odds (Section 6.2.1); PROC CATMOD provides the ADDCELL option in the MODEL statement for this purpose, but this option is ignored for maximum likelihood estimation. (b) Replace sampling zeros by some small number, typically 10^{-10} or smaller (Agresti, 1990). (c) Add a small quantity, like 0.1, to all zero cells (Evers and Namboordiri., 1977).

EXAMPLE 7.5   Race and politics in the 1980 U.S. Presidential vote

Table 7.1 shows data (Agresti (1990, Table 4.12) from Clogg and Shockey (1988)) from the 1982 General Social Survey on votes in the 1980 U.S. Presidential election for Reagan or for Carter or other in relation to race and conservatism (1=most liberal, 7=most conservative).[6] The dataset VOTE, containing the variables RACE, CONS, VOTEFOR, and COUNT is listed in Appendix B.15.

Table 7.1 1982 General Social Survey: Reagan vs. Carter, by Race and Conservatism

Political Conservatism	Race			
	White		Non-White	
	Reagan	Carter/other	Reagan	Carter/other
1	1	12	0	6
2	13	57	0	16
3	44	71	2	23
4	155	146	1	31
5	92	61	0	8
6	100	41	2	7
7	18	8	0	4

It is natural to treat Vote for Reagan vs. Carter/other as the response, and Race and Conservatism as predictors in this $2 \times 2 \times 7$ table, with variables VoteFor (V), Race (R), and Conservatism (C). Before fitting models, it is useful to take an exploratory look at the data. The fourfold display shown in Figure 7.6 shows separate panels for each level of conservatism. In order to focus on the tendency to vote for Reagan vs. Carter/other among Whites compared to Non-Whites, the number of White and Non-White respondents were equated in each panel in this figure. With this standardization, confidence rings will overlap in the left and right quadrants (Reagan vs. Carter or other) when the (conditional) odds ratio does not differ significantly from 1.

Thus, among Whites, in the bottom half of each panel, you can compare the areas of the left and right quadrants and see that the propensity to vote for Reagan increases with conservatism. A similar trend is evident among Non-White respondents, but there are a number of zero frequencies among Non-Whites who indicated they voted for Reagan.

---

[6]John R. Nesselroade and Raymond B. Cattell, editors, *Handbook of Multivariate Experimental Psychology, Second Edition*, 1988, copyright © Plenum Press. Reprinted by permission of Kluwer Academic/Plenum Publishers.

Figure 7.6   Fourfold display for Vote, by Race and Conservatism, equating the number of White and Non-White respondents at each level of Conservatism

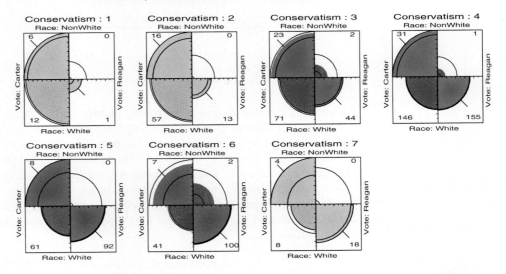

The conditional odds ratios for Vote and Race given Conservatism are all in the same direction, indicating that Whites were more likely to vote for Reagan at *any* level of Conservatism. The `fourfold` program gives the test of homogeneity of odds ratios shown in Output 7.7, which is equivalent to a test for lack-of-fit of the homogeneous association log-linear model $[RC][VR][VC]$. The tests of conditional independence, $V \perp R \mid C$, suggest that voting preference depends on race and possibly conservatism.

Output 7.7   Vote data: Test of Homogeneity of odds ratios

```
Test of Homogeneity of Odds Ratios (no 3-Way Association)


   TEST                            CHISQ      DF      PROB
   Homogeneity of Odds Ratios      4.961       6     0.5488


   Conditional Independence of Vote and Race | Conservatism
                    (assuming Homogeneity)


   TEST                            CHISQ      DF      PROB
   Likelihood-Ratio               77.335       1     0.0000
   Cochran-Mantel-Haenszel        61.969       1     0.0000
```

To illustrate the problem of zero cells, consider tests of fit of the saturated model, $[RCV]$, and of the homogeneous association model, $[RC][VR][VC]$, fit as log-linear models under three conditions: (a) no adjustment for zeros, (b) replace zeros by 10^{-10}, and (c) add 0.5 to each cell. In each case, the models are fit with the statements below, after possible adjustment to the `COUNT` variable. The results are summarized in Table 7.2.

```
proc catmod data=vote;
   weight count;
   model cons*race*votefor = _response_ / ml noiter noresponse noprofile;
   loglin cons|race|votefor / title='Saturated model';
   run;
   loglin cons|race|votefor @2 / title='No 3-way association';
```

Table 7.2   Effects of zero-cell actions on log-linear models for VOTE data

Action	Model: [RCV] df	[RCV] G^2	[RC][VR][VC] df	[RC][VR][VC] G^2
(a) None	0	.	2	1.89
(b) $n = 0 \rightarrow 10^{-10}$	1	0.00	6	4.96
(c) $n \rightarrow n + \frac{1}{2}$	0	.	6	3.45

In case (a), the four zero cells are treated as structural zeros and deleted, leaving only 2 df for the test of lack-of-fit in the no-3-way model. In case (b), the main effect parameter for Race cannot be estimated and there is, paradoxically, 1 df for the test of the saturated model. Case (c), adding 0.5 to each cell, has no anomalies, and this solution is used for this example. In other cases, it is recommended to compare several approaches to determine if any conclusions are affected by the presence of zero cells.

This example proceeds to fit a main effects logit model. Treating the Vote for Reagan vs. Carter/other as the response, the logit model with nominal main effects for Race and Conservatism is

$$\text{logit(Reagan/Carter)} = \alpha + \beta_i^{\text{Race}} + \beta_j^{\text{Cons}} . \tag{7.16}$$

Equation 7.16 may be fit with PROC CATMOD as follows:

```
data vote;
    set vote;
    count = count + 0.5;
proc catmod data=vote order=data;
   weight count;
   response / out=predict;
   model votefor = race cons / noiter noresponse noprofile;
```

The model fit statistics and parameter estimates for the logit model (Equation 7.16) are shown in Output 7.8. The model fits quite well.

To interpret the model, plot the observed and predicted logits, with 90% confidence intervals, as shown below. The CATPLOT macro produces Figure 7.7.

```
%pscale(lo=-5, hi=2.3, anno=pscale, prob=%str(0.01,.05,.1,.25,.5,.75,.9));

axis1 order=(-5 to 2) offset=(0,3)
     label=(a=90 'Logit (Reagan / Carter)');
axis2 label=('Conservatism') offset=(2);
symbol1 i=none v=circle h=1.9 c=black;
symbol2 i=none v=square h=1.7 c=red  ;
legend1 position=(bottom inside center) offset=(,2);
%catplot(data=predict, class=race, x=cons, z=1.65, anno=pscale,
   legend=legend1);
```

Notice that for both Whites and Non-Whites, the log odds of voting for Reagan increases with conservatism. This is also reflected in the parameter estimates for CONS in Output 7.8, which increase in approximately equal steps. Equation 7.16 does not use the ordinal nature of conservatism. A model that uses conservatism as a direct, quantitative independent variable (c) can be expressed as

$$\text{logit (Reagan / Carter)} = \alpha + \beta_i^{\text{Race}} + \beta^{\text{Cons}} c \tag{7.17}$$

Output 7.8   Vote data: Fit of the nominal main effects model

```
          Main Effects of Race and Conservatism
                    CATMOD PROCEDURE

     MAXIMUM-LIKELIHOOD ANALYSIS-OF-VARIANCE TABLE

     Source            DF    Chi-Square      Prob
     --------------------------------------------------
     INTERCEPT          1        43.75      0.0000
     RACE               1        41.37      0.0000
     CONS               6        67.84      0.0000


     LIKELIHOOD RATIO   6         3.45      0.7501

       ANALYSIS OF MAXIMUM-LIKELIHOOD ESTIMATES

                                    Standard    Chi-
     Effect        Parameter  Estimate   Error   Square    Prob
     --------------------------------------------------------------
     INTERCEPT         1      -1.4324   0.2166   43.75   0.0000
     RACE              2       1.1960   0.1859   41.37   0.0000
     CONS              3      -1.6144   0.6551    6.07   0.0137
                       4      -1.2000   0.2857   17.64   0.0000
                       5      -0.1997   0.2083    0.92   0.3377
                       6       0.2779   0.1672    2.76   0.0965
                       7       0.6291   0.1941   10.51   0.0012
                       8       1.1433   0.2052   31.03   0.0000
```

Figure 7.7   Observed (points) and fitted (lines) logits for main effects model. Dotted lines show a 90% confidence interval around the predicted log odds.

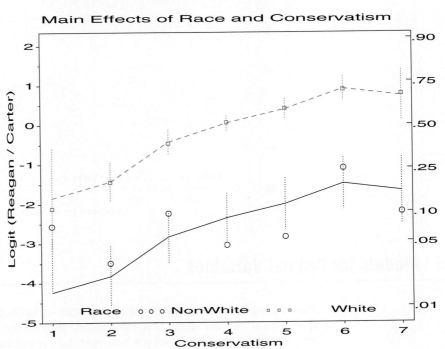

Note that there is just one parameter for conservatism, β^{Cons}, which is interpreted as an increase in the log odds of a Vote for Reagan for each change of 1 unit in Conservatism. Equation 7.17 may be fit with PROC CATMOD just by adding the statement DIRECT CONS;

```
proc catmod data=vote order=data;
   direct cons;
   weight count;
   response / out=predict;
   model votefor = race cons / noiter noresponse noprofile ;
   title 'Linear Effect for Conservatism' h=2.5 a=-90 ' ';
```

The likelihood-ratio G^2 for this model is $G^2(11) = 9.58$, and the difference in G^2 for Equations 7.17 and 7.16 is $\Delta G^2(5) = 6.13$, so the linear model cannot be rejected, given that the nominal model fits. The estimate $\widehat{\beta}^{\text{Cons}} = 0.472$ indicates that the odds of voting for Reagan increase by a factor of $\exp(0.472) = 1.60$ (60%) for each step of increasing conservatism.

The observed and fitted logits are plotted exactly as before, using the same CATPLOT macro call with the new output dataset PREDICT. The plot is shown in Figure 7.8. Note that the 90% confidence limits around predicted values are noticeably smaller than in Figure 7.7. This is just one advantage of models for ordinal variables, which are discussed in the following section. □

Figure 7.8   Observed (points) and fitted (lines) logits for linear effect of conservatism. Dotted lines show a 90% confidence interval around the predicted log odds.

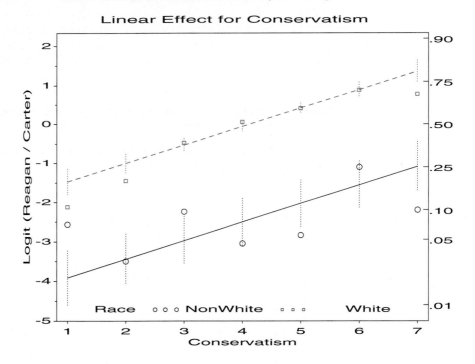

7.5   Models for Ordinal Variables

Standard log-linear models treat all classification variables as nominal, unordered factors; all statistical tests are identical and parameter estimates are equivalent if the categories of any variable are re-ordered. Yet you have seen that the ordering of categories often provides important information about the nature of associations, and Section 3.2.4 showed that non-parametric tests that take into account the ordered nature of a factor are more powerful.

In a mosaic display, an ordered associative effect is seen when the residuals have an opposite-corner pattern of positive and negative signs and magnitudes (e.g., for the Hair-color and Eye-color data, Figure 4.4, or the Titanic data, Figure 4.16(a)). In a correspondence analysis plot, an association has an ordered effect when the points for two factors are ordered similarly. In these cases, log-linear and logit models that use the ordered nature of the factors offer several advantages.

- Because they are more focused, tests that use the ordinal structure of the table variables are more powerful when the association varies systematically with the ordered values of a factor.

- Because they consume fewer degrees of freedom, you can fit unsaturated models where the corresponding model for nominal factors would be saturated. In a 2-way table, for example, a variety of models for ordinal factors may be proposed that are intermediate between the independence model and the saturated model.

- Parameter estimates from these models are fewer in number, are easier to interpret, and quantify the nature of effects better than corresponding quantities in models for nominal factors. Estimating fewer parameters typically gives smaller standard errors, as shown in Example 7.5.

These advantages are analogous to the use of tests for trends or polynomial effects in ANOVA models with quantitative factors.

Models for ordinal variables may be specified in log-linear form, as described in Section 7.5.1. When there is an ordinal response variable, related models may be specified in terms of logits for adjacent categories (Section 7.5.2) or cumulative logits (Section 7.5.3). The descriptions here are brief. For further information, refer to Agresti (1984), Agresti (1990, Chapter 9), and Goodman (1979, 1983).

7.5.1   Log-linear Models for Ordinal Variables

For a 2-way table, when either the row variable or the column variable, or both, are ordinal, one simplification comes from assigning ordered scores $\{a_i\}$, $a_1 \leq a_2 \leq \cdots a_I$ and/or $\{b_j\}$, $b_1 \leq b_2 \leq \cdots b_J$ to the categories so that the ordinal relations are necessarily included in the model. Typically, equally spaced scores are used, for example, integer scores, $\{a_i\} = i$, or the zero-sum equivalent, $\{a_i\} = i - (I + 1)/2$ (e.g., $\{a_i\} = \{-1, 0, 1\}$ for $I = 3$). These give simple interpretations of the association parameters in terms of *local odds ratios*,

$$\theta_{ij} = \frac{m_{ij}\, m_{i+1,j+1}}{m_{i,j+1}\, m_{i+1,j}} \ ,$$

the odds ratio for adjacent rows and adjacent columns.

When both variables are assigned scores, this gives the *linear-by-linear model*,

$$\log(m_{ij}) = \mu + \lambda_i^A + \lambda_j^B + \gamma\, a_i b_j \ . \tag{7.18}$$

Because the scores are fixed, this model has only one extra parameter, γ, compared to the independence model, which is the special case $\gamma = 0$. The terms $\gamma a_i b_j$ describe a pattern of association where deviations from independence increase linearly with a_i and b_j in opposite directions towards the opposite corners of the table.

In the linear-by-linear association model, the local log odds ratios are

$$\log \theta_{ij} = \gamma (a_{i+1} - a_i)(b_{j+1} - b_j) \ ,$$

which reduces to

$$\log \theta_{ij} = \gamma$$

for integer-spaced scores, so γ is the common local log odds ratio. As a result, the linear-by-linear model is sometimes called the model of *uniform association* (Goodman, 1979).

Generalizations of the linear-by-linear model result when only one variable is assigned scores. In the ***row-effects model***, the row variable (in this example, A) is treated as nominal, while the column variable (B) is assigned ordered scores $\{b_j\}$. The log-linear model is then

$$\log(m_{ij}) = \mu + \lambda_i^A + \lambda_j^B + \alpha_i b_j \ , \tag{7.19}$$

where the α_i parameters are the *row effects*. An additional constraint, $\sum_i \alpha_i = 0$ or $\alpha_I = 0$, is imposed so that Equation 7.19 has $(I-1)$ more parameters than the independence model. The linear-by-linear model is the special case where the row effects are equally spaced, and the independence model is the special case where all $\alpha_i = 0$.

The row-effects model (Equation 7.19) also has a simple odds ratio interpretation. The local log odds ratio for adjacent pairs of rows and columns is

$$\log \theta_{ij} = \alpha_{i+1} - \alpha_i \ ,$$

which is constant for all pairs of adjacent columns. Plots of the local log odds ratio against i would appear as a set of parallel curves.

In the analogous ***column-effects model***, $(J-1)$ linearly independent column effect parameters β_j are estimated for the column variable, while fixed scores $\{a_i\}$ are assigned to the row variable.

The linear-by-linear model (Equation 7.18) and the row-effects model (Equation 7.19) can be fit using `PROC CATMOD`, but to do so requires that you enter the complete model matrix explicitly. With `PROC GENMOD` you only need to create a numeric variable with score values in the input dataset, a much easier task.

EXAMPLE 7.6   Mental impairment and parents' SES

In Example 5.2 correspondence analysis was used to explore the relationship between ratings of the mental health status of young New Yorkers and their parents' socioeconomic status (SES). Figure 5.2 showed that most of the association in the table was accounted for by a single dimension along which both factors were ordered, consistent with the view that mental health increased in relation to parents' SES.

For comparison, we first fit the independence model with both `PROC CATMOD` and `PROC GENMOD`. As expected, this model fits quite badly, with $G^2 (15) = 47.418$.

```
%include catdata(mental);
proc catmod data=mental;
   weight count;
   model mental*ses = _response_ / noiter noprofile noresponse;
   loglin mental ses / title='Independence';
   run;
```

For illustration, the standardized (adjusted) deviance residuals, $g_i / \sqrt{(1 - h_i)}$, are obtained in the `PROC GENMOD` step (named `STRESDEV` in the `OBSTATS` dataset), and used with the `MOSAIC` macro to produce the mosaic display shown in the left panel of Figure 7.9.[7] The parameter `CELLFILL=DEV 0.5` causes the program to write the value of all residuals greater than 0.5 in absolute value in the corresponding tile.

---

[7]To ensure that the levels of both factors are ordered correctly, `MENTAL` and `SES` were entered as numeric variables in the dataset `MENTAL`, and user formats were used to provide the character labels shown in Figure 7.9. Because SAS/IML does not make use of formatted values, the `TABLE` macro was used to convert the numeric variables to character.

```
proc genmod data=mental;
   class mental ses;
   model count = mental ses / dist=poisson obstats residuals;
   make 'obstats' out=obstats noprint;
run;

%table(data=mental, var=Mental SES, weight=count, char=Y,
       format=mental mental. ses ses., order=data, out=mental2);
data obstats;
   merge mental2 obstats;
%mosaic(data=obstats, vorder=Mental SES, plots=2, split=H V, resid=stresdev,
   title=Mental Impairment and SES: Independence, cellfill=dev 0.5);
```

Figure 7.9   Mental health and SES: Residuals from Independence (left) and Row Effects (right) Models

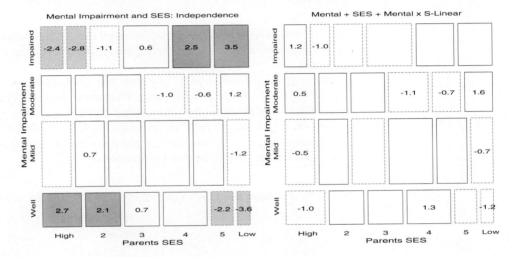

Note that the residuals in Figure 7.9 for the independence model have the opposite-corner pattern, which would arise if either the row-effects model (with ordered row effects) or the linear-by-linear association model described the association between mental health and SES.

To fit models in which the association terms for MENTAL and/or SES use quantitative scores, create copies (M and S) of these variables. They are used as quantitative variables when they appear in the MODEL statement, but are *not* listed as CLASS variables. The following statements fit the row-effects model, using SES as a linear effect, and then the linear-by-linear model. Goodness-of-fit statistics for all three models are shown in Table 7.3.

Table 7.3   Mental health data: Goodness-of-fit statistics for ordinal log-linear models

Model	df	χ^2	G^2	ΔG^2	AIC
Independence	15	45.985	47.418	.	17.42
Linear-by-linear	14	9.732	9.895	37.523	-18.18
Row-effects (Mental)	12	6.289	6.281	41.137	-17.72

```
data mental;
   set mental;
   m = mental;    *-- copy m and s as quantitative, non-class;
   s = ses;
```

```
title 'Linear SES';
proc genmod data=mental;
   class mental ses;
   model count = mental ses mental*s / dist=poisson obstats residuals;
   make 'obstats' out=obstats noprint;
run;
data obstats;
   merge mental obstats;
%mosaic(data=obstats, var=Mental SES, resid=stresdev,  split=H V,
   title=Mental + SES + Mental x S-Linear, cellfill=dev 0.5);

title 'Linear x Linear';
proc genmod data=mental;
   class mental ses;
   model count = mental ses m*s / dist=poisson obstats residuals;
run;
```

The ΔG^2 values in Table 7.3 each test whether the corresponding model results in a significant reduction in the residual G^2 compared to the independence model. Both are highly significant.

Similarly, the difference in G^2 between the linear-by-linear and row-effects model, $\Delta G^2 (2) = 9.732 - 6.289 = 3.443$, suggests that the row-effects model is *not* a significant improvement over the linear-by-linear model. The AIC values suggest a slight preference for the linear-by-linear model. The residuals for the row effects model are shown in the right panel of Figure 7.9; residuals for the linear-by-linear model (not shown) have the same signs, but are slightly smaller in some cells.

Output 7.9 Parameter estimates for the row-effects log-linear model, Mental health data

```
                              Linear SES

                  Analysis Of Parameter Estimates

        Parameter      DF    Estimate   Std Err   ChiSquare  Pr>Chi

        INTERCEPT       1      4.2528    0.0968   1929.6528   0.0001
        MENTAL    1     1      0.8256    0.1849     19.9359   0.0001
        MENTAL    2     1      1.0266    0.1661     38.2085   0.0001
        MENTAL    3     1      0.4545    0.1846      6.0579   0.0138
        MENTAL    4     0      0.0000    0.0000        .        .
        SES       1     1     -0.5439    0.1695     10.2931   0.0013
        SES       2     1     -0.4451    0.1438      9.5866   0.0020
        SES       3     1     -0.1308    0.1194      1.2007   0.2732
        SES       4     1      0.3068    0.0984      9.7211   0.0018
        SES       5     1      0.0727    0.0945      0.5911   0.4420
        SES       6     0      0.0000    0.0000        .        .
        S*MENTAL  1     1     -0.3068    0.0489     39.3076   0.0001
        S*MENTAL  2     1     -0.1617    0.0413     15.3281   0.0001
        S*MENTAL  3     1     -0.1434    0.0462      9.6370   0.0019
        S*MENTAL  4     0      0.0000    0.0000        .        .
        SCALE           0      1.0000    0.0000        .        .

NOTE:  The scale parameter was held fixed.
```

Under the linear-by-linear model, the estimate of the coefficient of M*S is $\hat{\gamma} = 0.0907$ (s.e.=0.015) with unit-spaced scores. This corresponds to a local odds ratio, $\hat{\theta}_{ij} = \exp(0.0907) = 1.095$. This single number describes the association succinctly: each step down the socioeconomic scale increases the odds of being classified one step poorer in mental health by 9.5%.

Parameter estimates for the row-effects model are shown in Output 7.9. The row effects are the values of the S*MENTAL terms. These values are ordered, consistent with mental health status having ordinal associative effects, but (with integer scores for both variables) they are not equally spaced, as the linear-by-linear model would imply. The spacing of these parameter estimates is similar to what you saw in the correspondence analysis plot (Figure 5.2), with the middle categories Mild Impairment and Moderate Impairment relatively close together compared to the extreme categories.

These log-linear models and the associated mosaic displays do not provide a clear preference between the row-effects and linear-by-linear models here. The next examples provide other models and graphical displays that may distinguish them better.

□

7.5.2   Adjacent Category Logit Models

When there is a single response variable, logit models provide a simple way to model the dependence of the response on the other explanatory variables. For an ordinal response, models for the logits between adjacent response categories allow the ordered nature of the response to be taken into account. For the model of independence, the ***adjacent category logits*** are

$$A_{j|i} \equiv \log\left(\frac{\pi_{j+1|i}}{\pi_{j|i}}\right) = \log\left(\frac{m_{i,j+1}}{m_{ij}}\right) = (\mu + \lambda_i^A + \lambda_{j+1}^B) - (\mu + \lambda_i^A + \lambda_j^B)$$

$$= \lambda_{j+1}^B - \lambda_j^B \qquad (7.20)$$

which are constants—for example, $\beta_j = (\lambda_{j+1}^B - \lambda_j^B)$—not depending on the explanatory variable(s). If an explanatory variable is also ordinal, you may use scores $\{a_i\}$ as before. The analog of the linear-by-linear model with unit-spaced scores allows the value of $A_{j|i}$ to vary linearly with the quantitative value,

$$A_{j|i} = \beta_j + \gamma\, a_i \qquad (7.21)$$

The slope parameter γ has a similar log odds interpretation: the log odds of a response in category $j + 1$ as opposed to category j increases by γ for each unit increase in the explanatory variable.

In a similar way, the fixed scores a_i may be replaced by row effect parameters α_i to be estimated (with the constraint $\sum_i \alpha_i = 0$ or $\alpha_I = 0$) to give the row-effects adjacent logit model

$$A_{j|i} = \beta_j + \alpha_i \qquad (7.22)$$

A plot of the fitted logits against i for this model appears as parallel curves (rather than parallel lines under the linear-by-linear model (Equation 7.21)).

Even less restrictive models, which are still unsaturated, may be fit if the row-effects model fits poorly. For example, each adjacent logit may be linearly related to an assigned score for an explanatory variable, but the slopes may differ over the adjacent response categories (the ***linear-interaction model***):

$$A_{j|i} = \beta_j + \gamma_j\, s_i \;. \qquad (7.23)$$

Alternatively, a quadratic relation between the adjacent logits $A_{j|i}$ and the scores $A_{j|i} = \beta_j + \gamma_1\, a_i + \gamma_2 a_i^2$ may be fit. These possibilities are illustrated in the following example.

EXAMPLE 7.7   Mental impairment and parents' SES

This example considers adjacent category logit models for the Mental Health data, treating MENTAL as an ordinal response. Adjacent logit models are easily fit with PROC CATMOD using the RESPONSE ALOGIT; statement. Differences among the logits for adjacent categories (the intercepts, β_j, in Equations 7.21 and 7.22) are specified by the _RESPONSE_ keyword in the MODEL statement. Nominal explanatory variables are included as main effects (and possibly, interactions) on the left-hand side of the MODEL statement. An explanatory variable is treated as quantitative when declared in a DIRECT statement.

The following statements fit a series of adjacent category logit models to the Mental Health data. Model 0 has only a _RESPONSE_ effect, and is analogous to the independence model. In Model 1, the adjacent logits for mental impairment are affected by SES, as a nominal variable. Model 2 is the linear-by-linear model for adjacent logits, with SES as a direct variable. Model 3 allows different slopes for each adjacent logit.

```
%include catdata(mental);

*-- Adjacent logit models;
proc catmod data=mental;
   weight count;
   population ses;
   response alogit / out=pred0;
   model mental = _response_ / noprofile noresponse title='Model 0:  _R_';
run;
   response alogit / out=pred1;
   model mental = _response_  ses / noprofile noresponse title='Model 1: _R_ SES';
run;
   direct ses;
   response alogit / out=pred2;
   model mental = _response_  ses / noprofile noresponse title='Model 2: _R_ S';
run;
   direct ses;
   response alogit / out=pred3;
   model mental = _response_ | ses / noprofile noresponse title='Model 3: _R_|S';
run;
```

For each model, an output dataset, which contains the observed and fitted logits, is requested with the OUT= option in the RESPONSE statement. Plotting the observed and fitted logits makes it easy to see what relationships are implied by each model. The plots for Model 1 and Model 2, shown in Figure 7.10, are produced with the CATPLOT macro as shown below. The macro call requests a plot of the observed logit (_OBS_) against SES, with separate curves for each adjacent logit (CLASS=_NUMBER_). By default, the macro also draws curves connecting the predicted values (_PRED_ in the output dataset) and ± 1 standard error bars around each fitted logit.

```
axis1 label=(a=90) order=(-1 to 1.5 by .5);
axis2 offset=(3,8);
proc format;
   value cum 1='1:2'  2='2:3'  3='3:4';
title 'Model 1: Mental = _R_ SES';
%catplot(data=pred1, x=ses, y=_obs_, class=_number_, clfmt=cum.,
   type=FUNCTION, ylab=Adjacent Logit);

title 'Model 2: Mental = _R_  S';
%catplot(data=pred2, x=ses, y=_obs_, class=_number_, clfmt=cum.,
   type=FUNCTION, ylab=Adjacent Logit);
```

Figure 7.10   Adjacent category logit models for Mental Health data: Model 1 and Model 2

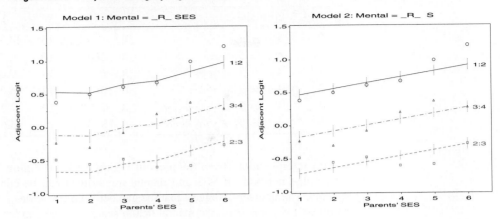

For illustration, we also fit less restrictive models, allowing a quadratic relation between the adjacent logit and SES (Model 4). Model 5 adds a quadratic term to the unequal slopes allowed in Model 3. Plots for Model 3 and Model 5 are shown in Figure 7.11.

```
proc catmod data=mental;
   weight count;
   population ses;
   direct ses;
   response alogit / out=pred4;
   model mental = _response_ ses ses*ses /
                  noprofile noiter title='Model 4: _R_ S S^2';
run;
   response alogit / out=pred5;
   model mental = _response_|ses ses*ses /
                  noprofile noiter title='Model 5: _R_|S S^2';
run;
```

Figure 7.11   Adjacent category logit models for Mental Health data: Model 3 and Model 5

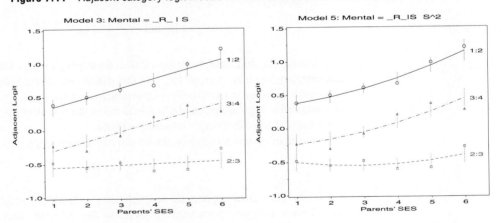

What can you conclude from this? From Table 7.4, all models except the independence model have acceptable fit according to the χ^2 values; Models 2–5 all have smaller AIC values than Model 1; of these, Model 2, the linear-by-linear model, is the most parsimonious, but Models 4 and 5 have slightly smaller AIC values.

Table 7.4   Adjacent category logit models for Mental Health data

Model	Formula	Terms	df	χ^2	p-value	AIC
0	$A_{j\|i} = \beta_j$	_R_	15	44.35	0.0001	14.35
1	$A_{j\|i} = \beta_j + \alpha_i$	_R_ SES	10	6.76	0.7478	-13.24
2	$A_{j\|i} = \beta_j + \gamma\, a_i$	_R_ S	14	9.68	0.7849	-18.32
3	$A_{j\|i} = \beta_j + \gamma_j a_i$	_R_|S	12	6.26	0.9023	-17.74
4	$A_{j\|i} = \beta_j + \gamma_1 a_i + \gamma_2 a_i^2$	_R_ S S^2	13	7.39	0.8809	-18.61
5	$A_{j\|i} = \beta_j + \gamma_j a_i + \delta a_i^2$	_R_|S S^2	11	3.69	0.9782	-18.69

One interpretation (from the plots in Figure 7.10 and Figure 7.11) is that there is evidence that not both of SES and mental impairment can be considered linear with unit spacing. The intercepts suggest that the gap between categories 1 and 2 ('Well', 'Mild impairment') is greatest on the mental health scale, and the gap between categories 2 and 3 ('Mild', 'Moderate impairment') is smallest. The evidence regarding the metric for SES is more ambiguous: there is a suggestion of a mildly quadratic relationship with SES, particularly for the logit between response categories 1 and 2, but this may be due to the points for (lowest) SES categories 5 and 6, where the large logit values imply a relatively larger number of people classified as mildly impaired as opposed to well.   □

7.5.3   Cumulative Logit Models

When there is an ordinal response factor, cumulative logit models (Williams and Grizzle, 1972) provide an alternative way to take the ordinal nature of the response into account, without assigning arbitrary scores to the response categories.

Let F_j be the cumulative probability of a response less than or equal to category j,

$$F_j = \pi_1 + \pi_2 + \cdots + \pi_j = \sum_{h=1}^{h=j} \pi_h \ .$$

Then the ***cumulative logit*** is defined as

$$C_j \equiv \mathrm{logit}(1 - F_j) = \log\left(\frac{1 - F_j}{F_j}\right) \ .$$

C_j gives the log odds that the response is in a category *greater* than category j, as opposed to a category less than or equal to j. By this definition, the cumulative logits are necessarily monotone decreasing over the response categories: $C_1 \geq C_2 \geq \cdots \geq C_{J-1}$. Models for the cumulative logit are particularly useful when the response may be considered a discrete realization of an underlying continuous variable.

In terms of cumulative logits, the model of independence is

$$C_{j\|i} = \beta_j \ ,$$

that is, the logit does not depend on explanatory variable(s) indexed by subscript i. Here, the response category parameters β_j refer to the cutpoints between adjacent categories, rather than to the distances between adjacent ones as in the analogous adjacent category logit model (Equation 7.20).

For quantitative scores, a_i, assigned to an explanatory variable, the analog of the linear-by-linear model is

$$C_{j\|i} = \beta_j + \gamma\, a_i \ . \tag{7.24}$$

which again has one more parameter than the independence model. For any two rows, the difference in logits, $C_{j|i} - C_{j|i'}$, is the log odds ratio in the 2×2 table for those two rows, with columns dichotomized following response category j. Under Equation 7.24, $C_{j|i} - C_{j|i'} = \gamma(a_i - a_{i'})$, so the log odds ratio is proportional to the difference in scale values and is the same at all cutpoints. When unit-spaced scores $\{a_i\} = i$ are used, the logit difference for adjacent rows is then constant:

$$C_{j|i} - C_{j|i'} = \gamma \ .$$

As with the adjacent category logits, a variety of models analogous to the row-effects model (Equation 7.22) and the linear-interaction model (Equation 7.23) may be defined for the cumulative logits. These are illustrated in the next example, primarily to look at the shapes of plots of observed and fitted logits and to compare them with what you saw for adjacent category logits.

EXAMPLE 7.8   Mental impairment and parents' SES

Cumulative logit models may be fit using PROC CATMOD with the RESPONSE CLOGIT; statement. The model is specified in the same way as for adjacent category logits, but now the _RESPONSE_ keyword refers to differences among the cumulative response probabilities. As before, an independent variable is treated as a quantitative variable, when it is declared in a DIRECT statement.

The following statements fit the same models as in Example 7.7: first Models 0–3 in which SES has no effect on mental health (Model 0), and then SES with a nominal effect (Model 1), a constant linear effect (Model 2), and different linear effects for each cumulative logit (Model 3).

```
%include catdata(mental);

*-- Cumulative logit models;
proc catmod data=mental;
   weight count;
   population ses;
   response clogit / out=pred0;
   model mental = _response_ / noprofile noresponse title='Model 0: _R_';
 run;
   response clogit / out=pred1;
   model mental = _response_  ses /
                  noprofile noresponse title='Model 1: _R_ SES';
 run;
   direct ses;
   response clogit / out=pred2;
   model mental = _response_  ses /
                  noprofile noresponse title='Model 2:  _R_ S';
 run;
   direct ses;
   response clogit / out=pred3;
   model mental = _response_ | ses /
                  noprofile noresponse title='Model 3:  _R_|S';
 run;
```

For comparison, you can also fit models with both linear and quadratic effects on the cumulative logits, first with equal slopes and curvature for all response categories (Model 4), and second with separate slopes and equal curvatures (Model 5).

```
data mental;
   set mental;
   ses2 = ses**2;
```

```
proc catmod data=mental;
  weight count;
  population ses;
  direct ses ses2;
  response clogit / out=pred4;
  model mental = _response_ ses ses2 /
               noprofile noiter title='Model 4: _R_ S S^2';
  run;
  response clogit / out=pred5;
  model mental = _response_|ses ses2 /
               noprofile noiter title='Model 5: _R_|S S^2';
  run;
```

The model fit statistics for these models are shown in Table 7.5. The values are quite similar to those for the adjacent category logits (Table 7.3).

Table 7.5   Cumulative logit models for Mental Health data

Model	Terms	df	χ^2	p-value	AIC
0	_R_	15	45.92	0.0001	15.92
1	_R_ | SES	10	7.75	0.6536	-12.25
2	_R_ S	14	10.72	0.7080	-17.28
3	_R_|S	12	6.48	0.8897	-17.52
4	_R_ S S^2	13	8.36	0.8192	-17.64
5	_R_|S S^2	11	3.94	0.9716	-18.06

For any such model, the CATPLOT macro displays the observed and fitted cumulative logits using the output dataset specified on the RESPONSE statement. The statements below produce the graphs of the logits for Model 0 and Model 1, shown in Figure 7.12. Similar statements, using the output datasets PRED2 and PRED4, give the graphs for Model 2 and Model 4 in Figure 7.13.

```
axis1 label=(a=90);
axis2 offset=(3,6);
proc format;
   value cum 1='>1'  2='>2'  3='>3';
title 'Model 0: Mental = _R_';
%catplot(data=pred0, x=ses, y=_obs_, class=_number_, clfmt=cum.,
   type=FUNCTION, ylab=Cumulative Logit);
title 'Model 1: Mental = _R_ SES';
%catplot(data=pred1, x=ses, y=_obs_, class=_number_, clfmt=cum.,
   type=FUNCTION, ylab=Cumulative Logit);
```

Figure 7.12   Cumulative logit models for Mental Health data: Model 0 and Model 1

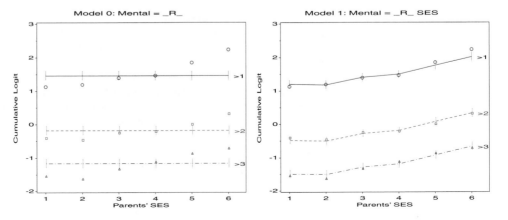

Figure 7.13 Cumulative logit models for Mental Health data: Model 2 and Model 4

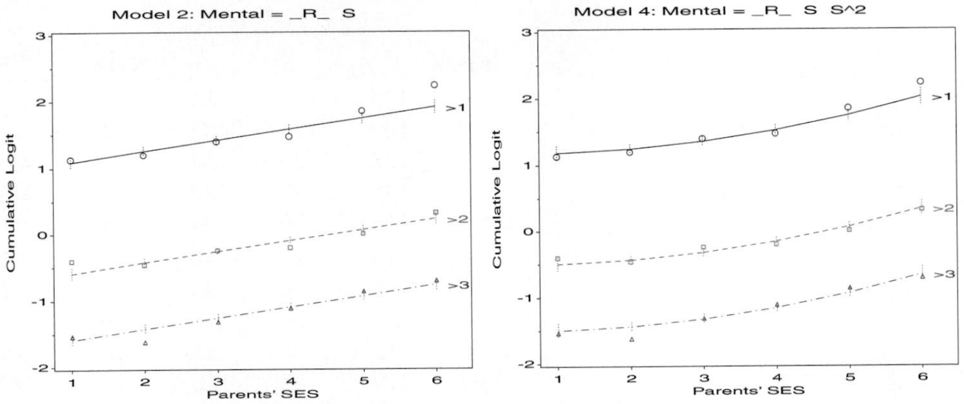

7.6 An Extended Example

Any model is a summary, and even a reasonably good-fitting model is not always sensible or faithful to the details of the data. The interplay between graphing and fitting is important in arriving at an understanding of the relationships among the variables and an adequate descriptive model. This section describes the analysis of a moderately large 3-way table, where we find that graphical displays play a crucial role in directing our understanding and model representation.

EXAMPLE 7.9   Student opinion about the Vietnam war

In May 1967, a survey of student opinion on U.S. policies toward the war in Vietnam was undertaken at the University of North Carolina at Chapel Hill. Students were asked which of four policies they supported. The alternatives stated that the U.S. should

A defeat North Vietnam by widespread bombing and by land invasion.

B follow the present policy.

C de-escalate military activity, stop bombing, and intensify efforts to begin negotiations.

D withdraw military forces immediately.

The responses were classified by gender and by student status (undergraduate year or graduate student), published in the student newspaper, and subsequently analyzed by Aitkin et al. (1989).[8] The data is shown in Table 7.6 and listed in the dataset VIETNAM in Appendix B.12.

The survey was not designed to yield a representative sample (survey ballots were merely made available in the student council building), and the response rates, shown in Table 7.6, were low overall and varied somewhat according to year and gender. You cannot, therefore, draw conclusions about the attitudes of the whole student population. However, you can study how the preferred policy varies with sex and year of study, among those who responded. This means that the total numbers of each sex and year should be regarded as fixed, and the [SexYear] term must be included in any model. Note that both the response and year might reasonably be treated as ordinal variables.

---

[8]Murray Aitkin, Dorothy Anderson, Brian Francis, and John Hinde, *Statistical Modeling in GLIM*, 1989, copyright © Murray Aitkin, Dorothy Anderson, Brian Francis, and John Hinde. Reprinted by permission of Oxford University Press.

Table 7.6   Student opinion on Vietnam war policy

| Sex | Year | Response | | | | Total | Enroll | % Resp |
		A	B	C	D			
Male	1	175	116	131	17	439	1768	24.8
	2	160	126	135	21	442	1792	24.7
	3	132	120	154	29	435	1693	25.7
	4	145	95	185	44	469	1522	30.8
	Grad	118	176	345	141	780	3005	26.0
Female	1	13	19	40	5	77	487	15.8
	2	5	9	33	3	50	326	15.3
	3	22	29	110	6	167	772	21.6
	4	12	21	58	10	101	608	16.6
	Grad	19	27	128	13	187	1221	15.3

The dataset VIETNAM, listed in Appendix B.12, is created in frequency form with the variables SEX, YEAR, RESPONSE, and COUNT. Both YEAR and RESPONSE are created as numeric variables to allow them to be treated as ordinal (or interval) variables, and formats are created to associate descriptive labels as needed.

Because response choice is the natural outcome variable, it is useful to begin with a simple graph showing the proportions of choices for each Sex-Year group, shown in Figure 7.14.

Figure 7.14   Response probabilities for Vietnam data. Point labels indicate the response category.

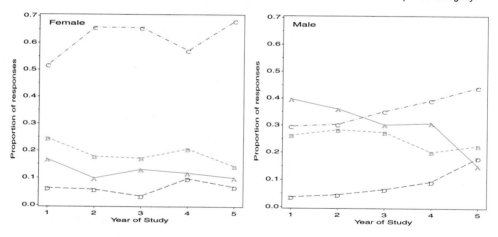

To create the graphs, find the total number of respondents in each group, merge this with the data, and calculate the proportions.

```
%include catdata(vietnam);

*-- Get row totals for sex-year;
proc summary data=vietnam nway;
   class sex year;
   var count;
   output out=totals sum=total;
```

```
*-- Merge, compute proportions;
data vietnam;
    merge vietnam totals(keep=sex year total);
    by sex year;
    p = count / total;
    label p='Proportion of responses';
```

Then, plot P against YEAR for each SEX, producing the graphs shown in Figure 7.14:

```
goptions hby=0;
proc gplot data=vietnam;
    plot p * year = response /
        frame vaxis=axis1 haxis=axis2 hm=0 vm=1 nolegend anno=label;
    by sex;
    symbol1 v=A h=2 i=join c=red  l=1;
    symbol2 v=B h=2 i=join c=red  l=20;
    symbol3 v=C h=2 i=join c=blue l=41;
    symbol4 v=D h=2 i=join c=blue l=21;
    axis1 label=(a=90) order=(0 to .7 by .1);
    axis2 offset=(3);
```

From these graphs, you can see that women choose response C, "begin negotiations," most often, and the ranking of their choices is relatively constant over years. For men, however, the proportions choosing "dovish" responses C and D increase consistently over years, while the proportions for A and B decrease. Keep these observations in mind as you begin to search for a descriptive model.

Begin by fitting the baseline "null" model, $[SY][R]$, which includes the $[SY]$ association but no association between RESPONSE and SEX or YEAR. This model implies that the response curves in Figure 7.14 should all be flat (no year effect) and at the same levels in the two panels (no sex effect). The model fit is very poor (G^2 (27) = 361.72), and the patterns in Figure 7.14 lead us to add sex and year effects, giving the model $[SY][RS][RY]$. These two models are fit using PROC CATMOD using the LOGLIN statement as follows:

```
*-- Fit as loglin models;
proc catmod data=vietnam;
    weight count;
    model response * sex * year = _response_ /
        ml noiter noresponse nodesign nogls noprofile;
    loglin response sex|year / title='Null model';
 run;
    loglin sex|year response|sex response|year / title='Sex+Year';
 run;
```

The model summary statistics from this step are shown in Output 7.10. For the second model, the $[RS]$ and $[RY]$ terms are both large, and the model fit is dramatically improved. Given the large sample size, you might accept this as an adequate model, particularly if you had not plotted the data.

The likelihood-ratio G^2 for the Sex+Year model, 19.19 on 12 df, corresponds to the 3-way term $[RSY]$. Excluding it from the model means that the relationship between RESPONSE and YEAR is the same for men and women, yet you have seen in Figure 7.14 that this is unlikely to be true. There is something wrong with the Sex+Year model.

You can confirm these suspicions by plotting predicted probabilities under the model together with the observed response probabilities. For a log-linear model, PROC CATMOD gives fitted *frequencies*, and you could divide these by the totals, as done in Figure 7.14.

Output 7.10   Model fit summaries for initial models: Vietnam war data

```
                           Null model

        MAXIMUM-LIKELIHOOD ANALYSIS-OF-VARIANCE TABLE

        Source                DF   Chi-Square      Prob
        ------------------------------------------------
        RESPONSE               3       604.29    0.0000
        SEX                    1       953.57    0.0000
        YEAR                   4       187.96    0.0000
        SEX*YEAR               4        59.36    0.0000


        LIKELIHOOD RATIO      27       361.72    0.0000

                           Sex+Year

        MAXIMUM-LIKELIHOOD ANALYSIS-OF-VARIANCE TABLE

        Source                DF   Chi-Square      Prob
        ------------------------------------------------
        SEX                    1       754.01    0.0000
        YEAR                   4       152.19    0.0000
        SEX*YEAR               4        50.55    0.0000
        RESPONSE               3       519.19    0.0000
        RESPONSE*SEX           3       124.76    0.0000
        RESPONSE*YEAR         12       179.83    0.0000


        LIKELIHOOD RATIO      12        19.19    0.0839
```

It is somewhat easier to fit the equivalent logit model for RESPONSE, for which the fitted values (with _TYPE_='PROB' in the output dataset) are probabilities. The CATPLOT macro produces Figure 7.15.

```
*-- Fit as logit models;
proc catmod data=vietnam;
   weight count;
   population sex year;
   response logit;
   model response = / ml noiter noprofile title='Null model';
 run;
   response logit / out=fit;
   model response = sex year/ ml noiter noprofile title='Sex+Year';
 run;

axis1 label=(a=90) order=(0 to .7 by .1);
axis2 offset=(3,5);
%catplot(data=fit,
   x=year, y=_obs_,
   type=PROB,
   class=response, clfmt=letter.,
   byvar=sex, byfmt=$sex.,
   vaxis=axis1, haxis=axis2,
   colors=red red blue blue,
   ylab=Probability of Response);
```

Figure 7.15   Observed and fitted probabilities for model [*SY*][*RS*][*RY*]

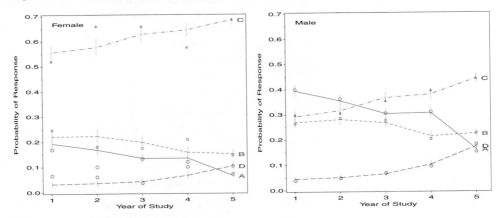

The fitted probabilities are reasonably close for males, but quite poor for females. Perhaps you need to fit different models for men and women. The saturated log-linear model, [*RSY*] corresponds to the logit model $R = S|Y = S + Y + S*Y$. You can examine the possibility of different year effects for men and women within the logit formulation by nesting the effect of YEAR within SEX. (This is equivalent to fitting separate models, $R = Y$, by SEX.)

```
*-- Year within Sex;
proc catmod data=vietnam;
   weight count;
   population sex year;
   model response = sex  year(sex='F')  year(sex='M')
     / ml noiter noprofile title='Year within Sex';
   response logit ;
```

The output, shown in Output 7.11, indicates that the year effect for women is quite small $(G^2(12) = 12.96)$ and can be dropped from the model. Removing the term YEAR(SEX='F') from the MODEL statement gives an adequate model; the residual $G^2(12) = 12.96$ in the revised model is (coincidentally) just that for the term dropped.

Output 7.11   Vietnam war data: Nested year effect model

```
                    Year within Sex


        MAXIMUM-LIKELIHOOD ANALYSIS-OF-VARIANCE TABLE

        Source              DF    Chi-Square     Prob
        ---------------------------------------------------

        INTERCEPT            3       453.92      0.0000
        SEX                  3       102.66      0.0000
        YEAR(SEX=F)         12        12.96      0.3718
        YEAR(SEX=M)         12       182.12      0.0000

        LIKELIHOOD RATIO     0          .          .
```

Remember that the response probabilities for men were consistently increasing or decreasing with year. Perhaps we can simplify the model by using year as a linear effect. To do this, we just add the statement DIRECT YEAR;.

```
*-- Year-linear within Males;
proc catmod data=vietnam;
   weight count;
   population sex year;
   direct year;
   model response = sex year(sex='M')
       / ml noiter noprofile title='Year-linear within Males';
   response / out=fit;
```

Output 7.12   Vietnam war data, Linear year effect for males

```
                Year-linear within Males

        MAXIMUM-LIKELIHOOD ANALYSIS-OF-VARIANCE TABLE

       Source              DF    Chi-Square     Prob
       ------------------------------------------------
       INTERCEPT            3       283.29     0.0000
       SEX                  3       218.11     0.0000
       YEAR(SEX=M)          3       158.88     0.0000

       LIKELIHOOD RATIO    21        38.10     0.0125
```

The model fit statistics for this model (Output 7.12) suggests there is some lack-of-fit, however, with $G^2(21) = 38.10$. To see why, plot the observed and fitted probabilities again. Because the plot is determined completely by the output dataset FIT, you can use exactly the same %CATPLOT call as for Figure 7.15. The result is shown in Figure 7.16.

Figure 7.16   Observed and fitted probabilities for model $R = S + Y_{lin}(M)$

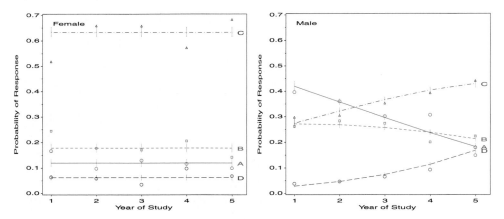

Most of the observed points in Figure 7.16 are quite close to the fitted values (the error bars show ±1 standard error around the predicted probability). However, there are a few scattered points for females and a couple for males (4th year, responses A and B) which appear poorly fit.

You should examine residuals more closely to see if the lack-of-fit is localized to these few cells or whether there is a more general way to improve the model. For example, the two points for 4th-year men indicate a tendency for them to select response B less than the model predicts, and to select response A more often. Aitkin et al. (1989) make the reasonable suggestion that these draft-eligible men would eschew the "present policy" under which their chances of being drafted would increase. But perhaps it is time to look at this data from another perspective. □

7.6.1 A Fresh Look

Plots of observed and fitted values can tell part of the story, but it is the *comparison* of the two, in relation to the structure of the data, which is most effective in suggesting ways to modify a given model. Probability plots or index plots of residuals can be useful, but these do not relate to the structure of the contingency table or to the pattern of association. Mosaic displays and correspondence analysis are more useful for understanding the nature of associations, which they reveal in different ways.

EXAMPLE 7.10 **Student opinion about the Vietnam war**

Because the associations of RESPONSE with YEAR differ for men and women, it is natural to examine partial mosaic plots for the two sexes. This is easily done with the MOSAIC macro, using BY=SEX. First, a DATA step is used to create more meaningful labels for RESPONSE and YEAR. These statements create the two graphs shown in Figure 7.17.

```
%include catdata(vietnam);
proc format;
    value yr  1='Fresh'  2='Soph'  3='Jr'  4='Sr'  5='Grad';
data vietnam;
    length sex $ 6;
    set vietnam;
    yr = put(year, yr.);
    resp = put(response, letter.);
    sex = put(sex, $sex.);
run;
%mosaic(data=vietnam, var=Sex Yr Resp, by=Sex,
    sort=no, vorder=Yr Resp Sex, htext=2, cellfill=dev);
```

Figure 7.17 Partial mosaic plots, by SEX, for Vietnam war data

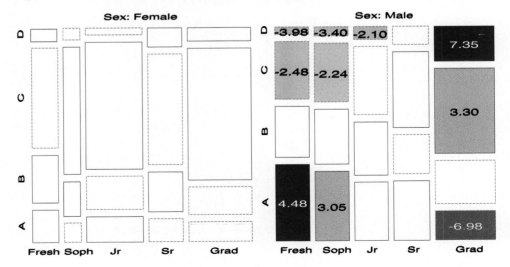

With the variables in each mosaic ordered by Year and Response, recall that the height of each bar shows the (conditional) proportion of students in each year who chose each response. There is no systematic pattern for women, but the pattern of heights of the boxes and of the residuals from independence for men is very systematic. The trend over years is easiest to see for responses A and D; note that there is a large jump in proportion choosing these responses between 4th-year students and graduate students. Perhaps our assumption of a linear trend with year for males needs adjustment.

A correspondence analysis plot also displays residuals from a background model. Here the null-response model of joint independence, $[SY][R]$, is used, so all associations between the response and the sex-year combinations will be shown. To do this, we first transpose the data so that the responses are columns and the sex-year populations are rows.

```
%include catdata(vietnam);

*-- Reshape to two-way table, SexYr x Response;
proc transpose data=vietnam prefix=R out=viet2way;
   var count;
   by sex year;

data viet2way;
   set viet2way;
   rename r1=A r2=B r3=C r4=D;
   sexyr = sex || put(year,1.);
   drop _name_;
proc print;

%corresp(data=viet2way, var=A--D, id=sexyr, interp=none join);
```

The plot shown in Figure 7.18 is quite revealing. The response points, A–D, largely define the first dimension, which accounts for 73.6% of the association from the null-response

Figure 7.18   Correspondence analysis display for model $[SY][R]$

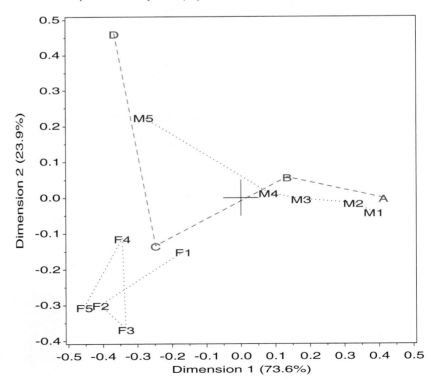

model. The year points for men, M1–M5, are also ordered along this dimension, but male graduate students are far from the male undergraduates. The year points for women are tightly clustered and aligned closest to response C, their most preferred alternative. The second dimension seems largely to do with the contrast between the relatively high choice for response D ("immediate withdrawal") among male graduate students and general preference for response C ("de-escalate") among most women.

Both Figure 7.17 and Figure 7.18 indicate that our assumption of linear spacing of year for men is incorrect, particularly for graduate students. A simple approach is to replace the variable YEAR with a new variable, YR, for which graduate students are some number greater than 5. Varying the year for graduate students over the range 5–10 gives the residual G^2 values (with 21 df) in Table 7.7, and suggests that 7 years for graduate students gives the best fit. The plot of fitted and observed values under the revised model is shown in Figure 7.19.

```
%include catdata(vietnam);

data vietnam;
   set vietnam;
   yr = year + 2*(year=5);
   label yr="Year + 2(Grad)";

*-- Yr-linear within Males;
proc catmod data=vietnam;
   weight count;
   population sex yr;
   direct yr;
   model response = sex yr(sex='M')
      / ml noiter noprofile title='Yr-linear within Males';
   response / out=fit;
```

Table 7.7 Profile deviance analysis of Year for Graduate Students

Grad Year	$G^2(21)$
5	38.10
6	26.69
7	23.87
8	23.99
9	25.13
10	26.58

Figure 7.19 Observed and fitted probabilities for model $R = S + Y_{lin}(M)$, Graduate students=7

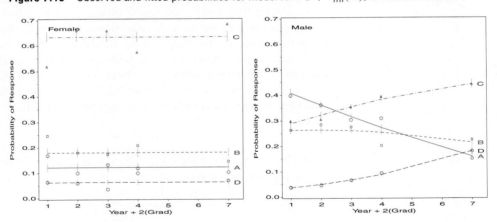

This model fits quite well overall, but there are still several discrepant points. Example 7.11 examines residuals and influence diagnostics for this model. □

7.7   Influence and Diagnostic Plots for Log-linear Models

Model diagnostic statistics provide important ancillary information regarding the adequacy of a log-linear model as a true summary of the relationships among the variables captured in the data. As in logistic regression models (see Section 6.6), there are analogs of leverage, Cook's D, and the leave-one-out $\Delta\chi^2$ statistics for log-linear models, described in Section 7.7.4. Half-normal plots (Section 7.7.2) are particularly useful for detecting outlier cells.

Most of the basic diagnostic quantities are calculated by PROC GENMOD and made available for plotting by use of the statement MAKE 'OBSTATS' OUT=[9] and the options OBSTATS RESIDUALS on the MODEL statement. A macro program, INFLGLIM (Section 7.7.3), is provided for calculating additional diagnostics (hat values and Cook's D) that are not supplied by PROC GENMOD and for producing useful plots of these measures. For models that can be fit using PROC GENMOD, the INFLGLIM macro makes model diagnosis easy.

These diagnostic quantities are not computed by PROC CATMOD; however, with some effort, they may also be obtained from the results of PROC CATMOD, as described in Section 7.7.4.

7.7.1   Residuals and Diagnostics for Log-linear Models

For a log-linear model, the simple, raw residual in cell i is $e_i \equiv n_i - \widehat{m}_i$. But this is of little use; with n_i distributed as $\text{Pois}(m_i)$, the variance of n_i is m_i, so cells with larger expected frequencies will have larger raw residuals. As a result, it is common to standardize by dividing by $\sqrt{\widehat{m}_i}$, giving the **Pearson residual**,

$$r_i \equiv \frac{n_i - \widehat{m}_i}{\sqrt{\widehat{m}_i}} \quad ,$$

which again are components of the overall Pearson χ^2, in the sense that $\chi^2 = \sum r_i^2$.

For a good-fitting model, one might expect these so-called "standardized" residuals to have a normal distribution with mean 0 and variance 1, that is, $e \sim N(\mathbf{0}, \sigma^2 \mathbf{I})$. But this expectation ignores the facts that parameters have been estimated, and the estimated residuals have degrees of freedom equal to the residual df = (number of cells) − (number of parameters).[10] When the constraints on the residuals are taken into account (Agresti (1990), Section 12.4), Christensen (1997, Section 10.7)), it turns out that the Pearson residuals for a correct log-linear model are distributed asymptotically with standard errors

$$\hat{\sigma}(r_i) = \sqrt{1 - h_{ii}}$$

where h_{ii} is the leverage or hat value defined in Equation 7.27 below.[11] Consequently, one may define **adjusted residuals** (Haberman, 1973, 1974),

$$r_i^\star \equiv \frac{n_i - \widehat{m}_i}{\sqrt{\widehat{m}_i(1 - h_{ii})}} \quad , \tag{7.25}$$

which are standardized to have unit asymptotic variance. Cells with large expected frequencies tend to have large hat values and, hence, small standard errors. The effect of ignoring the adjustment is to underestimate the magnitude of residuals in cells with large expected frequency. This effect is illustrated in Example 7.12.

---

[9]SAS software Version 7 and higher uses the Output Delivery System with the ODS statement instead.

[10]Following Christensen (1997), a better term would be "crude standardized residuals."

[11]This is similar to the situation in ordinary linear models, where the estimated residuals are distributed $N(\mathbf{0}, \sigma^2(\mathbf{I} - \mathbf{H}))$, and so have standard errors equal to $\sqrt{1 - h_{ii}}$.

From the perspective of maximum-likelihood estimation, **deviance residuals** may be defined as

$$g_i = \text{sign}(e_i) \left[2|n_i \log(n_i/\widehat{m}_i)| + (n_i - \widehat{m}_i) \right]^{1/2} , \tag{7.26}$$

the signed square root of the contribution of cell i to the likelihood-ratio G^2 (or deviance), so that $G^2 = \sum g_i^2$. Analogous **adjusted deviance residuals**, $g_i^\star$, are defined by dividing g_i by $\sqrt{1 - h_{ii}}$.

For any generalized linear model, the hat value h_{ii} may be calculated as the ith diagonal element of the matrix

$$\boldsymbol{H} = \boldsymbol{W}^{\frac{1}{2}} \boldsymbol{X} (\boldsymbol{X}^\mathsf{T} \boldsymbol{W} \boldsymbol{X})^{-1} \boldsymbol{X}^\mathsf{T} \boldsymbol{W}^{\frac{1}{2}} , \tag{7.27}$$

where $\boldsymbol{W}$ is the diagonal matrix of weights used in computing the Hessian. For log-linear models, $\boldsymbol{W} = \text{diag}(\boldsymbol{m})$.

Various measures of influence for logistic regression (Section 6.6.2) were defined to measure the effect of deleting each observation on model fit statistics or estimated parameters. Similar diagnostics for log-linear models may be defined for the contributions of each cell.

Cook's distance, C_i, is a squared measure of the impact the ith cell has on the estimated parameters and, hence, on the fitted frequencies. For a log-linear model, imagine that you drop each cell in turn, fit the model to the remaining cells, and estimate the expected frequency for the omitted cell. It would be computationally intensive to calculate this by refitting the model for each cell, but a simple one-step approximation (Christensen, 1997, Section 10.7) may be calculated as

$$C_i = \frac{r_i^2 h_{ii}}{k(1 - h_{ii})} \tag{7.28}$$

where k is the number of parameters estimated in the model. This measure is equivalent to the statistic $\overline{C}_i$ defined for logistic regression (Equation 6.13) divided by k.

Similarly, one-step estimates of the change in deviance and Pearson χ^2 associated with deleting cell i may be calculated as

$$\Delta G^2_{(-i)} = \frac{g_i^2}{1 - h_{ii}} = (g_i^\star)^2 ,$$

and

$$\Delta \chi^2_{(-i)} = \frac{r_i^2}{1 - h_{ii}} = (r_i^\star)^2 .$$

7.7.2   Half-Normal Probability Plots of Residuals

As you have just seen, the adjusted Pearson and deviance residuals have a standard normal distribution (in large samples) when the fitted model is correct. This suggests that a plot of the ordered residuals, $r_{(i)}$, against the corresponding approximate expected values of an equal-sized sample (of N contingency table cells, here) would have in a normal distribution $z_{(i)} = \Phi^{-1}\{(i - \frac{3}{8})/(N + \frac{1}{4})\}$, where $\Phi^{-1}(\bullet)$ is the inverse normal or probit function. Such plots, called **normal quantile plots** or **normal QQ plots**, are commonly used for GLMs with a quantitative response variable. These plots are described in *SAS System for Statistical Graphics, First Edition*, Section 3.5 and illustrated there in Section 5.4.2.

The graphical principle is that standardized residuals from a specified distribution against quantiles from that distribution should plot along a line through the origin with slope 1. The NQPLOT macro (see *SAS System for Statistical Graphics, First Edition*, Section A.1.10) plots residuals against their normal quantiles with a 95% confidence envelope, which makes it easier to determine when residuals stray far enough from the line to be considered worrisome.

For generalized linear models, several enhancements to these ideas have been suggested. First, model departures and outliers are often easier to see for discrete data when the *absolute values* of residuals are plotted because large positive and negative values are sorted together. This gives the *half-normal plot*, in which the absolute values of residuals, arranged in increasing order, $|r|_{(i)}$, are plotted against $|z|_{(i)} = \Phi^{-1}\{(N + i - \frac{1}{8})/(2N + \frac{1}{2})\}$. All outliers will then appear in the upper-right corner of such a plot, as points separated from the trend of the remaining cells.

Second, the normal-theory reference line $|r|_{(i)} = |z|_{(i)}$ and the normal-theory confidence envelope may not be appropriate for generalized linear models (or even ordinary linear models with small sample size). Atkinson (1981) proposed replacing these with a *simulated envelope* and reference line obtained by simulating residuals from the assumed distribution. These reference quantities are calculated in the following way for a log-linear model.

For each cell, 19 additional observations are generated from a Poisson distribution with mean $\widehat{m}_i$, the expected frequency in this cell under the fitted model. The same model fitted to the actual data is then fit to each of these simulated datasets, giving a new set of residuals for each simulation. For each set, sort the absolute residuals, and obtain the mean, minimum, and maximum. In the half-normal plot, the curve for the mean absolute simulated residual serves as the data-based reference line instead of the normal-theory line $|r|_{(i)} = |z|_{(i)}$; similarly, curves for the minimum and maximum of the 19 simulated datasets may replace the normal-theory confidence limits.

The HALFNORM macro (Appendix A.10) performs this simulation for any generalized linear model fit with PROC GENMOD with the standard error distributions (normal, binomial, Poisson, gamma) and produces a half-normal plot with the simulated mean and 95% reference curves.[12] These plots are illustrated in the examples that follow.

7.7.3 Model Diagnostics with PROC GENMOD and the INFLGLIM Macro

The observation statistics calculated by PROC GENMOD include most of the residuals described for logistic regression models in Section 6.6, but they do not include the "hat" value measure of leverage or the influence measures, Cook's D (C_i), $\Delta G^2_{(-i)}$, and $\Delta \chi^2_{(-i)}$.

In terms of the variables in the OBSTATS dataset, the hat values, h_{ii}, may be calculated as HAT = HESSWGT * STD**2, where STD is the standard error of $x_i^\mathsf{T} \beta$. Cook's D, as defined in Equation 7.28, may be calculated as COOKD = HAT * STRESCHI**2 / (K*(1-HAT)), where STRESCHI is the adjusted Pearson residual ($r_i^\star$), and K is the number of parameters in the model. The value of K may be obtained from PROC GENMOD as the sum of the DF values in the PARMEST dataset.

In addition, the OBSTATS dataset does not include the factor (CLASS) variables from the input dataset, so these variables must be merged with the OBSTATS dataset to create plots in which the observations (cells of the contingency table) are labeled meaningfully.

These calculations and a variety of plots are carried out by the INFLGLIM macro (see Appendix A.11). The following example illustrates how to do these calculations directly and the use of the INFLGLIM macro.

---

[12] Flores and Flack (1990) make the reasonable suggestion to replace the mean, minimum, and maximum by resistant, but otherwise equivalent, values—namely, the median and median ±1.5IQR, where IQR is the interquartile range. This suggestion is not yet implemented in the HALFNORM macro.

EXAMPLE 7.11   Student opinion about the Vietnam war

The revised model, with linear effects of year on each logit and with graduate students treated as YR=7 as shown in Figure 7.19, was fit using PROC CATMOD. However, influence diagnostics are easier to obtain using PROC GENMOD. The same model can be fit using PROC GENMOD by defining a dummy variable for women and an interaction between YR and a dummy variable for men.

```
data vietnam;
   set vietnam;
   yr = year + 2*(year=5);
   mlin =  yr * (sex='M');
   female = (sex='F');
   cell = trim(sex)|| put(year,1.)|| trim(put(response,letter.));
   label yr="Year + 2(Grad)";

proc genmod data=vietnam;
   class year sex response;
   model count = year|sex response|mlin  response|female /
         dist=poisson obstats residuals;
   make 'obstats' out=obstats;
```

Normally, one would need to merge the input dataset with the OBSTATS and calculate hat values, Cook's D, or other quantities for plotting:

```
%let k=8;
data obstats;
   merge vietnam obstats;
   h = hesswgt * std**2;
   cookd = streschi**2 * h/((1-h) * &k);
```

where K=8 is the number of estimated parameters.

Instead, the INFLGLIM macro (Appendix A.11) automates these steps and gives various influence plots of residuals from a given model. The macro plots all combinations of the variables given by the GY parameter against the variables given by the GX parameter, using a bubble symbol whose size is proportional to the BUBBLE parameter, usually Cook's D.

This example plots the one-step estimates of change in deviance ($\Delta G^2_{(-i)}$, or DIFDEV) due to deleting each cell against hat values, using bubble symbols with area proportional to Cook's D. The INFL parameter determines the criterion for labeling potentially influential points.

```
%inflglim(data=vietnam, resp=count,
    class=year sex response,
    model= year|sex  response|mlin  response|female,
    dist=poisson, id=cell,
    infl=%str(difdev>4 or &bubble>1 or hat>1.5*&hcrit),
    gy=difdev, gx=hat, bubble=cookd);
```

This plot (Figure 7.20) shows that there are still two large residuals: 4th-year men choose response B substantially less often than predicted (accounting for over one-third of the model deviance), and first-year women choose response C less than predicted. The analysis is completed with a half-normal plot of these residuals, shown in Figure 7.21. Although there is evidence of non-normality in the distribution of residuals, even the largest values are within the simulated envelope.

Figure 7.20   Influence plot for model $R = S + Y_{lin}(M)$, Graduate students=7

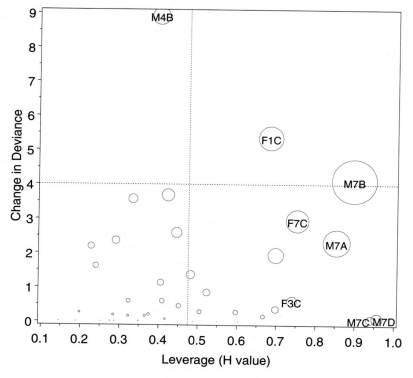

Figure 7.21   Half-normal plot for model $R = S + Y_{lin}(M)$, Graduate students=7

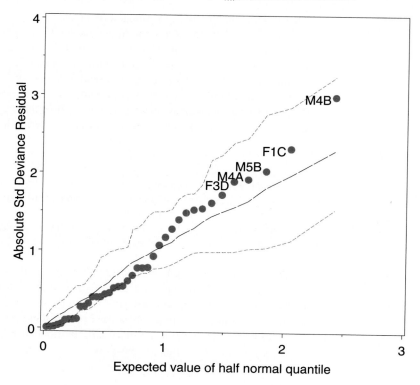

```
%halfnorm(data=vietnam, resp=count,
   class=sex year response,
   model=year|sex response|mlin response|female,
   dist=poisson, id=cell);
```

□

EXAMPLE 7.12   Berkeley admissions

These diagnostic plots may also be illustrated with the Berkeley admissions data using the log-linear model $[AD][GD]$ or the equivalent logit model, logit(Admit) $= \alpha + \beta_i^D$. Recall that this model fit well, except in Department A. To give useful labels for influential cells, first combine the factor variables into a character identifier, CELL.

```
data berkeley;
   set berkeley;
   cell = trim(put(dept,dept.)) ||
          gender ||
          trim(put(admit,yn.));
```

Ask for an influence plot of adjusted Pearson residuals against hat values (showing Cook's D by bubble size, by default):

```
%inflglim(data=berkeley, class=dept gender admit,
        resp=freq, model=admit|dept gender|dept, dist=poisson, id=cell,
        gx=hat, gy=streschi);
```

The plot (Figure 7.22) clearly indicates that the only cells that do not fit ($|r_i| > 2$) are for Department A. Notice, also, that the cells for males applying to this department (with high expected frequencies) have large leverage and, therefore, large influence (Cook's D) on this model.

Figure 7.22   Influence plot for Berkeley admissions data, Model $[AD][GD]$. Bubble areas are proportional to Cook's D.

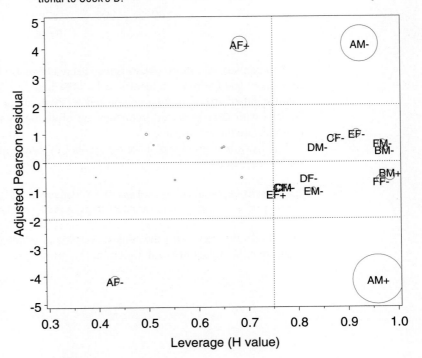

To illustrate why adjusted residuals are preferable to the (crudely standardized) residuals, plot the estimated residual standard error, $\sqrt{1 - h_{ii}}$, against fitted cell frequency for this model. This plot (Figure 7.23) is produced as follows:

```
%inflglim(data=berkeley, class=dept gender admit,
        resp=freq, model=dept|gender dept|admit, dist=poisson, id=cell,
        gx=pred, gy=seres);
```

Figure 7.23   Residual standard errors vs. fitted frequencies for Berkeley admissions data, Model [*AD*][*GD*]

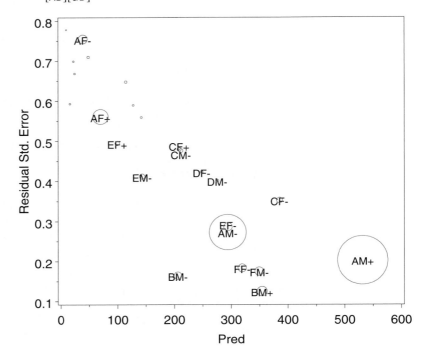

You can see that the standard errors decrease nearly linearly with estimated expected frequency, and the most influential cells (AM+ and AM– for males in Department A) have small standard errors, so their unadjusted residuals are most severely underestimated. That is, cells with large expected frequency are often highly influential, but their (unadjusted) residuals are underestimated.

Finally, a half-normal plot for this model is shown in Figure 7.24, produced with the HALFNORM macro.

```
%halfnorm(data=berkeley, class=dept gender admit,
    resp=freq, model=dept|gender dept|admit, dist=poisson, id=cell);
```

By default, the cells with the largest 5 absolute residuals are labeled. This plot clearly shows that the model fits well, except in Department A.   □

Figure 7.24   Half-normal residual plot for Berkeley admissions data, Model [AD][GD]

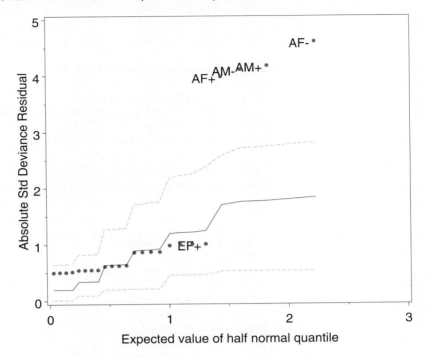

7.7.4   Model Diagnostics with PROC CATMOD

For situations where an equivalent model cannot be fit with PROC GENMOD, the hat values and Cook's D can still be obtained from the output dataset from PROC CATMOD. The technique described here is based on the idea (Christensen, 1997) that a log-linear model is essentially a regression model for log frequency, which can be fit by weighted least-squares regression. Here are the steps:

1. Fit the log-linear model, obtaining the cell frequencies n_i and estimated expected frequencies $\widehat{m}_i$ in a dataset (use the statement RESPONSE / OUT=*datasetname*, as illustrated in Example 7.9).

2. Use PROC REG to calculate a weighted regression and obtain the regression diagnostics (e.g., H and COOKD) with an OUTPUT statement. Fit the regression with:

   independent variables: Dummy variables for all marginals and association terms in the log-linear model. (PROC REG does not provide a CLASS statement.)

   dependent variable: The "working" response, $y_i = \log(\widehat{m}_i) + (n_i - \widehat{m}_i)/\widehat{m}_i$

   weights: $\widehat{m}_i$

3. Leverages will be correctly reported in the output. The adjusted residuals, however, will have been divided by $\sqrt{MSE}$, and the Cook's D values will have been divided by MSE. For a model with k parameters and N cells, the average leverage will be k/N, so a value $h_{ii} > 2k/N$ would be considered "large".

EXAMPLE 7.13   Berkeley admissions

This example continues with the results from model $[AD][GD]$ to illustrate the computations with the results from PROC CATMOD. The expected frequencies were obtained using the option PRED=FREQ in the MODEL statement, as shown here:

```
proc catmod order=data data=berkeley;
   weight freq;
   model dept*gender*admit=_response_ /
         ml  noiter noresponse nodesign noprofile pred=freq ;
   response / out=predict;
   loglin admit|dept dept|gender / title='Model (AD,DG)';
```

In the PREDICT dataset, $\widehat{m}_i$ is named _PRED_, n_i is _OBS_, and $e_i = n_i - \widehat{m}_i$ is _RESID_. The working response may be calculated in a DATA step as follows:

```
data rdat;
   set predict;
   drop _sample_ _type_ _number_;
   where (_type_='FREQ');
   cell = trim(put(dept,dept.)) ||
          gender ||
          trim(put(admit,yn.));
    *-- Working response;
   y = log(_pred_) + _resid_/_pred_;
```

Fitting the regression model for the working response using PROC REG is conceptually simple, though tedious because PROC REG (like PROC LOGISTIC) cannot generate the dummy variables itself. This may be done in a DATA step, or with PROC GLMMOD, or using the DUMMY macro (Appendix A.7) and the INTERACT macro (Appendix A.13). This example illustrates using the macro programs; by default, they append the new variables to the input dataset.

```
%dummy(data=rdat, var=admit gender dept, prefix=a g d);
%interact(v1=a0, v2=d1 d2 d3 d4 d5, prefix=ad);
%interact(v1=gf, v2=d1 d2 d3 d4 d5, prefix=gd);

proc reg data=rdat outest=est;
   id cell;
   weight _pred_;
   model y = a0 gf d1-d5 ad11-ad15 gd11-gd15;
   output out=regdiag
          h=hat cookd=cookd student=studres;
```

In the final step, the $\sqrt{MSE}$ is obtained from the OUTEST dataset, and the adjusted residuals and Cook's D may be calculated.

```
data regdiag;
   set regdiag;
   retain _rmse_;
   if _n_=1 then set est(keep=_rmse_ );
   adjres = studres * _rmse_;
   cookd = cookd * _rmse_**2;
```

These quantities, shown in Output 7.13, may then be plotted in the forms shown earlier using the INFLGLIM macro.   □

Output 7.13   Diagnostics for the model [*AD*][*GD*] calculated from PROC CATMOD output

```
                    Diagnostics by weighted regression

     CELL    _OBS_     _PRED_     _RESID_     COOKD      HAT      ADJRES

     AM+       512    531.431    -19.431     22.305     0.959    -4.153
     AM-       313    293.569     19.431     11.893     0.925     4.153
     AF+        89     69.569     19.431      2.087     0.685     4.153
     AF-        19     38.431    -19.431      0.724     0.430    -4.153
     BM+       353    354.188     -1.188      0.883     0.984    -0.504
     BM-       207    205.812      1.188      0.507     0.973     0.504
     BF+        17     15.812      1.188      0.026     0.648     0.504
     BF-         8      9.188     -1.188      0.009     0.395    -0.504
     CM+       120    113.998      6.002      0.058     0.581     0.868
     CM-       205    211.002     -6.002      0.143     0.773    -0.868
     CF+       202    208.002     -6.002      0.140     0.770    -0.868
     CF-       391    384.998      6.002      0.295     0.876     0.868
     DM+       138    141.633     -3.633      0.036     0.687    -0.546
     DM-       279    275.367      3.633      0.086     0.839     0.546
     DF+       131    127.367      3.633      0.031     0.652     0.546
     DF-       244    247.633     -3.633      0.076     0.821    -0.546
     EM+        53     48.077      4.923      0.055     0.496     1.001
     EM-       138    142.923     -4.923      0.273     0.831    -1.001
     EF+        94     98.923     -4.923      0.172     0.755    -1.001
     EF-       299    294.077      4.923      0.620     0.918     1.001
     FM+        22     24.031     -2.031      0.026     0.553    -0.620
     FM-       351    348.969      2.031      0.672     0.969     0.620
     FF+        24     21.969      2.031      0.022     0.511     0.620
     FF-       317    319.031     -2.031      0.613     0.966    -0.620
```

7.8   Multivariate Responses

In many studies, there may be *several* categorical responses observed along with one or more explanatory variables. In a clinical trial, for example, the efficacy of a drug might be the primary response, but the occurrence of side-effects might give rise to additional response variables of substantive interest. Or, in a study of occupational health, the occurrence of two or more distinct symptoms might be treated as response variables.

If there are no explanatory variables, then the problem is simply to understand the joint distribution of the response categories; and the log-linear models and graphical displays described earlier are sufficient. Otherwise, in these cases, one usually wants to understand how the various responses are affected by the explanatory variables. Moreover, it may also be important to understand how the association between the categorical responses depends on the explanatory variables, that is, how *both* the marginal distributions of the responses and their joint distribution depends on the predictors.

Although the general log-linear model is often used in these situations, there are special reparameterizations that may be used to separate the marginal dependence of each response on the explanatory variables from the interdependence among the responses.

Suppose that categorical responses, $R_1, R_2, \ldots$, have been observed, together with possible explanatory variables, $E_1, E_2, \ldots$, and let $\pi_{ij\cdots}$ be the joint probability of all the responses and explanatory variables; also use x to refer to the values of $E_1, E_2, \ldots$.

Note that the minimal model of independence of all responses from each other and from the explanatory variables is the log-linear model $[R_1][R_2]\cdots[E_1E_2\cdots]$ (i.e., all associations among the E_i must be included). A no-effect model in which the responses do not depend on the explanatory variables, but may be associated among themselves, is $[R_1 R_2 \cdots][E_1 E_2 \cdots]$. However, these models do not separate the individual (marginal) effects of $E_1, E_2 \ldots$ on each R_i from their associative effects.

There are three useful general approaches which *do* separate these effects:

- Model the marginal dependence of each response, R_i separately on $E_1, E_2, \ldots$, and, in addition, model the interdependence among the responses.
- Model the joint dependence of all responses on $E_1, E_2, \ldots$, parameterized so that marginal and associative effects are delineated.
- Construct simultaneous models, estimated together, for the marginal and joint dependence of the responses on the explanatory variables.

The first approach is the simplest, an informative starting place, and is satisfactory in the (unlikely) case that the responses are not associated, or that the associations among responses do not vary much over the explanatory variables (i.e., no terms like $[R_1 R_2 E_j]$ are required). In the clinical trial example, you would construct separate log-linear or logit models for efficacy of the drug and for occurrence of side-effects, and supplement these analyses with mosaic or other displays showing the relations between efficacy and side-effects. This approach is carried out with PROC CATMOD by using the RESPONSE LOGITS statement.

In the second approach, the joint probabilities, $\pi_{ij\ldots}$, are recast to give separate information regarding the dependence of the univariate marginal probabilities $\pi_{i\bullet}, \pi_{\bullet j}, \ldots$, on the explanatory variables and the dependence of the intra-response associations on the explanatory variables. This approach is carried out by specifying a transformation of the joint probabilities on the RESPONSE statement.

The third approach, exemplified by Lang and Agresti (1994), is the most general, but it requires specialized software for model fitting.

Two related models are discussed by McCullagh and Nelder (1989, Section 6.5). This example considers only the case of two binary responses. Let x refer to the values of the explanatory variables and let $\pi_{ij}(x)$ be the joint probabilities in cell $R_1 = i$, $R_2 = j$. The ***bivariate logistic model*** arises from a linear transformation of the cell probabilities to probabilities γ, which include the univariate margins, given by

$$\gamma = L\pi \tag{7.29}$$

where L is a matrix of 0s and 1s of the form of a factorial design matrix transposed. In the 2×2 case,

$$\gamma = \begin{pmatrix} \pi_{1\bullet} \\ \pi_{2\bullet} \\ \pi_{\bullet 1} \\ \pi_{\bullet 2} \\ \pi_{11} \\ \pi_{12} \\ \pi_{21} \\ \pi_{22} \end{pmatrix} = \begin{bmatrix} 1 & 1 & 0 & 0 \\ 0 & 0 & 1 & 1 \\ 1 & 0 & 1 & 0 \\ 0 & 1 & 0 & 1 \\ 1 & 0 & 0 & 0 \\ 0 & 1 & 0 & 0 \\ 0 & 0 & 1 & 0 \\ 0 & 0 & 0 & 1 \end{bmatrix} \begin{pmatrix} \pi_{11} \\ \pi_{12} \\ \pi_{21} \\ \pi_{22} \end{pmatrix} \tag{7.30}$$

There are, of course, only three linearly independent probabilities because $\sum \sum \pi_{ij} = 1$. The bivariate logistic model is formulated in terms of factorial contrasts on the elements of γ, which express separate models for the two logits and the log odds ratio. The model is expressed as

$$\eta = C \log \gamma = C \log L\pi \ ,$$

where C is a matrix of contrasts. In the 2×2 case, the usual contrasts may be defined by

$$
\boldsymbol{\eta} = \begin{pmatrix} \eta_1 \\ \eta_2 \\ \eta_{12} \end{pmatrix} = \begin{pmatrix} \text{logit } \pi_{1\bullet} \\ \text{logit } \pi_{\bullet 1} \\ \theta \end{pmatrix} = \begin{bmatrix} 1 & -1 & 0 & 0 & 0 & 0 & 0 & 0 \\ 0 & 0 & 1 & -1 & 0 & 0 & 0 & 0 \\ 0 & 0 & 0 & 0 & 1 & -1 & -1 & 1 \end{bmatrix} \begin{pmatrix} \pi_{1\bullet} \\ \pi_{2\bullet} \\ \pi_{\bullet 1} \\ \pi_{\bullet 2} \\ \pi_{11} \\ \pi_{12} \\ \pi_{21} \\ \pi_{22} \end{pmatrix}
$$

(7.31)

Thus, this is modeling the marginal odds of each response, together with the log odds ratio θ simultaneously.

Specific models are then formulated for the dependence of $\eta_1(\boldsymbol{x})$, $\eta_2(\boldsymbol{x})$ and $\eta_{12}(\boldsymbol{x})$ on the explanatory variables. For example, with one quantitative explanatory variable, x, the model

$$
\begin{pmatrix} \eta_1 \\ \eta_2 \\ \eta_{12} \end{pmatrix} = \begin{pmatrix} \alpha_1 + \beta_1 x \\ \alpha_2 + \beta_2 x \\ \theta \end{pmatrix}
$$

(7.32)

asserts that the log odds of each response changes linearly with x, while the odds ratio between the responses remains constant. In the general form given by McCullagh and Nelder (1989), the submodels in Equation 7.32 may each depend on the explanatory variables in different ways. For example, the logits η_1 and η_2 could both depend quadratically on x, while an intercept-only model could be posited for the log odds ratio η_{12}.

In PROC CATMOD, such general models can be tested only by specifying the design matrix directly in the MODEL statement. The matrices L and C in Equations 7.30 and 7.31 are specified in the RESPONSE statement.

The second model is a ***bivariate log-linear model***, obtained by taking $L = I$ in Equation 7.29, so that $\boldsymbol{\gamma} = \boldsymbol{\pi}$. Then a log-linear model of the form

$$\boldsymbol{\eta}(\boldsymbol{x}) = C \log \boldsymbol{\pi}$$

expresses contrasts among log probabilities as linear functions of the explanatory variables. For the 2×2 case, take the contrasts as

$$
\boldsymbol{\eta} = \begin{pmatrix} l_1 \\ l_2 \\ \eta_{12} \end{pmatrix} = \begin{bmatrix} 1 & 1 & -1 & -1 \\ 1 & -1 & 1 & -1 \\ 1 & -1 & 1 & -1 \end{bmatrix} \begin{pmatrix} \log \pi_{11} \\ \log \pi_{12} \\ \log \pi_{21} \\ \log \pi_{22} \end{pmatrix}
$$

(7.33)

and models for the dependence of $l_1(\boldsymbol{x})$, $l_2(\boldsymbol{x})$ and $\eta_{12}(\boldsymbol{x})$ are expressed in the same way as Equation 7.32. The estimates of the odds ratio η_{12} are the same under both models. The marginal functions are parameterized differently, however, but lead to similar predicted probabilities. The fitting and graphing of these models is illustrated in the next example.

EXAMPLE 7.14   Breathlessness and wheeze in coal miners

Example 3.9 examined the association between the occurrence of two pulmonary conditions, breathlessness and wheeze, among coal miners, classified by age (Ashford and Snowden, 1970). Figure 3.7 showed fourfold displays focused on the odds ratio for the co-occurrence of these symptoms; and Figure 3.8 plotted these odds ratios against age directly. Here, consider models that examine the changes in prevalence of the two symptoms over age, together with the changes in their association.

As a first step, calculate the log odds for breathlessness and for wheeze, and calculate the log odds ratio for their association in each 2×2 table. These values are shown in Output 7.14. The log odds ratios are the same values plotted in Figure 3.8 (but the youngest age group was not included in the earlier analysis).

```
data ashford;
   input age @;
   age2 = age**2;
   do breath = 1, 0;
      do wheeze = 1, 0;
         input count @;
         output;
         end;
      end;
   label breath='Breathlessness'
      wheeze='Wheeze'
      age='Age Group';
datalines;
20     9     7        95 1841
25    23     9       105 1654
30    54    19       177 1863
35   121    48       257 2357
40   169    54       273 1778
45   269    88       324 1712
50   404   117       245 1324
55   406   152       225  967
60   372   106       132  526
;
proc transpose out=ashford1 prefix=r;
   var count;
   by age;

data ashford1;
   set ashford1;
   drop _name_;
   logit1 = log( (r1 + r2 + .5) / (r3 + r4 + .5) );
   logit2 = log( (r1 + r3 + .5) / (r2 + r4 + .5) );
   logodds= log( ((r1+.5)*(r4+.5))/((r2+.5)*(r3+.5)) );
   label logit1='Logit(Breathlessness)'
      logit2='Logit(Wheeze)';
proc print;  id age;
```

Output 7.14   Empirical logits and log odds ratios for breathlessness and wheeze

AGE	R1	R2	R3	R4	LOGIT1	LOGIT2	LOGODDS
20	9	7	95	1841	-4.76528	-2.87294	3.19560
25	23	9	105	1654	-3.99154	-2.56075	3.65825
30	54	19	177	1863	-3.32366	-2.09578	3.37903
35	121	48	257	2357	-2.73598	-1.84930	3.13269
40	169	54	273	1778	-2.21692	-1.42100	3.00688
45	269	88	324	1712	-1.73985	-1.10978	2.77699
50	404	117	245	1324	-1.10180	-0.79724	2.92171
55	406	152	225	967	-0.75855	-0.57254	2.43681
60	372	106	132	526	-0.31931	-0.22611	2.63176

Figure 7.25   Empirical logits and log odds ratios for breathlessness and wheeze. The lines show separate linear regressions for each function.

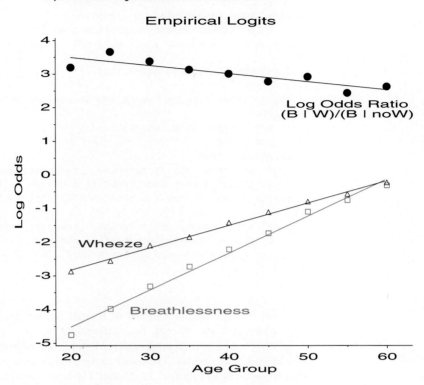

Plotting both logits and the log odds against age gives the graph shown in Figure 7.25. The plotting step is straight-forward and is not shown. Notice that both symptoms, while quite rare among young miners, increase steadily with age (or years working in the mine). There is a hint of curvilinearity, particularly in the logit for breathlessness. The decline in the odds ratio with age reflects selection, as miners who had retired for health or other reasons were excluded from the study.

You can fit ordinary log-linear models to this data as shown below, giving likelihood-ratio goodness-of-fit G^2 values shown in Table 7.8. Note that in Models 0–2, age is treated as a 9-level factor. In Models 3–4, age is treated as a quantitative variable (symbolized as x in the model terms) by declaring AGE and AGE2 (x^2) in a DIRECT statement.[13] PROC CATMOD does not allow quantitative variables to appear on the left-hand side in a MODEL statement. Consequently, these models are fit in a separate PROC CATMOD step, where they are expressed as _RESPONSE_*AGE and _RESPONSE_*AGE2 on the right-hand side.

Table 7.8   Log-linear models fit to Ashford & Snowden data

Model	Terms	df	G^2	p-value	G^2/df
0	$[B][W][A]$	25	6939.07	0.0000	277.56
1	$[BW][A]$	24	2701.94	0.0000	112.58
2	$[BW][BA][WA]$	8	26.69	0.0008	3.34
3	$[BW][Bx][Wx]$	21	41.46	0.0049	1.97
4	$[BW][Bx^2][Wx^2]$	18	17.60	0.4825	0.97

---

[13] In these model formulae, a term like $[Bx^2]$ refers to a quadratic model, $\eta_1 = \alpha_1 + \beta_{11}x + \beta_{11}x^2$ in Equation 7.32.

```
title 'Loglinear models for B and W';
proc catmod order=data data=ashford;
   weight count;
   model breath*wheeze*age = _response_ /
      ml noiter noresponse noprofile nodesign nogls;
   loglin breath wheeze age / title='0: Minimal model: [B] [W] [A]';
run;
   loglin breath|wheeze age / title='1: Null age: [BW] [A]';
run;
   loglin breath|wheeze breath|age wheeze|age/ title='2: [BW] [BA] [WA]';

proc catmod order=data data=ashford;
   weight count;
   direct age age2;
   model breath*wheeze = _response_ _response_*age/
      ml noiter noresponse noprofile nodesign nogls;
   loglin breath|wheeze / title='3: [BW] [Bx] [Wx]';
run;
   model breath*wheeze = _response_ _response_*age _response_*age2/
      ml noiter noresponse noprofile nodesign nogls;
   loglin breath|wheeze / title='4: [BW] [Bx^2] [Wx^2]';
run;
```

Model 0 is the minimal model of mutual independence; Model 1 allows association of breathlessness and wheeze, but independent of age. Neither of these makes any sense, given what we have seen graphically. Model 2 allows both breathlessness and wheeze to depend on age as a factor. The quantitative models for age, Models 3 and 4 correspond to what is apparent in Figure 7.25. Model 3 is equivalent in goodness-of-fit to the bivariate log-linear model (Equation 7.33), but is parameterized in terms of generalized logits

$$
\begin{pmatrix} l_{11,22} \\ l_{12,22} \\ l_{21,22} \end{pmatrix} = \begin{pmatrix} \log \pi_{11}/\pi_{22} \\ \log \pi_{12}/\pi_{22} \\ \log \pi_{21}/\pi_{22} \end{pmatrix} = \begin{pmatrix} \alpha_1 + \beta_1 x \\ \alpha_2 + \beta_2 x \\ \alpha_{12} + \beta_{12} x \end{pmatrix} .
$$

Model 4 adds terms in x^2 to each of these equations. From the G^2 and G^2/df values in Table 7.8, it appears that only Model 4 is acceptable.

Log-linear models parameterized as in Equation 7.33 may be fit by specifying the logit contrasts shown there in the RESPONSE statement. For instance, the following model has the same G^2 as Model 3, but the fitted function values are those of $\hat{l}_1$, $\hat{l}_2$ and the odds ratio $\hat{\eta}_{12}$.

```
proc catmod order=data data=ashford;
   direct age ;
   weight count;
   response  1  1 -1 -1,
             1 -1  1 -1,
             1 -1 -1  1  log / out=predict;
   model breath*wheeze = age  /  noiter nogls prob noprofile;
   title '[BW] [Bx] [Wx], Loglinear, logit contrasts';
```

The bivariate logit model is more complex because the RESPONSE statement must include both the *L* matrix and the *C* matrix (both from Equation 7.30). Nevertheless, the fitted functions correspond exactly to what is plotted in Figure 7.25. Model fit statistics and the parameter estimates for the linear model are shown in Output 7.15.

```
proc catmod order=data data=ashford;
   direct age ;
   weight count;
   response                          /* C matrix */
      1 -1  0  0  0  0  0  0,        /* logit1 */
      0  0  1 -1  0  0  0  0,        /* logit2 */
      0  0  0  0  1 -1 -1  1         /* logodds */
      log
         1  1  0  0,                 /* L matrix */
         0  0  1  1,
         1  0  1  0,
         0  1  0  1,
         1  0  0  0,
         0  1  0  0,
         0  0  1  0,
         0  0  0  1 / out=predict;
   model breath*wheeze = age  /  noiter nogls;
   title '[BW] [Bx] [Wx], Bivariate logit model';
```

Output 7.15   Model fit and parameter estimates for the linear bivariate logit model

```
               [BW] [Bx] [Wx], Bivariate logit model

                   ANALYSIS-OF-VARIANCE TABLE


         Source               DF    Chi-Square      Prob
         ------------------------------------------------------

         INTERCEPT             3       3957.55     0.0000
         AGE                   3       2145.10     0.0000


         RESIDUAL             21         30.15     0.0890

             ANALYSIS OF WEIGHTED-LEAST-SQUARES ESTIMATES
```

Effect	Parameter	Estimate	Standard Error	Chi-Square	Prob
INTERCEPT	1	-6.3543	0.1210	2757.08	0.0000
	2	-4.0894	0.0815	2515.74	0.0000
	3	4.0665	0.2879	199.55	0.0000
AGE	4	0.1025	0.00248	1703.20	0.0000
	5	0.0651	0.00180	1310.15	0.0000
	6	-0.0262	0.00594	19.41	0.0000

The observed and fitted function values (the logits and odds ratio) are plotted as shown below, giving the graph in Figure 7.26. The fitted relations are very similar to those shown in Figure 7.25, although the models for the marginal functions are parameterized quite differently.

```
proc sort data=predict;
    where (_type_='FUNCTION');
    by _number_;
%label(data=predict, x=age, y=_pred_,
    color=scan('red blue black', _number_),
    text=scan('Breathlessness Wheeze Odds_Ratio', _number_),
    pos=scan('9 1 3', _number_), subset=(age=35), out=_lab_);
%points(data=predict, x=age, y=_obs_,
    color=scan('red blue black', _number_),
    symbol=scan('square triangle dot', _number_), size=2, out=_pts_);
data _anno_;
    set _lab_ _pts_;

proc gplot data=predict;
    plot  _pred_ * age = _number_ /
          vaxis=axis1 vm=1 hm=1 haxis=axis2 anno=_anno_ nolegend;
    symbol1 v=none i=join c=red;
    symbol2 v=none i=join c=blue;
    symbol3 v=none i=join c=black;
    axis1 label=(a=90) order=(-5 to 4) offset=(4);
    axis2 offset=(3,5);
    label _pred_ = 'Log Odds';
```

Figure 7.26   Observed (points) and fitted (lines) logits and log odds ratios for the linear bivariate logit model

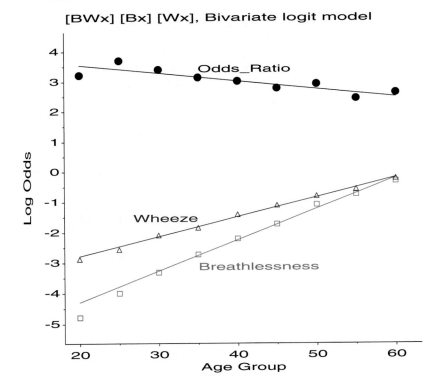

The quadratic model, corresponding to Model 4 may be fit and plotted exactly in the same way, changing the MODEL statement in the lines above to

```
model breath*wheeze = age age2;
```

where AGE2 has also been declared in the DIRECT statement. The quadratic model is graphed in Figure 7.27.

Figure 7.27 Observed (points) and fitted (curves) logits and log odds ratios for quadratic bivariate logit model

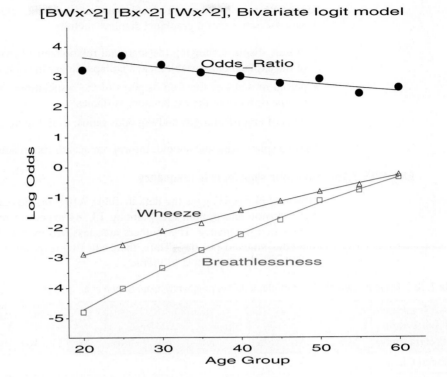

The model fit statistics for these bivariate logit models (Table 7.9) indicate that both models fit better than their log-linear counterparts. The table also shows an intermediate model, Model 4m, which was fit by specifying the design matrix numerically in the MODEL statement. In this model, the log odds ratio has only a linear term in age, while breathlessness and wheeze vary quadratically.

Table 7.9 Bivariate logit models fit to Ashford & Snowden data

Model	Terms	df	χ^2	p-value	χ^2/df
3	$[BWx][Bx][Wx]$	21	30.15	0.0890	1.44
4m	$[BWx][Bx^2][Wx^2]$	19	17.07	0.5853	0.94
4	$[BWx^2][Bx^2][Wx^2]$	18	16.94	0.5270	0.94

On statistical grounds, you might be led to choose the quadratic model as the best fit, but the graphical evidence suggests that the difference between them is slight. Figure 7.26 and Figure 7.27 are also both quite similar to the plot of the empirical logits in Figure 7.25, but the fitted models give a simplified description. Thus, Model 3 may be summarized as

$$\begin{pmatrix} \eta_B \\ \eta_W \\ \eta_{BW} \end{pmatrix} = \begin{pmatrix} -6.354 + 0.102 \text{ age} \\ -4.089 + 0.065 \text{ age} \\ 4.066 - 0.026 \text{ age} \end{pmatrix}$$

For each five years, the odds of a miner showing breathlessness are multiplied by $\exp(5 \times 0.102) = 1.67$, a 67% increase; the odds of wheeze increase by $\exp(5 \times 0.065) = 1.38$, a 38% increase. Whatever model we accept, the respiratory health of these miners clearly decreases with age. □

7.8.1 Examining Relations

When there is more than one explanatory variable and several responses, it is useful to begin with a more thorough visual examination of the relationships within and between these sets. Some useful graphical displays include

- mosaic displays showing the marginal relationships among the response variables and of the explanatory variables, each collapsed over the other set;
- partial mosaics or fourfold displays of the associations among the responses, stratified by one or more of the explanatory variables;
- plots of empirical logits and log odds ratios, as in Figure 7.25.

These displays can, and should, inform our search for an adequate descriptive model.

EXAMPLE 7.15 Toxaemic symptoms in pregnancy

Brown, et al. (1983) gave the data in Table 7.10[14] on the occurrence of signs of toxaemia (hypertension and protein urea) among 13,384 expectant mothers in Bradford, England, in their first pregnancy. The mothers are classified by social class and by the number of cigarettes smoked per day. Thus, there are two response variables and two explanatory variables in this $2 \times 2 \times 5 \times 3$ table.

Table 7.10   Toxaemic symptoms of mothers during pregnancy, from Brown et al. (1983)

Smoking	0				1-19				20+			
Hypertension	Yes		No		Yes		No		Yes		No	
Protein urea	Yes	No	Yes	No	Yes	No	Yes	No	Yes	No	Yes	No
Social Class												
1	28	82	21	286	5	24	5	71	1	3	0	13
2	50	266	34	785	13	92	17	284	0	15	3	34
3	278	1101	164	3160	120	492	142	2300	16	92	32	383
4	63	213	52	656	35	129	46	649	7	40	12	163
5	20	78	23	245	22	74	34	321	7	14	4	65

The questions of main interest are how the occurrence of each symptom varies with class and smoking, and how the association between them varies. It is useful, however, to examine first the marginal relationship between the two responses and between the two predictors. These are produced with the MOSAIC macro as shown below. The parameter PLOTS=2 gives a plot of the first two variables, according to the order in which the data is sorted. Re-sorting to make HYPER and UREA vary most rapidly gives the second plot. Both plots are shown in Figure 7.28.

```
%include catdata(toxaemia);

data toxaemia;
   set toxaemia;
   sm = put(smoke, smoke.);

%mosaic(data=toxaemia, var=Class Sm Hyper Urea, plots=2, htext=2,
   title=%str(Predictors: Class, Smoke));

proc sort data=toxaemia;
   by class sm descending urea descending hyper;
%mosaic(data=toxaemia, var= Hyper Urea Sm Class, plots=2, sort=no, htext=2,
   title=%str(Hypertension and Protein Urea));
```

---

[14]P. J. Brown, J. Stone, C. Ord-Smith, "Toxaemic Signs during Pregnancy," *Journal of the Royal Statistical Society, Series C, Applied Statistics.* Copyright © 1983 by the Royal Statistical Society.

Figure 7.28 Mosaic displays for toxaemia data: Predictor and Response associations

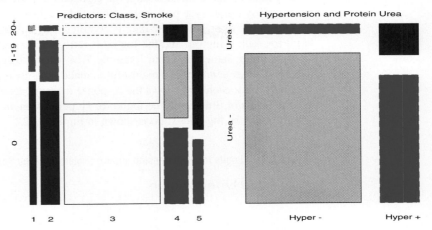

Notice in Figure 7.28 that the majority of the mothers are in the third social class and that Smoking is negatively related to Social Class, with the highest levels of Smoking in classes 4 and 5. Within the responses, the great majority of women exhibit neither symptom, but showing one symptom makes it more likely to show the other. Marginally, Hypertension is somewhat more prevalent than Protein Urea.

Next examine how the association between responses varies with Social Class and with Smoking. Figure 7.29 shows a collection of partial mosaic plots of the association between Hypertension and Urea, for each level of Smoking, collapsed over Social Class. Figure 7.30 is similar, but stratified by Social Class. These statements produce Figure 7.29:

```
proc freq data=toxaemia order=data;
    tables hyper * urea * smoke / out=sum1;
    weight count;
%mosaic(data=sum1,  var= Hyper Urea Smoke, sort=no, by=Smoke, htext=3);
```

Figure 7.29 Toxaemia data: Response associations by Smoking

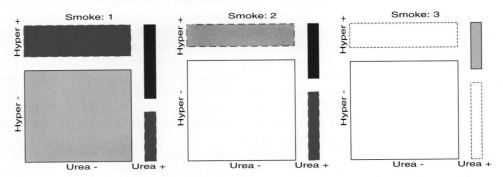

Figure 7.30 Toxaemia data: Response associations by Social Class

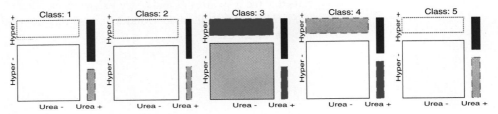

Ignoring Social Class, the association between Hypertension and Protein Urea decreases with Smoking. Ignoring Smoking, the association is greatest in Social Class 3. However, these two symptoms are positively associated in all cases.

Our initial overview of the data is completed by calculating and plotting the empirical logit for each symptom and the log odds ratio, within each class-smoke population. This is done in the same way as in Example 7.14, except that there are now two explanatory factors. Consequently, it is most useful to make separate plots for each of the logits and the log odds ratio; each plot shows the response measure against Class, with separated curves for the levels of Smoking. The logits for Hypertension and for Protein Urea are shown in Figure 7.31; the log odds ratio is shown in Figure 7.32.

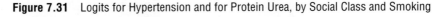

Figure 7.31   Logits for Hypertension and for Protein Urea, by Social Class and Smoking

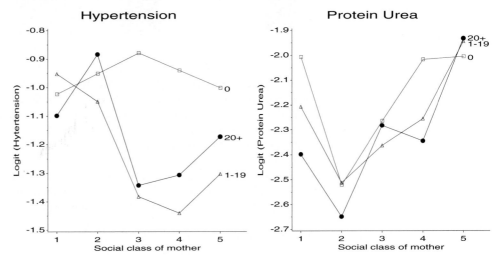

From Figure 7.31 it may be seen that the prevalence of these symptoms has a possibly complex relation to Social Class and Smoking. However, the mosaic for these predictors in Figure 7.28 has shown that several of the class-smoking categories are quite small (particularly heavy smokers in Class 1), so the response effects for these classes will be poorly estimated. Taking this into account, you may suspect that Protein Urea varies with Social Class, but not with Smoking, while the prevalence of Hypertension may truly vary with neither, just one, or both of these predictors.

The association between the response symptoms, shown in Figure 7.32, is clearer, once you take the variation in sample sizes into account. Except for the heavy smokers, particularly in social classes 1 and 2, the log odds ratio appears to be relatively constant.

When there are no quantitative predictors, and when the odds ratio is relatively constant, it is easier to fit ordinary log-linear models than to use the bivariate logit formulation of the previous example.

You can fit these models using the LOGLIN statement as shown below. There are two zero cells in Table 7.10. In the log-linear formulation, PROC CATMOD treats these as structural zeros, so first replace the zeros with a small positive number. The minimal model $[CS][H][U]$ fits the marginal association of the numbers in each Class-Smoking category, but asserts that the responses H and U are independent, which is contradicted by the data. Take $[CS][HU]$ as the null model (Model 0), asserting no relationship between response and predictor variables.

Figure 7.32   Log odds ratio for Hypertension, given Protein Urea, by Social Class and Smoking

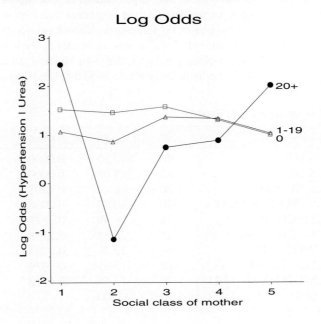

```
%include catdata(toxaemia);
data toxaemia;
   set toxaemia;
   if count=0 then count=1E-10;

*-- Loglinear models;
proc catmod order=data
            data=toxaemia;
   weight count;
   model hyper*urea*class*smoke = _response_ /
      ml noiter noresponse noprofile nodesign;
   loglin  class|smoke hyper urea / title='Model -1: CS  H  U';
run;
   loglin  class|smoke hyper|urea / title='Model 0: CS  HU';
run;
   loglin  class|smoke  hyper|urea  hyper|smoke  urea|class /
        title='Model 1: CS  HU  SH  CU';
run;
   loglin  class|smoke|hyper|urea @2 /
        title='Model 2: CS  CH  CU  HU  SH  CU';
run;
   loglin class|smoke|hyper  class|urea  hyper|urea /
        title='Model 3: CSH  CU  HU';
run;
   loglin class|smoke|hyper  class|urea  smoke|urea  hyper|urea /
        title='Model 4: CSH  CU  SU  HU';
run;
   loglin class|smoke|hyper  class|smoke|urea  hyper|urea /
        title='Model 5: CSH  CSU  HU';
run;
```

The fit statistics and some model selection criteria for these and other models are shown in Table 7.11. The large residual G^2 for Model 0 (179.03 on 42 df) indicates substantial associations between the responses and explanatory variables. Model 1 adds the simple dependence of Hypertension on Smoking ($[SH]$) and that of Urea on Class ($[CU]$); Model 2 includes all 2-way terms. In Model 3, Hypertension is allowed to depend on both Class and Smoking jointly ($[CSH]$). In Model 4, an additional dependence of Urea on Smoking ($[SU]$) is included, while in Model 5, Urea depends on Class and Smoking jointly ($[CSU]$).

Table 7.11 Log-linear models fit to Toxaemia data

Model	Terms	df	χ^2	p-value	χ^2/df	AIC	R^2	Adj. R^2
-1	CS H U	43	672.85	0.0000	15.65	586.85	.	.
0	CS HU	42	179.03	0.0000	4.26	95.03	0.000	0.000
1	CS HU SH CU	36	46.12	0.1203	1.28	-25.88	0.742	0.699
2	CS CH CU HU SH CU	30	40.47	0.0960	1.35	-19.53	0.774	0.684
3	CSH CU HU	24	26.00	0.3529	1.08	-22.00	0.855	0.746
4	CSH CU SU HU	22	25.84	0.2588	1.17	-18.16	0.856	0.724
5	CSH CSU HU	14	22.29	0.0729	1.59	-5.71	0.875	0.626
6	CSH CSU SHU	12	15.65	0.2079	1.30	-8.35	0.913	0.694
7	CSH CSU CHU SHU	8	12.68	0.1233	1.59	-3.32	0.929	0.628
8	CSHU	0	0.00	.	.	0.00	1.000	.

None of these models contain 3-way terms involving both H and U, so these models assume that the log odds ratio for Hypertension given Urea is constant over the explanatory variables. Recalling the partial mosaics (Figure 7.29 and Figure 7.30), Models 6 and 7 add terms that allow the odds ratio to vary, first with Smoking ($[SHU]$), and then with Class ($[CHU]$) as well.

How do you choose among these models? Model 1 is the smallest whose deviance is non-significant. Models 3 and 4 both have a smaller ratio of χ^2df. For comparing nested models, also examine the change in deviance as terms are added (or dropped). Thus, going from Model 1 to Model 2 decreases the deviance by 5.65 on 6 df, while the step from Model 2 to Model 3 gives a decrease of 14.47, also on 6 df. The AIC statistic, balancing parsimony and goodness-of-fit, has its minimum value for Model 1, which is adopted here for this example.

Whatever model is chosen, as a final step, it is important to determine what that model implies about the original research questions. Because the focus here is on the prevalence of each symptom and their association, it is helpful to graph the fitted logits and log odds ratios implied by the model, as done in Figure 7.26 and Figure 7.27.

Example 7.14 fit the bivariate logit model, for which the response functions were the desired logits and log odds. Here, where we have fit ordinary log-linear models, the fitted logits can be calculated from the fitted frequencies. To obtain predicted frequencies under Model 1, use the option PRED=FREQ in the MODEL statement.

```
proc catmod order=data data=toxaemia;
   weight count;
   response  / out=predict;
   model hyper*urea*class*smoke =  _response_ / pred=freq
      ml noiter noresponse noprofile nodesign;
   loglin  class|smoke hyper|urea hyper|smoke urea|class /
      title='Model 1: CS  HU  SH  CU';
```

Then, the observed and fitted frequencies can be extracted from the output dataset and rearranged so that logits and log odds may be calculated.

```
data predict;
   set predict;
   where (_type_='FREQ');
   drop _sample_ _number_ _type_;
proc sort data=predict;
   by class smoke hyper urea;

proc transpose data=predict out=fit(drop=_label_) prefix=fit;
   by class smoke;
   var _pred_;
proc transpose data=predict out=obs(drop=_label_) prefix=obs;
   by class smoke;
   var _obs_;

data pred;
   merge fit obs;
   drop _name_;
   array f{4} fit1-fit4;   *-- Fitted frequencies;
   array o{4} obs1-obs4;   *-- Observed frequencies;

   fhyper = log( (f[1] + f[2] + .5) / (f[3] + f[4] + .5) );
   furea =  log( (f[1] + f[3] + .5) / (f[2] + f[4] + .5) );
   fodds=  log( ((f[1]+.5)*(f[4]+.5))/((f[2]+.5)*(f[3]+.5)) );

   ohyper = log( (o[1] + o[2] + .5) / (o[3] + o[4] + .5) );
   ourea =  log( (o[1] + o[3] + .5) / (o[2] + o[4] + .5) );
   oodds=  log( ((o[1]+.5)*(o[4]+.5))/((o[2]+.5)*(o[3]+.5)) );

   label fhyper = 'Logit (Hytertension)'
      furea =    'Logit (Protein Urea)'
      fodds = 'Log Odds (Hypertension | Urea)';
   format smoke smoke.;
```

Finally, each measure is plotted separately, showing the fitted values with curves and the observed values with points. The statements below are repeated for Urea and for Log Odds. The three graphs are shown in Figure 7.33.

```
%label(data=pred, x=class, y=fhyper, subset=(class=5),
   text=put(smoke, smoke.), pos=6, xoff=.1, out=lab);

%points(data=pred, x=class, y=ohyper,
   symbol=scan('square triangle dot',smoke),
   color=scan('red blue black', smoke), size=2, out=_pts_);
data lab;
   set lab _pts_;

proc gplot data=pred;
   plot fhyper  * class = smoke / anno=lab nolegend
      vaxis=axis1 haxis=asix2 hm=0 vm=1;
   symbol1 v=square   h=1 i=join c=red;
   symbol2 v=triangle h=1 i=join c=blue;
   symbol3 v=dot      h=1 i=join c=black;
   axis1 label=(a=90) order=(-1.5 to -0.8 by .1);
   axis2 offset=(3,9);
   title 'Hypertension';
```

Figure 7.33   Toxaemia data: Observed and fitted logits and log odds ratios for Model 1: [*CS*][*HU*][*SH*][*CU*]

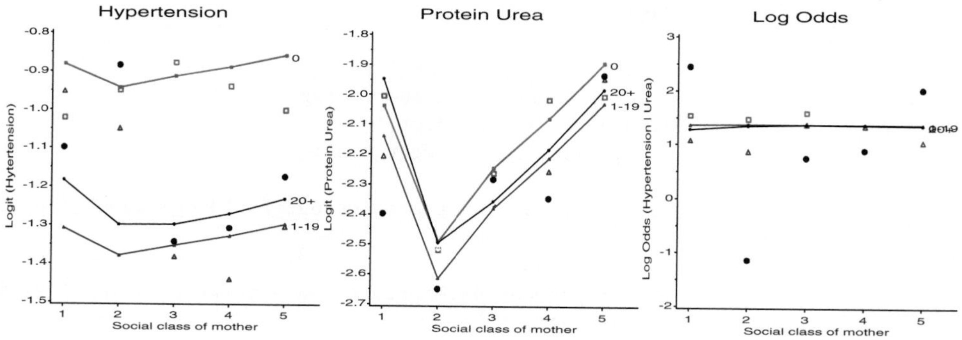

We can see from Figure 7.33 that the fitted log odds ratio is in fact nearly constant, while the log odds for Hypertension depends mainly on Smoking, and that for Protein Urea depends mainly on Social Class. Yet, the great variability of the observed points around the fitted curves indicates that these relationships are not well-determined. Adding error bars showing the standard error around each fitted point would indicate that the data conforms as closely to the model as can be expected, given the widely different sample sizes. However, this would make the plots more complex, so it was omitted here. In addition to showing the pattern of the results according to the fitted model, such graphs also help us to appreciate the model's limitations.   □

7.9   Chapter Summary

- Log-linear models provide a comprehensive scheme to describe and understand the associations among two or more categorical variables. It is helpful to think of these as discrete analogs of ANOVA models or of regression models, where the log of cell frequency is modeled as a linear function of predictors.

- Log-linear models may be fit using PROC CATMOD, PROC GENMOD, SAS/INSIGHT, or SAS/IML. Each of these offers certain advantages and disadvantages.

- Log-linear models typically make no distinction between response and explanatory variables. When one variable *is* a response, however, any logit model for that response has an equivalent log-linear model. The logit form is usually simpler to formulate and test, and plots of the observed and fitted logits are easier to interpret. Plotting the results of logit models fit with PROC CATMOD is facilitated by the CATPLOT macro.

- Standard log-linear models treat all variables as unordered factors. When one or more factors are ordinal, however, log-linear and logit models may be simplified by assigning quantitative scores to the levels of an ordered factor. Such models are often more sensitive and have greater power because they are more focused.

- The interplay between graphing and fitting is important in arriving at an understanding of the relationships among variables and an adequate descriptive model that is faithful to the details of the data.

- Model diagnostic statistics (adjusted residuals, leverage, Cook's D, etc.) provide important ancillary information regarding the adequacy of a log-linear model as a summary of the relationships in the data. Half-normal probability plots, tuned to the discrete nature of categorical data, help to detect outlying cells and are provided by the `HALFNORM` macro. A variety of diagnostic plots provided by the `INFLGLIM` macro aid in detecting unduly influential cells.

- When there are several categorical responses, along with one or more explanatory variables, some special forms of log-linear and logit models can be used to separate the marginal dependence of each response on the explanatory variables from the interdependence among the responses.

Appendix

A

SAS Programs and Macros

Introduction

> Programming graphics in X is like finding the square root of π using Roman numerals.

Henry Spencer

Many of the programs used in the book were developed as general-purpose SAS macros or SAS/IML modules that could be used for any set of data. This generality, however, makes them more complex than is useful to describe completely in the body of the text. In most cases, therefore, the text discusses the application and use of the program.

The SAS programs and macros listed in the contents above are documented in this appendix. The program code is supplied in the archives.

General Usage Notes

Installing the Programs

The set of programs and macros for *Visualizing Categorical Data* is available in two forms: `vcdprog.tar.gz` for Unix-like systems and `vcdprog.zip` for other systems. The distribution archives contain the following directories:

catdata	all the data sets listed in Appendix B
macros	all the macro programs
mosaics	the SAS/IML programs for mosaic displays
iml	other SAS/IML programs
sample	some example applications

For ease of use, you should copy these directories to similarly named directories under your SASUSER directory. In a DOS or Windows environment, for example, this might be `C:\SAS\SASUSER\`; under a Unix-like system, this might be `~/sasuser/` where ~ refers to your home directory.

The macro programs are most easily used if you add the name of the `macros` directory to the list of directories recognized by the SAS Autocall Facility. Then, SAS software will search this directory automatically for macro programs that you invoke. You can do this by adding a statement like the following to your AUTOEXEC.SAS file:

```
options sasautos=('vcdmacros', SASAUTOS);
```

substituting for `vcdmacros` the directory to which you copied the macros.[1] For further information, refer to the *SAS Guide to Macro Processing, Version 6, Second Edition*, Chapter 7, "The Autocall Facility," and to the SAS documentation for your operating system.

Instructions for installing the SAS/IML programs for mosaic displays are given in the `INSTALL` file in the `mosaics` directory.

Macro Parameters and Values

All of the macro programs (except for a few of the Graphics utility macros described in A.31) use keywords for the required and optional parameters. Default values (if any) are described in the Parameters section (and are given after the = sign in the parameter list in the `%macro` statement in each program). Thus, it is only necessary to specify required parameters and those parameters that differ from the default value, and these parameters can be specified in any order in the macro call.

- Most of the macros use keywords as values of some of the macro parameters. All keyword values are case insensitive; for example, using `plot=dist infl` in the `DISTPLOT` macro gives both the distribution and influence plot for a discrete distribution.

- Some of the macros use the keywords `YES` and `NO` as values of some parameters. In all cases, these keywords can be abbreviated to their initial letter.

A.1   The ADDVAR Macro: Added Variable Plots for Logistic Regression

The `ADDVAR` macro produces added variable plots (TYPE=AVP) for the effect of adding a variable to a logistic regression model, or a constructed variable plot (TYPE=CVP) for the effect of transforming a variable. The method is described in Section 6.6.5 and illustrated in Example 6.13.

For a model with a binary response, Y, and predictors in the list X, an added variable plot can be constructed for a new predictor, Z, by plotting the residuals of Y given X against the residuals of Z given X. A linear relation in this plot indicates that Z should be included in the model, but observations with extreme Z-residuals would be highly influential in this decision. A line fitted to this plot should have an intercept approximately zero and a slope approximating the coefficient of Z in the full model.

The constructed variable plot is designed to detect nonlinear dependence of Y on one of the X variables, say X_j. It is an added variable plot for the constructed variable, $X_j \log X_j$. A smoothed lowess curve (specified by the SMOOTH= parameter) will often show the form of a nonlinear relation.

Usage

The `ADDVAR` macro is called with keyword parameters. The X=, Y=, and Z= parameters are required. A TRIALS= variable can be specified if the data is in events/trials form. The arguments can be listed within parentheses in any order, separated by commas. For example:

```
%addvar(data=icu, y=Died,  x=age admit cancer uncons, z=Systolic,
    id=patient, loptions=order=data noprint);
```

This gives an AVP for the variable `Systolic` when added to the X= variables in the model predicting Y=DIED.

---

[1] If you are running SAS software from a networked installation, you may need to modify the `-autoexec` option for SAS invocation so that your local `AUTOEXEC.SAS` is used, rather than the system-wide version.

Parameters

`DATA=`	Specifies the name of the input dataset to be analyzed. [Default: `DATA=_LAST_`]
`Y=`	Specifies the name of the binary response variable.
`TRIALS=`	Name of a trials variable, for event/trials syntax.
`X=`	Specifies the names of the predictor variables in the model. Any discrete, classification variables with more than two levels must be represented by dummy variables.
`Z=`	Name of the added variable.
`ID=`	Name of a character observation ID variable.
`LOPTIONS=`	Any options for `PROC LOGISTIC`, such as `ORDER=DATA`. [Default: `LOPTIONS=NOPRINT`]
`SMOOTH=`	Lowess smoothing parameter. Use `SMOOTH=0` to suppress the smoothed lowess curve. [Default: `SMOOTH=0.5`]
`SUBSET=`	A logical expression (which can involve any variables in the output dataset) used to define the subset of points to label in the plot. `SUBSET=0` means that no points are labeled; `SUBSET=1` means that all points are labeled. [Default: `SUBSET=ABS(STUDRES)>2`]
`OUT=`	Specifies the name of the output dataset. [Default: `OUT=_RES_`]
`SYMBOL=`	Defines the plotting symbol for points. [Default: `SYMBOL=DOT`]
`INTERP=`	Interpolation option(s) for points (used in the `SYMBOL` statement). [Default: `INTERP=RL CI=RED`]
`TYPE=`	Type of plot: AVP or CVP. [Default: `TYPE=AVP`]
`NAME=`	Name of graph in graphic catalog. [Default: `NAME=ADDVAR`]
`GOUT=`	Name of the graphics catalog.

A.2 The AGREE Program: Observer Agreement Chart

The AGREE program is a collection of SAS/IML modules for preparing observer agreement charts that portray the agreement between two raters, as described in Section 3.7.

Usage

The modules are typically loaded into the SAS/IML workspace with the `%include` statement. The required input parameters are specified with SAS/IML statements, and the agree module is called as follows:

```
proc iml;
   %include iml(agree);
  *-- set global variables, if desired;
   font = 'hwpsl009';
   htext=1.3;
  *-- specify required parameters;
   table  = { ... };   *-- contingency table;
   weight = { ... };   *-- disagreement weights;
   vnames = { ... };   *-- variable names;
   lnames = { ... };   *-- level names;
   title  = " ...";
   run agree(table, weight, vnames, lnames, title);
```

Parameters

The required parameters for the `run agree` statement are

`table`	A square numeric matrix containing the contingency table to be analyzed.
`weight`	A vector of one or more weights used to give "partial credit" for disagreements by one or more categories. To ignore all but exact agreements, let `weight=1`. To take into account agreements one step apart (with a weight of 5/6), let `weight={1 5/6}`.
`vnames`	A character vector of two elements, containing the names of the row and column variables.
`lnames`	A character vector containing the names of the row and column categories. If `table` is $n \times n$, then `lnames` should contain n elements.
`title`	A character string containing the title for the plot.

Global Input Variables

The program uses two global variables to determine the font and character height for text in the agreement chart.

`font`	A character string specifying the font used. The default is Helvetica (`font='hwpsl009'`) if a PostScript driver is being used, `SWISS` otherwise.
`htext`	A numeric value specifying the height of text characters.

A.3   The BIPLOT Macro: Generalized Biplots

The `BIPLOT` macro produces generalized biplot displays for multivariate data, and for 2-way and multi-way tables of either quantitative or frequency data. It also produces labeled plots of the row and column points in two dimensions, with a variety of graphic options, and the facility to equate the axes automatically.

Input Dataset

The macro takes input in one of two forms:

(a) A dataset in table form, where the columns are separate variables and the rows are separate observations (identified by a row ID variable). In this arrangement, use the `VAR=` argument to specify this list of variables and the `ID=` variable to specify an additional variable whose values are labels for the rows.

Assume a dataset of reaction times to four topics in three experimental tasks, in a SAS dataset like this:

```
TASK     TOPIC1   TOPIC2   TOPIC3   TOPIC4
Easy      2.43     3.12     3.68     4.04
Medium    3.41     3.91     4.07     5.10
Hard      4.21     4.65     5.87     5.69
```

For this arrangment, the macro would be invoked as follows:

```
%biplot(var=topic1-topic4, id=task);
```

(b) A contingency table in frequency form (e.g., the output from PROC FREQ), or multi-way data in the univariate format used as input to PROC GLM. In this case, there will be two or more factor (class) variables, and one response variable, with one observation per cell. For this form, you must use the VAR= argument to specify the two (or more) factor (class) variables and specify the name of the response variable as the RESPONSE= parameter. Do not specify an ID= variable for this form.

For contingency table data, the response will be the cell frequency, and you will usually use the POWER=0 parameter to perform an analysis of the log frequency.

The same data in this format would have 12 observations and look like this:

```
TASK   TOPIC    RT
Easy     1     2.43
Easy     2     3.12
Easy     3     3.68
...
Hard     4     5.69
```

For this arrangment, the macro would be invoked as follows:

```
%biplot(var=topic task, response=RT);
```

In this arrangement, the order of the VAR= variables does not matter. The columns of the 2-way table are determined by the variable that varies most rapidly in the input dataset (topic, in the example).

Usage

The BIPLOT macro is defined with keyword parameters. The VAR= parameter must be specified, together with either one ID= variable or one RESPONSE= variable.

The arguments can be listed within parentheses in any order, separated by commas. For example,

```
%biplot(var=topic task, response=RT);
```

The plot can be re-drawn or customized using the output OUT= dataset of coordinates and the ANNO= Annotate dataset.

The graphical representation of biplots requires that the axes in the plot are equated, so that equal distances on the ordinate and abscissa represent equal data units (to perserve distances and angles in the plot). A '+', whose vertical and horizontal lengths should be equal, is drawn at the origin to indicate whether this has been achieved.

If you do not specifiy the HAXIS= and YAXIS= parameters, the EQUATE macro is called to generate the AXIS statements to equate the axes. In this case the INC=, XEXTRA=, and YEXTRA= parameters can be used to control the details of the generated AXIS statements.

By default, the macro produces and plots a two-dimensional solution.

Parameters

DATA=	Specifies the name of the input dataset to be analyzed. [Default: DATA=_LAST_]
VAR=	Specifies the names of the column variables when the data is in table form, or the names of the factor variables when the data is in frequency form or GLM form. [Default: VAR=_NUM_]
ID=	Observation ID variable when the data is in table form.
RESPONSE=	Name of the response variable (for GLM form).

DIM=	Specifies the number of dimensions of the CA/MCA solution. Only two dimensions are plotted by the PPLOT and GPLOT options, however. [Default: DIM=2]
FACTYPE=	Biplot factor type: GH, SYM, JK or COV. [Default: FACTYPE=SYM]
VARDEF=	Variance def for FACTYPE=COV: DF | N. [Default: VARDEF=DF]
SCALE=	Scale factor for variable vectors. [Default: SCALE=1]
POWER=	Power transform of response. [Default: POWER=1]
OUT=	Specifies the name of the output dataset of coordinates. [Default: OUT=BIPLOT]
ANNO=	Specifies the name of the annotate dataset of labels produced by the macro. [Default: ANNO=BIANNO]
STD=	How to standardize columns: NONE | MEAN | STD. [Default: STD=MEAN]
COLORS=	Colors for OBS and VARS. [Default: COLORS=BLUE RED]
SYMBOLS=	Symbols for OBS and VARS. [Default: SYMBOLS=NONE NONE]
INTERP=	Markers/interpolation for OBS and VARS. [Default: INTERP=NONE VEC]
LINES=	Lines for OBS and VARS interpolation. [Default: LINES=33 20]
PPLOT=	Produce a printer plot? [Default: PPLOT=NO]
VTOH=	The vertical to horizontal aspect ratio (height of one character divided by the width of one character) of the printer device, used to equate axes for a printer plot, when PPLOT=YES. [Default: VTOH=2]
GPLOT=	Produce a graphics plot? [Default: GPLOT=YES]
PLOTREQ=	The dimensions to be plotted. [Default: PLOTREQ=DIM2*DIM1]
HAXIS=	AXIS statement for horizontal axis. If both HAXIS= and VAXIS= are omitted, the program calls the EQUATE macro to define suitable axis statements. This creates the axis statements AXIS98 and AXIS99, whether or not a graph is produced.
VAXIS=	The name of an AXIS statement for the vertical axis.
INC=	The length of X and Y axis tick increments, in data units (for the EQUATE macro). Ignored if HAXIS= and VAXIS= are specified. [Default: INC=0.5 0.5]
XEXTRA=	Number of extra X axis tick marks at the left and right. Use to allow extra space for labels. [Default: XEXTRA=0 0]
YEXTRA=	Number of extra Y axis tick marks at the bottom and top. [Default: YEXTRA=0 0]
MO=	Length of origin marker, in data units. [Default: MO=0.5]
DIMLAB=	Prefix for dimension labels. [Default: DIMLAB=Dimension]
NAME=	Name of the graphics catalog entry. [Default: NAME=BIPLOT]

A.4 The CATPLOT Macro: Plot Results from PROC CATMOD

The CATPLOT macro is designed to plot observed and/or predicted values for logit models fit by the CATMOD procedure. The macro uses the output dataset produced with the OUT= option on the RESPONSE statement. This dataset normally contains both logit values (_TYPE_='FUNCTION') and probability values (_TYPE_='PROB'). Either set can be plotted, as specified by the TYPE= parameter.

The horizontal variable can be character (XC=) or numeric (X=). A separate curve is drawn for each value of the CLASS= variable, connecting predicted values with optional standard error bars, and separate plots are drawn for each value of the BYVAR= variable.

Usage

The CATPLOT macro is called with keyword parameters. Either the X= or the XC= parameter is required. Use the CLASS= parameter to give multiple curves in each plot for the levels of the CLASS variable. Use the BYVAR= parameter to give multiple plots for the levels of the BYVAR variable. The arguments can be listed within parentheses in any order, separated by commas. For example,

```
proc catmod;
   direct husinc;
   response / out=logits;
   model labour = husinc children;
%catplot(data=logits, x=husinc, y=_pred_, class=labor, byvar=children);
```

Parameters

DATA=   The name of the SAS dataset to be plotted, which must be an output dataset from PROC CATMOD. If DATA= is not specified, the most recently created dataset is used.

X=   Name of a numeric factor variable to be used as the horizontal variable in plots. Use the XC= parameter to specify a character variable. You must specify either the X= or XC= variable.

XC=   Name of a character factor variable used as the horizontal variable in plots.

Y=   Name of the ordinate variable. Y=_PRED_ plots the predicted value; Y=_OBS_ plots the observed value. The default is Y=_OBS_, but the predicted values are also drawn, connected by lines. [Default: Y=_OBS_]

CLASS=   The name of a factor variable, used to define separate curves that are plotted for each level of this variable.

BYVAR=   The name(s) of one or more factor variables to be used to define multiple panels in plots. A separate plot is produced for each combination of values of the BYVAR= variables.

BYFMT=   The name of a SAS format used to format the value of BYVARs for display in one panel of the plot(s). [Default: BYFMT=$16.]

TYPE=   The type of observations to be plotted. TYPE=FUNCTION (the default) gives plots of the logit value; TYPE=PROB gives plots of the probability value. [Default: TYPE=FUNCTION]

Z=   Standard error multiple for confidence intervals around predicted values, e.g., Z=1.96 gives 95% CI. To suppress error bars, use Z=0. The default is Z=1, giving 67% CI.

CLFMT=   Name of a SAS format used to format the value of the CLASS= variable for display in each panel of the plot(s).

CLSIDE=   Specifies whether the values of the CLASS= variable should be labeled by annotation in the plot or by a legend. If CLSIDE=LEFT or CLSIDE=FIRST, CLASS= values are written at the left side of each curve. If CLSIDE=RIGHT or CLSIDE=LAST, CLASS= values are written at the right side of each curve. If CLSIDE=NONE, or if a LEGEND= legend is specified, the CLASS= values appear in the legend. You should then define a LEGEND statement and use the LEGEND= parameter. [Default: CLSIDE=LAST]

XFMT=   Name of a SAS format used to format the values of the horizontal variable.

POSFMT=   Format to translate the value of the CLASS variable to a SAS/GRAPH annotate position. This will almost always be a user-specified format created with PROC FORMAT.

ANNO=   Name of an additional input annotate dataset. The graphic commands in this dataset are performed for each plot.

SYMBOLS=	List of SAS/GRAPH symbols for the levels of the CLASS= variable. The specified symbols are reused cyclically if the number of distinct values of the CLASS= variable exceeds the number of symbols. [Default: SYMBOLS=CIRCLE SQUARE TRIANGLE]
COLORS=	List of SAS/GRAPH colors for the levels of the CLASS= variable. The specified colors are reused cyclically if the number of distinct values of the CLASS= variable exceeds the number of colors. [Default: COLORS=BLACK RED BLUE GREEN]
LINES=	List of SAS/GRAPH line styles for the levels of the CLASS= variable. The specified line styles are reused cyclically if the number of distinct values of the CLASS= variable exceeds the number of line styles. [Default: LINES=1 20 41 21 7 14 33 12]
VAXIS=	Axis statement for custom response axis, e.g., VAXIS=AXIS1. [Default: VAXIS=AXIS1]
HAXIS=	Axis statement for custom horizontal axis, e.g., HAXIS=AXIS2. [Default: HAXIS=AXIS2]
LEGEND=	Legend statement for custom CLASS legend, e.g., LEGEND=LEGEND1.
PLOC=	For multiple plots (with a BYVAR= variable), PLOC defines the X, Y position of the panel label, in graph percentage units. [Default: PLOC=5 95]
PRINT=	Print the summarized input dataset? [Default: PRINT=NO]
NAME=	Name of graphic catalog entry. [Default: NAME=CATPLOT]

A.5 The CORRESP Macro: Plotting PROC CORRESP Results

The CORRESP macro carries out simple correspondence analysis of a 2-way contingency table, correspondence analysis of stacked multi-way tables (when the CROSS option is included in the OPTIONS= parameter), or multiple correspondence analysis (when the MCA option is included in the OPTIONS= parameter). See Section 5.2.4 for further description and examples.

The macro optionally produces labeled plot(s) of the category points with equated axes and produces output datasets from which more customized plots (e.g., a 3-D plot) can be constructed. It is a completely revised version of the CORRESP macro presented in *SAS System for Statistical Graphics, First Edition*, Section A1.6, which uses PROC CORRESP for the calculations, rather than SAS/IML.

Input Dataset

The macro takes an input dataset in one of two forms:

1. A dataset in contingency table form, where the columns are separate variables and the rows are separate observations (identified by a row ID variable). That is, the input dataset contains R observations and C variables (whose values are cell frequencies) for an $R \times C$ table. Do not use the COUNT= parameter in this case, but you should specify:

```
ID=ROWVAR, VAR=C1 C2 C3 C4 C5
```

2. A contingency table in frequency form (e.g., the output from PROC FREQ), or raw data, where there is one variable for each factor. In frequency form, there will be one observation for each cell. For this form, specify the table variables in the TABLES= parameter:

```
TABLES=A B C
```

Include the WEIGHT= parameter when the observations are in frequency form.

Usage

The CORRESP macro is called with keyword parameters. Either the VAR= parameter or the TABLES= parameter (but not both) must be specified, but other parameters or options may be needed to carry out the analysis you want. The arguments can be listed within parentheses in any order, separated by commas. For example,

```
%corresp(var=response, id=sex year);
```

The plot can be re-drawn or customized using the output OUT= dataset of coordinates and the ANNO= Annotate dataset.

The graphical representation of correspondence analysis plots requires that the axes in the plot are equated, so that equal distances on the ordinate and abscissa represent equal data units (to perserve distances and angles in the plot). A large '+', whose vertical and horizontal lengths should be equal, is drawn at the origin to indicate whether this has been achieved.

If you do not specifiy the HAXIS= and YAXIS= parameters, the EQUATE macro (A.31.2) is called to generate the AXIS statements to equate the axes. In this case the INC=, XEXTRA=, and YEXTRA= parameters can be used to control the details of the generated AXIS statements.

By default, the macro produces and plots a two-dimensional solution.

Parameters

DATA=   Specifies the name of the input dataset to be analyzed.
             [Default: DATA=_LAST_]
VAR=   Specifies the names of the column variables for simple CA, when the data is in contingency table form. Not used for MCA (use the TABLES= parameter instead).
ID=   Specifies the name(s) of the row variable(s) for simple CA. Not used for MCA.
TABLES=   Specifies the names of the factor variables used to create the rows and columns of the contingency table. For a simple CA or stacked analysis, use a ',' or '/' to separate the the row and column variables, but the TABLES= value must be quoted with %str( ) if a ',' is used as the separator.
WEIGHT=   Specifies the name of the frequency (WEIGHT) variable when the dataset is in frequency form. If WEIGHT= is omitted, the observations in the input dataset are not weighted.
SUP=   Specifies the name(s) of any variables treated as supplementary. The categories of these variables are included in the output but not otherwise used in the computations. These must be included among the variables in the VAR= or TABLES= option.
DIM=   Specifies the number of dimensions of the CA/MCA solution. Only two dimensions are plotted by the PPLOT option, however.
OPTIONS=   Specifies options for PROC CORRESP. Include MCA for an MCA analysis, CROSS=ROW|COL|BOTH for stacked analysis of multiway tables,

	PROFILE=BOTH|ROW|COLUMN for various coordinate scalings, etc. [Default: OPTIONS=SHORT]
OUT=	Specifies the name of the output dataset of coordinates. [Default: OUT=COORD]
ANNO=	Specifies the name of the annotate dataset of labels produced by the macro. [Default: ANNO=LABEL]
PPLOT=	Produce printer plot? [Default: PPLOT=NO]
GPLOT=	Produce graphics plot? [Default: GPLOT=YES]
PLOTREQ=	Specifies the dimensions to be plotted in a PLOT statement or SCATTER statement. [Default: PLOTREQ=DIM2*DIM1 when DIM=2, PLOTREQ=DIM2*DIM1=DIM3 when DIM=3]
HTEXT=	Height for row/col labels. If not specified, the global HTEXT goption is used. Otherwise, specify one or two numbers to be used as the height for row and column labels. The HTEXT= option overrides the separate ROWHT= and COLHT= parameters (maintained for backward compatibility).
ROWHT=	Height for row labels, if HTEXT= is not specified.
COLHT=	Height for column labels.
COLORS=	Colors for row and column points, labels, and interpolations. In an MCA analysis, only one color is used. [Default: COLORS=BLUE RED]
POS=	Annotate positions for the row and column labels relative to the SYMBOL points. In addition to the standard Annotate position values, the CORRESP macro also understands the special characters "/", "|", or "–". See the LABEL macro (A.31.6) for a description of these special position values. [Default: POS=5 5]
SYMBOLS=	Symbols used for row and column points, as in a SYMBOL statement. Ordinarily, no symbols are plotted because the point labels identify the locations and symbols would often overplot the labels. [Default: SYMBOLS=NONE NONE]
INTERP=	Interpolation options for row and column points. In addition to the standard interpolation options provided by the SYMBOL statement, the CORRESP macro also understands the option VEC to mean a vector from the origin to the row or column point. The option JOIN may be useful for an ordered factor, and the option NEEDLE may be useful to focus on the positions of the row/column points on the horizontal variable. [Default: INTERP=NONE NONE, INTERP=VEC for MCA]
HAXIS=	The name of an AXIS statement for the horizontal axis. If both HAXIS= and VAXIS= are omitted, the program calls the EQUATE macro to define suitable axis statements. This creates the axis statements AXIS98 and AXIS99, whether or not a graph is produced.
VAXIS=	The name of an AXIS statement for the vertical axis.
VTOH=	The vertical to horizontal aspect ratio (height of one character divided by the width of one character) of the printer device, used to equate axes for a printer plot, when PPLOT=YES. [Default: VTOH=2]
INC=	The length of X and Y axis tick increments, in data units (for the EQUATE macro). Ignored if HAXIS= and VAXIS= are specified. [Default: INC=0.1 0.1]
XEXTRA=	The number of extra X axis tick marks at the left and right. Use to allow extra space for labels. [Default: XEXTRA=0 0]
YEXTRA=	The number of extra Y axis tick marks at the bottom and top. [Default: YEXTRA=0 0]
MO=	Length of the origin (+) marker, in data units. [Default: MO=0.05]
DIMLAB=	Prefix for dimension labels. [Default: DIMLAB=Dimension]
NAME=	Name of graphic catalog entry. [Default: NAME=CORRESP]

A.6   The DISTPLOT Macro: Plots for Discrete Distributions

The DISTPLOT macro constructs plots of a discrete distribution designed to diagnose whether the data follows one of the standard distributions: the Poisson, Binomial, Negative Binomial, Geometric, or Log Series. The type of distribution is specified by the DIST= parameter.

The usual distribution diagnostic plot (PLOT=DIST) is constructed so that the points lie along a straight line when the data follows that distribution. An influence plot (PLOT=INFL) shows the influence of each observation on the choice of the distribution parameter(s). The macro is illustrated in Section 2.5.5.

Usage

The DISTPLOT macro is called with keyword parameters. You must specify the distribution to be fit (DIST=), and the COUNT= and FREQ= variables. The arguments can be listed within parentheses in any order, separated by commas. For example,

```
%distplot(data=queues, count=women, freq=queues, dist=binomial,
     parm=0.435);
```

Parameters

DATA=	The name of the input dataset. [Default: DATA=_LAST_]
COUNT=	The name of the basic count variable.
FREQ=	The name of the variable giving the observed frequency (number of occurrences) associated with the COUNT= variable.
LABEL=	Axis label for the horizontal (COUNT=) variable. If not specified, the label of that variable in the input dataset is used.
DIST=	Name of the distribution to be assessed, one of POISSON, BINOMIAL, NEGBIN, GEOMETRIC, or LOGSERIES.
PARM=	Trial value of the distribution parameter(s) to level the plot. For the Binomial distribution, PARM=p, the binomial probability of success; for the Poisson, PARM=λ, the Poisson mean. For the Geometric, PARM=p. For the Negative binomial, one or two values can be supplied. The first is taken as n; a second value is taken as p.
Z=	Specifies the multiplier used for error bars in the PLOT=DIST plot. [Default: Z=1.96]
PLOT=	What to plot: DIST and/or INFL. [Default: PLOT=DIST]
HTEXT=	Height of text labels in the plots. [Default: HTEXT=1.4]
OUT=	The name of the output dataset. [Default: OUT=DISTPLOT]
NAME=	Name of the graphics catalog entry. [Default: NAME=DISTPLT]

A.7   The DUMMY Macro: Create Dummy Variables

Given one or more character or discrete numerical variables, the DUMMY macro constructs dummy (0/1) variables to represent the categories of a discrete variable in a regression model with PROC LOGISTIC or PROC REG. If the original variable has c levels, $c - 1$ new variables are produced.

The dummy variables can be named by appending numbers to a prefix or by appending the value of the discrete variable to the prefix.

Usage

The DUMMY macro is called with keyword parameters. The VAR= variable(s) must be specified. The arguments can be listed within parentheses in any order, separated by commas. For example,

```
%dummy(var=region sex);
```

Parameters

DATA=
: The name of the input dataset. If not specified, the most recently created dataset is used.

OUT=
: The name of the output dataset. If not specified, the new variables are appended to the input dataset.

VAR=
: The name of the input variable(s) to be dummy coded. Must be specified. The variable(s) can be character or numeric.

PREFIX=
: Prefix used to create the names of dummy variables. Use an empty string to suppress the prefix. The default is 'D_'.

NAME=
: Determines how the dummy variables are named. If NAME=VAL, the dummy variables are named by appending the value of the VAR= variable to the prefix. For example, with a character variable sex, taking on value 'M' and 'F', the dummy variable would be named 'D_M'. Otherwise, the dummy variables are named by appending numbers, 1, 2, ... to the prefix. The resulting name must be 8 characters or fewer. [Default: NAME=VAL]

BASE=
: Indicates the level of the baseline category, which is given values of 0 on all the dummy variables. BASE=_FIRST_ specifies that the lowest value of the VAR= variable is the baseline group; BASE=_LAST_ specifies the highest value of the variable. Otherwise, you can specify BASE=value to make a different value the baseline group. [Default: BASE=_LAST_]
FULLRANK= Is either 0 or 1, where 1 indicates that the dummy variable for the BASE= category is eliminated. [Default: FULLRANK=1]

Example

With the input dataset,

```
data test;
  input y group $ @@;
 datalines;
 10  A  12  A   13  A   18  B  19  B  16  C  21  C  19  C
  ;
%dummy (data = test, var = group) ;
```

the DUMMY macro produces two new variables, 'D_A' and 'D_B'. Group C is the baseline category (corresponding to BASE=_LAST_).

OBS	Y	GROUP	D_A	D_B
1	10	A	1	0
2	12	A	1	0
3	13	A	1	0
4	18	B	0	1
5	19	B	0	1
6	16	C	0	0
7	21	C	0	0
8	19	C	0	0

A.8   The FOURFOLD Program: Fourfold Displays for 2 × 2 × *k* Tables

The FOURFOLD program is a collection of SAS/IML modules for constructing fourfold displays of a 2 × 2 table, or a collection of 2 × 2 tables for multiple strata or groups. This graphical method is described and illustrated in Section 3.4.

Usage

The modules are typically loaded into the SAS/IML workspace with the %include statement. The required inputs consist of the contingency table, its dimensions, the variable names, and names for the variable levels. These are usually specified with SAS/IML statements, and the fourfold module is called as follows:

```
proc iml;
   %include iml(fourfold);
  *-- specify required parameters;
   dim =    { ... };   *-- table dimensions;
   table  = { ... };   *-- contingency table;
   vnames = { ... };   *-- variable names;
   lnames = { ... };   *-- level names;
  *-- specify desired global variables;
   config = {1};
   run fourfold( dim, table, vnames, lnames );
```

The FOURFOLD program also provides a variety of optional parameters to be specified as global SAS/IML variables. All of these are given default values if not specified.

Required Parameters

The required parameters for the run fourfold statement are listed here. These are positional parameters and can be given any valid SAS name in the PROC IML step.

dim   A numeric vector containing the dimensions of the contingency table. The first two elements must be {2 2}.

table   A numeric matrix containing dim[1]=2 columns and number of rows equal to the product of the remaining elements of dim. The table must be entered so that the first variable varies most quickly (row-major order) and the last variable varies most slowly, in accord with the conventions for multi-way tables used by the SAS/IML routines marg and ipf.

vnames   A 1× ncol(dim) character vector, containing the names of the variables in the order corresponding to dim.

lnames   A character matrix containing the names of the categories (levels) of the variables, whose rows correspond to dim and vnames. Any short rows must be filled in with blank character strings, because matrices in SAS/IML must have the same number of elements in each row. For example, for the 2×2×6 table for the Berkeley data, the dim, vnames and lnames can be entered as follows:

```
dim = {2 2 6};
vnames = {"Admit?" "Sex" "Department"};
lnames = {"Yes" "No" " " " " " " " " " ",
          "Male" "Female" " " " " " " " " " ",
          "A" "B" "C" "D" "E" "F"};
```

Global Input Variables

The following global variables are used by the program if they have been assigned values of the correct type (character or numeric). Because they all have default values, it is necessary to specify only those you want to change. All character-valued variables are case-insensitive.

`std`	Specifies how the 2×2 tables are standardized. [Default: `std='MARG'`]

	`MARG`	Standardizes each 2×2 table to equal margins, keeping the odds ratio fixed. The `config` variable determines which margins are equated.
	`MAX`	Standardizes each table to a maximum cell frequency of 100. This has the effect of equating the totals in each table.
	`MAXALL`	Standardizes *all* tables so that the maximum cell entry is 100.

`config`	Specifies the margins to standardize, when `std='MARG'`. `config={1 2}` equates both the row and column variable in each table; `config={1}` equates the margin only for the column variable in each table; `config={2}` equates only the row variable.
`down`	Specifies the number of fourfold panels down each page.
`across`	Specifies the number of panels across each page.
`sangle`	The angle for side labels (0|90). [Default: `sangle=90`]
`colors`	The names of two colors to use for the smaller and larger diagonals of each 2×2 table. The positions of first color indicate the direction of association. [Default: `colors={BLUE RED}`]
`patterns`	The names of two fill patterns. For grayscale, use `patterns={SOLID SOLID}` and `colors={GRAYC0 GRAY80}`. [Default: `patterns={SOLID SOLID}`]
`alpha`	The error rate used for confidence rings on the odds ratios. Use `alpha=0;` to suppress the confidence rings.
`conf`	The type of confidence rings, either `'Individual'` (for each 2×2 table) or `'Joint'` (for simultaneous confidence intervals covering all k 2×2 tables). [Default: `conf='Individual'`]
`font`	A character string specifying the font used. The default is Helvetica (`font='hwpsl009'`) if a PostScript driver is being used, `SWISS` otherwise.
`frame`	The line style for the boxed frame (0=none).

A.9 The GOODFIT Macro: Goodness-of-Fit for Discrete Distributions

The GOODFIT macro carries out chi-square goodness-of-fit tests for discrete distributions, as described in Section 2.3. These include the uniform, binomial, Poisson, negative binomial, geometric, and logarithmic series distributions, as well as any discrete (multinomial) distribution whose probabilities you can specify. Both the Pearson chi-square and likelihood-ratio chi-square are computed.

The data can consist either of individual observations on a single variable or a grouped frequency distribution.

The parameter(s) of the distribution can be specified as constants or can be estimated from the data.

Usage

The GOODFIT macro is called with keyword parameters. The arguments can be listed within parentheses in any order, separated by commas. For example,

```
%goodfit(var=k, freq=freq, dist=binomial);
```

You must specify a VAR= analysis variable and the keyword for the distribution to be fit with the DIST= parameter. All other parameters are optional.

Parameters

DATA=   Specifies the name of the dataset to be analyzed. If not specified, the most recently created dataset is used.

VAR=   The name of the variable to be analyzed, the basic count variable.

FREQ=   The name of a frequency variable for a grouped dataset. If no FREQ= variable is specified, the program assumes the dataset is ungrouped and calculates frequencies using PROC FREQ. In this case you can specify a SAS format with the FORMAT= parameter to control the way the observations are grouped.

DIST=   Specifies the name of the discrete frequency distribution to be fit. The allowable values are UNIFORM, DISCRETE, BINOMIAL, POISSON, NEGBIN, GEOMETRIC, LOGSERIES.

PARM=   Specifies fixed parameter(s) for the distribution. If PARM= is not specified, the parameter(s) are estimated using maximum likelihood or method of moment estimators. For the Poisson distribution, you can specify parm=λ to specify the rate parameter; otherwise, λ is estimated from the data (and an extra degree of freedom is subtracted). Similarly, for the binomial distribution, specifying parm=p fits the distribution with that value of p. For the general DIST=DISCRETE (multinomial) distribution PARM= a list of numbers proportional to the theoretical cell probabilities. For example, for a multinomial distribution with probabilities $\frac{1}{4}, \frac{1}{2}, \frac{1}{4}$, you can specify PARM=1 2 1.

SUMAT=   For a distribution where the frequencies greater than or equal to some value of k have been lumped into a single category, specifing SUMAT=value causes the macro to sum the probabilities and expected frequencies for all values of k greater than or equal to value.

FORMAT=   The name of a SAS format used when no FREQ= variable has been specified.

OUT=   The name of an output dataset containing the grouped frequency distribution, estimated expected frequencies, and residuals.

OUTSTAT=   The name of an output dataset containing goodness-of-fit statistics.

A.10 The HALFNORM Macro: Half-Normal Plots for Generalized Linear Models

The HALFNORM macro plots the ordered absolute values of residuals from a generalized linear model against expected values of normal order statistics. A simulated envelope, correponding to an approximate 95% confidence interval, is added to the plot to aid assessment of whether the distribution of residuals corresponds to a good-fitting model. The method is described in Section 7.7.2 and illustrated in Example 7.11 and Example 7.12.

Usage

The `HALFNORM` macro is called with keyword parameters. The `RESP=` (or `Y=`) and `MODEL=` parameters are required. The `DIST=` must usually be specified for the analysis to be appropriate for your data. The arguments can be listed within parentheses in any order, separated by commas. For example,

```
%halfnorm(resp=count, class=sex response, model=sex|year|response@2);
```

Parameters

`DATA=`   Specifies the name of the input dataset to be analyzed.
[Default: `DATA=_LAST_`]

`Y=`

`RESP=`   Either `Y=` or `RESP=` specifies the name of the response variable to be analyzed.

`TRIALS=`   The name of a trials variable, for `DIST=BINOMIAL`, when the data is in events/trials form.

`MODEL=`   Specifies the model formula, the right-hand side of the `MODEL` statement. You can use the | and @ shorthands for crossed effects. For example, `MODEL = A|B|C@2` specifies a model with all main effects and 2-way interactions.

`CLASS=`   The names of any class variables used in the model. By default, all variables are treated as continuous, as in `PROC GENMOD`.

`DIST=`   Specifies the error distribution for a generalized linear model. Any of the keywords `NORMAL`, `BINOMIAL`, `POISSON`, `GAMMA`, or `IGAUSSIAN` (or their abbreviations) allowed in `PROC GENMOD` can be used. For frequency data, `DIST=POISSON` should usually be specified. [Default: `DIST=NORMAL`]

`LINK=`   Specifies the link function to be used in the generalized linear model. The default is the canonical link for the `DIST=` error distribution.

`OFFSET=`   The name(s) of any offset variables in the model.

`MOPT=`   Other options for the `MODEL` statement (e.g., `MOPT=NOINT` to fit a model without an intercept).

`FREQ=`   The name of a frequency variable, when the data is in frequency (grouped) form.

`ID=`   The name of a character variable used as an observation identifier in the plot. For contingency tables in frequency form, it is useful to combine abbreviations of the factor levels to produce an ID= variable for each cell.

`OUT=`   Specifies the name of the output dataset. The output dataset contains the input variables, absolute residuals (`_ARES_`), half-normal expected value (`_Z_`). [Default: `OUT=_RES_`]

`LABEL=`   Specifies whether and how to label observations in the plot. `LABEL=ALL` means that all observations are labeled with the `ID=` variable value; `LABEL=NONE` means that no observations are labeled; `LABEL=ABOVE` means that observations above the mean of the simulations are labeled; `LABEL=TOP` *n* means that the highest *n* observations are labeled. [Default: `LABEL=TOP 5`]

`SEED=`   Specifies the seed for the random number generators. `SEED=0` uses the time-of-day as the seed, so a different set of simulated observations is drawn each time the program is run. Any positive integer causes the same set of simulated observations to be drawn every time. [Default: `SEED=0`]

`RES=`   Specifies the type of residual to plot. Possible values are `STRESCHI` (adjusted Pearson residual) and `STRESDEV` (adjusted deviance residual). [Default: `RES=STRESDEV`]

NRES=	Number of simulations used for the confidence envelope. [Default: `NRES=19`]
SYMBOL=	Plotting symbol used for residuals. [Default: `SYMBOL=dot`]
INTERP=	Interpolation option used for residuals. [Default: `INTERP=none`]
COLOR=	Color for plotting the residuals. [Default: `COLOR=red`]
NAME=	Graph name in graphics catalog. [Default: `NAME=halfnorm`]
GOUT=	The name of the graphics catalog. [Default: `GOUT=GSEG`]

A.11   The INFLGLIM Macro: Influence Plots for Generalized Linear Models

The `INFLGLIM` macro produces various influence plots for a generalized linear model fit by `PROC GENMOD`, described and illustrated in Section 7.7.3. Each of these is a bubble plot of one diagnostic measure (specified by the `GY=` parameter) against another (`GX=`), with the bubble size proportional to a measure of influence (usually, `BUBBLE=COOKD`). One plot is produced for each combination of the `GY=` and `GX=` variables.

Usage

The macro normally takes an input dataset of raw data and fits the GLM specified by the `RESP=` and `MODEL=` parameters, using an error distribution given by the `DIST=` parameter. It fits the model, obtains the `OBSTATS` and `PARMEST` datasets, and uses these to compute some additional influence diagnostics (HAT, COOKD, DIFCHI, DIFDEV, SERES), any of which can be used as the `GY=` and `GX=` parameters.

Alternatively, if you have fit a model with `PROC GENMOD` and saved the `OBSTATS` and `PARMEST` datasets (e.g., using a `MAKE` statement), you can specify these with the `OBSTATS=` and `PARMEST=` parameters. The same additional diagnostics are calculated and plotted.

The `INFLGLIM` macro is called with keyword parameters. The `MODEL=` and `RESP=` parameters are required, and you must supply the `DIST=` parameter for any model with non-normal errors. The arguments can be listed within parentheses in any order, separated by commas. For example,

```
%include catdata(berkeley);
%inflglim(data=berkeley,
   class=dept gender admit,
   resp=freq, model=dept|gender dept|admit,
   dist=poisson,
   id=cell,
   gx=hat, gy=streschi);
```

Parameters

DATA=	Name of input (raw data) dataset. [Default: `DATA=_LAST_`]
RESP=	The name of the response variable. For a log-linear model, this is usually the frequency or cell count variable when the data is in grouped form (specify `DIST=POISSON` in this case).
MODEL=	Gives the model specification, the right-hand side of the `MODEL` statement. You can use the | and @ shorthands. For example, `MODEL = A|B|C@2` specifies a model with all main effects and 2-way interactions.
CLASS=	Specifies the names of any class variables used in the model.

DIST=	Specifies the error distribution for a generalized linear model. Any of the keywords NORMAL, BINOMIAL, POISSON, GAMMA, or IGAUSSIAN (or their abbreviations) allowed in PROC GENMOD can be used. For frequency data, DIST=POISSON should usually be specified. If you don't specify the error distribution, PROC GENMOD uses DIST=NORMAL.
LINK=	Specifies the link function to be used in the generalized linear model. The default is the canonical link for the DIST= error distribution.
MOPT=	Other options on the MODEL statement (e.g., MOPT=NOINT to fit a model without an intercept).
FREQ=	The name of a frequency variable when the data is in frequency (grouped) form.
WEIGHT=	The name of an observation weight (SCWGT) variable; used, for example, to specify structural zeros in a log-linear model.
ID=	Gives the name of a character observation ID variable that is used to label influential observations in the plots. Usually you will want to construct a character variable that combines the CLASS= variables into a compact cell identifier.
GY=	The names of variables in the OBSTATS dataset used as ordinates in the plot(s). One plot is produced for each combination of the words in GY by the words in GX. [Default: GY=DIFCHI STRESCHI]
GX=	Abscissa(s) for the plot, usually PRED or HAT. [Default: GX=HAT]
OUT=	Name of the output dataset containing the observation statistics. This is the dataset that is plotted. [Default: OUT=COOKD]
OBSTATS=	Specifies the name of the OBSTATS dataset (containing residuals and other observation statistics) for a model already fitted.
PARMEST=	Specifies the name of the PARMEST dataset (containing parameter estimates) for a model already fitted,
BUBBLE=	Gives the name of the variable to which the bubble size is proportional. [Default: BUBBLE=COOKD]
LABEL=	Determines which observations, if any, are labeled in the plots. If LABEL=NONE, no observations are labeled; if LABEL=ALL, all are labeled; if LABEL=INFL, only possibly influential points are labeled, as determined by the INFL= parameter. [Default: LABEL=INFL]
INFL=	A logical expression that specifies the criterion used to determine whether an observation is influential (when used with LABEL=INFL). Any variables in the OBSTAT dataset can be used. The value p/n is calculated and assigned to the macro variable HCRIT, which can also be used. [Default: INFL=%str(DIFCHI>4 OR HAT>&HCRIT OR &BUBBLE>1)]
LSIZE=	Observation label size. The height of other text (e.g., axis labels) is controlled by the HTEXT= graphics option. [Default: LSIZE=1.5]
LCOLOR=	Observation label color. [Default: LCOLOR=BLACK]
LPOS=	Observation label position. [Default: LPOS=5]
BSIZE=	Bubble size scale factor. [Default: BSIZE=10]
BSCALE=	Specifies whether the bubble size is proportional to AREA or RADIUS. [Default: BSCALE=AREA]
BCOLOR=	The color of the bubble symbol. [Default: BCOLOR=RED]
REFCOL=	Color of reference lines. Reference lines are drawn at nominally 'large' values for HAT values (HAT = &HCRIT) standardized residuals (0, ±2), and change in chi square values (4). [Default: REFCOL=BLACK]
REFLIN=	Line style for reference lines. Use REFLIN=0 to suppress these reference lines. [Default: REFLIN=33]
NAME=	Name of the graph in the graphic catalog. [Default: NAME=INFLGLIM]
GOUT=	Name of the graphics catalog.

A.12   The INFLOGIS Macro: Influence Plots for Logistic Regression Models

The INFLOGIS macro produces influence plots similar to the INFLGLIM macro but uses PROC LOGISTIC for a logistic regression model. The diagnostic measures are described in Section 6.6, and the macro is illustrated in Example 6.12. These plots show a measure of badness of fit for a given case (DIFDEV and/or DIFCHISQ, specified by the GY= parameter) vs. the fitted probability (PRED) and/or leverage (HAT, specified by the GX= parameter), using an influence measure (C or CBAR) as the size of a bubble symbol. One plot is produced for each combination of the GY= and GX= variables.

Usage

The INFLOGIS macro is called with keyword parameters. The Y= and X= parameters are required. The arguments can be listed within parentheses in any order, separated by commas. For example,

```
%include catdata(arthrit);
%inflogis(data=arthrit,
      y=better,
      x=_sex_ _treat_ age,
      id=case);
```

Parameters

DATA=   Specifies the name of the input dataset to be analyzed.
           [Default: DATA=_LAST_]
Y=   The name of the response variable.
TRIALS=   The name of a trials variable (when the data is in event/trials form).
X=   Names of the predictors in the model. All variables should be listed explicitly; the variable list shorthands (e.g., X1-X8) cannot be used.
ID=   Name of an observation ID variable (character or numeric). If no ID= variable is specified, the observation index number is used.
OUT=   Name of the output dataset. [Default: OUT=_DIAG_]
GY=   Ordinate(s) for plot: DIFDEV and/or DIFCHISQ. One plot is produced for each combination of GY and GX. [Default: GY=DIFDEV]
GX=   Abscissa(s) for plot: PRED and/or HAT. [Default: GX=PRED]
BUBBLE=   Gives the name of the variable to which the bubble size is proportional, one of C (Equation 6.12) or CBAR (Equation 6.13). [Default: BUBBLE=C]
LABEL=   Determines which observations, if any, are labeled in the plots. If LABEL=NONE, no observations are labeled; if LABEL=ALL, all are labeled; if LABEL=INFL, only possibly influential points are labeled.
           [Default: LABEL=INFL]
DEV=   The value of the DIFDEV or DIFCHISQ criterion used to decide whether a point is influential. [Default: DEV=4]
INFL=   A logical expression that specifies the criterion used to determine whether an observation is influential (when used with LABEL=INFL). Any variables in the OBSTAT dataset can be used. The value p/n is calculated and assigned to the dataset variable HCRIT, which can also be used.
           [Default: INFL=%str(DIFCHISQ>4 OR &BUBBLE>1)]
LSIZE=   Observation label size. The height of other text is controlled by the HTEXT= goption. [Default: LSIZE=1.5]
LCOLOR=   Observation label color. [Default: LCOLOR=BLACK]

LPOS=	Observation label position. [Default: LPOS=5]
BSIZE=	Bubble size scale factor. [Default: BSIZE=10]
BSCALE=	Bubble size proportional to AREA or RADIUS. [Default: BSCALE=AREA]
BCOLOR=	Bubble color. [Default: BCOLOR=BLACK]
REFCOL=	Color of reference lines. [Default: REFCOL=BLACK]
REFLIN=	Line style for reference lines; 0 = NONE. [Default: REFLIN=33]
LOPTIONS=	Options for PROC LOGISTIC. [Default: LOPTIONS=NOPRINT]
NAME=	Name of the graph in the graphic catalog. [Default: NAME=INFLOGIS]
GOUT=	Name of the graphics catalog.

A.13   The INTERACT Macro: Create Interaction Variables

The interact macro creates interaction variables, formed as the product of each of the variables given in one set (V1=) with each of the variables given in a second set (V2=).

Usage

The interact macro is called with keyword parameters. The arguments can be listed within parentheses in any order, separated by commas. For example,

```
%interact(v1=age sex, v2=I1 I2 I3);
```

Parameters

DATA=	The name of the input dataset. If not specified, the most recently created dataset is used.
V1=	Specifies the name(s) of the first set of variable(s).
V2=	Specifies the name(s) of the second set of variable(s).
OUT=	The name of the output dataset. If not specified, the new variables are appended to the input dataset.
PREFIX=	Prefix(s) used to create the names of interaction variables. The default is I_. The names are of the form I_11 I_12 ... I_1m I_21 I_22 ... I_nm, where there are n variables in V1 and m variables in V2.
CENTER=	If non-blank, the V1 and V2 variables are mean-centered prior to forming their interaction products.

A.14   The LAGS Macro: Lagged Frequencies for Sequential Analysis

The LAGS macro tabulates joint frequencies of events at various lags for sequential analysis. Given a variable containing event codes (character or numeric), this macro creates

- a dataset containing $n + 1$ lagged variables, _lag0–_lagN. (_lag0 is just a copy of the input event variable).
- optionally, an $(n + 1)$-way contingency table containing frequencies of all combinations of events at lag0–lagN.

Either or both of these datasets can be used for subsequent analysis of sequential dependencies. One or more BY= variables can be specified, in which case separate lags and frequencies are produced for each value of the BY variables.

Usage

Exactly one event variable must be specified with the VAR= option. All other options have default values. If one or more BY= variables are specified, lags and frequencies are calculated separately for each combination of values of the BY= variable(s).

The arguments can be listed within parentheses in any order, separated by commas. For example,

```
%lags(data=codes, var=event, nlag=2);
```

Parameters

DATA=   The name of the SAS dataset to be lagged. If DATA= is not specified, the most recently created dataset is used.

VAR=   The name of the event variable to be lagged. The variable can be either character or numeric.

BY=   The name(s) of one or more BY variables. Lags will be restarted for each level of the BY variable(s). The BY variables can be character or numeric.

VARFMT=   An optional format for the event VAR= variable. If the codes are numeric, and a format specifying what each number means is used (e.g., 1='Active' 2='Passive'), the output lag variables will be given the character values.

NLAG=   Specifies the number of lags to compute. [Default: NLAG=1]

OUTLAG=   Name of the output dataset containing the lagged variables. This dataset contains the original variables plus the lagged variables, named according to the PREFIX= option.

PREFIX=   Prefix for the name of the created lag variables. The default is PREFIX=_LAG, so the variables created are named _LAG1, _LAG2, up to _LAG&nlag. For convenience, a copy of the event variable is created as _LAG0.

FREQOPT= Options for the TABLES statement used in PROC FREQ for the frequencies of each of lag1–lagN vs lag0 (the event variable). [Default: FREQOPT= NOROW NOCOL NOPERCENT CHISQ]

Arguments pertaining to the *n*-way frequency table:

OUTFREQ= Name of the output dataset containing the *n*-way frequency table. The table is not produced if this argument is not specified.

COMPLETE= NO or ALL specifies whether the *n*-way frequency table is to be made 'complete' by filling in 0 frequencies for lag combinations that do not occur in the data. [Default: COMPLETE=ALL]

Example

Assume a series of 16 events have been coded with the three codes a, b, c, for two subjects, as follows:

```
Sub1:   c   a   a   b   a   c   a   c   b   b   a   b   a   a   b   c
Sub2:   c   c   b   b   a   c   a   c   c   a   c   b   c   b   c   c
```

and these have been entered as the two variables SEQ (subject) and CODE in the dataset CODES:

```
SEQ     CODE

1       c
1       a
1       a
1       b
....
2       c
2       c
2       b
2       b
....
```

Then, the macro call:

```
%lags(data=codes, var=code, by=seq, outfreq=freq);
```

produces the lags dataset `_lags_` for `NLAG=1` that looks like this:

```
SEQ     CODE     _LAG0     _LAG1

1       c        c
        a        a         c
        a        a         a
        b        b         a
        a        a         b
        ....

2       c        c
        c        c         c
        b        b         c
        b        b         b
        a        a         b
        ....
```

The output 2-way frequency table (`outfreq=freq`) is a $3 \times 3 \times 2$ contingency table, which looks like this:

```
SEQ     _LAG0     _LAG1     COUNT

1       a         a         2
        b         a         3
        c         a         2
        a         b         3
        b         b         1
        c         b         1
        a         c         2
        b         c         1
        c         c         0
```

2	a	a	0
	b	a	0
	c	a	3
	a	b	1
	b	b	1
	c	b	2
	a	c	2
	b	c	3
	c	c	3

A.15   The LOGODDS Macro: Plot Empirical Logits for Binary Data

For a binary response variable, Y, taking values 0 or 1, and a continuous independent variable, X, the LOGODDS macro groups the X variable into some number of ordered, non-overlapping intervals. It plots the empirical log-odds of $Y = 1$ (and/or $\Pr(Y = 1)$) against X for each interval of X, together with the fitted linear logistic relation, an optional smoothed curve (using the LOWESS macro), and the observed binary responses. These plots are described and illustrated in Section 6.2.1.

Usage

The input data to be plotted must be in case form. The LOGODDS macro is called with keyword parameters. The X= and Y= variables are required. The arguments can be listed within parentheses in any order, separated by commas. For example,

```
%include catdata(icu);
%logodds(data=icu, x=age, y=died, smooth=0.25, ncat=16,
   options=order=data);
```

Parameters

X=	Name of the continuous independent variable.
Y=	Name of the binary response variable.
EVENT=	Value of Y for the event of interest. [Default: EVENT=1]
DATA=	The name of the input dataset. [Default: DATA=_LAST_]
OPTIONS=	Options for PROC LOGISTIC—for example, OPTIONS=DESCENDING.
NCAT=	Number of categories of the X variable. For example, if deciles of X are desired, use NCAT=10. [Default: NCAT=10]
PLOT=	Scale(s) for the response. PLOT=LOGIT gives a plot on the logit scale, PLOT=PROB on the probability scale. [Default: PLOT=LOGIT PROB]
SMOOTH=	Smoothing parameter for a lowess smooth, in the interval (0−1). No smooth curve is produced unless a SMOOTH= value is specified.
SHOW=	Specifies whether to plot the binary observations. [Default: SHOW=OBS]
OBS=	Specifies how to display the binary observations. If OBS=STACK, the observations are plotted in vertical columns at the top (Y=1) or bottom (Y=0) of the plot. If OBS=JITTER, a small random quantity is added (Y=0) or subtracted (Y=1) to the Y value. [Default: OBS=STACK]
NAME=	The name of the graph in the graphic catalog. [Default: NAME=LOGODDS]
GOUT=	The name of the graphic catalog. [Default: GOUT=GSEG]

A.16 The MOSAICS Program: SAS/IML Modules for Mosaic Displays

The MOSAICS program contains the SAS/IML modules for constructing mosaic displays for an *n*-way contingency table. This graphical method is described and illustrated extensively in Chapter 4. The complete documentation and many examples are contained in the distribution archive in the directory mosaics/doc/ in PDF and PostScript formats. The latest version of the program and documentation are also available on the Web at http://www.math.yorku.ca/SCS/mosaics/mosaics.html.

Usage

The modules are typically loaded into the SAS/IML workspace with the %include statement, or with the load statement from a SAS/IML storage library. The SYMSIZE option in PROC IML is often useful for efficiency because the program is quite large.

The required inputs include the contingency table dimensions, table frequencies, the variable names, and names for the variable levels. These can be specified directly with SAS/IML statements (or read in from a SAS dataset), and the mosaics module is called as follows:

```
proc iml symsize=256;
   reset storage=mosaic.mosaic;
   load module=_all_;        *-- or, %include mosaics(mosaics);
   *-- specify data parameters;
   levels = { ... };   *-- variable levels;
   table  = { ... };   *-- contingency table;
   vnames = { ... };   *-- variable names;
   lnames = { ... };   *-- level names;

   *-- specify non-default global inputs;
   fittype='USER';
   config = { 1  1,
              2  3 };

   run mosaic(levels, table, vnames, lnames, plots, title);
```

The MOSAICS program also provides a large number of optional parameters, which are specified as global SAS/IML variables. All of these are given default values if not specified.

Required Parameters

The required parameters for the run mosaics statement are listed below. These are positional parameters and can be given any valid SAS name in the PROC IML step.

levels   A numeric vector that specifies the number of variables and the dimensions of the contingency table. If levels is $n \times 1$, then the table has n dimensions, and the number of levels of variable i is levels[i]. The order of the variables in levels is the order in which they are entered into the mosaic display.

table   A matrix or vector giving the frequency, $n_{ij...}$, of observations in each cell of the table. The table variables are arranged in accordance with the conventions of the SAS/IML IPF and MARG functions, so the **first** variable varies most rapidly across the columns of table and the last variable varies most slowly down the rows. The table must be *complete*. If you use PROC FREQ to sum a larger dataset, use the SPARSE option in the TABLES statement so that all combinations are created.

vnames	A $1 \times n$ character vector of variable (factor) names, in an order corresponding to levels.
lnames	A character matrix of labels for the variable levels, one row for each variable. The number of columns is the maximum value in levels. When the number of levels is unequal, the rows for smaller factors must be padded with blank entries.
plots	A vector containing any of the integers 1 to n that specifies the list of marginal tables to be plotted. If plots contains the value i, the marginal sub-table for variables 1 to i will be displayed. For a 3-way table, plots={1 2 3} displays each sequential plot, showing the [A], [AB] and [ABC] marginal tables; while plots=3 displays only the final 3-way [ABC] mosaic.
title	A character string or vector of strings containing title(s) for the plots. If title is a single character string, it is used as the title for all plots. Other-wise, title can be a vector of up to max(plots) strings, and title[i] is used as the tile for the plot produced when plots contains i. If the number of strings is less than max(plots), the last string is used for all remaining plots.

Global Input Variables

The following global variables are used by the program if they have been assigned values of the correct type (character or numeric). Because they all have default values, it is necessary to specify only those you want to change. All character-valued variables are case-insensitive.

Analysis Options

config	A numeric or character matrix specifying which marginal totals to fit when fittype='USER' is also specified. config is ignored for all other fit types. Each column specifies a high-order marginal in the model, either by the names of the variables or by their indices, according to their order in vnames. For example, the log-linear model $[AB][AC][BC]$ for a 3-way table is specified by the 2 by 3 matrix,

```
config = { 1  1  2,
           2  3  3};
```

or by variable names,

```
config = { A  A  B,
           B  C  C};
```

The same model can be specified more easily row-wise, and then transposed:

```
config = t( 1 2, 1 3, 2 3 );
```

devtype	A character string that specifies the type of deviations (residuals) to be represented by shading. devtype='GF' is the default. GF calculates components of Pearson goodness-of-fit chi-square; LR calculates components of the likelihood ratio (deviance) chi-square Equation 7.26. FT calculates Freeman-Tukey residuals. Appending ADJ to one of the above options causes adjusted residuals ($= d_i/\sqrt{(1 - h_i)}$, where h_i is the diagonal element of the "hat" matrix) to be calculated, e.g., Equation 7.25. Because $0 < h_i < 1$, the adjusted residuals are always larger in magnitude than the unadjusted values. The ADJ keyword increases the computation time for each model, because the design matrix

of the log-linear model must then be generated to find the h values. Nevertheless, the adjusted residuals are generally better indicants of unusual cells.

fittype   A character string that specifies the type of sequential log-linear models to fit. `fittype='JOINT'` is the default. For 2-way tables, (or 2-way margins of larger tables), all fittypes fit the independence model.

JOINT*k* specifies sequential models of joint independence, $[A][B]$, $[AB][C]$, $[ABC][D]$,... These models specify that the last variable in a given plot is independent of all previous variables jointly.
Optionally, the keyword JOINT can be followed by a digit, k, to specify which of the n ordered variables is independent of the rest jointly.

MUTUAL specifies sequential models of mutual independence, $[A][B]$, $[A][B][C]$, $[A][B][C][D]$, ...

CONDIT*k* specifies sequential models of conditional independence that hypothesize that all previous variables are independent, given the last, i.e., $[A][B]$, $[AC][BC]$, $[AD][BD][CD]$, ... For the 3-way model, A and B are hypothesized to be conditionally independent, given C; for the 4-way model, A, B, and C are conditionally independent, given D.
Optionally, the keyword CONDIT can be followed by a digit, k, to specify which of the n ordered variables is conditioned upon.

PARTIAL specifies sequential models of partial independence of the first pair of variables, conditioning on all remaining variables one at a time: $[A][B]$, $[AC][BC]$, $[ACD][BCD]$, ... For the 3-way model, A and B are hypothesized to be conditionally independent, given C; for the 4-way model, A and B are conditionally independent, given C and D.

MARKOV*k* specifies a sequential series of Markov chain models fit to the table, whose dimensions are assumed to represent discrete ordered time points, such as lags in a sequential analysis. The keyword MARKOV can be optionally followed by a digit to specify the order of the Markov chains; e.g., `fittype='MARKOV2';` specifies a second-order Markov chain. First-order is assumed if not specified. Such models assume that the table dimensions are ordered in time, e.g., Lag0, Lag1, Lag2,...

MARKOV (or MARKOV1) fits the models $[A][B]$, $[AB][BC]$, $[AB][BC][CD]$, ... where the categories at each lag are associated only with those at the previous lag. MARKOV2 fits the models $[A][B]$, $[A][B][C]$, $[ABC][BCD]$, $[ABC][BCD][CDE]$, ...

USER If `fittype='USER'`, specify the hypothesized model in the global matrix `config`. The models for plots of marginal tables are based on reducing the hypothesized configuration, eliminating all variables not participating in the current plot.

order   Specifies whether and how to perform a correspondence analysis to assist in reordering the levels of each factor variable as it is entered into the mosaic display. This analysis is not performed if `order='NONE'`. Otherwise, order can be a character vector containing either 'DEV' or 'JOINT' to specify that the CA is performed on residuals from the model for the current subtable (DEV) or on residuals from the model of joint independence for this subtable (JOINT). In addition, order can contain either 'ROW' or 'COL' or both to specify which dimensions of the current subtable are considered for reordering. The usual options for this reordering are order = {JOINT COL};
At present this analysis merely produces printed output that suggests an ordering, but it does not actually reorder the table or the mosaic display.

| zeros | A matrix of the same size and shape as the input `table` containing entries of 0 or 1, where 0 indicates that the corresponding value in `table` is to be ignored or treated as missing or a structural zero. |

Zero entries cause the corresponding cell frequency to be fitted exactly; one degree of freedom is subtracted for each such zero. The corresponding tile in the mosaic display is outlined in black.

If an entry in any marginal subtable in the order [A], [AB], [ABC] ... corresponds to an all-zero margin, that cell is treated similarly as a structural zero in the model for the corresponding subtable. Note, however, that tables with zero margins may not always have estimable models.

If the `table` contains zero frequencies that should be treated as structural zeros, assign the `zeros` matrix like this:

```
zeros = table > 0;
```

For a square table, to fit a model of quasi-independence ignoring the diagonal entries, assign the `zeros` matrix like this (assuming a 4×4 table):

```
zeros = J(4,4) - I(4);
```

Display Options

| abbrev | If `abbrev`> 0, variable names are abbreviated to that many letters in the model formula (and in the plot title if `title='&MODEL'`). |
| cellfill | Provides the ability to display a symbol in the cell representing the coded value of large residuals. This is particularly useful for black-and-white output, where it is difficult to portray both sign and magnitude distinctly. |

NONE Nothing (default)

SIGN draws + or − symbols in the cell, whose *number* corresponds to the shading density.

SIZE draws + or − symbols in the cell, whose *size* corresponds to the shading density.

DEV writes the value of the standardized residual in the cell, using format 6.1.

FREQ writes the value of the cell frequency in the cell, using format 6.0.

	If a numeric value, *min*, is also specified (e.g., `cellfill='DEV 2'`), then only cells whose residual exceeds that value in magnitude are so identified.
colors	A character vector of one or two elements specifying the colors used for positive and negative residuals. The default is {BLUE RED}. For a monochrome display, specify `colors='BLACK'` and use two distinct fill patterns for the fill type, such as `filltype={MO M45}` or `filltype={GRAY M45}`.
filltype	A character vector of one or two elements that specifies the type of fill pattern to use for shading. `filltype[1]` is used for positive residuals; `filltype[2]`, if present, is used for negative residuals. If only one value is specified, a complementary value for negative residuals is generated internally. `filltype={HLS HLS}` is the default.

M45 uses SAS/GRAPH patterns MdN135 and Md45 with hatching at 45 and 135°. d is the density value determined from the residual and the `shade` parameter.

LR uses SAS/GRAPH patterns Ld and Rd.

MO uses SAS/GRAPH patterns M*d*N0 and M*d*N90 with hatching at 0 and 90°.

GRAY*step* uses solid, greyscale fill using the patterns GRAY*nn* starting from GRAYF0 for density=1 and increasing darkness by *step* for each successive density level. The default for *step* is 16, so 'GRAY' gives GRAYF0, GRAYE0, GRAYD0, and so forth.

HLS uses solid, color-varying fill based on the HLS color scheme. The colors are selected attempting to vary the lightness in approximately equal steps. For this option, the colors values must be selected from the following hue names: RED GREEN BLUE MAGENTA CYAN YELLOW.

fuzz	A numeric value that specifies the smallest absolute residual to be considered equal to zero. Cells with $|d_{ij}| <$ fuzz are outlined in black. The default is fuzz = 0.20.
htext	A numeric value that specifies the height of text labels in character cells. The default is htext=1.3. The program attempts to avoid overlap of category labels, but this cannot always be achieved. Adjust htext (or make the labels shorter) if they collide.
legend	Orientation of legend for shading of residual values in mosaic tiles. 'V' specifies a vertical legend at the right of the display; 'H' specifies a horizontal legend beneath the display. Default: 'NONE'.
shade	A vector of up to 5 values of $|d_{ij}|$, which specify the boundaries between shading levels. If shade={2 4} (the default), then the shading density number d is

d	residuals
0	$0 \le |d_{ij}| < 2$
1	$2 \le |d_{ij}| < 4$
2	$4 \le |d_{ij}|$

Use shade= a big number to suppress all shading.

space	A vector of two values that specify the x, y percent of the plotting area reserved for spacing between the tiles of the mosaic. The default value is 10 times the number of variables allocated to each of the vertical and horizontal directions in the plot.
split	A character vector consisting of the letters V and H that specifies the directions in which the variables divide the unit square of the mosaic display. If split={H V} (the default), the mosaic alternates between horizontal and vertical splitting. If the number of elements in split is less than the maximum number in plots, the elements in split are reused cyclically.
vlabels	An integer from 0 to the number of variables in the table. It specifies that variable names (in addition to level names) are to be used to label the first vlabels variables. The default is vlabels=2, meaning variable names are used in plots of the first two variables only.

A.17 The MOSAIC Macro: Mosaic Displays

The MOSAIC macro provides an easily used macro interface to the SAS/IML modules MOSAICS (mosaic displays, with model fitting via IPF), MOSAICD (mosaic displays, with externally-calculated residuals) and MOSPART (partial mosaic displays) included in the MOSAICS package (A.16).

Using the SAS/IML programs directly means that you must compose a PROC IML step and invoke the mosaic module (or mospart). Instead, the MOSAIC macro can be used with any SAS dataset in frequency form (e.g., the output from PROC FREQ or the TABLE macro). The macro simply creates the PROC IML step, reads the input dataset, and runs either the mosaic module, the mosaicd module, or the mospart module, depending on the options specified. If your data is in case form, just use PROC FREQ first (or the TABLE macro) to construct the contingency table.

Ordinarily, the program fits a model (specified by the FITTYPE= parameter) and displays residuals from this model in the mosaic. A separate model and mosaic display are produced for each marginal subtable specified by the PLOTS= parameter.

However, if you have already fit a model and calculated residuals some other way (e.g., using PROC CATMOD or PROC GENMOD), specify a RESID= variable in the macro call. The macro will then produce the mosaic for that model (using the mosaicd module).

If a BY= variable is specified, the macro calls the mospart module, which produces one (partial) mosaic plot for each level of the BY variable(s).

The MOSAIC macro is easier to use but is not as flexible as direct use of the SAS/IML programs. The SORT macro (Appendix A.28) and the TABLE macro (Appendix A.29) were designed to ease these limitations:

- Factor levels are labeled using the values of the factor variables in the input dataset. You cannot simply attach a SAS format to a factor to convert numeric values to character labels (because SAS/IML reads variables as-is and cannot access SAS formats). However, you *can* use a DATA step to create character equivalents of numeric variables using the put() function, or use the TABLE macro with your own formats.

- You cannot reorder the factors or the levels of a factor quite as flexibly as you can in SAS/IML. If you use the SORT= parameter, take care that an ordered factor ('Low', 'Medium', 'High') is not sorted alphabetically. However, you *can* use the SORT macro to sort the dataset in any desired way.

Usage

Almost all of the parameters of the MOSAICS program have equivalents in the macro. The parameters for the MOSAIC macro are like those of the SAS/IML MOSAICS program, except:

DATA=	Specifies the name of the input dataset. The dataset should contain one observation per cell. The variables should include those listed in VAR= and COUNT=, and possibly RESID= and BY=.
VAR=	Specifies the names of the factor variables for the contingency table. Abbreviated variable lists (e.g., V1-V3) are *not* allowed. The levels of the factor variables can be character or numeric, but they are used 'as is' in the input data. You can omit the VAR= variables if variable names are used in the VORDER= parameter.
BY=	Specifies the names of one (or more) By variables. Partial mosaic plots are produced for each combination of the levels of the BY= variables. The BY= variable(s) *must* be listed among the VAR= variables.
COUNT=	Specifies the name of the frequency variable in the dataset.
CONFIG=	For a user-specified model, CONFIG= gives the terms in the model, separated by '/'. For example, to fit the model of no-3-way association, specify

```
config=1 2 / 1 3 / 2 3
```

or (using variable names)

```
config = A B / A C / B C
```

Note that the numbers in the configuration refer to the variables after they have been reordered, either by sorting the dataset or by specifying the VORDER= parameter.

VORDER=   Specifies either the names of the variables or their indices in the desired order in the mosaic. Note that using the VORDER= parameter keeps the factor levels in their order in the input dataset.

SORT=   Specifies whether and how the input dataset is to be sorted to produce the desired order of variables in the mosaic. SORT=YES sorts the data in the reverse order that it is listed in the VAR= paraemter, so that the variables are entered in the order given in the VAR= parameter. Otherwise, SORT= lists the variable names, possibly with the DESENDING or NOTSORTED options, in the reverse of the desired order, e.g., SORT=C DESCENDING B DESCENDING A. The default is SORT=YES, unless VORDER= has been specified; in the latter case, the default is SORT=NO.

RESID=   Specifies that a model has already been fit and that externally calculated residuals are contained in the variable named by the RESID= parameter.

A.18   The MOSMAT Macro: Mosaic Matrices

The MOSMAT macro provides an easily used macro interface to the MOSAICS and MOSMAT SAS/IML programs to create a scatterplot matrix of mosaic displays for all pairs of categorical variables, as illustrated in Section 4.4.

Each pairwise plot shows the marginal frequencies to the order specified by the PLOTS= parameter. When PLOTS=2, these are the bivariate margins, and the residuals from marginal independence are shown by shading. When PLOTS>2, the observed frequencies in a higher-order marginal table are displayed, and the model fit to that marginal table is determined by the FITTYPE= parameter.

Usage

The parameters for the MOSMAT macro are like those of the SAS/IML MOSAICS program, except the following:

DATA=   Specifies the name of the input dataset. This dataset should contain one observation per cell, the variables listed in VAR= and COUNT=. [Default: DATA=_LAST_]

VAR=   Specifies the names of the factor variables for the contingency table. Abbreviated variable lists (e.g., V1–V3) are not allowed. The levels of the factor variables can be character or numeric, but they are used as-is in the input data. Upper/lower case in the variable names is respected in the diagonal label panels. You can omit the VAR= variables if variable names are used in the VORDER= parameter.

COUNT=   Specifies the name of the frequency variable in the dataset. The COUNT= variable must be specified.

PLOTS=   The PLOTS= parameter determines the number of table variables displayed in each pairwise mosaic. [Default: PLOTS=2]

CONFIG=	For a user-specified model, config= gives the terms in the model, separated by '/'. For example, to fit the model of no-3-way association, specify CONFIG=1 2 / 1 3 / 2 3, or (using variable names) CONFIG = A B / A C / B C. Note that the numbers refer to the variables after they have been reordered, either by sorting the dataset or by specifying the VORDER= parameter.
VORDER=	Specifies either the names of the variables or their indices in the desired order in the mosaic. Note that using the VORDER= parameter keeps the factor levels in their order in the data.
SORT=	Specifies whether and how the input dataset is to be sorted to produce the desired order of variables in the mosaic. SORT=YES sorts the data in the reverse order that it is listed in the VAR= parameter, so that the variables are entered in the order given in the VAR= parameter. Otherwise, SORT= lists the variable names, possibly with the DESCENDING or NOTSORTED option in the reverse of the desired order. e.g., SORT=C DESCENDING B DESCENDING A.

A.19 The ORDPLOT Macro: Ord Plot for Discrete Distributions

The ORDPLOT macro constructs a plot whose slope and intercept can diagnose the form of a discrete frequency distribution, as described in Section 2.4. This is a plot of $k n_k / n_{k-1}$ against k, where k is the basic count and n_k is the frequency of occurrence of k. The macro displays both a weighted and unweighted least squares line and uses the slope and intercept of the weighted line to determine the form of the distribution. Rough estimates of the parameters of the distribution are also computed from the slope and intercept.

Usage

The ORDPLOT macro is called with keyword parameters. The COUNT= and FREQ= variables are required. The arguments can be listed within parentheses in any order, separated by commas. For example,

```
%include catdata(vonbort);   *-- creates horskick data set;
%ordplot(data=horskick, count=Deaths, freq=corpsyrs);
```

Parameters

DATA=	Name of the input dataset. [Default: DATA=_LAST_]
COUNT=	The name of the basic count variable.
FREQ=	The name of the variable giving the number of occurrences of the COUNT= variable.
LABEL=	Label for the horizontal (COUNT=) variable. If not specified the variable label for the COUNT= variable in the input dataset is used.
LEGLOC=	*X, Y* location (in screen percent) for interpretive legend. [Default: LEGLOC=3 88]
LEGCLR=	Legend color. [Default: LEGCLR=RED]
OUT=	The name of the output dataset. [Default: OUT=ORDPLOT]
NAME=	Name of the graphics catalog entry. [Default: NAME=ORDPLOT]

A.20 The PANELS Macro: Arrange Multiple Plots in Panels

The PANELS macro constructs a template in which to replay a series of graphs, assumed all the same size, in a rectangular array of *R* rows and *C* columns. By default, the panels are displayed left-to-right across rows, starting either from the top (ORDER=DOWN) or bottom (ORDER=UP). If the number of rows and columns are unequal, the aspect ratio of individual panels can be maintained by setting EQUATE=Y. It is assumed that all the plots have already been created and stored in a graphics catalog (the default, WORK.GSEG, is used automatically by SAS/GRAPH procedures).

For interactive use within the SAS Session Manager, you should be aware that all plots are stored cumulatively in the graphics catalog throughout your session, unless explicitly changed with the GOUT= option in graphics procedures or macros. To create multiple paneled plots, you can use the FIRST= and LAST= parameters or a REPLAY= list to specify which plots are used in a given call.

Usage

Call the PANELS macro after the steps that create the graphs in the graphics catalog. The GDISPLA macro (A.31.3) can be used to suppress the display of the original full-sized graphs as they are generated. The ROWS= and COLS= parameters must be specified. For example,

```
goptions hsize=7in vsize=5in;
%gdispla(OFF);
proc gplot data=mydata;
   plot y * x = group;
   by sex;

%gdispla(ON);
%panels(rows=1, cols=2);
```

Parameters

ROWS=

COLS= The ROWS= and COLS= arguments are required, and they specify the size of the array of plots to be displayed. These are the only required arguments.

PLOTS= If there are fewer than &ROWS*&COLS plots, specify the number as the PLOTS= argument. Optionally, there can be an additional plot, which is displayed (as a GSLIDE title, for example) in the top nn% of the display, as specified by the TOP= argument.

TOP= If TOP=nn is specified, the top nn% of the display is reserved for one additional panel (of width 100%), to serve as the plot title or annotation.

ORDER= The ORDER= argument specifies the order of the panels in the REPLAY= list when REPLAY= is not specified. Typically, the panels are displayed across the columns. ORDER=UP means that the panels in the bottom row are drawn first and numbered 1, 2,..., &COLS. ORDER=DOWN means that the panels in the top row are drawn first and numbered 1, 2,..., &COLS.

If you add the keyword BYROWS to ORDER=, the panels are displayed up or down the rows. For example, when ROWS=3, and COLS=5, ORDER=DOWN BYROWS generates the REPLAY= list as

```
replay=1:1  2:4  3:7  4:10  5:13
       6:2  7:5  8:8  9:11 10:14
      11:3 12:6 13:9 14:12 15:15
```

EQUATE=	The EQUATE= argument determines if the size of the panels is adjusted so that the aspect ratio of the plots is preserved. If EQUATE=Y, the size of each plot is adjusted to the maximum of &ROWS and &COLS. This is usually desired, as long as the graphic options HSIZE and VSIZE are the same when the plots are replayed in the panels template as when they were originally generated. [Default: EQUATE=Y]
REPLAY=	The REPLAY= argument specifies the list of plots to be replayed in the constructed template, in one of the forms used with the PROC GREPLAY REPLAY statement, for example, REPLAY=1:1 2:3 3:2 4:4 or REPLAY=1:plot1 2:plot3 3:plot2 4:plot4.
TEMPLATE=	The name of the template constructed to display the plots. [Default: TEMPLATE=PANEL&ROWS.&COLS]
TC=	The name of the template catalog used to store the template. You can use a two-part SAS dataset name to save the template permanently.
FIRST=	By default, the REPLAY= argument is constructed to replay plot *i* in panel *i*. If the REPLAY= argument is not specified, you can override this default assignment by specifying FIRST= the sequential number of the first graph in the graphics catalog to plot (default: FIRST=1), where:

> 0 A positive integer means the absolute number of the first graph in the input catalog to be replayed. For example, FIRST=3 starts with the third graph.

$\leq$ 0 An integer less than 1 means the number of first graph relative to last graph in the input catalog (i.e. FIRST=0 means last graph only, FIRST=-1 means the first is the one before last, etc.).

LAST=	The LAST= parameter can be used to specify the number of the last graph in the input graphics catalog to be replayed. The default is LAST=0, which refers to the last plot in the graphics catalog. The LAST= value is interpreted as follows:

> 0 A positive integer means the absolute number of last graph in the input catalog to be replayed. For example, LAST=4 ends with the fourth graph.

$\leq$ 0 An integer less than 1 means the number of last graph relative to last graph in the input catalog (i.e. LAST=0 means last graph only, LAST=-1 means to end with the one before last, etc.).

GIN=	Specifies the name of the input graphics catalog from which the plots to be replayed are taken. [Default: GIN=WORK.GSEG]
GOUT=	Specifies the name of the graphics catalog in which the paneled plot is stored. [Default: GOUT=WORK.GSEG]

A.21 The POISPLOT Macro: Poissonness Plot

The POISPLOT macro constructs a "Poissonness plot" for determining if discrete data follows the Poisson distribution, as described and illustrated in Section 2.5. When the data follows a Poisson distribution, the plot has a linear relation between the count metameter $n_{(k)}$ and the basic count, k. An influence plot displays the effect of each observed frequency on the choice of the Poisson parameter, λ. The DISTPLOT macro (A.6) generalizes these displays to other discrete distributions.

Usage

The POISPLOT macro is called with keyword parameters. The COUNT= and FREQ= parameters are required. The arguments can be listed within parentheses in any order, separated by commas. For example,

```
data horskick;
    input deaths corpsyrs;
    label deaths='Number of Deaths'
        corpsyrs='Number of Corps-Years';
datalines;
      0    109
      1     65
      2     22
      3      3
      4      1
;
%poisplot(count=Deaths,freq=corpsyrs, plot=dist);
```

Parameters

DATA=	The name of the input dataset. [Default: DATA=_LAST_]
COUNT=	The name of the basic count variable.
FREQ=	The name of the variable giving the number of occurrences of COUNT.
LABEL=	Label for the horizontal (COUNT=) variable. If not specified the variable label for the COUNT= variable in the input dataset is used.
LAMBDA=	Trial value of the Poisson parameter λ to level the plot. If LAMBDA=0 (the default) the plot is not leveled.
Z=	Multiplier for error bars. [Default: Z=1.96]
PLOT=	What to plot: DIST and/or INFL. [Default: PLOT=DIST INFL]
HTEXT=	Height of text labels. [Default: HTEXT=1.4]
OUT=	The name of the output dataset. [Default: OUT=POISPLOT]
NAME=	Name of the graphics catalog entry. [Default: NAME=POISPLT]

A.22   The POWERLOG Macro: Power Analysis for Logistic Regression Table

The POWERLOG macro calculates sample size required to achieve given power values for a logistic regression model with one or more quantitative predictors, as described in Section 6.9. Results are displayed as a table of sample sizes required for a range of power values and as a graph.

Usage

The POWERLOG macro is called with keyword parameters. The arguments can be listed within parentheses in any order, separated by commas. You must supply either

- an input dataset containing the variables P1, P2, ALPHA, POWER, and RSQ (one observation for each combination for which power is desired)
- the macro parameters P1= and P2=

For example,

```
%powerlog(p1=.08, p2=%str(.16, .24));
```

Parameters

DATA=	Specifies the name of an input dataset containing the variables P1, P2, AL-PHA, POWER, and RSQ in all combinations for which power is desired. If an input DATA= dataset is specified, the program ignores values for the P1=, P2=, ALPHA=, POWER=, and RSQ= parameters.
P1=	The estimated probability of the event at the mean value of the quantitative predictor.
P2=	The estimated probability of the event at an X-value equal to the X-mean plus one standard deviation. You can specify a list of values separated by commas, a range of the form x TO y BY z, or a combination of these. However, you must surround the P2= value with %STR() if any commas appear in it. For example,

```
p2=.10 to .30 by .05
p2=%str(.10, .13, .20)
```

ALPHA=	The desired Type I error probability for a *one-sided* test of $H_0 : \beta(x) = 0$.
POWER=	The desired power of the test.
RSQ=	The squared multiple correlation of the predictor with all other predictors. Use RSQ=0 for a 1-predictor model.
PLOT=	A specification for plotting the results. The default is PLOT=N * POWER=RSQ. No plots are produced if PLOT= is blank.
PLOTBY=	Another variable in the OUT= dataset.
OUT=	Specifies the name of the output dataset.

Example

Assume we are modeling the relation of the probability of heart disease on X = cholesterol. If previous studies suggest that heart disease occurs with P1=0.08 at the mean level of cholesterol, what is the sample size required to detect a 50% increase (P2 = 1.5*.08 = .12), or an 87.5% increase (P2 = 1.875*.08 = .15) in the probability of heart disease, when cholesterol increases by one standard deviation?

If age is another predictor, how does sample size vary with the RSQ between cholesterol and age? These questions are answered with the following macro call:

```
%powerlog(p1=.08, p2=%str(.12, .15), rsq=%str(.2, .4) );
```

A.23   The POWERRxC Macro: Power for 2-Way Frequency Tables

The POWERRXC macro computes approximate power for Pearson and Likelihood Ratio χ^2 tests of independence in 2-way tables. When power is calculated for a range of sample sizes, the macro can produce a plot of power against sample size.

Usage

The `POWERRXC` macro takes 10 keyword arguments. The `ROW=` and `COL=` variables must be specified. You must also specify the `COUNT=` variable when the data is in frequency form.

Parameters

`DATA=`	The name of the input dataset. [Default: `DATA=_last_`]
`ROW=`	Specifies the variable defining the rows of the table.
`COL=`	Specifies the variable defining the columns of the table.
`COUNT=`	The variable of frequency counts, if the input data is cell counts of a contingency table in frequency form. If not specified, the input data is considered to be raw data in case form.
`LEVEL=`	The significance level (α) of the test of independence. [Default: `LEVEL=.05`]
`ALPHA=`	Synonym for `LEVEL`. [Default: `ALPHA=&LEVEL`]
`NRANGE=`	The sample size or range of sample sizes for which power is desired. If not specified, the actual sample size is used. For example: `nrange=20 to 200 by 20`, or `nrange=%str(20, 50 to 100 by 10)`. Note that `%STR()` should be used when commas appear in your range specification.
`PLOT=`	[Default: `PLOT=POWERP * N`]
`FREQOPT=`	Specifies options for `PROC FREQ`. [Default: `FREQOPT=NOROW NOCOL NOPERCENT`]
`OUT=`	The name of the output dataset. [Default: `OUT=_POWER_`]

A.24   The POWER2x2 Macro: Power for 2 × 2 Frequency Tables

The `POWER2X2` macro computes the power of a test comparing proportions from two equal-sized, independent samples. Power is calculated for various sizes of the total sample, or the required sample size is calculated for various power values, allowing you to pick the sample size that achieves the desired power.

Usage

The `POWER2X2` macro takes nine keyword arguments. You must supply the `DIFF=` parameter. By default the macro computes power for a range of sample sizes (given by `NMIN=` and `NMAX=`). Alternatively, you can specify a range of power values (given by `POWER=`) for which the required sample size is calculated.

Parameters

`P1=`	Specifies an estimate of the "success" rate in one group, the baseline group. [Default: `P1=.50`]
`DIFF=`	Specifies the difference in the proportions that you want to detect. This is the specification of the alternative hypothesis at which power is computed. The difference *must* be specified; there is *no* default. You can specify a list of values separated by commas, a range of the form x `TO` y `BY` z, or a combination of these. However, you must surround the `DIFF=` value with `%STR()` if any commas appear in it. For example,

```
diff=.10 to .30 by .05
diff=%str(.10, .13, .20)
```

ALPHA=	Specifies the significance level or size of the test. It is a decimal value less that 1. For example, ALPHA=.05 sets the probability of a Type 1 error at 0.05. You can specify a single value, or a list of values separated by commas, or a range of the form x TO y by z. [Default: ALPHA=.05]
POWER=	Values of power for sample size calculation. You can specify a list of values separated by commas, a range of the form x TO y by z, or a combination of these, as in a DO statement. However, you must surround the POWER= value with %STR() if any commas appear in it.
NMIN=	Specifies the minimum total sample size at which power will be computed. [Default: NMIN=10]
NMAX=200	Specifies the minimum total sample size at which power will be computed. [Default: NMAX=200] To get power for a single total sample size, set NMIN and NMAX to half of the total sample size.
PLOT=	A specification for plotting the results, in the form Y * X or Y * X = Z, where X, Y, and Z can be any of the variables N, DIFF, P2, POWER or OR. No plots are produced if PLOT= is blank. [Default: PLOT=POWER * N= DIFF]
PLOTBY=	Another variable in the OUT= dataset. Separate plots are drawn for each level of the PLOTBY= variable.
OUT=	The name of the output dataset. [Default: OUT=_POWER_]

Example

```
%power2x2( p1=.6,  diff=.10 to .20 by .05,  nmin=50);
```

With the settings above, the expected baseline success rate is 60%. Power for detecting a difference of 10–20% in the two proportions will be computed for a .05 level test and for sample sizes ranging from 50 to 200.

Details

Hypotheses in the test are

$$H_0 : p_1 = p_2$$
$$H_a : p_1 \neq p_2$$

where p_1 and p_2 are the success probabilities in the two populations. The Pearson chi-square statistic tests the null hypothesis (H_0) against the alternative hypothesis (H_a) and is available in the FREQ procedure when the CHISQ option is specified on the TABLES statement.

The power is the probability of rejecting H_0 and is a function of the true difference in proportions. Power is often computed assuming many different settings of the true proportions. The type 2 error rate (denoted β) is the probability of accepting H_0 for some non-zero true difference and is equal to 1-power. The power and β are computed for a range of total sample sizes at a particular alternative hypothesis that you specify. It is assumed that the total sample size will be split equally between the two samples.

A.25 The ROBUST Macro: Robust Fitting for Linear Models

The ROBUST macro uses iteratively reweighted least squares to fit linear models by M-estimation. The weights are determined by the BISQUARE, HUBER, LAV or OLS function. The fitting procedure can be PROC REG, PROC GLM or PROC LOGISTIC.

Usage

The ROBUST macro is called with keyword parameters. The RESPONSE= and MODEL= parameters are required. The arguments can be listed within parentheses in any order, separated by commas. For example,

```
%include catdata(icu);
%robust(data=icu, response=died, model=age cancer uncons admit,
    proc=logistic, id=id, iter=3);
```

Parameters

DATA=   The name of the input dataset. [Default: DATA=_LAST_]
RESPONSE=   The name of the response variable in the model.
MODEL=   The right-hand-side of the MODEL statement.
PROC=   The name of the estimation procedure to be used, one of REG, GLM, or LOGISTIC. [Default: PROC=LOGISTIC]
CLASS=   The names of any CLASS variables in the MODEL (for GLM only).
ID=   The names of any observation ID variables. These are simply copied to the OUT= dataset.
OUT=   The name of the output dataset of observation statistics. [Default: OUT=RESIDS]
OUTPARM=   The name of the output dataset of parameter estimates on the final iteration.
FUNCTION=   Weight function, one of HUBER, LAV (least absolute value), BISQUARE, or OLS. [Default: FUNCTION=BISQUARE]
TUNE=   Tuning constant for BISQUARE or HUBER. The weighting function is applied to the value _RESID_ / (&TUNE * MAD) where MAD is the median absolute value of the residuals. The default is TUNE=6 for the BISQUARE function, and TUNE=2 for the HUBER function.
ITER=   The maximum number of iterations. [Default: ITER=10]
CONVERGE=   The maximum change in observation weights for convergence. The value must have a leading 0. [Default: CONVERGE=0.05]
PRINT=   Controls printing of intermediate and final results. [Default: PRINT=NOPRINT]

A.26 The ROOTGRAM Macro: Hanging Rootograms

The ROOTGRAM macro produces histograms, rootograms, and hanging rootograms for the distribution of a discrete variable compared with expected frequencies according to a theoretical distribution. The use of the macro is illustrated in Section 2.3.3.

Usage

The VAR= and OBS= variables must be specified. The expected frequencies can be obtained with the GOODFIT macro (A.9).

The ROOTGRAM macro is called with keyword parameters. The arguments can be listed within parentheses in any order, separated by commas. For example,

```
%include catdata(madison);
%goodfit(data=madison, var=count, freq=blocks, dist=poisson);
%rootgram(data=fit, var=count, obs=blocks);
```

Parameters

DATA=	Specifies the name of the input dataset. [Default: DATA=_LAST_]
VAR=	Specifies the name of the analysis variable, used as the abscissa in the plot.
OBS=	Specifies the name of the observed frequency variable.
EXP=	Specifies the name of the expected or fitted frequency variable. [Default: EXP=EXP]
FUNC=	The name of the function applied to ordinate. Use FUNC=NONE to give a plot on the scale of observed frequency, or FUNC=SQRT for a rootogram. [Default: FUNC=SQRT]
BWIDTH=	Bar width, in data units. [Default: BWIDTH=.5]
BCOLOR=	Bar color. [Default: BCOLOR=GRAYB0]
BTYPE=	Bar type: One of HANG (bars hanging from the fitted frequency curve), DEV (bars showing observed−expected deviations), or NEEDLE (bars showing observed frequencies). [Default: BTYPE=HANG]
ANNO=	The name of an input Annotate dataset.
NAME=	Name of the graphics catalog entry.

A.27   The SIEVE Program: Sieve Diagrams

The SIEVE program is a collection of SAS/IML modules for drawing sieve (or parquet) diagrams for a 2-way contingency table, as described in Section 3.5.

Usage

The modules are typically loaded into the SAS/IML workspace with the %include statement. The required input parameters are specified with SAS/IML statements, and the sieve module is called as follows:

```
proc iml;
   %include iml(sieve);
 *-- specify required parameters;
   table  = { ... };   *-- contingency table;
   vnames = { ... };   *-- variable names;
   lnames = { ... };   *-- level names;
   title  = " ...";      *-- plot title
   run sieve( table, vnames, lnames, title );
```

Several options can be specified through global input variables.

Required Parameters

The required parameters for the `run sieve` statement are listed below. These are positional parameters and can be given any valid SAS name in the `PROC IML` step.

table
: A numeric matrix of r rows and c columns containing the contingency table to be displayed.

vnames
: A character vector of two elements, containing the names of the row and column variables.

lnames
: A character matrix of size $2 \times \max(r, c)$ containing the names of the row categories in the first row and column categories in the second row. If $r \neq c$, the shorter row must be filled in with blank character strings.

title
: A character string containing the title for the plot.

Global Input Variables

The following global variables are used by the program if they have been assigned values of the correct type (character or numeric). Because they all have default values, it is only necessary to specify those you want to change. All character-valued variables are case-insensitive.

filltype
: A character string that provides options for filling each cell in the sieve diagram. Possible values are

OBS	Fill cells in proportion to observed frequencies
OBSP	Like OBS, but also write observed frequency in the cell
DEV	Fill cells in proportion to the deviation from independence
EXL	No fill, write expected frequency in cell
EXL	Fills cells in proportion to the expected frequency, write expected frequency in cell

margins
: A character string, which specifies whether the marginal totals for the row and column variables are drawn in the sieve diagram.

  `''` margins are not drawn

  `TOTALS` the row/col totals in margins

font
: Font for text.

colors
: Names of two colors to use for the positive and negative residuals. [Default: `colors={BLUE RED}`]

A.28   The SORT Macro: Sort a Dataset by the Value of a Statistic

The `SORT` macro generalizes the idea of sorting the observations in a dataset to include

- sorting according to the values of a user-specified format. With appropriate user-defined formats, this can be used to arrange the observations in a dataset in any desired order.
- reordering according to the values of a summary statistic computed on the values in each of several groups—for example, the mean or median of an analysis variable.

Usage

You must specify one or more BY= variables. To sort by the value of a statistic, specify the name of the statistic with the BYSTAT= parameter, and specify the analysis variable with VAR=. To sort by formatted values, specify the variable names and associated formats with BYFMT=. If neither the BYSTAT= or BYFMT= parameter is specified, an ordinary sort is performed.

The SORT macro is called with keyword parameters. The arguments can be listed within parentheses in any order, separated by commas. For example,

```
%sort(by=age sex, bystat=mean, var=income);
```

  or

```
proc format;
    value age   0='Child' 1='Adult';
%sort(by=age decending sex,  byfmt=age:age.);
```

Parameters

DATA=   Name of the input dataset to be sorted. The default is the most recently created dataset.

VAR=   Specifies the name of the analysis variable used for BYSTAT sorting.

OUT=   Name of the output dataset. If not specified, the output dataset replaces the input dataset.

BY=   Names of one or more classification (factor, grouping) variables to be used in sorting. The BY= argument can contain the keyword DESCENDING before a variable name for ordinary or formatted-value sorting. For BYSTAT sorting, use ORDER=DESCENDING. The BY= variables can be character or numeric.

BYFMT=   A list of one or more terms, of the form, VAR:FMT or VAR=FMT, where VAR is one of the BY= variables, and FMT is a SAS format. Do not specify BYSTAT= when sorting by formatted values.

VAR=   Name of the analysis variable to be used in determining the sorted order.

BYSTAT=   Name of the statistic, calculated for the VAR= variable for each level of the BY= variables. The BYSTAT= value can be the name of any statistic computed by PROC UNIVARIATE.

FREQ=   For BYSTAT sorting, specify the name of a frequency variable if the input data consists of grouped frequency counts.

ORDER=   Specify ORDER=DESCENDING to sort in descending order when sorting by a BYSTAT. The ORDER= parameter applies to all BY= variables in this case.

Example

Given a frequency table of Faculty by Income, sort the faculties so they are arranged by mean income:

```
%sort(data=salary, by=Faculty, bystat=mean, var=income, freq=count);
```

A.29 The TABLE Macro: Construct a Grouped Frequency Table, with Recoding

The TABLE macro constructs a grouped frequency table suitable for input to the MOSAIC macro or the MOSMAT macro. The input data can be individual observations or a contingency table, which can be collapsed to fewer variables. Numeric factor variables can be converted to character using user-supplied formats.

Usage

The TABLE macro takes seven keyword arguments. The VAR= parameter is required. When the input dataset is already in frequency form, you must also specify the WEIGHT= parameter.

Parameters

DATA=   The name of the input dataset. [Default: DATA=_LAST_]

VAR=   Names of all factor (classification) variables to be included in the output dataset. The observations are summed over any other factors, weighted by the WEIGHT= variable, if any.

CHAR=   If WEIGHT is non-blank, this forces the VAR= variables to be converted to character variables (using formatted values) in the output dataset. If CHAR= a numeric value (e.g., CHAR=8), it specifies the length of each character variable; otherwise, the character variables default to length 16.

WEIGHT=   The name of a frequency variable, if the input dataset is already in frequency form. If not specified, each observation is assumed to be one case.

ORDER=   Specifies the order of the variable levels used in the PROC FREQ step. The valid option values are INTERNAL, FREQ, DATA, and FORMATTED.

FORMAT=   A list of variable(s), format pairs (suitable for a FORMAT statement). The FORMAT= option can be used to recode the values of any of the VAR= variables.

OUT=   The name of the output dataset. The variables in the output dataset are the VAR= variables, plus COUNT, the frequency variable for each cell. [Default: OUT=TABLE]

Limitations

None of the factor variables can be named COUNT.

Example

This example reads a 3-way frequency table (Gender x Admit x Dept), where admit and dept are numeric variables, and collapses it (over Dept) to a 2-way table, with gender and admit as character variables. The option order=data keeps the factor level values in the order encountered in the input data.

```
%include catdata(berkeley);
%table(data=berkeley, var=gender admit, weight=freq, char=Y,
       format=admit admit. gender $sex., order=data, out=berk2);
%mosaic(data=berk2, var=Gender Admit);
```

The formats `admit.` and `$sex.` are created with `PROC FORMAT`:

```
proc format;
   value admit  1="Admitted" 0="Rejected";
   value $sex  'M'='Male'   'F'='Female';
```

A.30   The TRIPLOT Macro: Trilinear Plots for *n* × 3 Tables

The `TRIPLOT` macro plots three variables (rows of an *n* × 3 table) in an equilateral triangle, so that each point represents the proportions of each variable to the total for that observation. These plots are described and illustrated in Section 3.8.

Usage

The `TRIPLOT` macro is called with keyword parameters. The names of three variables must be given in the `VAR=` parameter. The arguments can be listed within parentheses in any order, separated by commas. For example, Figure 3.18 was produced using

```
data tridemo;
   input A B C point $12.;
   label point='Point';
datalines;
40 30 30  (40,30,30)
20 60 20  (20,60,20)
10 10 80  (10,10,80)
;
%triplot(var=A B C, class=Point, id=point, gridby=25,
   symbols=dot dot dot, idht=1.6, axes=bot,
   symht=4, gridclr=gray);
```

Parameters

DATA=	The name of dataset to be plotted. [Default: DATA=_LAST_]
VAR=	The names of three variables used as the axes in the plot. The values of each observation are normally all non-negative. Missing values are treated as 0.
CLASS=	The name of a class variable determining plotting symbol. Different values of the CLASS= variable are represented by the values in the COLORS= and SYMBOLS= lists, used sequentially.
ID=	The name of an observation identifier (label) variable.
BY=	The name of a BY variable. If specified, a separate plot is produced for each level of the BY variable.
WHERE=	A WHERE-clause to subset observations to be plotted.
IDHT=	Height of ID label. [Default: IDHT=2]
IDCLR=	Color of ID label. [Default: IDCLR='BLACK']
IDPOS=	Position of ID label. [Default: IDPOS=8]
IDSUBSET=	A SAS expression (which can use any dataset variables) used to subset ID labels. If an ID= variable is given and the IDSUBSET= expression evaluates to non-zero, the observation is labeled in the plot. [Default: IDSUBSET=1]

INTERP=	Interpolation between points, a SYMBOL statement option. If INTERP=JOIN, points within the same CLASS= value are connected by lines. Most other SYMBOL statement interpolation options would give bizare results. [Default: INTERP=NONE]
SYMHT=	Height of point symbols. [Default: SYMHT=2]
SYMBOLS=	A list of one or more symbols for points, corresponding to the levels of the CLASS= variable. The symbols are reused cyclically if there are more class levels than symbols. [Default: SYMBOLS=DOT CIRCLE SQUARE $: TRIANGLE = X _ Y]
COLORS=	A list of one or more colors for points, corresponding to the levels of the CLASS= variable. The colors are also reused cyclically as required. [Default: COLORS=BLACK RED BLUE GREEN BROWN ORANGE PURPLE YELLOW]
BACKCLR=	Background color inside the trilinear plot. [Default: BACKCLR=WHITE]
BACKPAT=	Background fill pattern. For a plot with a light gray background—for example, specify BACKPAT=SOLID and BACKCLR=GRAYD0. [Default: BACKPAT=EMPTY]
GRIDBY=	Grid line interval. For grid lines at 25, 50, and 75%—for example, specify GRIDBY=25. [Default: GRIDBY=20]
GRIDCLR=	Grid line color. [Default: GRIDCLR=GRAY]
GRIDLINE=	Style of grid lines. [Default: GRIDLINE=34]
AXES=	Type of axes, one of NONE, FULL, TOP, or BOT. AXES=NONE draws no coordinate axes; AXES=FULL draws a line from 0 to 100% for each of the three coordinates; AXES=TOP draws a line from the apex to the centroid only; AXES=BOT draws a line from the centroid to the base only. [Default: AXES=NONE]
AXISCLR=	Color of axis lines. [Default: AXISCLR=BLUE]
AXISLINE=	Style of axis lines. [Default: AXISLINE=1]
XOFF=	X offset, in %, for adjusting the plot. [Default: XOFF=2]
XSCALE=	X scale factor for adjusting the plot. Before plotting the X coordinates are adjusted by X = XOFF + XSCALE * X. [Default: XSCALE=.96]
YOFF=	X offset, in %, for adjusting the plot. [Default: YOFF=2]
YSCALE=	Y scale factor for adjusting the plot. Before plotting the Y coordinates are adjusted by Y = YOFF + YSCALE * Y. [Default: YSCALE=.96]
LEGEND=	The name of SAS/GRAPH legend statement or 'NONE'. If LEGEND= is not specified and there is more than one group defined by a CLASS= variable, a legend statement is constructed internally. If LEGEND=NONE, no legend is drawn; otherwise, the LEGEND= value is used as the name of a legend statement.
LABHT=	Height of variable labels, in GUNITs. [Default: LABHT=2]
LABLOC=	Location of variable label: 0 or 100. [Default: LABLOC=100]
NAME=	Name of the graphics catalog entry. [Default: NAME=TRIPLT]

A.31   Utility Macros

A.31.1   BARS: Create an Annotate Dataset to Draw Error Bars

The BARS macro creates an Annotate dataset to draw vertical or horizontal error bars in a plot produced with PROC GPLOT. That is, the error bars can be drawn for a response variable displayed on the Y axis or on the X axis. The other (CLASS=) variable can be character or numeric.

Usage

The BARS macro is called with keyword parameters. The VAR= and CLASS= variables must both be specified. The length of the error bars should be specified with either the BARLEN= parameter or the LOWER= and UPPER= parameters.

The arguments can be listed within parentheses in any order, separated by commas. For example,

```
%bars(class=age, var=logodds, lower=lower, upper=upper);
proc gplot data=mydata;
   plot logodds * age / anno=_bars_;
```

Parameters

DATA=	Name of the input dataset. [Default: DATA=_LAST_]
VAR=	Name of the response variable, to be plotted on the axis given by the BAXIS= parameter.
CLASS=	Name of the independent variable, plotted on the other axis.
CVAR=	Name of a curve variable, when PROC GPLOT is used with the statement PLOT &VAR * &CLASS = &CVAR.
BY=	Name of a BY variable for multiple plots, when PROC GPLOT is used with the statement BY &BY;.
BAXIS=	One of X or Y, indicating the response variable axis along which error bars are drawn. [Default: BAXIS=Y]
BARLEN=	The name of a numeric variable or a numeric constant giving the error bar length. Use the name of a variable when the input dataset contains a standard error variable or multiple thereof. If BARLEN= is given, the LOWER= and UPPER= values are ignored, and error bars are drawn at the values &VAR +- &Z * &BARLEN.
Z=	A numeric value giving the multiplier of the BARLEN= value used to determine the lower and upper error bar values.
LOWER=	A numeric variable or constant giving the lower error bar value. Use the LOWER= and UPPER= parameters if the error bars are non-symmetric or if the lower and upper values are contained as separate variables in the input dataset.
UPPER=	A numeric variable or constant giving the upper error bar value.
TYPE=	Type of error bars to be drawn: one of UPPER, LOWER, or BOTH and possibly one of ALT or ALTBY. TYPE=LOWER draws only the lower error bars; TYPE=UPPER draws only the upper error bars; TYPE=BOTH draws both upper and lower error bars. Use TYPE=ALT BOTH to have the error bars alternate (lower, upper) over observations in the input dataset; use TYPE=ALTBY BOTH to have the error bars alternate over values of the BY= variable. [Default: TYPE=BOTH]
SYMBOL=	The plotting symbol, drawn at (&CLASS, &VAR). If not specified, no symbols are drawn.
COLOR=	Color for lines and symbols, a character constant (enclosed in quotes), or variable name. [Default: COLOR='BLACK']
LINE=	The Annotate line style used for error bars. [Default: LINE=1]
SIZE=	Size of symbols and thickness of lines. [Default: SIZE=1]
BARWIDTH=	The width of error bar tops, in data units. [Default: BARWIDTH=.5]
OUT=	Name of the output dataset, to be used as an Annotate dataset with PROC GPLOT. [Default: OUT=_BARS_]

A.31.2 EQUATE: Create AXIS Statements for a GPLOT with Equated Axes

The EQUATE macro creates AXIS statements for a GPLOT with equated axes and optionally produces a plot using point labels (supplied in an input Annotate dataset). It is a modified version of the same macro appearing in the SAS Sample Library.

It creates an AXIS statement for the vertical variable Y and an AXIS statement for horizontal variable X such that an inch on the vertical axis represents the same data range as an inch on the horizontal axis. Equated axes are necessary whenever distances between points or angles between vectors from the origin are to be interpreted.

Usage

The EQUATE macro takes 15 keyword arguments. The X= and Y= parameters are required.

You may want to reset the defaults below to be more suited to the graphic devices you typically use. As well, you should use GOPTIONS HSIZE= VSIZE=; to allow the maximum plot size if you specify the XMAX= and YMAX= parameters as null values.

As an additional convenience (particularly for use within other macros) EQUATE will calculate reasonable tick mark increments from the data, to give about 6 tick marks on an axis (with a "nice number" increment) if the XINC= or YINC= parameters are specified as null values.

Parameters

DATA=   Name of the input dataset. [Default: DATA=_LAST_]
ANNO=   Name of an Annotate dataset (used only if PLOT=YES). [Default: ANNO=&DATA]
X=   Name of the X variable. [Default: X=X]
Y=   Name of the Y variable. [Default: Y=Y]
XMAX=   Maximum X axis length (inches). If XMAX= (a null value) the macro queries the device driver (using the DSGI) to determine the maximum axis length. [Default: XMAX=6.5]
YMAX=   Maximum Y axis length (inches). If YMAX= (a null value) the macro queries the device driver (using the DSGI) to determine the maximum axis length. [Default: YMAX=8.5]
XINC=   X axis tick increment. If XINC= (a null value), the macro calculates an increment from the data that is 1, 2, 2.5, 4, or 5 times a power of 10 so that about 6 tick marks will appear on the X axis. [Default: XINC=0.1]
YINC=   Y axis tick increment. If XINC= (a null value), the macro calculates an increment from the data that is 1, 2, 2.5, 4, or 5 times a power of 10 so that about 6 tick marks will appear on the X axis. [Default: YINC=0.1]
XPEXTRA= Number of extra X axis tick marks at the high end. Use the XPEXTRA= and XMEXTRA= parameters to extend the range of the X variable beyond the data values, e.g., to accommodate labels for points in a plot. [Default: XPEXTRA=0]
XMEXTRA= Number of extra X axis tick marks at the low end. [Default: XMEXTRA=0]
YPEXTRA= Number of extra Y axis tick marks at the high end. Use the YPEYTRA= and YMEYTRA= parameters to extend the range of the Y variable beyond the data values, e.g., to accommodate additional annotations in a plot. [Default: YPEXTRA=0]
YMEXTRA= Number of extra Y axis tick marks at the low end. [Default: XMEXTRA=0]
VAXIS=   Name of the AXIS statement for Y axis. [Default: VAXIS=AXIS98]
HAXIS=   Name of the AXIS statement for X axis. [Default: HAXIS=AXIS99]
PLOT=   Draw the plot? [Default: PLOT=NO]

A.31.3   GDISPLA: Device-Independent DISPLAY/NODISPLAY Control

The GDISPLA macro is used to switch graphics display off or on in a device-independent way. It is usually used with the PANELS macro (A.20) or the SCATMAT macro (*SAS System for Statistical Graphics, First Edition* Section A1.13) or other programs that produce multiple plots and then join those plots in a template using PROC GREPLAY. Thus, one can suppress the output of the initially separate graphs and display the final combined plot.

It also allows for the fact that for direct output to the display device, the required GOPTIONS are NODISPLAY or DISPLAY, whereas for output to a GSF, GIF, or EPS file, the options are GSFMODE=NONE or GSFMODE=APPEND. With output to such graphic files, only the combined plot is produced.

Usage

The GDISPLA macro is called with positional parameters. The first (SWITCH) parameter must be specified (or nothing is done).

```
%let devtype=SCREEN;
%gdispla(OFF);
proc gplot;
    plot y * x;
    by group;
%gdispla(ON);
%panels(rows=1, cols=3);
```

Parameters

SWITCH   A string value, either OFF or ON.
IML   Specify any non-blank value as the second argument to use the GDISPLA macro within SAS/IML.

Global Parameters

The macro uses one global macro parameter, DEVTYP, to determine the appropriate action. This parameter is normally initialized either in the AUTOEXEC.SAS file or in device-specific macros.

DEVTYP   String value, the type of graphic device driver. The value DEVTYP=SCREEN causes the macro to use the DISPLAY or NODISPLAY option. The values EPS, GIF, CGM, and WMF cause the macro to use the GSMODE=REPLACE option when %GDISPLA(ON) is called. All other values cause the macro to use the GSMODE=APPEND option when %GDISPLA(ON) is called.

A.31.4   GENSYM: Generate SYMBOL Statements for Multiple Curves

The GENSYM macro generates a series of SYMBOL statements for multiple group plots of the form

```
proc gplot;
    plot y * x = group;
```

Separate plot symbols, colors, line styles and interpolation options can be generated for each group.

Usage

The GENSYM macro is called with keyword parameters. All parameters have default values, but the N= parameter must usually be specified to give the number of goups. The arguments can be listed within parentheses in any order, separated by commas. For example,

```
%gensym(n=4);
```

The INTERP=, LINE=, SYMBOLS=, and COLORS= parameters are each lists of one or more values. If fewer than N (blank delimited) values are given, the available values are reused cyclically as needed.

Parameters

N=	The number of groups. N= symbol statements are constructed, named SYM-BOL1, SYMBOL2, ..., SYMBOLN.
H=	The height of the plotting symbol. The same H= value is used for all SYM-BOL statements. [Default: H=1.5]
INTERP=	List of one or more interpolation options. [Default: INTERP=NONE]
LINE=	List of one or more numbers in the range 1–46 giving SAS/GRAPH line styles [Default: LINE=1]
SYMBOLS=	A list of one or more names of SAS/GRAPH plotting symbols. [Default: SYMBOLS=SQUARE TRIANGLE : $ = X _ Y]
COLORS=	A list of one or more names of SAS/GRAPH colors. [Default: COLORS=BLACK RED GREEN BLUE BROWN YELLOW ORANGE PURPLE]

Example

To plot the four combinations of age group (old, young) and sex, with separate plotting symbols (circle, dot) for old vs. young, and separate colors (red, blue) for females vs. males, use the macro as follows:

```
proc gplot;
   plot y * x = agesex;
   %gensym(n=4, symbols=circle circle dot dot, colors=red blue,
       interp=rl);
```

A.31.5   GSKIP: Device Independent Macro for Multiple Plots

The GSKIP macro is designed to handle difficulties in producing multiple plots in one SAS job or session in a device-independent way. This makes it easier to change from one device to another without modifying your program code.

For EPS, GIF, CGM, and WMF drivers, it assigns a new output filename for the next plot. For FOILS (on continuous forms) it skips the normally blank non-foil separator page. Otherwise, (e.g., for screen output) it has no effect.

Usage

The GSKIP macro has one optional positional parameter but is usually called simply as

```
proc gplot;
    plot y * x;
%gskip;
```

after a procedure or macro that produces only one plot.

It relies on global macro parameters, DISPLAY, DEVTYP, FIG, GSASFILE, and GSASDIR. These parameters are normally initialized either in the AUTOEXEC.SAS file or in device-specific macros. For example, for normal graphic output to the Graph Window, assign DISPLAY and DEVTYP as

```
%let devtyp=SCREEN;
%let displa=ON;
```

For EPS file output, assign devtype=EPS, initialize fig to 1 before the first graph, and assign the basename for graphic output files with the gsasfile macro variable.

```
%let devtyp=EPS;
%let fig=1;
%let gsasfile=myfig;
```

GSKIP is normally used after each graphic procedure or macro to advance the FIG counter and open a new graphic output file. For example,

```
proc gplot;
    plot y * x;
%gskip();
```

Parameters

INC   The value by which the FIG counter is incremented, normally 1 (the default). Use the INC parameter after a plot with a BY statement. For example,

```
proc gplot;
    plot y * x; by sex;
%gskip(2);
```

Global Parameters

DISPLAY   String value, ON or OFF, usually set by the GDISPLA macro. The GISKP macro takes no action if DISPLAY=OFF.

DEVTYP   String value, the type of graphic device driver. The values EPS, GIF, CGM, and WMF cause FIG= to be incremented and a new output filename to be assigned. If DEVTYP=FOILS, a blank graphic page is produced. All others are ignored.

FIG   A numeric value, the number of the current figure.

GSASFILE   String value, the basename of the graphic output file(s). The output files are named according to the macro expression

```
%scan(&gsasfile,1,.)&fig..%lowcase(&devtyp)
```

This gives, e.g., myfile1.eps, myfile2.eps, ...

GSASDIR   String value, the output directory in which the graphic files are written. If not specified, output goes to the current directory.

A.31.6   LABEL: Label Points on a Plot

The LABEL macro creates an Annotate dataset used to label observations in a 2-D (PROC GPLOT) or 3-D (PROC G3D) scatterplot. The points that are labeled can be selected by an arbitrary logical expression from those in the input dataset. The macro offers flexible ways to position the text label relative to either the data point or the center of the plot. The resulting Annotate dataset would then be used with the ANNO= option of PROC GPLOT or PROC G3D.

Usage

The LABEL macro is called with keyword parameters. Values must be supplied for the X=, Y= and TEXT= parameters. For a PROC G3D plot, supply a value for the Z= parameter as well. The arguments can be listed within parentheses in any order, separated by commas. For example,

```
%label(x=age, y=response, text=name);
```

Parameters

DATA=	The name of the input dataset. [Default: DATA=_LAST_]
X=	The name of the X variable for the scatterplot.
Y=	The name of the Y variable for the scatterplot.
Z=	The name of the Z variable for a 3-D scatterplot.
BY=	The name(s) of any BY variable(s) to be used for multiple plots.
XOFF=	An X-offset for the text label. You can specify a numeric constant (e.g., XOFF=-1) in data units, or the name of a variable in the input dataset. Positive values move the label toward larger X values relative to the point; negative values move it toward smaller X values.
YOFF=	A Y-offset for the text label. Positive values move the label towards larger Y values.
ZOFF=	A Z-offset for the text label, for a 3-D plot.
TEXT=	The text used to label each point. TEXT= can be specified as a variable in the dataset or a SAS expression involving dataset variables (e.g., TEXT=SCAN(MODEL,1)) and/or string constants. If you supply an expression, use the %str() macro function, e.g., TEXT=%str(trim(name || '-' || place)) to protect special characters.
LEN=	Length of the TEXT variable. [Default: LEN=16]
POS=	Specifies the position of the label relative to the data point. The POS= value can be a character constant (one of the characters in 123456789ABCDE+-/|, as used by the Annotate POSITION variable), an expression involving dataset variables that evaluates to one of these characters (e.g., POS=SCAN('9 1 3', _NUMBER_)), or one of the special characters, "/", "|", or "–". The special position values cause the point label to be out-justified (moved outward toward the edges of the plot relative to the data point) by comparing the coordinates of the point to the mean of X and Y (/), or to the mean of X only (|), or to the mean of Y only (–).
SYS=	Specifies the Annotate XSYS & YSYS value. [Default: SYS=2]
COLOR=	Label color (the name of a dataset character variable or a string constant enclosed in quotes). [Default: COLOR='BLACK']
SIZE=	The size of label (in whatever units are given by the GUNIT goption). There is no default, which means that the labels inherit the global HTEXT setting.

FONT=	The name of the font used for the label. There is no default, which means that the labels inherit the global FTEXT setting.
ANGLE=	Baseline angle for the text label.
ROTATE=	Character rotate for the text label.
SUBSET=	An expression (which can involve any dataset variables) to select points. A point will be labeled if the expression evaluates to non-zero for the current observation. [Default: SUBSET=1]
COPY=	The names of any input variables to be copied to the output dataset.
IN=	The name of an optional input annotate dataset. If specified, the IN= dataset is concatenated with the OUT= dataset.
OUT=	The name of the annotate dataset produced. [Default: OUT=_LABEL_]

Example

This example plots Weight against Price for American cars in the Auto data, labeling the most expensive cars.

```
%label(data=auto, x=price, y=weight,
        color='red', size=1.2,
        subset=origin='A' and price>10000,
        pos=1, text=scan(model,1));

proc gplot data=auto(where=(origin='A'));
    plot weight * price / frame anno=_label_;
    symbol1 v='+'  i=none color=black h=1.5;
```

A.31.7   POINTS: Create an Annotate Dataset to Draw Points in a Plot

The POINTS macro creates an Annotate dataset to draw point symbols in a 2-D or 3-D scatterplot. This is useful when you need to plot two variables (e.g, observed, predicted) against a common X, with separate curves for the levels of a class variable. In PROC GPLOT, for example, you cannot plot both observed and fitted values against a common X, stratified by GROUP as,

```
proc gplot;
    plot (obs fit) * X = group;
```

However, you can add the OBS points with the POINTS macro to a plot of fit * X = group (drawing lines, but no points):

```
%points(x=X, y=obs, out=_pts_);
 proc gplot;
    plot fit * X = group / anno=_pts_;
 symbol1 i=join v=none c=red;
 symbol2 i=join v=none c=blue;
```

Usage

The POINTS macro is called with keyword parameters. The X= and Y= parameters are required. For a plot with PROC G3D, you must also give the Z= variable. The arguments can be listed within parentheses in any order, separated by commas.

Parameters

DATA=   The name of the input dataset. [Default: DATA=_LAST_]
X=   The name of the X variable for the scatterplot.
Y=   The name of the Y variable for the scatterplot.
Z=   The name of the Z variable for a 3-D scatterplot.
BY=   The name(s) of any BY variable(s) to be used for multiple plots.
CLASS= The name of a class variable to be used with PROC GPLOT in the PLOT statement for multiple curves, in the form

        plot Y * X = CLASS;

SYS=   Specifies the Annotate XSYS and YSYS value. [Default: SYS=2]
COLOR= Point color(s): the name of a dataset character variable, or an expression that evaluates to a SAS/GRAPH color, or a string constant enclosed in quotes. [Default: COLOR='BLACK']
SYMBOL= Point symbol(s): the name of a dataset character variable, or an expression that evaluates to a SAS/GRAPH color, or a string constant enclosed in quotes. [Default: SYMBOL='DOT']
SIZE=   The size of the symbol (in GUNIT units). If not specified, the global graphics option HTEXT value is used.
FONT=   Font for symbol(s): the name of a dataset character variable, or an expression that evaluates to a SAS/GRAPH color, or a string constant enclosed in quotes. Use for special symbols, e.g., FONT='MARKER'. If not specified, the standard symbol font is used.
SUBSET= An expression (which can involve any dataset variables) to select points. A point will be plotted if the expression evaluates to non-zero for the current observation. [Default: SUBSET=1]
COPY=   The names of any variables to be copied to the output dataset.
IN=   The name of an optional input annotate dataset. If specified, the IN= dataset is concatenated with the OUT= dataset.
OUT=   Name of the annotate dataset produced. [Default: OUT=_PTS_]

A.31.8   PSCALE: Construct an Annotate Dataset for a Probability Scale

The PSCALE macro constructs an Annotate dataset to draw an unequally spaced scale of probability values on the vertical axis of a plot (at either the left or right). The probabilities are assumed to correspond to equally spaced values on a scale corresponding to Normal quantiles (using the probit transformation) or Logistic quantiles (using the logit transformation).

Usage

The PSCALE macro is called with keyword parameters. The arguments can be listed within parentheses in any order, separated by commas.

When the probability scale is to be drawn as the right vertical axis, it is usually necessary to reserve space at the right side of the plot and to draw an axis label. This can be accomplished by using the option ANGLE=-90 on a TITLE statement. For example,

```
%pscale(out=pscale);
title  h=1.5 a=-90 'Probability'
       h=3.0 a=-90 ' ';     *-- extra space for tick labels;
proc gplot;
   plot logit * X / anno=pscale;
```

Parameters

ANNO=	Name of the output Annotate dataset. [Default: ANNO=PSCALE]
OUT=	Synonym for ANNO=.
SCALE=	Linear scale: LOGIT or PROBIT. [Default: SCALE=LOGIT]
LO=	Low scale value. [Default: LO=-3]
HI=	High scale value. [Default: HI=3]
PROB=	List of probability values to be displayed on the axis, in the form of a list acceptable in a DO statement. The macro calculates the linear scale transform (as specified by the SCALE= parameter) of each probability to find the Y-axis value for that probability. [Default: PROB=\%str(.05, .1 to .9 by .1, .95)]
AT=	X-axis percent for the axis. AT=100 plots the axis at the right; AT=0 plots the axis at the left. [Default: AT=100]
TICKLEN=	Length of tick marks. [Default: TICKLEN=1.3]
SIZE=	Size of the axis value labels.
FONT=	Font for the axis value labels.

Appendix

B Datasets

Overview

> 'Data! data!' he cried impatiently. I can't make bricks without clay.

> Arthur Conan-Doyle, *The Adventures of Sherlock Holmes, "The Copper Beeches"*

This appendix lists the DATA steps used to create the principal datasets used in the book. We give references to the principal examples where the data is discussed (or see the Example Index) and additional description and/or data in some cases.

Categorical variables, both factors and responses, often need to be re-ordered for analysis, either because they are intrinsically ordinal, or their effects are more sensible when ordered in some fashion. For flexibility, we often define these as numeric variables, but provide VALUE formats that may be used to display the numeric value as a character string or to sort the factor levels according to the formatted value.

Where contingency tables are described, we list the factor variables in the order where the first factor varies most rapidly over observations and the last variable named varies least rapidly.

These datasets are contained in the `catdata` directory in the VCD distribution archives. Some additional data sets, in SAS/IML format are provided in the `mosaics` directory.

B.1 `arthrit.sas`: Arthritis Treatment Data

The arthritis treatment data comes from Koch and Edwards (1988) and is also used for examples in Stokes et al. (1995). The data comes from a double-blind clinical trial investigating a new treatment for rheumatoid arthritis. This dataset is introduced (in contingency table form) in Example 3.3.

The predictors are treatment (TREAT), age (AGE) and sex (SEX). The response (IMPROVE) records whether the patient experienced no improvement, some improvement or marked improvement in symptoms; a binary variable (BETTER) is created to distinguish between no improvement vs. improvement. Dummy variables for the character variables treatment (_TREAT_) and sex (_SEX_) are also created to facilitate analysis with PROC LOGISTIC.

The DATA step below creates a dataset in case form with 84 observations and 9 variables. There are two observations on each dataline.

```
proc format;
    value outcome 0 = 'not improved'
                  1 = 'improved';
data arthrit;
    length treat $7. sex $6. ;
    input id treat $ sex $ age improve @@ ;
    case = _n_;
    better  = (improve > 0);
    _treat_ = (treat ='Treated') ;      /* dummy variables */
    _sex_   = (sex = 'Female');
datalines;
57 Treated Male   27 1    9 Placebo Male   37 0
46 Treated Male   29 0   14 Placebo Male   44 0
77 Treated Male   30 0   73 Placebo Male   50 0
17 Treated Male   32 2   74 Placebo Male   51 0
36 Treated Male   46 2   25 Placebo Male   52 0
23 Treated Male   58 2   18 Placebo Male   53 0
75 Treated Male   59 0   21 Placebo Male   59 0
39 Treated Male   59 2   52 Placebo Male   59 0
33 Treated Male   63 0   45 Placebo Male   62 0
55 Treated Male   63 0   41 Placebo Male   62 0
30 Treated Male   64 0    8 Placebo Male   63 2
 5 Treated Male   64 1   80 Placebo Female 23 0
63 Treated Male   69 0   12 Placebo Female 30 0
83 Treated Male   70 2   29 Placebo Female 30 0
66 Treated Female 23 0   50 Placebo Female 31 1
40 Treated Female 32 0   38 Placebo Female 32 0
 6 Treated Female 37 1   35 Placebo Female 33 2
 7 Treated Female 41 0   51 Placebo Female 37 0
72 Treated Female 41 2   54 Placebo Female 44 0
37 Treated Female 48 0   76 Placebo Female 45 0
82 Treated Female 48 2   16 Placebo Female 46 0
53 Treated Female 55 2   69 Placebo Female 48 0
79 Treated Female 55 2   31 Placebo Female 49 0
26 Treated Female 56 2   20 Placebo Female 51 0
28 Treated Female 57 2   68 Placebo Female 53 0
60 Treated Female 57 2   81 Placebo Female 54 0
22 Treated Female 57 2    4 Placebo Female 54 0
27 Treated Female 58 0   78 Placebo Female 54 2
```

```
 2 Treated Female 59 2    70 Placebo Female 55 2
59 Treated Female 59 2    49 Placebo Female 57 0
62 Treated Female 60 2    10 Placebo Female 57 1
84 Treated Female 61 2    47 Placebo Female 58 1
64 Treated Female 62 1    44 Placebo Female 59 1
34 Treated Female 62 2    24 Placebo Female 59 2
58 Treated Female 66 2    48 Placebo Female 61 0
13 Treated Female 67 2    19 Placebo Female 63 1
61 Treated Female 68 1     3 Placebo Female 64 0
65 Treated Female 68 2    67 Placebo Female 65 2
11 Treated Female 69 0    32 Placebo Female 66 0
56 Treated Female 69 1    42 Placebo Female 66 0
43 Treated Female 70 1    15 Placebo Female 66 1
                          71 Placebo Female 68 1
                           1 Placebo Female 74 2
;
```

B.2 `berkeley.sas`: Berkeley Admissions Data

The Berkeley admission data was described and analyzed by Bickel et al. (1975). The data we have used here reflects the six largest departments in 1971, as listed by Freedman, et al. (1978). The departments are labeled A–F, in decreasing order of their overall rate of admission.

The DATA step below creates a dataset in frequency form with 24 observations and 4 variables, representing a $2 \times 2 \times 6$ contingency table, with factors ADMIT, GENDER, and DEPT, and frequency variable FREQ.

```
title 'Berkeley Admissions data';
proc format;
    value admit 1="Admitted" 0="Rejected"            ;
    value yn    1="+"         0="-"                   ;
    value dept  1="A" 2="B" 3="C" 4="D" 5="E" 6="F";
data berkeley;
    do dept = 1 to 6;
        do gender = 'M', 'F';
            do admit = 1, 0;
                input freq @@;
                output;
    end; end; end;
/* Admit  Rej   Admit Rej */
datalines;
     512   313    89    19
     353   207    17     8
     120   205   202   391
     138   279   131   244
      53   138    94   299
      22   351    24   317
;
```

B.3 `haireye.sas`: Hair-color and Eye-color Data

The data on hair color and eye color came originally as a 2-way table from Snee (1974). The division by sex is fictitious, created for didactic purposes.[1]

The DATA step below creates a dataset in frequency form with 32 observations and 4 variables, representing a $4 \times 4 \times 2$ contingency table, with factors HAIR, EYE, and SEX, and frequency variable COUNT.

```
title 'Hair - Eye color data';
data haireye;
    length  hair $8 eye $6 sex $6;
    drop c i black brown red blond;
    array h{*} black brown red blond;
    c='Black Brown Red Blond';
    input sex $ eye $ black brown red blond;
    do i=1 to dim(h);
        count = h(i); hair=scan(c,i);
        output;
        end;
datalines;
M  Brown        32        53        10        3
M  Blue         11        50        10        30
M  Hazel        10        25        7         5
M  Green        3         15        7         8
F  Brown        36        66        16        4
F  Blue         9         34        7         64
F  Hazel        5         29        7         5
F  Green        2         14        7         8
;
```

B.4 `icu.sas`: ICU Data

This data comes from Hosmer and Lemeshow (1989, App. 2). The dataset consists of a sample of 200 subjects who were part of a much larger study on survival of patients following admission to an adult intensive care unit (Lemeshow, et al., 1988).

The response variable (DIED) records only whether the patient died before being discharged; further longevity is unknown. Among the explanatory variables, a number of originally continuous measures (those dealing with blood chemistry) was recorded dichotomously, using arguably accepted standards for "low" vs. "high".

The variables RACE and COMA are both trichotomous but have highly unbalanced freqencies. Two binary variables, WHITE and UNCONS, are created to contrast the seemingly important comparisons for these variables.

---

[1]The relation between hair color and eye color seems surprisingly murky in data such as this. Genetically, hair color, eye color, and skin color are related to melanin, and it is known that there are (at least) two types of melanin, one of which is reddish (fair), the other darkish. People with a lot of the darker form of melanin in the skin presumably have it in the hair and eyes also. However, there are numerous racial characteristics that are unrelated genetically but happen to occur together in a race. The students in Snee's dataset were not classified by race, so we shall never know. Whether there is any relation between hair color, eye color, and sex is even more of a mystery.

The DATA step below creates a dataset in case form with 200 observations and 23 variables. The data lines are abbreviated here to conserve space.

```
proc format;
    value yn    0='No' 1='Yes';
    value sex   0='Male'  1='Female';
    value race  1='White' 2='Black'  3='Other';
    value ser   0='Medical' 1='Surgery';
    value admit 0='Elective' 1='Emergency';
    value po    0='>60'      1='<=60';
    value ph    0='>=7.25'  1='<7.25';
    value pco   0='<=45'    1='>45';
    value cre   0='<=2'      1='>2';

data icu;
    input id died age sex race service cancer renal infect
        cpr systolic hrtrate previcu admit fracture po2 ph pco bic
        creatin coma;
    label
        id = 'Patient id code'
        died = 'Died before discharge'       /* 0=No, 1=Yes */
        age = 'Age'                          /* years */
        sex = 'Sex'                          /* 0 = Male, 1 = Female */
        race = 'Race'                        /* 1 = White, 2=Black, 3 = Other */
        service = 'Service at Admission'     /* 0 = Medical, 1 = Surgical */
        cancer = 'Cancer Part of Problem'   /* 0=No, 1=Yes */
        renal = 'History of Chronic Renal'  /* 0=No, 1=Yes */
        infect = 'Infection Probable'        /* 0=No, 1=Yes */
        cpr = 'CPR Prior to ICU Admission'  /* 0=No, 1=Yes */
        systolic = 'Systolic Blood Pressure' /* mm Hg */
        hrtrate = 'Heart Rate at Admission' /* beats/min */
        previcu = 'Previous Admit to ICU'    /* 0=No, 1=Yes */
        admit = 'Type of Admission'          /* 0=Elec 1=Emerg */
        fracture = 'Fracture'                /* 0=No, 1=Yes */
        po2 = 'PO2, inital Blood Gas'        /* 0=>60, 1=<=60 */
        ph = 'PH, inital Blood Gas'          /* 0=7.25, 1= <7.25 */
        pco = 'PCO2, inital Blood Gas'       /* 0=45, 1= >45 */
        bic = 'Bicarbonate, inital Blood'    /* 0=18, 1= <18 */
        creatin = 'Creatinine, inital Blood' /* 0=2, 1= >2 */
        coma = 'Consciousness at ICU'        /* 0=None 1=Stupor 2=Coma */
        uncons = 'Stupor or coma at ICU';

    white = (race=1);
    uncons= (coma>0);

    format died cancer renal infect cpr previcu fracture yn.;
    format sex sex. race race. admit admit. ph ph. pco pco. creatin cre.;
/*
            D           R                                               C
            I   A S A S C C I C   S   H   P T F P       P B C O
        I   E   G E C E A R N P   Y   R   R Y R O P C I R M
        D   D   E X E R N N F R   S   A   E P A 2 H O C E A
*/
datalines;
     8 0 27 1 1 0 0 0 1 0 142  88 0 1 0 0 0 0 0 0 0
    12 0 59 0 1 0 0 0 0 0 112  80 1 1 0 0 0 0 0 0 0
```

```
       14   0  77  0  1  1  0  0  0  0  100   70  0  0  0  0  0  0  0  0  0
       28   0  54  0  1  0  0  0  1  0  142  103  0  1  1  0  0  0  0  0  0
       32   0  87  1  1  1  0  0  1  0  110  154  1  1  0  0  0  0  0  0  0
       38   0  69  0  1  0  0  0  1  0  110  132  0  1  0  1  0  0  1  0  0
       40   0  63  0  1  1  0  0  0  0  104   66  0  0  0  0  0  0  0  0  0
       41   0  30  1  1  0  0  0  0  0  144  110  0  1  0  0  0  0  0  0  0
       42   0  35  0  2  0  0  0  0  0  108   60  0  1  0  0  0  0  0  0  0
       50   0  70  1  1  1  1  0  0  0  138  103  0  0  0  0  0  0  0  0  0
       51   0  55  1  1  1  0  0  1  0  188   86  1  0  0  0  0  0  0  0  0
       53   0  48  0  2  1  1  0  0  0  162  100  0  0  0  0  0  0  0  0  0
       58   0  66  1  1  1  0  0  0  0  160   80  1  0  0  0  0  0  0  0  0
       61   0  61  1  1  0  0  1  0  0  174   99  0  1  0  0  1  0  1  1  0
       73   0  66  0  1  0  0  0  0  0  206   90  0  1  0  0  0  0  0  1  0
       75   0  52  0  1  1  0  0  1  0  150   71  1  0  0  0  0  0  0  0  0
       82   0  55  0  1  1  0  0  1  0  140  116  0  0  0  0  0  0  0  0  0
       84   0  59  0  1  0  0  0  1  0   48   39  0  1  0  1  0  1  1  0  2
       92   0  63  0  1  0  0  0  0  0  132  128  1  1  0  0  0  0  0  0  0
       96   0  72  0  1  1  0  0  0  0  120   80  1  0  0  0  0  0  0  0  0
       98   0  60  0  1  0  0  0  1  1  114  110  0  1  0  0  0  0  0  0  0
      100   0  78  0  1  1  0  0  0  0  180   75  0  0  0  0  0  0  0  0  0
      102   0  16  1  1  0  0  0  0  0  104  111  0  1  0  0  0  0  0  0  0
      111   0  62  0  1  1  0  1  0  0  200  120  0  0  0  0  0  0  0  0  0
      112   0  61  0  1  0  0  0  1  0  110  120  0  1  0  0  0  0  0  0  0
      136   0  35  0  1  0  0  0  0  0  150   98  0  1  0  0  0  0  0  0  0
      ... more data lines ...
      789   1  60  0  1  0  0  0  1  0   56  114  1  1  0  0  1  0  1  0  0
      871   1  60  0  3  1  0  1  1  0  130   55  0  1  0  0  0  0  0  0  1
      921   1  50  1  2  0  0  0  0  0  256   64  0  1  0  0  0  0  0  0  1
   ;
proc sort;
   by descending died age;
```

B.5 `lifeboat.sas`: Lifeboats on the *Titanic*

The information in the dataset LIFEBOAT comes from the report by the British Board of Trade (Mersey, 1912, p. 38) on the sinking of the *S. S. Titanic*, as described in Example 3.18. A second dataset, LIFEBOA2, presents more accurate and detailed figures.

The table in Lord Mersey's report lists the numbers of the male crew, male passengers, and women (including female crew) and children who, according to the evidence presented by survivors, left the ship in each of the 18 lifeboats launched (out of 20) before the ship sank.

The report notes that "in three or four instances the number of women and children are only arrived at by subtracting the numbers of crew and male passengers from the total said to be in the boat." The total of 854 listed here far exceeds the 712 actually saved, so the report concludes that "it is obvious that these figures are quite unreliable," and "the real proportion of women to men saved was much less than the proportion appearing in the evidence from the boats." Similarly, this data also understates the number of male crew in the boats (107 vs. the 189 actually saved).

The DATA step shown next creates the dataset LIFEBOAT in table form with 18 observations (the lifeboats) and 10 variables. Information on launch times and boat capacity is found elsewhere in the report. The variable SIDE is coded 'p' for Port and 's' for Starboard. A subsequent PROC RANK step is used to classify the launch times into three levels for the boats launched from each side.

```
title 'Lifeboats on the Titanic';
/* from the Board of Trade (1912)
    "Report on the Loss of the S.S. Titanic", p, 38
*/
proc format;
    value $side 'p'='Port'  's'='Starboard';
    value period 0='Early'  1='Middle'  2='Late';

data lifeboat;
    input  launch time5.2 side $ boat $ crew men women;
    total = sum(crew, men, women);
    format launch hhmm. side $side.;
    port = (side='p');
    int = launch * port;
    select (boat);
        when ('C', 'D')  cap=47;
        when ('1', '2')  cap=40;
        otherwise        cap=65;
    end;
    label launch='Launch Time'
        boat = 'Boat label'
        crew = 'Men of crew'
        men = 'Men passengers'
        women = 'Women and Children'
        cap = 'Boat capacity'
        total = 'Total loaded';
datalines;
 0:45  p  7   3  4  20
 0:55  p  5   5  6  30
 1:00  p  3  15 10  25
 1:10  p  1   7  3   2
 1:20  p  9   8  6  42
 1:25  p 11   9  1  60
 1:35  p 13   5  0  59
 1:35  p 15  13  4  53
 1:40  p  C   5  2  64
 0:55  s  6   2  2  24
 1:10  s  8   4  0  35
 1:20  s 10   5  0  50
 1:25  s 12   2  0  40
 1:30  s 14   8  2  53
 1:35  s 16   6  0  50
 1:45  s  2   4  1  21
 1:55  s  4   4  0  36
 2:05  s  D   2  2  40
;

proc rank out=lifeboat groups=3;
    var launch;
    ranks period;
    by side;
```

The LIFEBOA2 Data

The dataset LIFEBOA2 was constructed from information extracted from the *Encyclopedia Titanica* Web site (Hind, 1997). This data has never previously been tabulated. This Web site includes all available information about the occupants of the lifeboats (as far as can be reconstructed from all historical records and accounts), each identified by name, and classified in the categories "First class passengers", "First class servants", "Second class passengers", "Second class servants" (only one), "Third class passengers", and Crew, broken down into "Deck crew", "Engineering crew" and "Victualling crew". The occupants include those loaded onto the boats, as well as those who jumped to the boat or were pulled from the water, and also indicates the few (10) who made their way onto boats, but died, either in the boat or after arrival at the *Carpathia*.

This dataset LIFEBOA2 contains 20 observations (for all 20 lifeboats, including the two never launched but used by those in the water) and 14 variables. The variables MEN and WOMEN include only male and female passengers, excluding servants. The variables CLASS1-CLASS3 include both passengers and servants. The OTHER variable includes those who got into the boats by other means. It is of some interest that the other category includes five stowaways (four on boat C), as well as people who jumped onto the boats or were pulled from the water. Two surviving canine pets (one named "Sun Yat Sen") are listed in the Web pages but are not included in the counts that follow. In this dataset, the CLASS1-CLASS3 and CREW variables are non-overlapping, so the TOTAL is calculated as their sum.

```
proc format;
    value $side 'p'='Port'   's'='Starboard';
data lifeboa2;
    input boat $ order side $ men women class1-class3 crew other
          launch time5.2;
    format launch hhmm. side $side.;
    total=sum(of class1-class3 crew);
    label launch='Launch Time'  order='Launch order'
        boat = 'Boat label'        side='Side'
        men = 'Men passengers'    women = 'Women and Children'
        class1 = '1st Class passengers'  class2='2nd Class passengers'
        class3 = '3rd Class passengers'  other ='Other lifeboat occupants'
        crew = 'Men of crew'
        cap = 'Boat capacity'     total = 'Total loaded';
    port = (side='p');
    select (boat);
        when ('C', 'D') cap=47;
        when ('1', '2') cap=40;
        otherwise       cap=65;
    end;
datalines;
  1    5 s    3  1    5  0   0  7 0   1:10
  2   15 p    3  9    8  0   6  4 0   1:45
  3    4 s   11  8   26  0   0 13 0   1:00
  4   16 p    3 16   24  2   0 12 9   1:50
  5    2 s   13 14   27  0   0  8 2   0:55
  6    3 p    2 16   19  0   1  4 1   0:55
  7    1 s   13 12   24  1   0  3 0   0:45
  8    5 p    0 17   23  0   0  4 0   1:10
  9   10 s    9 16    6 17   3 15 0   1:30
 10    7 p    5 28    9 18   6  4 0   1:20
 11   12 s    7 16    6 14   5 26 0   1:35
 12   10 .    1 18    0 17   2  3 1   1:30
 13   13 s   15 24    1 12  26 24 2   1:40
 14    8 p   10 23    5 21   7  9 4   1:25
```

```
15  13  s  23  15   1   1  36  25  0   1:40
16  .   p   2  23   0   3  22  12  0   1:35
A   .   s   9   2   3   0   8   5  0   .
B   .   p  10   0   3   1   6  18  0   .
C  17   s  13  25   2   0  36   6  4   1:40
D   .   s   6  13   8   2   9   5  3   2:05
;
```

B.6 `marital.sas`: Pre-marital Sex, Extra-marital Sex, and Divorce

This data comes from a study of divorce patterns by Thornes and Collard (1979; reported in Gilbert, 1981), described in Example 4.4.

The dataset `MARITAL` is created in frequency form with 16 observations and 4 variables to represent the 2^4 contingency table, with factors `MARITAL`, `EXTRA`, `PRE`, and `GENDER`, and frequency variable `COUNT`.

```
data marital;
   input gender $ pre $ extra $ @;
   pre = 'Pre:' || pre;
   extra = 'X:' || extra;
   marital='Divorced';  input count @;  output;
   marital='Married';   input count @;  output;
datalines;
Women  Yes  Yes   17    4
Women  Yes  No    54   25
Women  No   Yes   36    4
Women  No   No   214  322
Men    Yes  Yes   28   11
Men    Yes  No    60   42
Men    No   Yes   17    4
Men    No   No    68  130
;
```

B.7 `mental.sas`: Mental Impairment and Parents' SES

This 2-way contingency table comes from *The Midtown Manhattan Study* (Srole, et al., 1978, p. 289), and reports a classification of 1600 young people by their mental health status and by their parents' socioeconomic status (SES), as described in Example 5.2.

The DATA step `MENTAL` creates the 5×4 contingency table in frequency form, with ordinal factors `SES` and `MENTAL` and frequency variable `COUNT`.

```
proc format;
   value mental 1='Well' 2='Mild' 3='Moderate' 4='Impaired';
   value ses    1='High' 2='2' 3='3' 4='4' 5='5' 6='Low';
data mental;
   input ses mental count @@;
   label ses="Parents SES"
      mental='Mental Impairment';
```

```
datalines;
1  1  64    1  2  94    1  3  58    1  4  46
2  1  57    2  2  94    2  3  54    2  4  40
3  1  57    3  2 105    3  3  65    3  4  60
4  1  72    4  2 141    4  3  77    4  4  94
5  1  36    5  2  97    5  3  54    5  4  78
6  1  21    6  2  71    6  3  54    6  4  71
;
```

B.8 `msdiag.sas`: Diagnosis of Multiple Sclerosis

The data on diagnosis of multiple sclerosis came originally from a study by Westlund and Kurland (1953). It was later used by Landis and Koch (1977), Agresti (1990, Table 10.13) and others. The data is described in Example 3.14 and Example 3.15.

Two samples of patients, one from Winnipeg and one from New Orleans, were each rated by two neurologists (one from each city) in four diagnostic categories for multiple sclerosis. The dataset `MSDIAG` is thus a $4 \times 4 \times 2$ contingency table, with factors `W_RATING`, `N_RATING`, and `PATIENTS` and frequency variable `COUNT`.

```
proc format;
    value rating 1="Certain MS" 2="Probable" 3="Possible" 4="Doubtful MS";
data msdiag;
    do patients='Winnipeg  ', 'New Orleans';
        do N_rating = 1 to 4;
            do W_rating = 1 to 4;
                input count @;
                output;
                end;
            end;
        end;
    format N_rating W_rating rating.;
    label N_rating = 'New Orleans neurologist'
          W_rating = 'Winnipeg nurologist';
datalines;
38  5  0  1
33 11  3  0
10 14  5  6
 3  7  3 10
 5  3  0  0
 3 11  4  0
 2 13  3  4
 1  2  4 14
;

*-- Agreement, separately, and conrolling for Patients;
proc freq data=msdiag;
    weight count;
    tables patients * N_rating * W_rating / norow nocol nopct agree;
run;
```

B.9 `orings.sas`: NASA Space Shuttle O-Ring Failures

The data on O-ring failures in the NASA space shuttle program comes from Dalal, et al. (1989, Table 1). Tufte (1997) discusses this data at length and is the source of the "damage index" variable. This data is discussed in Example 6.5 in this book.

The dataset ORINGS contains 24 observations (the launches before the *Challenger*) and 8 variables. For analysis purposes, we regard the data in events/trials form, with FAILURES as the number of events and ORINGS=6 as the number of trials.

```
data orings;
    flt_num = _n_;
    input flight $ temp pressure fail failures damage;
    orings = 6;
    label temp='Temperature'  pressure='Leak check pressure'
        fail = 'Any failure?'  failures='Number of O-ring failures'
        damage = 'Damage index';
datalines;
    1   66   50   0   0   0
    2   70   50   1   1   4
    3   69   50   0   0   0
    4   80   50   .   .   .
    5   68   50   0   0   0
    6   67   50   0   0   0
    7   72   50   0   0   0
    8   73   50   0   0   0
    9   70  100   0   0   0
  41B   57  100   1   1   4
  41C   63  200   1   1   2
  41D   70  200   1   1   4
  41G   78  200   0   0   0
  51A   67  200   0   0   0
  51C   53  200   1   2  11
  51D   67  200   0   0   0
  51B   75  200   0   0   0
  51G   70  200   0   0   0
  51F   81  200   0   0   0
  51I   76  200   0   0   0
  51J   79  200   0   0   0
  61A   75  200   1   2   4
  61C   58  200   1   1   4
  61I   76  200   0   0   4
;
```

B.10 `suicide.sas`: Suicide Rates in Germany

The data on suicide rates in West Germany classified by age, sex, and method of suicide used is from Heuer (1979, Table 1). The original $2 \times 17 \times 9$ table contains 17 age groups from 10 to 90 in 5-year steps and 9 categories of suicide method, in the dataset SUICIDE0.

```
title 'Suicide Rates by Age, Sex and Method';
data suicide0;
    input sex $1 age poison cookgas toxicgas hang drown gun knife
                        jump other;
    length sexage $ 4;
    sexage=trim(sex)||trim(left(put(age,2.)));
datalines;
M 10     4   0   0   247    1  17    1    6    0
M 15   348   7  67   578   22 179   11   74  175
M 20   808  32 229   699   44 316   35  109  289
M 25   789  26 243   648   52 268   38  109  226
M 30   916  17 257   825   74 291   52  123  281
M 35  1118  27 313  1278   87 293   49  134  268
M 40   926  13 250  1273   89 299   53   78  198
M 45   855   9 203  1381   71 347   68  103  190
M 50   684  14 136  1282   87 229   62   63  146
M 55   502   6  77   972   49 151   46   66   77
M 60   516   5  74  1249   83 162   52   92  122
M 65   513   8  31  1360   75 164   56  115   95
M 70   425   5  21  1268   90 121   44  119   82
M 75   266   4   9   866   63  78   30   79   34
M 80   159   2   2   479   39  18   18   46   19
M 85    70   1   0   259   16  10    9   18   10
M 90    18   0   1    76    4   2    4    6    2
F 10    28   0   3    20    0   1    0   10    6
F 15   353   2  11    81    6  15    2   43   47
F 20   540   4  20   111   24   9    9   78   47
F 25   454   6  27   125   33  26    7   86   75
F 30   530   2  29   178   42  14   20   92   78
F 35   688   5  44   272   64  24   14   98  110
F 40   566   4  24   343   76  18   22  103   86
F 45   716   6  24   447   94  13   21   95   88
F 50   942   7  26   691  184  21   37  129  131
F 55   723   3  14   527  163  14   30   92   92
F 60   820   8   8   702  245  11   35  140  114
F 65   740   8   4   785  271   4   38  156   90
F 70   624   6   4   610  244   1   27  129   46
F 75   495   8   1   420  161   2   29  129   35
F 80   292   3   2   223   78   0   10   84   23
F 85   113   4   0    83   14   0    6   34    2
F 90    24   1   0    19    4   0    2    7    0
;
```

For the purposes of this book, I have collapsed the age groups into five age ranges, amalgamated the two gas-related methods, and dropped the categories 'knife' and 'other', which have rather small frequencies.

```
%include catdata(suicide0);
proc format;
    value agegp 10-20 = '10-20'
                25-35 = '25-35'
                40-50 = '40-50'
                55-65 = '55-65'
                70-90 = '70-90';
```

```
%let vars = poison gas hang drown gun jump;
data suicide0;
   set suicide;
   by sex notsorted;
   drop cookgas toxicgas other;
   gas = cookgas + toxicgas;
   *-- collapse age groups;
   cage= put(age,agegp.);
   Sexage = sex || cage;
proc summary data=suicide nway idmin order=data;
   id SexAge ;
   class sex cage;
   var &vars ;
   output out=suicide(drop=_type_) sum=&vars;
```

With the equivalent of a PROC TRANSPOSE step, we get the dataset SUICIDE used in the examples here:

```
data suicide;
   input sex $ age $ @;
   do method = 'Poison', 'Gas', 'Hang', 'Drown', 'Gun', 'Jump';
      input count @;
      output;
      end;
   input;
datalines;
   M  10-20  1160   335  1524    67   512   189
   M  25-35  2823   883  2751   213   852   366
   M  40-50  2465   625  3936   247   875   244
   M  55-65  1531   201  3581   207   477   273
   M  70-90   938    45  2948   212   229   268

   F  10-20   921    40   212    30    25   131
   F  25-35  1672   113   575   139    64   276
   F  40-50  2224    91  1481   354    52   327
   F  55-65  2283    45  2014   679    29   388
   F  70-90  1548    29  1355   501     3   383
;
```

B.11 `titanic.sas`: Survival on the *Titanic*

The *Titanic* data was presented by Dawson (1995) as a file of 2201 observations.[2] The file was processed with PROC FREQ and converted to the DATA step that follows.

The dataset TITANIC comprises a $4 \times 2 \times 2 \times 2$ contingency table in frequency form. The factor variables are CLASS, SEX, AGE, and SURVIVE; the cell frequencies are in the variable COUNT.

---

[2]URL: http://www.amstat.org/publications/jse/v3n3/datasets.dawson.html

```
                title 'Survival on the Titanic';

            proc format;
              value class 1='1st' 2='2nd' 3='3rd' 4='crew';
              value age   0='Child' 1='Adult';
              value sex   0='Female' 1='Male';
              value surv  1='Survived' 0='Died';

            data titanic;
              input survive  age  sex  @;
              format age age. class class. sex sex. survive surv.;
              do class = 1 to 4;
                 input count @;
                 output;
                 end;
            datalines;
            0   1   1       118     154     387     670
            0   1   0         4      13      89       3
            0   0   1         0       0      35       0
            0   0   0         0       0      17       0
            1   1   1        57      14      75     192
            1   1   0       140      80      76      20
            1   0   1         5      11      13       0
            1   0   0         1      13      14       0
            ;
```

B.12 `vietnam.sas`: Student Opinion about the Vietnam War

This data, given by Aitkin et al. (1989), comes from a survey of student opinion on U.S. policies toward the war in Vietnam that was conducted in May 1967 at the University of North Carolina at Chapel Hill. The survey is described in detail in Example 7.9.

The DATA step that follows creates the dataset VIETNAM, representing the $4 \times 5 \times 2$ contingency table in frequency form, with 40 observations and four variables. The factors are RESPONSE, YEAR, and SEX.

```
            proc format;
              value resp    1='Defeat North Vietnam'  2='Present policy'
                            3='Negotiate'             4='Immediate withdrawal';
              value letter 1='A'  2='B'  3='C'  4='D';
              value yr      1='Freshmen'  2='Sophomore'  3='Junior'
                            4='Senior'    5='Grad student';
              value $sex   'M'='Male'    'F'='Female';

            data vietnam;
              do sex = 'F', 'M';
                 do year = 1 to 5;
                    do response = 1 to 4;
                       input count @;
                       output;
                       end;
                    end;
                 end;
```

```
      label year= 'Year of Study'
            sex = 'Sex';
 datalines;
  13   19   40    5
   5    9   33    3
  22   29  110    6
  12   21   58   10
  19   27  128   13
 175  116  131   17
 160  126  135   21
 132  120  154   29
 145   95  185   44
 118  176  345  141
 ;
```

B.13 `vision.sas`: Visual Acuity in Left and Right Eyes

Kendall and Stuart (1961, Tables 33.2 and 33.5) gave the data below on unaided distance vision among 3,242 men and 7,477 women, all aged 30–39 and employed in the U.K. Royal Ordnance factories 1943–1946. For each person, unaided visual acuity of each eye was measured and categorized into four grades. Example 3.11 presents a graphic analysis of the data for women. See Bishop et al. (1975, p. 284) and Friendly (1992) for further analyses of this data.

The DATA steps that follow create two 4×4 contingency tables: one for women and one for men. These are combined to produce the dataset VISION, representing the $2 \times 4 \times 4$ contingency table in frequency form. The factor variables are GENDER, LEFT, and RIGHT.

```
data women;
   input right left count @@;
datalines;
1 1 1520    1 2  266    1 3  124    1 4  66
2 1  234    2 2 1512    2 3  432    2 4  78
3 1  117    3 2  362    3 3 1772    3 4 205
4 1   36    4 2   82    4 3  179    4 4 492
;

data men;
   input right left count @@;
datalines;
1 1  821    1 2 112    1 3  85    1 4  35
2 1  116    2 2 494    2 3 145    2 4  27
3 1   72    3 2 151    3 3 583    4 4  87
4 1   43    4 2  34    4 3 106    4 4 331
;
*-- Join the two data sets;
data vision;
   set women (in=w)
       men   (in=m);
   if w then gender='F';
       else gender='M';
```

B.14 `vonbort.sas`: Deaths by Horse Kicks in the Prussian Army

The data from von Bortkiewicz (1898) is given by Andrews and Herzberg (1985, p. 18) in the form of a 14 × 20 2-way table. The data is read in frequency form by the DATA step VONBORT below. The frequency variable is DEATHS.

Four of the army corps, G, I, VI, and XI were noted as having a somewhat different organization from the rest, and Fisher (1925) excluded these in his 1-way table, shown in Table 2.1. The DATA step VONBORT2 selects the remaining army corps and uses PROC FREQ to construct the frequency distribution analysed in Chapter 2.

```
title 'von Bortkiewicz data';
data vonbort;
   input year @;
   do corps = 1 to 14;
      input deaths @;
      output;
      end;
/*  1 2  3   4   5 6  7  8    9  10 11 12 13 14 */
/*  G I II III IV V VI VII VIII IX X XI XIV XV */
datalines;
75 0 0 0 0 0 0 0 1 1 0 0 0 1 0
76 2 0 0 0 1 0 0 0 0 0 0 0 1 1
77 2 0 0 0 0 0 1 1 0 0 1 0 2 0
78 1 2 2 1 1 0 0 0 0 0 1 0 1 0
79 0 0 0 1 1 2 2 0 1 0 0 2 1 0
80 0 3 2 1 1 1 0 0 0 2 1 4 3 0
81 1 0 0 2 1 0 0 1 0 1 0 0 0 0
82 1 2 0 0 0 0 1 0 1 1 2 1 4 1
83 0 0 1 2 0 1 2 1 0 1 0 3 0 0
84 3 0 1 0 0 0 0 1 0 0 2 0 1 1
85 0 0 0 0 0 0 1 0 0 2 0 1 0 1
86 2 1 0 0 1 1 1 0 0 1 0 1 3 0
87 1 1 2 1 0 0 3 2 1 1 0 1 2 0
88 0 1 1 0 0 1 1 0 0 0 0 1 1 0
89 0 0 1 1 0 1 1 0 0 1 2 2 0 2
90 1 2 0 2 0 1 1 2 0 2 1 1 2 2
91 0 0 0 1 1 1 0 1 1 0 3 3 1 0
92 1 3 2 0 1 1 3 0 1 1 0 1 1 0
93 0 1 0 0 0 1 0 2 0 0 1 3 0 0
94 1 0 0 0 0 0 0 0 1 0 1 1 0 0
;
data vonbort2;
   set vonbort;
   where corps not in (1,2,7,12);

proc freq data=vonbort2;
   tables deaths / out=horskick;
```

B.15 `vote.sas`: Race and Politics in the 1980 U.S. Presidential Vote

This data, concerning votes in the 1980 U.S. Presidential election in relation to race and conservatism (1=most liberal, 7=most conservative), comes from the 1982 General Social Survey, as reported by Clogg and Shockey (1988). This dataset is analyzed in Example 7.5.

The dataset VOTE contains 28 observations and four variables, representing a $2 \times 7 \times 2$ contingency table in frequency form. The factor variables are VOTEFOR, CONS, and RACE; the frequency variable is COUNT. Note that the VOTEFOR variable is categorized as "Reagan" vs. "Carter or other".

```
title  'Race and Politics in the 1980 Presidential vote';
proc format;
   value race 0='NonWhite'
              1='White';
data vote;
   input @10 race cons @;
   do votefor='Reagan', 'Carter';
      input count @;
      output;
      end;
datalines;
White     1 1    1    12
White     1 2   13    57
White     1 3   44    71
White     1 4  155   146
White     1 5   92    61
White     1 6  100    41
White     1 7   18     8
NonWhite  0 1    0     6
NonWhite  0 2    0    16
NonWhite  0 3    2    23
NonWhite  0 4    1    31
NonWhite  0 5    0     8
NonWhite  0 6    2     7
NonWhite  0 7    0     4
;
```

B.16 `wlfdata.sas`: Women's Labor-force Participation

This data on Canadian women's labor-force participation comes from a sample survey of young married women (age 21–30), carried out by York Institute for Social Research, in the *Social Change in Canada Project*, as given by Fox (1984, 1997). The data is described in Example 6.15.

The dataset WLFPART contains 263 observations and 11 variables in case form. The response variable, LABOR, is trichotomous. For analysis purposes, two nested dichotomies are created: WORKING (full-time or part-time vs. not working) and FULLTIME (full-time vs. part-time, missing for those not working). Explanatory variables include HUSINC (Husband's income, in $1000s), KIDS (one or more children in the household) and REGION (of Canada, represented by four dummy variables, R1–R4).

```
proc format;
   value labor    /* labor-force participation */
      1 ='working full-time'
      2 ='working part-time'
      3 ='not working';
   value kids     /* presence of children in the household */
      0 ='Children absent'
      1 ='Children present';
```

```
                    value region    /* region of Canada */
                       1 ='Atlantic Canada'
                       2 ='Quebec'
                       3 ='Ontario'
                       4 ='Prairie provinces'
                       5 ='British Columbia';

                 data wlfpart;
                    input case labor husinc children region @@;
                    working = labor < 3;
                    if working then
                       fulltime = (labor = 1);
                    /* dummy variables for region */
                    r1 = (region=1);
                    r2 = (region=2);
                    r3 = (region=3);
                    r4 = (region=4);
                    label husinc="Husband's Income";
                 datalines;
                    1  3  15  1  3      2  3  13  1  3      3  3  45  1  3      4  3  23  1  3
                    5  3  19  1  3      6  3   7  1  3      7  3  15  1  3      8  1   7  1  3
                    9  3  15  1  3     10  3  23  1  3     11  3  23  1  3     12  1  13  1  3
                   13  3   9  1  4     14  3   9  1  4     15  3  45  1  1     16  3  15  1  1
                   17  3   5  1  3     18  3   9  1  3     19  3  13  1  3     20  3  13  0  3
                   21  2  19  0  3     22  3  23  1  4     23  1  10  0  4     24  1  11  0  3
                   25  3  23  1  3     26  3  23  1  3     27  3  19  1  3     28  3  19  1  3
                   29  3  17  1  4     30  1  14  1  4     31  3  13  1  3     32  3  13  1  3
                   33  3  15  1  3     34  3   9  0  3     35  3   9  0  3     36  3  19  0  3
                   37  3  15  1  3     38  1  20  0  3     39  3   9  1  1     40  2   6  0  1
                   41  3   9  1  5     42  2   4  1  3     43  2  28  0  3     44  3  23  1  3
                   45  2   5  1  3     46  3  28  1  3     47  3   7  1  3     48  3   7  1  3
                   49  3  23  1  4     50  1  15  0  4     51  2  10  1  4     52  2  10  1  4
                   53  3   9  0  3     54  3   9  0  3     55  2   9  1  1     56  3  17  0  1
                   57  3  23  1  1     58  3  23  1  1     59  3   9  1  3     60  3   9  1  3
                   61  1   9  0  3     62  1  28  0  3     63  2  10  1  3     64  2  23  0  4
                   65  3  11  1  4     66  3  15  1  3     67  3  15  1  3     68  3  19  1  3
                   69  3  19  1  3     70  3  23  1  3     71  3  17  1  3     72  3  17  1  3
                   73  3  17  1  3     74  3  17  1  3     75  3  17  1  3     76  2  38  1  3
                   77  2  38  1  3     78  3   7  1  1     79  3  19  1  4     80  2  19  1  5
                   81  1  13  0  3     82  2  15  1  3     83  1  17  1  3     84  1  17  1  3
                   85  2  23  1  3     86  1  27  0  5     87  1  16  1  5     88  1  27  0  3
                   89  3  35  0  3     90  3  35  0  3     91  3  35  0  3     92  2   9  1  3
                   93  2   9  1  3     94  2   9  1  3     95  3  13  1  3     96  3  17  1  3
                   97  3  17  1  3     98  1  15  0  3     99  1  15  0  3    100  3  15  1  3
                  101  1  11  0  1    102  3  23  1  1    103  3  15  1  1    104  3  15  0  5
                  105  2  12  0  5    106  2  12  0  5    107  3  13  1  4    108  3  19  1  3
                  109  3  19  1  1    110  3   3  1  1    111  3   9  1  1    112  1  17  1  1
                  113  3   1  1  1    114  3   1  1  1    115  2  13  1  4    116  3  13  1  4
                  117  3  19  0  5    118  3  19  0  5    119  1  15  0  5    120  2  30  1  3
                  121  3   9  1  1    122  3  23  1  1    123  1   9  0  3    124  1   9  0  3
                  125  3  13  1  4    126  2  13  1  3    127  3  17  1  1    128  2  13  1  4
                  129  2  13  1  4    130  2  19  1  3    131  2  19  1  3    132  3   3  1  3
                  133  1  14  0  3    134  1  14  0  3    135  1  11  1  3    136  1  11  1  3
                  137  2  14  1  3    138  3  13  1  3    139  3  28  1  3    140  3  28  1  3
                  141  3  14  1  3    142  3  14  1  3    143  3  11  1  4    144  3  13  1  4
                  145  3  13  1  4    146  2  11  1  1    147  2  11  1  1    148  3  19  1  5
                  149  1   6  0  5    150  3  28  0  5    151  1  13  0  5    152  1  13  0  5
                  153  3   5  0  5    154  2  28  1  5    155  2  11  1  5    156  3  23  1  5
```

157	2	15	1	5	158	3	13	1	5	159	1	22	0	3	160	1	15	0	3
161	3	15	1	3	162	3	15	1	1	163	1	5	1	1	164	1	1	0	4
165	1	1	0	4	166	3	9	1	1	167	3	15	1	3	168	1	13	0	3
169	3	19	1	1	170	2	8	1	5	171	1	7	1	4	172	3	19	1	3
173	3	7	1	3	174	1	9	0	3	175	1	9	0	3	176	1	24	0	3
177	3	15	1	3	178	1	13	0	3	179	3	13	0	5	180	1	13	0	5
181	1	17	1	1	182	1	16	0	1	183	1	18	0	3	184	1	18	0	3
185	3	13	0	3	186	2	15	1	5	187	3	13	1	5	188	3	7	1	5
189	1	9	1	1	190	3	23	1	5	191	3	17	1	4	192	3	15	1	5
193	3	11	1	4	194	3	17	1	4	195	3	17	1	4	196	1	5	1	4
197	1	5	1	4	198	3	26	1	3	199	1	10	0	2	200	1	11	0	2
201	1	20	1	2	202	3	13	1	2	203	3	15	1	2	204	3	28	1	2
205	2	9	1	2	206	3	19	1	2	207	3	11	1	2	208	1	11	0	2
209	3	9	1	2	210	1	10	0	2	211	3	19	1	2	212	3	13	1	2
213	1	3	0	2	214	3	15	1	2	215	3	15	1	2	216	2	17	1	2
217	3	7	1	2	218	2	15	0	2	219	3	19	1	2	220	1	16	0	2
221	3	5	0	2	222	3	11	1	2	223	3	11	1	2	224	3	19	1	2
225	3	15	1	2	226	3	15	1	2	227	3	11	1	2	228	1	5	0	2
229	2	23	1	2	230	2	23	1	2	231	3	7	1	2	232	3	13	1	2
233	1	15	0	2	234	1	5	0	2	235	3	7	1	2	236	1	6	0	2
237	1	5	1	2	238	1	5	1	2	239	3	13	1	2	240	3	13	1	2
241	3	13	1	2	242	3	13	0	2	243	3	17	1	2	244	1	6	1	2
245	3	5	1	2	246	2	19	1	2	247	1	3	1	2	248	3	23	0	2
249	3	23	0	2	250	1	15	0	2	251	3	11	0	2	252	3	23	0	2
253	3	13	1	2	254	2	23	1	2	255	1	11	0	2	256	3	9	0	2
257	1	2	0	2	258	3	15	1	2	259	3	15	0	2	260	3	15	1	2
261	3	11	1	2	262	3	11	0	2	263	3	15	1	2					

;

Appendix

C Tables

> Isolated facts, those that can only be obtained by rough estimate and that require development, can only be presented in memoires; but those that can be presented in a body, with details, and on whose accuracy one can rely, may be expounded in tables.
>
> E. Duvillard, *Mémoire sur le travail du Bureau de statistique*, 1806

The tables of percentage points of the Chi-Square distribution usually printed in texts rarely have enough detail, in the range of degrees of freedom (df) or in the upper-tail probability values, to meet the needs for everyone.

It is relatively easy to generate any table you want by using the CINV function in a DATA step. Two such tables are provided here. A traditional table (Table C.1) gives the values of χ^2 for a wide range of upper-tail probabilities and df. A second table gives entries of χ^2/df (Table C.2) whose values tend to be relatively constant and are provided by PROC GENMOD. Both tables are printed to 4 significant digits.

Both tables were generated using the statements in the "CHI2TAB Program" in this Appendix. If the printed versions are not adequate, you may change the %LET statements or the CVALUE picture format to meet your needs. The DIVISOR macro variable determines which table is printed. Plots of the values in the table may be produced easily from the dataset CHISQ.

C.1   CHI2TAB Program

```
options ls=110;
%let df=  1 to 20,
         25 to 50 by 5,
         60 to 100 by 10,
         200 to 400 by 50;
%let np=12;    %*-- Number of p-values;
%let pvalue=.25 .10 .09 .08 .07 .06 .05 .025 .01 .005 .0025 .001;
%let divisor = 1;      *-- Chi-square values;
*let divisor = df;     *-- Chi-square / df values;

data chisq;
   array pr(*) p1-p&np   (&pvalue);
   keep df p c;
   label p='Upper Tail Prob'
         df='df';
   do k = 1 to dim(pr);        /* for each P-value */
      p = 100*pr(k);
     do df = &df;
         c = cinv(1-pr(k), df) / &divisor;
         output;
         end;
      end;

proc sort;
   by df;
proc transpose out=chi2tab;
   by df; var c;

%*-- Generate variable labels;
%macro lab(k, prefix, values);
   %do i=1 %to &k;
      &&prefix.&i = "%scan(&values,&i,%str( ))"
      %end;
%mend;

proc format;
   picture cvalue low-<100  = '00.00'
                  100-high  = '000.0';
data chi2tab;
   set chi2tab;
   drop _name_;
   format col1-col&np cvalue. df 4.;
   label   %lab(&np, COL, &pvalue);
proc print label;
   id df;
```

C.2 χ^2 Values

Table C.1 Values of χ^2 for Various Upper-Tail Probabilities

df	.25	.10	.09	.08	.07	.06	.05	.025	.01	.005	.0025	.001
						Upper-Tail Probability						
1	1.32	2.70	2.87	3.06	3.28	3.53	3.84	5.02	6.63	7.87	9.14	10.82
2	2.77	4.60	4.81	5.05	5.31	5.62	5.99	7.37	9.21	10.59	11.98	13.81
3	4.10	6.25	6.49	6.75	7.06	7.40	7.81	9.34	11.34	12.83	14.32	16.26
4	5.38	7.77	8.04	8.33	8.66	9.04	9.48	11.14	13.27	14.86	16.42	18.46
5	6.62	9.23	9.52	9.83	10.19	10.59	11.07	12.83	15.08	16.74	18.38	20.51
6	7.84	10.64	10.94	11.28	11.65	12.08	12.59	14.44	16.81	18.54	20.24	22.45
7	9.03	12.01	12.33	12.69	13.08	13.53	14.06	16.01	18.47	20.27	22.04	24.32
8	10.21	13.36	13.69	14.06	14.48	14.95	15.50	17.53	20.09	21.95	23.77	26.12
9	11.38	14.68	15.03	15.42	15.85	16.34	16.91	19.02	21.66	23.58	25.46	27.87
10	12.54	15.98	16.35	16.75	17.20	17.71	18.30	20.48	23.20	25.18	27.11	29.58
11	13.70	17.27	17.65	18.06	18.53	19.06	19.67	21.92	24.72	26.75	28.72	31.26
12	14.84	18.54	18.93	19.36	19.84	20.39	21.02	23.33	26.21	28.29	30.31	32.90
13	15.98	19.81	20.21	20.65	21.15	21.71	22.36	24.73	27.68	29.81	31.88	34.52
14	17.11	21.06	21.47	21.93	22.44	23.01	23.68	26.11	29.14	31.31	33.42	36.12
15	18.24	22.30	22.73	23.19	23.72	24.31	24.99	27.48	30.57	32.80	34.94	37.69
16	19.36	23.54	23.97	24.45	24.99	25.59	26.29	28.84	31.99	34.26	36.45	39.25
17	20.48	24.76	25.21	25.70	26.25	26.87	27.58	30.19	33.40	35.71	37.94	40.79
18	21.60	25.98	26.44	26.94	27.50	28.13	28.86	31.52	34.80	37.15	39.42	42.31
19	22.71	27.20	27.66	28.18	28.75	29.39	30.14	32.85	36.19	38.58	40.88	43.82
20	23.82	28.41	28.88	29.40	29.99	30.64	31.41	34.16	37.56	39.99	42.33	45.31
25	29.33	34.38	34.90	35.47	36.10	36.82	37.65	40.64	44.31	46.92	49.43	52.61
30	34.79	40.25	40.81	41.43	42.11	42.88	43.77	46.97	50.89	53.67	56.33	59.70
35	40.22	46.05	46.65	47.31	48.03	48.85	49.80	53.20	57.34	60.27	63.07	66.61
40	45.61	51.80	52.43	53.12	53.89	54.76	55.75	59.34	63.69	66.76	69.69	73.40
45	50.98	57.50	58.16	58.89	59.70	60.60	61.65	65.41	69.95	73.16	76.22	80.07
50	56.33	63.16	63.86	64.62	65.46	66.41	67.50	71.42	76.15	79.48	82.66	86.66
60	66.98	74.39	75.14	75.96	76.87	77.90	79.08	83.29	88.37	91.95	95.34	99.60
70	77.57	85.52	86.32	87.20	88.17	89.27	90.53	95.02	100.4	104.2	107.8	112.3
80	88.13	96.57	97.42	98.35	99.38	100.5	101.8	106.6	112.3	116.3	120.1	124.8
90	98.64	107.5	108.4	109.4	110.5	111.7	113.1	118.1	124.1	128.2	132.2	137.2
100	109.1	118.4	119.4	120.4	121.5	122.8	124.3	129.5	135.8	140.1	144.2	149.4
200	213.1	226.0	227.3	228.7	230.2	232.0	233.9	241.0	249.4	255.2	260.7	267.5
250	264.6	279.0	280.4	282.0	283.7	285.6	287.8	295.6	304.9	311.3	317.3	324.8
300	316.1	331.7	333.3	335.0	336.9	338.9	341.3	349.8	359.9	366.8	373.3	381.4
350	367.4	384.3	385.9	387.7	389.8	392.0	394.6	403.7	414.4	421.9	428.8	437.4
400	418.6	436.6	438.4	440.3	442.4	444.8	447.6	457.3	468.7	476.6	483.9	493.1

C.3 χ^2/df Values

Table C.2 Values of χ^2/df for Various Upper-Tail Probabilities

df	.25	.10	.09	.08	.07	.06	.05	.025	.01	.005	.0025	.001
1	1.323	2.706	2.874	3.065	3.283	3.537	3.841	5.024	6.635	7.879	9.141	10.828
2	1.386	2.303	2.408	2.526	2.659	2.813	2.996	3.689	4.605	5.298	5.991	6.908
3	1.369	2.084	2.164	2.253	2.353	2.469	2.605	3.116	3.782	4.279	4.773	5.422
4	1.346	1.945	2.011	2.084	2.167	2.261	2.372	2.786	3.319	3.715	4.106	4.617
5	1.325	1.847	1.904	1.967	2.038	2.119	2.214	2.567	3.017	3.350	3.677	4.103
6	1.307	1.774	1.825	1.881	1.943	2.015	2.099	2.408	2.802	3.091	3.375	3.743
7	1.291	1.717	1.762	1.813	1.870	1.934	2.010	2.288	2.639	2.897	3.149	3.475
8	1.277	1.670	1.712	1.759	1.810	1.870	1.938	2.192	2.511	2.744	2.972	3.266
9	1.265	1.632	1.670	1.713	1.762	1.816	1.880	2.114	2.407	2.621	2.829	3.097
10	1.255	1.599	1.635	1.675	1.720	1.771	1.831	2.048	2.321	2.519	2.711	2.959
11	1.246	1.570	1.605	1.643	1.685	1.733	1.789	1.993	2.248	2.432	2.612	2.842
12	1.237	1.546	1.578	1.614	1.654	1.699	1.752	1.945	2.185	2.358	2.527	2.742
13	1.230	1.524	1.555	1.589	1.627	1.670	1.720	1.903	2.130	2.294	2.453	2.656
14	1.223	1.505	1.534	1.567	1.603	1.644	1.692	1.866	2.082	2.237	2.388	2.580
15	1.216	1.487	1.515	1.547	1.581	1.621	1.666	1.833	2.039	2.187	2.330	2.513
16	1.211	1.471	1.499	1.529	1.562	1.600	1.644	1.803	2.000	2.142	2.278	2.453
17	1.205	1.457	1.483	1.512	1.544	1.581	1.623	1.776	1.965	2.101	2.232	2.399
18	1.200	1.444	1.469	1.497	1.528	1.563	1.604	1.751	1.934	2.064	2.190	2.351
19	1.196	1.432	1.456	1.483	1.513	1.547	1.587	1.729	1.905	2.031	2.152	2.306
20	1.191	1.421	1.444	1.470	1.500	1.532	1.571	1.708	1.878	2.000	2.117	2.266
25	1.174	1.375	1.396	1.419	1.444	1.473	1.506	1.626	1.773	1.877	1.977	2.105
30	1.160	1.342	1.361	1.381	1.404	1.429	1.459	1.566	1.696	1.789	1.878	1.990
35	1.149	1.316	1.333	1.352	1.372	1.396	1.423	1.520	1.638	1.722	1.802	1.903
40	1.140	1.295	1.311	1.328	1.347	1.369	1.394	1.484	1.592	1.669	1.742	1.835
45	1.133	1.278	1.293	1.309	1.327	1.347	1.370	1.454	1.555	1.626	1.694	1.779
50	1.127	1.263	1.277	1.292	1.309	1.328	1.350	1.428	1.523	1.590	1.653	1.733
60	1.116	1.240	1.252	1.266	1.281	1.298	1.318	1.388	1.473	1.533	1.589	1.660
70	1.108	1.222	1.233	1.246	1.260	1.275	1.293	1.357	1.435	1.489	1.540	1.605
80	1.102	1.207	1.218	1.229	1.242	1.257	1.273	1.333	1.404	1.454	1.501	1.560
90	1.096	1.195	1.205	1.216	1.228	1.242	1.257	1.313	1.379	1.426	1.470	1.525
100	1.091	1.185	1.194	1.205	1.216	1.229	1.243	1.296	1.358	1.402	1.443	1.494
200	1.066	1.130	1.137	1.144	1.151	1.160	1.170	1.205	1.247	1.276	1.304	1.338
250	1.059	1.116	1.122	1.128	1.135	1.143	1.152	1.183	1.220	1.245	1.269	1.299
300	1.054	1.106	1.111	1.117	1.123	1.130	1.138	1.166	1.200	1.223	1.245	1.271
350	1.050	1.098	1.103	1.108	1.114	1.120	1.128	1.153	1.184	1.205	1.225	1.250
400	1.047	1.092	1.096	1.101	1.106	1.112	1.119	1.143	1.172	1.192	1.210	1.233

References

Agresti, A. *Analysis of Ordinal Categorical Data*. Wiley, New York, 1984.

Agresti, A. *Categorical Data Analysis*. Wiley-Interscience, New York, 1990.

Agresti, A. *An Introduction to Categorical Data Analysis*. Wiley Interscience, New York, 1996.

Aitchison, J. *The Statistical Analysis of Compositional Data*. Chapman and Hall, London, 1986.

Aitkin, M. A., Anderson, D., Francis, B., and Hinde, J. *Statistical Modelling in GLIM*. Clarendon Press, Oxford, UK, 1989.

Akaike, H. Information theory and an extension of the maximum likelihood principal. In Petrov, B. N. and Czaki, F., editors, *Proceedings of the 2nd International Symposium on Information*, Budapest, 1973. Akademiai Kiado.

Allison, P. D. *Logistic Regression Using the SAS System*. SAS Institute Inc., Cary, NC, 1999.

Anderson, E. B. *Statistical Analysis of Categorical Data*. Springer-Verlag, Berlin, 1991.

Andrews, D. F. and Herzberg, A. M. *Data: A Collection of Problems from Many Fields for the Student and Research Worker*. Springer-Verlag, New York, NY, 1985.

Ashford, J. R. and Snowden, R. D. Multivariate probit analysis. *Biometrics*, 26:535–546, 1970.

Atkinson, A. C. Two graphical displays for outlying and influential observations in regression. *Biometrika*, 68:13–20, 1981.

Bangdiwala, K. Using SAS software graphical procedures for the observer agreement chart. *Proceedings of the SAS Users Group International Conference*, 12:1083–1088, 1987.

Bartlett, M. S. Contingency table interactions. *Journal of the Royal Statistical Society, Supplement*, 2:248–252, 1935.

Benzécri, J.-P. Sur l'analyse des tableaus binaires associés a une correspondense multiple. *Cahiers de l'Analyse des Données*, 2:55–71, 1977.

Bertin, J. *Graphics and Graphic Information-processing*. de Gruyter, New York, 1981.

Bickel, P. J., Hammel, J. W., and O'Connell, J. W. Sex bias in graduate admissions: Data from Berkeley. *Science*, 187:398–403, 1975.

Birch, M. W. An algorithm for the logarithmic series distributions. *Biometrics*, 19:651–652, 1963.

Bishop, Y. M. M., Fienberg, S. E., and Holland, P. W. *Discrete Multivariate Analysis: Theory and Practice*. MIT Press, Cambridge, MA, 1975.

Box, G. E. P. and Cox, D. R. An analysis of transformations (with discussion). *Journal of the Royal Statistical Society, Series B*, 26:211–252, 1964.

Bradley, R. A. and Terry, M. E. Rank analysis of incomplete block designs. I. the method of paired comparisons. *Biometrika*, 39:324–345, 1952.

Bradu, D. and Gabriel, R. K. The biplot as a diagnostic tool for models of two-way tables. *Technometrics*, 20:47–68, 1978.

Brown, P. J., Stone, J., and Ord-Smith, C. Toxaemic signs during pregnancy. *Journal of the Royal Statistical Society, Series C (Applied Statistics)*, 32:69–72, 1983.

Burt, C. The factorial analysis of qualitative data. *British Journal of Statistical Psychology*, 3:166–185, 1950.

Christensen, R. *Log-Linear Models and Logistic Regression*. Springer, New York, NY, 2nd edition, 1997.

Cicchetti, D. V. and Allison, T. A new procedure for assessing reliability of scoring EEG sleep recordings. *American Journal of EEG Technology*, 11:101–109, 1971.

Cleveland, W. S. Robust locally weighted regression and smoothing scatterplots. *Journal of the American Statistical Association*, 74:829–836, 1979.

Cleveland, W. S. A model for studying display methods of statistical graphics. *Journal of Computational and Statistical Graphics*, 2:323–343, 1993a.

Cleveland, W. S. *Visualizing Data*. Hobart Press, Summit, NJ, 1993b.

Cleveland, W. S. and McGill, R. Graphical perception: Theory, experimentation and application to the development of graphical methods. *Journal of the American Statistical Association*, 79:531–554, 1984.

Cleveland, W. S. and McGill, R. Graphical perception and graphical methods for analyzing scientific data. *Science*, 229:828–833, 1985.

Clogg, C. and Shockey, J. W. Multivariate analysis of discrete data. In Nesselroade, J. R. and Cattell, R. B., editors, *Handbook of Multivariate Experimental Psychology*. Plenum Press, New York, 1988.

Cohen, A. On the graphical display of the significant components in a two-way contingency table. *Communications in Statistics– Theory and Methods*, A9:1025–1041, 1980.

Cohen, J. A coefficient of agreement for nominal scales. *Educational and Psychological Measurement*, 20:37–46, 1960.

Cohen, J. Weighted kappa: Nominal scale agreement with provision for scaled diasgreement or partial credit. *Psychological Bulletin*, 70:213–220, 1968.

Collett, D. R. *Modelling Binary Data*. Chapman and Hall, London, 1st edition, 1991.

Cook, R. D. and Weisberg, S. *Residuals and Influence in Regression*. Chapman and Hall, New York, 1982.

Copas, J. B. Plotting P against X. *Applied Statistics*, 32:25–31, 1983.

Cowles, M. and Davis, C. The subject matter of psychology: Volunteers. *British Journal of Social Psychology*, 26:97–102, 1987.

Cressie, N. and Read, T. R. C. Multinomial goodness-of-fit tests. *Journal of the Royal Statistical Society, Series B*, 46:440–464, 1984.

Dalal, S., Fowlkes, E. B., and Hoadley, B. Risk analysis of the space shuttle: Pre-*Challenger* prediction of failure. *Journal of the American Statistical Association*, 84 (408):945–957, 1989.

Dawson, R. J. M. The "unusual episode" data revisited. *Journal of Statistics Education*, 3 (3), 1995.

Dittrich, R., Hatzinger, R., and Katzenbeisser, W. Modelling the effect of subject-specific covariates in paired comparison studies with an application to university rankings. *Applied Statistics*, 47:511–525, 1998.

Evers, M. and Namboordiri, N. K. A Monte Carlo assessment of the stability of log-linear estimates in small samples. In *Proceedings of the Social Statistics Section*, Alexandria, VA, 1977. American Statistical Association.

Fedenczuk, L. L. and Bercov, M. TERNPLOT - SAS creation of ternary plots. *Proceedings of the SAS Users Group International Conference*, 16:771–778, 1991.

Fienberg, S. E. Perspective Canada as a social report. *Social Indicators Research*, 2: 153–174, 1975.

Fienberg, S. E. *The Analysis of Cross-Classified Categorical Data*. MIT Press, Cambridge, MA, 2nd edition, 1980.

Fienberg, S. E. and Gong, G. D. Comment (on Landswehr-et al). *Journal of the American Statistical Association*, 79:72–77, 1984.

Findlay, M. A. *Titanic* passenger list. In Eaton, J. P. and Haas, C. A., editors, *Titanic, triumph and tragedy*, Norton, New York, 1986.

Fisher, R. A. *Statistical Methods for Research Workers*. Oliver & Boyd, London, 1925.

Fisher, R. A., Corbet, A. S., and Williams, C. B. The relation between the number of species and the number of individuals. *Journal of Animal Ecology*, 12:42, 1943.

Fleiss, J. L. *Statistical Methods for Rates and Proportions*. John Wiley and Sons, New York, 1973.

Fleiss, J. L. and Cohen, J. The equivalence of weighted kappa and the intraclass correlation coefficient as measures of reliability. *Educational and Psychological Measurement*, 33: 613–619, 1972.

Fleiss, J. L., Cohen, J., and Everitt, B. S. Large sample standard errors of kappa and weighted kappa. *Psychological Bulletin*, 72:332–327, 1969.

Flores, F. and Flack, V. F. Program to generate Atkinson's and resistant envelopes for normal probability plots of regression residuals. *Proceedings of the SAS Users Group International Conference*, 15:1345–1352, 1990.

Fowlkes, E. B. Some diagnostics for binary logistic regression via smoothing. *Biometrika*, 74(3):503–5152, 1987.

Fox, J. *Linear Statistical Models and Related Methods*. John Wiley and Sons, New York, 1984.

Fox, J. Effect displays for generalized linear models. In Clogg, C. C., editor, *Sociological Methodology, 1987*, pp. 347–361. Jossey-Bass, San Francisco, 1987.

Fox, J. *Regression Diagnostics: An Introduction*. Sage Publications, Beverly Hills, CA, 1991.

Fox, J. *Applied Regression Analysis, Linear Models, and Related Methods*. Sage Publications, Thousand Oaks, CA, 1997.

Freedman, D., Pisani, R., and Purves, R. *Statistics*. Norton, New York, 1978.

Friendly, M. *SAS System for Statistical Graphics*. SAS Institute Inc., Cary, NC, 1st edition, 1991.

Friendly, M. Mosaic displays for loglinear models. In *ASA, Proceedings of the Statistical Graphics Section*, pp. 61–68, Alexandria, VA, 1992.

Friendly, M. A fourfold display for 2 by 2 by K tables. Technical Report 217, York University, Psychology Dept, 1994a.

Friendly, M. Mosaic displays for multi-way contingency tables. *Journal of the American Statistical Association*, 89:190–200, 1994b.

Friendly, M. SAS/IML graphics for fourfold displays. *Observations*, 3(4):47–56, 1994c.

Friendly, M. Conceptual and visual models for categorical data. *The American Statistician*, 49:153–160, 1995.

Friendly, M. Mosaic displays. WWW application, 1996.

Friendly, M. Conceptual models for visualizing contingency table data. In Greenacre, M. and Blasius, J., editors, *Visualization of Categorical Data*, chapter 2, pp. 17–35. Academic Press, San Diego, CA, 1997.

Friendly, M. Extending mosaic displays: Marginal, conditional, and partial views of categorical data. *Journal of Computational and Statistical Graphics*, 8:373–395, 1999a.

Friendly, M. Visualizing categorical data. In Sirken, M., Herrmann, D., Schechter, S., Schwarz, N., Tanur, J., and Tourangeau, R., editors, *Cognition and Survey Research*, chapter 20, pp. 319–348. John Wiley and Sons, New York, 1999b.

Gabriel, K. R. The biplot graphic display of matrices with application to principal components analysis. *Biometrics*, 58(3):453–467, 1971.

Gabriel, K. R. Biplot. In Johnson, N. L. and Kotz, S., editors, *Encyclopedia of Statistical Sciences*, volume 1, pp. 263–271. John Wiley and Sons, New York, 1980.

Gabriel, K. R. Biplot display of multivariate matrices for inspection of data and diagnosis. In Barnett, V., editor, *Interpreting Multivariate Data*, chapter 8, pp. 147–173. John Wiley and Sons, London, 1981.

Gabriel, K. R. Biplot display of multivariate categorical data, with comments on multiple correspondence analysis. In Kraznowski, W. J., editor, *Recent Advances in Descriptive Multivariate Analysis*, chapter 9, pp. 190–226. Oxford University Press, Oxford, UK, 1995a.

Gabriel, K. R. MANOVA biplots for two-way contingency tables. In Kraznowski, W. J., editor, *Recent Advances in Descriptive Multivariate Analysis*, chapter 10, pp. 227–268. Oxford University Press, Oxford, UK, 1995b.

Gabriel, K. R., Galindo, M. P., and Vincente-Villardón, J. L. Use of biplots to diagnose independence models in three-way contingency tables. In Greenacre, M. and Blasius, J., editors, *Visualization of Categorical Data*, chapter 27, pp. 391–404. Academic Press, San Diego, CA, 1997.

Gart, J. J. and Zweiful, J. R. On the bias of various estimators of the logit and its variance with applications to quantal bioassay. *Biometrika*, 54:181–187, 1967.

Gifi, A. *Nonlinear Multivariate Analysis*. Department of Data Theory, University of Leiden, The Netherlands, 1981.

Gifi, A. *Nonlinear Multivariate Analysis*. John Wiley and Sons, Chichester, UK, 1990.

Gilbert, G. N. *Modelling Society: An Introduction to Loglinear Analysis for Social Researchers*. Allen and Unwin, London, 1981.

Goodman, L. A. The multivariate analysis of qualitative data: Interactions among multiple classifications. *Journal of the American Statistical Association*, 65:226–256, 1970.

Goodman, L. A. The analysis of multidimensional contingency tables: Stepwise procedures and direct estimates for building models for multiple classifications. *Technometrics*, 13:33–61, 1971.

Goodman, L. A. The analysis of multidimensional contingency tables when some variables are posterior to others: A modified path analysis approach. *Biometrika*, 60:179–192, 1973.

Goodman, L. A. Simple models for the analysis of association in cross-classifications having ordered categories. *Journal of the American Statistical Association*, 74:537–552, 1979.

Goodman, L. A. Association models and canonical correlation in the analysis of cross-classifications having ordered categories. *Journal of the American Statistical Association*, 76(374):320–334, 1981.

Goodman, L. A. The analysis of dependence in cross-classifications having ordered categories, using log-linear models for frequencies and log-linear models for odds. *Biometrics*, 39:149–160, 1983.

Goodman, L. A. The analysis of cross-classified data having ordered and/or unordered categories: Association models, correlation models, and asymmetry models for contingency tables with or without missing entries. *Annals of Statistics*, 13(1):10–69, 1985.

Goodman, L. A. Some useful extensions of the usual correspondence analysis approach and the usual log-linear models approach in the analysis of contingency tables. *International Statistical Review*, 54(3):243–309, 1986. With a discussion and reply by the author.

Goodman, L. A. Measures, models, and graphical displays in the analysis of cross-classified data. *Journal of the American Statistical Association*, 86(416):1085–1138, 1991. With comments and a rejoinder by the author.

Gower, J. C. and Hand, D. J. *Biplots*. Chapman & Hall, London, 1996.

Greenacre, M. *Theory and Applications of Correspondence Analysis*. Academic Press, London, 1984.

Greenacre, M. Correspondence analysis of multivariate categorical data by weighted least squares. *Biometrika*, 75:457–467, 1988.

Greenacre, M. The Carroll-Green-Schaffer scaling in correspondence analysis: A theoretical and empirical appraisal. *Journal of Marketing Research*, 26:358–365, 1989.

Greenacre, M. Some limitations of multiple correspondence analysis. *Computational Statistics Quarterly*, 3:249–256, 1990.

Greenacre, M. Biplots in correspondence analysis. *Journal of Applied Statistics*, 2:251–269, 1993.

Greenacre, M. Diagnostics for joint displays in correspondence analysis. In Blasius, J. and Greenacre, M., editors, *Visualization of Categorical Data*, pp. 221–238. Academic Press, 1997.

Greenacre, M. and Hastie, T. The geometric interpretation of correspondence analysis. *Journal of the American Statistical Association*, 82:437–447, 1987.

Greenwood, M. and Yule, G. U. An inquiry into the nature of frequency distributions of multiple happenings, with particular reference to the occurrence of multiple attacks of disease or repeated accidents. *Journal of the Royal Statistical Society, Series A*, 83:255–279, 1920.

Haberman, S. J. The analysis of residuals in cross-classified tables. *Biometrics*, 29:205–220, 1973.

Haberman, S. J. *The Analysis of Frequency Data*. University of Chicago Press, Chicago, 1974.

Haberman, S. J. *The Analysis of Qualitative Data: New Developments*, volume II. Academic Press, New York, 1979.

Haldane, J. B. S. The estimation and significance of the logarithm of a ratio of frequencies. *Annals of Human Genetics*, 20:309–311, 1955.

Hartigan, J. A. and Kleiner, B. Mosaics for contingency tables. In Eddy, W. F., editor, *Computer Science and Statistics: Proceedings of the 13th Symposium on the Interface*, pp. 268–273. Springer-Verlag, New York, NY, 1981.

Hartigan, J. A. and Kleiner, B. A mosaic of television ratings. *The American Statistician*, 38:32–35, 1984.

Heuer, J. *Selbstmord Bei Kinder Und Jugendlichen*. Ernst Klett Verlag, Stuttgard, 1979. [Suicide by children and youth.].

Hind, P. Encyclopedia Titanica. WWW document, 1997. http://www.encyclopedia-titanica.org.

Hirschfeld, H. O. A connection between correlation and contingency. *Cambridge Philosophical Society Proceedings*, 31:520–524, 1935.

Hoaglin, D. C. A poissonness plot. *The American Statistician*, 34:146–149, 1980.

Hoaglin, D. C. and Tukey, J. W. Checking the shape of discrete distributions. In Hoaglin, D. C., Mosteller, F., and Tukey, J. W., editors, *Exploring Data Tables, Trends and Shapes*, chapter 9. John Wiley and Sons, New York, 1985.

Hosmer, D. W. and Lemeshow, S. *Applied Logistic Regression*. John Wiley and Sons, New York, 1989.

Hout, M., Duncan, O. D., and Sobel, M. E. Association and heterogeneity: Structural models of similarities and differences. *Sociological Methodology*, 17:145–184, 1987.

Hsieh, F. Y. Sample size tables for logistic regression. *Statistics in Medicine*, 8(7):795–802, 1989.

Jinkinson, R. A. and Slater, M. Critical discussion of a graphical method for identifying discrete distributions. *The Statistician*, 30:239–248, 1981.

Johnson, N. L., Kotz, S., and Kemp, A. W. *Univariate Discrete Distributions*. John Wiley and Sons, New York, NY, 2nd edition, 1992.

Johnson, W. Influence measures in logistic regression: Another point of view. *Biometika*, 72:59–65, 1985.

Joiner, B. Lurking variables: Some examples. *The American Statistician*, 35:227–233, 1981.

Kemp, A. W. and Kemp, C. D. Weldon's dice data revisited. *The American Statistician*, 45:216–222, 1991.

Kendall, M. G. and Stuart, A. *The Advanced Theory of Statistics*, volume 2. Griffin, London, 1961.

Kendall, M. G. and Stuart, A. *The Advanced Theory of Statistics*, volume 1. Griffin, London, 1963.

Koch, G. and Edwards, S. Clinical efficiency trials with categorical data. In Peace, K. E., editor, *Biopharmaceutical Statistics for Drug Development*, pp. 403–451. Marcel Dekker, New York, 1988.

Kosambi, D. D. Characteristic properties of series distributions. *Proceedings of the National Institute of Science of India*, 15:109–113, 1949.

Kosslyn, S. M. Graphics and human information processing: A review of five books. *Journal of the American Statistical Association*, 80:499–512, 1985.

Kosslyn, S. M. Understanding charts and graphs. *Applied Cognitive Psychology*, 3:185–225, 1989.

Landis, J. R. and Koch, G. G. The measurement of observer agreement for categorical data. *Biometrics*, 33:159–174, 1977.

Landwehr, J. M., Pregibon, D., and Shoemaker, A. C. Graphical methods for assessing logistic regression models. *Journal of the American Statistical Association*, 79:61–71, 1984.

Lang, J. B. and Agresti, A. Simultaneously modeling joint and marginal distributions of multivariate categorical responses. *Journal of the American Statistical Association*, 89 (426):625–632, 1994.

Larsen, W. A. and McCleary, S. J. The use of partial residual plots in regression analysis. *Technometrics*, 14:781–790, 1972.

Lavine, M. Problems in extrapolation illustrated with space shuttle O-ring data. *Journal of the American Statistical Association*, 86:912–922, 1991.

Lebart, L., Morineau, A., and Tabard, N. *Techniques De La Description Statistique*. Dunod, Paris, 1977.

Lebart, L., Morineau, A., and Warwick, K. M. *Multivariate Descriptive Statistical Analysis: Correspondence Analysis and Related Techniques for Large Matrices*. John Wiley and Sons, New York, 1984.

Lee, A. J. Modelling scores in the Premier League: Is Manchester United really the best? *Chance*, 10(1):15–19, 1997.

Lemeshow, S., Avrunin, D., and Pastides, J. S. Predicting the outcome of intensive care unit patients. *Journal of the American Statistical Association*, 83:348–356, 1988.

Lewandowsky, S. and Spence, I. The perception of statistical graphs. *Sociological Methods & Research*, 18:200–242, 1989.

Lindsey, J. K. *Analysis of Frequency and Count Data*. Oxford University Press, Oxford, UK, 1995.

Lindsey, J. K. and Mersch, G. Fitting and comparing probability distributions with log linear models. *Computational Statistics and Data Analysis*, 13:373–384, 1992.

Luce, R. D. *Individual Choice Behavior: A Theoretical Analysis*. John Wiley and Sons, New York, 1959.

Mallows, C. L. Some comments on C_p. *Technometrics*, 15:661–675, 1973.

McCullagh, P. and Nelder, J. A. *Generalized Linear Models*. Chapman and Hall, London, 1989.

Mersey, L. Report on the loss of the "Titanic" (S. S.). Parliamentary command paper 6352, 1912.

Meulman, J. J. and Heiser, W. J. Visual display of interaction in multiway contingency tables by use of homogeneity analysis: the $2 \times 2 \times 2 \times 2$ case. In Greenacre, M. and Blasius, J., editors, *Visualization of Categorical Data*, chapter 20, pp. 277–296. Academic Press, San Diego, CA, 1997.

Mosteller, F. and Wallace, D. L. *Applied Bayesian and Classical Inference: The Case of the Federalist Papers*. Springer-Verlag, New York, NY, 1984.

Nishisato, S. *Analysis of Categorical Data: Dual Scaling and Its Applications*. Univeristy of Toronto Press, Toronto, 1980.

Noack, A. A class of random variables with discrete distributions. *Annals of Mathematical Statistics*, 21:127–132, 1950.

Ord, J. K. Graphical methods for a class of discrete distributions. *Journal of the Royal Statistical Society, Series A*, 130:232–238, 1967.

Pearson, K. On the criterion that a given system of deviations from the probable in the case of a correlated system of variables is such that it can be reasonably supposed to have arisen by random sampling. *Philosophical Magazine*, 50(5th Series):157–175, 1900.

Pregibon, D. Logistic regression diagnostics. *Annals of Statistics*, 9:705–724, 1981.

Read, T. R. C. and Cressie, N. A. C. *Goodness-of-Fit Statistics for Discrete Multivariate Data*. Springer-Verlag, New York, 1988.

Reiss, A. J. J. Victim proneness by type of crime in repeat victimization. In Fienberg, S. E. and Reiss, A. J. J., editors, *Indicators of Crime and Criminal Justice*. U. S. Government Printing Office, Washington, DC, 1980.

Riedwyl, H. and Schüpbach, M. Siebdiagramme: Graphische darstellung von kontingenztafeln. Technical Report 12, Institute for Mathematical Statistics, University of Bern, Bern, Switzerland, 1983.

Riedwyl, H. and Schüpbach, M. Parquet diagram to plot contingency tables. In Faulbaum, F., editor, *Softstat '93: Advances In Statistical Software*, pp. 293–299. Gustav Fischer, New York, 1994.

Sall, J. The conceptual model for categorical responses. *ASA Statistical Computing and Statistical Graphics Newsletter*, 3:33–36, Nov. 1991.

SAS Institute Inc. *SAS/STAT User's Guide, Version 6, Fourth Edition*. SAS Institute Inc., Cary, NC, 1990.

Schwartz, G. Estimating the dimensions of a model. *Annals of Statistics*, 6:461–464, 1978.

Shrout, P. E. and Fleiss, J. L. Intraclass correlations: Uses in assessing rater reliability. *Psychological Bulletin*, 86:420–428, 1979.

Simpson, E. H. The interpretation of interaction in contingency tables. *Journal of the Royal Statistical Society, Series B*, 30:238–241, 1951.

Snee, R. D. Graphical display of two-way contingency tables. *The American Statistician*, 28:9–12, 1974.

Sokal, R. R. and Rholf, F. J. *Biometry. The Principles and Practice of Statistics*. W. H. Freeman, San Francisco, CA, 1969.

Spence, I. Visual psychophysics of simple graphical elements. *Journal of Experimental Psychology: Human Perception and Performance*, 16:683–692, 1990.

Srole, L., Langner, T. S., Michael, S. T., Kirkpatrick, P., Opler, M. K., and Rennie, T. A. C. *Mental Health in the Metropolis: The Midtown Manhattan Study*. NYU Press, New York, 1978.

Stokes, M. E., Davis, C. S., and Koch, G. G. *Categorical Data Analysis Using the SAS System*. SAS Institute Inc., Cary, NC, 1995.

Strauss, D. The many faces of logistic regression. *The American Statistician*, 46(4):321–327, 1992.

Theus, M. and Lauer, S. R. W. Visualizing loglinear models. *Journal of Computational and Statistical Graphics*, 8(3):396–412, 1999.

Thornes, B. and Collard, J. *Who Divorces?* Routledge & Kegan, London, 1979.

Tufte, E. R. *The Visual Display of Quantitative Information*. Graphics Press, Cheshire, CT, 1983.

Tufte, E. R. *Envisioning Information*. Graphics Press, Cheshire, CT, 1990.

Tufte, E. R. *Visual Explanations: Images and Quantities, Evidence and Narrative*. Graphics Press, Cheshire, CT, 1997.

Tukey, J. W. A quick, compact, two sample test to duckworth's specifications. *Technometrics*, 1:31–48, 1959.

Tukey, J. W. *Exploratory Data Analysis*. Addison Wesley, Reading, MA, 1977.

Tukey, J. W. Graphic comparisons of several linked aspects: Alternative and suggested principles. *Journal of Computational and Statistical Graphics*, 2(1):1–33, 1993.

Upton, G. J. G. The diagrammatic representation of three-party contests. *Political Studies*, 24:448–454, 1976.

Upton, G. J. G. Picturing the 1992 British general election. *Journal of the Royal Statistical Society, Series A*, 157(Part 2):231–252, 1994.

van der Heijden, P. G. M. *Correspondence Analysis of Longitudinal Categorical Data*. DSWO Press, Leiden, Netherlands, 1987.

van der Heijden, P. G. M., de Falguerolles, A., and de Leeuw, J. A combined approach to contingency table analysis using correspondence analysis and log-linear analysis. *Applied Statistics*, 38(2):249–292, 1989.

van der Heijden, P. G. M. and de Leeuw, J. Correspondence analysis used complementary to log-linear analysis. *Psychometrika*, 50:429–447, 1985.

von Bortkiewicz, L. *Das Gesetz der Kleinen Zahlen*. Teubner, Leipzig, 1898.

Wainer, H. Using trilinear plots for NAEP state data. *Journal of Educational Measurement*, 33(1):41–55, 1996.

Wang, P. C. Adding a variable in generalized linear models. *Technometrics*, 27:273–276, 1985.

Wang, P. C. Residual plots for detecting nonlinearity in generalized linear models. *Technometrics*, 29:435–438, 1987.

Westlund, K. B. and Kurland, L. T. Studies on multiple sclerosis in Winnipeg, Manitoba and New Orleans, Louisiana. *American Journal of Hygiene*, 57:380–396, 1953.

Whittemore, A. S. Sample size for logistic regression with small response probability. *Journal of the American Statistical Association*, 76(1):27–32, 1981.

Williams, O. D. and Grizzle, J. E. Analysis of contingency tables having ordered categories. *Journal of the American Statistical Association*, 67:55–63, 1972.

Young, F. W. ViSta: The visual statistics system. Technical Report RM 94-1, L.L. Thurstone Psychometric Laboratory, UNC, 1994.

Zelterman, D. *Models for Discrete Data*. Oxford University Press, New York, 1999.

Author Index

Y

Z

Example Index

Index

A

absolute values of residuals 310
ADDCELL option, MODEL statement 284
added-variable plots 237, 238–240
ADDVAR macro 238–240, 337
adjacent category logit models 293, 294–296
adjusted deviance residuals 309
adjusted R^2 statistic 271
adjusted residual, log-linear models 308
AGGREGATE option, MODEL statement 214
AGREE option, FREQ procedure 93
AGREE program 97, 338
agreement, measuring strength 92
    observer agreement chart 94–97
    partial agreement 94–96
Akaike Information Criterion (AIC) statistic 271
ALPHA parameter, POWERLOG macro 262
analysis graphs 10
ANGLE parameter, TITLE statement 220
ANOVA models, discrete 266–268
arthritis treatment (example) 3, 390
    contingency table 61
    homogeneity of association 73
    logistic regression model 197–199, 204–207
    logistic regression model with interaction 224
    logistic regression model, quantitative predictors 203
    logit model 212–215
    multiple logistic regression model 218–221
    overall analysis 65–67
    plotting LOGISTIC procedure results 215
    power analysis, logistic regression 260
    presentation graphs 10–12
    proportional odds model 241–245
    stratified analysis 70–72
    trilinear plot 98
association plots 90
asymmetric map 144
asymptotic distributions 33
AXIS statement
    GPLOT procedure 147, 381
    PSCALE macro 281

B

Bangdiwala's observer agreement chart 94–97
BARS macro 257, 379
Bartlett's data (example) 180–187
baseball fielding dataset (example) 99
baseball standings (1987) (example) 254–259
Berkeley graduate admissions (example) 2, 391
    conditional mosaic matrix 133
    contingency tables 60
    fitting log-linear model 272–276, 278
    fourfold display 75–77
    log-linear model diagnostics 313–315, 316
    logit model 279–283
    mosaic matrix 131–132

odds ratio 65
    sieve diagram 12, 88
    stratified analysis 79–81
    two-way contingency tables 62–63
BIC criterion 271
binary predictor 259–261
binary variables 2
binomial distributions 20, 22–26, 34–36, 37
    negative 29–31, 40
binomial samples 63
binomialness plot 55, 56
BIPLOT macro 189–193, 339
biplots for contingency tables 188–193
    2-way tables 188–191
    3-way tables 191–193
bivariate data 4
bivariate log-linear model 319
bivariate logistic model 318
bivariate MCA 165–168
Bowker's test 94
Bradley-Terry-Luce model 254–259
breathlessness in coal miners (example)
    fourfold display 82–84
    multivariate responses, log-linear model 319–325
Breslow-Day test 73
BTL model for paired comparisons 254–259
Burt matrix 169–170
butterfly species (example) 21
BY parameter, MOSAIC macro 128
BY statement, GPLOT procedure 219
BYVAR parameter, MOSPART module 126

C

C keyword, OUTPUT statement (LOGISTIC procedure) 230
CA
    See correspondence analysis (CA)
canonical analysis of categorical data 142
    See also correspondence analysis (CA)
case form 3
    CORRESP procedure 145
    LOGISTIC procedure 204
categorical data 2–5
    canonical analysis 142
    graphical methods 11–13
    mosaic matrices 129–134
categorical variables 2
category scores, properties of 154–159
CATMOD procedure 73, 268, 301, 319
    adjacent logit models 294–296
    CONTRAST statement 251
    cumulative logit model 297–299
    DIRECT statement 251
    fitting log-linear models 272
    fitting logit models 279
    generalized logits 240, 250–253

Z

zero frequencies 283–288
zeros
    fixed 283
    random 283
    sampling 283
    structural 153, 283

Call your local SAS® office to order these books available through the Books by Users℠ program:

An Array of Challenges — Test Your SAS® Skills
by **Robert Virgile**......................Order No. A55625

Annotate: Simply the Basics
by **Art Carpenter**........................Order No. A57320

Applied Multivariate Statistics with SAS® Software, Second Edition
by **Ravindra Khattree**
and **Dayanand N. Naik**.................Order No. A56903

Applied Statistics and the SAS® Programming Language, Fourth Edition
by **Ronald P. Cody**
and **Jeffrey K. Smith**...................Order No. A55984

Beyond the Obvious with SAS® Screen Control Language
by **Don Stanley**...........................Order No. A55073

Carpenter's Complete Guide to the SAS® Macro Language
by **Art Carpenter**........................Order No. A56100

The Cartoon Guide to Statistics
by **Larry Gonick**
and **Woollcott Smith**...................Order No. A55153

Categorical Data Analysis Using the SAS® System, Second Edition
by **Maura E. Stokes, Charles S. Davis,**
and **Gary G. Koch**......................Order No. A57998

Cody's Data Cleaning Techniques Using SAS® Software
by **Ron Cody**...............................Order No. A57198

Common Statistical Methods for Clinical Research with SAS® Examples
by **Glenn A. Walker**.....................Order No. A55991

Concepts and Case Studies in Data Management
by **William S. Calvert**
and **J. Meimei Ma**........................Order No. A55220

Efficiency: Improving the Performance of Your SAS® Applications
by **Robert Virgile**........................Order No. A55960

Essential Client/Server Survival Guide, Second Edition
by **Robert Orfali, Dan Harkey,**
and **Jeri Edwards**........................Order No. A56285

Extending SAS® Survival Analysis Techniques for Medical Research
by **Alan Cantor**...........................Order No. A55504

A Handbook of Statistical Analyses Using SAS®
by **B.S. Everitt**
and **G. Der**.................................Order No. A56378

The How-To Book for SAS/GRAPH® Software
by **Thomas Miron** ....Order No. A55203

In the Know ... SAS® Tips and Techniques From Around the Globe
by **Phil Mason** ....Order No. A55513

Integrating Results through Meta-Analytic Review Using SAS® Software
by **Morgan C. Wang**
and **Brad J. Bushman** ....Order No. A55810

Learning SAS® in the Computer Lab
by **Rebecca J. Elliott** ....Order No. A55273

The Little SAS® Book: A Primer
by **Lora D. Delwiche**
and **Susan J. Slaughter** ....Order No. A55200

The Little SAS® Book: A Primer, Second Edition
by **Lora D. Delwiche**
and **Susan J. Slaughter** ....Order No. A56649
(updated to include Version 8 features)

Logistic Regression Using the SAS System: Theory and Application
by **Paul D. Allison** ....Order No. A55770

Mastering the SAS® System, Second Edition
by **Jay A. Jaffe** ....Order No. A55123

Multiple Comparisons and Multiple Tests Using the SAS® System
by **Peter H. Westfall, Randall D. Tobias, Dror Rom, Russell D. Wolfinger,**
and **Yosef Hochberg** ....Order No. A56648

The Next Step: Integrating the Software Life Cycle with SAS® Programming
by **Paul Gill** ....Order No. A55697

Multivariate Data Reduction and Discrimination with SAS® Software
by **Ravindra Khattree**
and **Dayanand N. Naik**................Order No. A56902

Painless Windows 3.1: A Beginner's Handbook for SAS® Users
by **Jodie Gilmore** ....Order No. A55505

Painless Windows: A Handbook for SAS® Users
by **Jodie Gilmore** ....Order No. A55769
(for Windows NT and Windows 95)

Painless Windows: A Handbook for SAS® Users, Second Edition
by **Jodie Gilmore** ....Order No. A56647
(updated to include Version 7 and Version 8 features)

JMP® Books

Basic Business Statistics: A Casebook
by **Dean P. Foster, Robert A. Stine,**
and **Richard P. Waterman**........................Order No. A56813

Business Analysis Using Regression: A Casebook
by **Dean P. Foster, Robert A. Stine,**
and **Richard P. Waterman**........................Order No. A56818

JMP® Start Statistics, Version 3
by **John Sall** and **Ann Lehman** ....Order No. A55626

*Welcome * Bienvenue * Willkommen * Yohkoso * Bienvenido*

SAS Publishing Is Easy to Reach

Visit our Web page at www.sas.com/pubs

You will find product and service details, including

- **sample chapters**
- **tables of contents**
- **author biographies**
- **book reviews**

Learn about

- **regional user-group conferences**
- **trade-show sites and dates**
- **authoring opportunities**
- **custom textbooks**

Explore all the services that SAS Publishing has to offer!

Your Listserv Subscription Automatically Brings the News to You

Do you want to be among the first to learn about the latest books and services available from SAS Publishing? Subscribe to our listserv **newdocnews-l** and, once each month, you will automatically receive a description of the newest books and which environments or operating systems and SAS release(s) that each book addresses.

To subscribe,

1. Send an e-mail message to **listserv@vm.sas.com**.

2. Leave the "Subject" line blank.

3. Use the following text for your message:

   subscribe NEWDOCNEWS-L *your-first-name your-last-name*

   For example: subscribe NEWDOCNEWS-L John Doe

Create Customized Textbooks Quickly, Easily, and Affordably

SelecText® offers instructors at U.S. colleges and universities a way to create custom textbooks for courses that teach students how to use SAS software.

For more information, see our Web page at **www.sas.com/selectext**, or contact our SelecText coordinators by sending e-mail to **selectext@sas.com**.

You're Invited to Publish with SAS Institute's Books by Users℠ Program

If you enjoy writing about SAS software and how to use it, the Books by Users Program at SAS Institute offers a variety of publishing options. We are actively recruiting authors to publish books, articles, and sample code. Do you find the idea of writing a book or an article by yourself a little intimidating? Consider writing with a co-author. Keep in mind that you will receive complete editorial and publishing support, access to our users, technical advice and assistance, and competitive royalties. Please contact us for an author packet. E-mail us at **sasbbu@sas.com** or call 919-677-8000, extension 7921. See the SAS Institute Publishing Web page at **www.sas.com/pubs** for complete information.

See *Observations*®, Our Online Technical Journal

Feature articles from *Observations*®: *The Technical Journal for SAS*® *Software Users* are now available online at **www.sas.com/obs**. Take a look at what your fellow SAS software users and SAS Institute experts have to tell you. You may decide that you, too, have information to share. If you are interested in writing for *Observations*, send e-mail to **sasbbu@sas.com** or call 919-677-8000, extension 7921.

Book Discount Offered at SAS Public Training Courses!

When you attend one of our SAS Public Training Courses at any of our regional Training Centers in the U.S., you will receive a 15% discount on book orders that you place during the course. Take advantage of this offer at the next course you attend!

SAS Institute
SAS Campus Drive
Cary, NC 27513-2414
Fax 919-677-4444

E-mail: sasbook@sas.com
Web page: www.sas.com/pubs
To order books, call Fulfillment Services at 800-727-3228*
For other SAS Institute business, call 919-677-8000*

* Note: Customers outside the U.S. should contact their local SAS office.